INTERNATIONAL SERIES IN PURE AND APPLIED PHYSICS

Leonard I. Schiff, *Consulting Editor*

INTRODUCTION TO MODERN PHYSICS

INTERNATIONAL SERIES IN PURE AND APPLIED PHYSICS

LEONARD I. SCHIFF, *Consulting Editor*

Allis and Herlin   Thermodynamics and Statistical Mechanics
Becker   Introduction to Theoretical Mechanics
Clark   Applied X-rays
Edwards   Analytic and Vector Mechanics
Evans   The Atomic Nucleus
Finkelnburg   Atomic Physics
Ginzton   Microwave Measurements
Green   Nuclear Physics
Gurney   Introduction to Statistical Mechanics
Hall   Introduction to Electron Microscopy
Hardy and Perrin   The Principles of Optics
Harnwell   Electricity and Electromagnetism
Harnwell and Livingood   Experimental Atomic Physics
Harnwell and Stephens   Atomic Physics
Houston   Principles of Mathematical Physics
Houston   Principles of Quantum Mechanics
Hughes and DuBridge   Photoelectric Phenomena
Hund   High-frequency Measurements
Kemble   The Fundamental Principles of Quantum Mechanics
Kennard   Kinetic Theory of Gases
Marshak   Meson Physics
Morse   Vibration and Sound
Morse and Feshbach   Methods of Theoretical Physics
Muskat   Physical Principles of Oil Production
Read   Dislocations in Crystals
Richtmyer, Kennard, and Lauritsen   Introduction to Modern Physics
Schiff   Quantum Mechanics
Seitz   The Modern Theory of Solids
Slater   Introduction to Chemical Physics
Slater   Microwave Transmission
Slater   Quantum Theory of Matter
Slater and Frank   Electromagnetism
Slater and Frank   Introduction to Theoretical Physics
Slater and Frank   Mechanics
Smythe   Static and Dynamic Electricity
Squire   Low Temperature Physics
Stratton   Electromagnetic Theory
Thorndike   Mesons: A Summary of Experimental Facts
Townes and Schawlow   Microwave Spectroscopy
White   Introduction to Atomic Spectra

The late F. K. Richtmyer was Consulting Editor of the series from its inception in 1929 to his death in 1939. Lee A. DuBridge was Consulting Editor from 1939 to 1946; and G. P. Harnwell from 1947 to 1954.

Introduction to
MODERN PHYSICS

F. K. RICHTMYER

*Late Professor of Physics
at Cornell University*

E. H. KENNARD

*Formerly Professor of Physics
at Cornell University*

T. LAURITSEN

*Professor of Physics
California Institute of Technology*

FIFTH EDITION

New York   Toronto   London

McGRAW-HILL BOOK COMPANY, INC.

1955

INTRODUCTION TO MODERN PHYSICS

VI

52509

PREFACE TO THE FIFTH EDITION

After the death of Professor Richtmyer in 1939, it was arranged that the preparation of a third edition of his "Introduction to Modern Physics," originally published in 1928, should be undertaken by E. H. Kennard, then professor of physics at Cornell University. So extensively had the physical scene changed that many additions were needed and extensive curtailment or recasting of existing material was necessary. In making these changes, the intention was to retain the characteristic features of the book, especially the historical approach to new fields and the choice of a limited number of topics for careful discussion rather than an inclusive summary of everything. In a later fourth edition only limited further changes were made.

In the present fifth edition, further curtailments have been made in order to make room for important new material, and many passages have been rewritten. The former chapter on electromagnetic theory has been relegated to an appendix, and "Relativity" now precedes the photo-electric effect because of its fundamental nature. Older material on the quantum theory and the nuclear atom has been abbreviated, but the treatment of wave mechanics has been expanded somewhat so as to exhibit an actual example of the mathematical method and to give the student a precise idea of perturbation theory and of the approximate treatment of electron spin. "Spectroscopy" has been partly rewritten, and additions here include the measurement of nuclear moments, micro-wave work on the hydrogen fine structure, the ammonia inversion line, and alternating intensities in band spectra.

The chapter on x-rays has been greatly abbreviated. Specific heats are treated only briefly as the first third of a new chapter on "The Wave Mechanics of Matter in Bulk," which contains also a summary of the wave mechanics of ideal gases and a short description of the application of wave mechanics to solids. Space has not been taken, however, for a survey of the somewhat incoherent experimental facts in the physics of solids, with which the student is presumed to acquire sufficient general familiarity in other courses.

The revision of the chapters on nuclear physics and cosmic rays has been largely the responsibility of the new junior author. Both chapters

v

have been extensively rearranged to accommodate new material and to present as systematically as possible current thinking in these two closely related fields. In Chapter 10, considerable emphasis has been placed on the experimental foundations of the present theory of nuclear structure and the course of nuclear reactions, and some account of the theory itself, admittedly tentative at points, is presented. The subject matter of Chapter 11 has been expanded to include a description of some of the newly discovered fundamental particles which appear in high-energy nuclear interactions and whose bearing on the structure of matter presents one of the most important unsolved problems of present-day physics.

E. H. Kennard
T. Lauritsen

PREFACE TO THE FIRST EDITION

For several years, the author has given at Cornell University, and, occasionally, in summer sessions elsewhere, a course of lectures under the title "Introduction to Modern Physical Theories." These lectures have been adapted, as far as possible, to meet the needs of two groups of students: (1) those special students in physics who, before entering the specialized graduate courses, desire a survey of the origin and development of modern physics in order the better to understand the interrelations of the more advanced courses; and (2) those students who, pursuing either academic or professional curricula and having had the usual elementary undergraduate courses in physics, wish a further bird's-eye view of the whole subject. This book is based upon these lectures and has been prepared, although rather reluctantly, as a result of the importunities of former students and other friends.

The purpose of this book is, frankly, pedagogical. The author has attempted to present such a discussion of the origin, development, and present status of *some* of the more important concepts of physics, *classical as well as modern*, as will give to the student a correct perspective of the growth and present trend of physics as a whole. Such a perspective is a necessary basis—so the author, at least, believes—for a more intensive study of any of the various subdivisions of the subject. While for the student whose interests are cultural, or who is to enter any of the professions directly or indirectly related to physics, such as engineering, chemistry, astronomy, or mathematics, an account of modern physics which gives the *origin* of current theories is likely to be quite as interesting and valuable as in a categorical statement of the theories themselves. Indeed, in *all* branches of human knowledge the "why" is an absolutely indispensable accompaniment to the "what." Why?" is the proverbial question of childhood. "Why?" inquires the *thoughtful* (!) student in classroom or lecture hall. "Why?" demands the venerable scientist when listening to an exposition of views held by a colleague. Accordingly, if this book seems to lay somewhat greater emphasis on matters which are frequently regarded as historical, or, if here and there a classical experiment is described in greater detail than is customary, it is with a desire to recognize the importance of "why."

If one were to attempt to answer all of the "why's" raised by an intelligent auditor in answer to a categorical statement, such as, "The atom of oxygen is composed of eight electrons surrounding a nucleus containing four alpha particles," one would have to expound a large part of physical science from Copernicus to Rutherford and Bohr. To attempt a statement of even the more important concepts, hypotheses, and laws of modern physics and of their origin and development would be an encyclopedic task which, at least in so far as concerns the aim of this book, would fall of its own weight. Accordingly, it has been necessary to select those parts of the subject which best serve our purpose. This selection, as well as the method of presentation, has been based upon the experience gained in giving the above-mentioned lectures to numerous groups of students. Many very important developments, particularly the more recent ones, either have been omitted entirely or have been given only a passing comment. And even in those parts of the subject which have been discussed, there has been no attempt to bring the discussion strictly up to date. Indeed, with the present rapid growth of physics, it would be quite impossible for any *book*, even a special treatise, to be strictly up to date. Happily, for our purpose, up-to-date-ness is not an imperative requisite, since it is assumed that the student who wishes the *latest* knowledge will consult the current periodicals.

In this connection, it should be emphasized that this book is an *introduction* to modern physical theories and is intended neither as a compendium of information nor as a critical account of any of the subjects discussed. In preparing the manuscript, the author has consulted freely the many very excellent texts which deal with the various special topics. Save for here and there a very minor item, or an occasional novelty in presentation, the book makes no claim to originality, except, perhaps, as regards the viewpoint from which some parts have been written.

It is assumed that the student is familiar with the elementary principles of calculus, for no account of modern physics can dispense with at least a limited amount of mathematical discussion, if for no other reason than to emphasize the fact that, in the progress of physics, *theory* and *experiment* have gone hand in hand. Partly, however, for the sake of brevity and partly in the attempt always to keep the underlying physical principles in the foreground, numerous "short cuts" and simplifications, some of them perhaps rather questionable from a precise standpoint, have been introduced. These elisions should cause no confusion.

The student who, in his educational career, has reached the point where he can, with profit, pursue a course based on such a book as this, has passed beyond the stage where he assimilates only the material presented in lecture or class and has come to regard a "course" as a channel to guide his own independent studies, branching out from the "course" in such directions as his fancy or interests may lead him. It is hoped that students reading this book will do likewise. Deliberately, the author has not given a collected bibliography at the end of each chapter, or a list of problems and suggested topics for study. Rather, references, in most cases to original sources, have been given at appropriate points in the text, and it is hoped that, starting from these references, the student will prepare his own bibliography of such parts of the subject as appeal to him. The advantage to the student of such a procedure is obvious. Quite apart from the value of the experience gained in making contact with, and in studying, the literature of any subject, the reading of *first-hand* accounts of at least some of the more important developments will give the student a better understanding of the subject than can, in general, be gained by textbook study only. Accordingly, he will find here and there throughout this book suggestions of important articles which should be read in the original. Likewise, in many places the discussion has, of necessity, been brief, and the student is referred to special treatises for further details. Various supplementary questions and problems will also arise at numerous points as the student reads the text.

There is no more fascinating story than an account of the development of physical science as a whole. (*Any* scientist would probably make the same statement about *his own* science!) Such a study leads to certain broad generalizations which are of outstanding importance in evaluating current theories and concepts. For example, one finds that, taken by and large, the evolution of physics has been characterized by *continuity*. That is to say: With few exceptions, the ideas, concepts, and laws of physics have evolved *gradually;* only here and there do we find *outstanding* discontinuities. The discovery of photoelectricity, of x-rays, and of radioactivity represent such discontinuities and are correctly designated "discoveries." But we must use "discover" in a quite different sense when we say that J. J. Thomson "discovered" the electron. The history of the electron goes back at least to Faraday. Thomson's experiments are all the more brilliant because he succeeded in demonstrating, by direct experiment, the existence of something, evidence concerning which had been previously *indirect*. Then, there are the respective roles played by qualitative and by quantitative work. Numerous important discoveries have been made "by investigating the next decimal place." Witness the discovery of argon. And ever since Kepler proved that the orbits of the planets are ellipses, relations expressible in *quantitative* form have carried greater weight than those which could be stated only qualitatively. For example, Rumford's experiments on the production of heat by mechanical means were suggestive. But Joule's measurement of the mechanical equivalent of heat was *convincing*. If, directly, or indirectly by inference, the author has succeeded here and there in the text in pointing out such generalizations as these, one more object which he has had in mind will have been accomplished.

The author wishes to take this occasion to acknowledge his obligations to those who have aided in the preparation of this book: to his wife, for assistance in preparing the manuscript and in proofreading; and to his many students, whose generous approbation of the lecture courses upon which the book is based has, in a large part, inspired its preparation. He is particularly indebted to Dr. J. A. Becker, of the Bell Telephone Laboratories, Inc., for his invaluable aid in reading the manuscript, pointing out numerous errors, and suggesting important improvements.

F. K. Richtmyer

Ithaca, N.Y.
July, 1928

CONTENTS

Preface to the Fifth Edition   v

Preface to the First Edition   vii

CHAPTER 1.   HISTORICAL SKETCH   1

FIRST PERIOD: EARLIEST TIMES TO 1550 A.D.   5

1. The Greeks. 2. Thales of Miletus. 3. Pythagoras. 4. Anaxagoras
and Empedocles. 5. Democritus. 6. Aristotle. 7. Aristarchus. 8.
Archimedes. 9. From the Greeks to Copernicus. 10. The Copernican
System.

SECOND PERIOD (1550–1800 A.D.): RISE OF THE EXPERIMENTAL METHOD .   12

11. Galileo Galilei. 12. Tycho Brahe and Kepler. 13. The Experimental
Method Spreads. 14. Sir Isaac Newton. 15. Newton's Contemporaries.
16. Mechanics during the Eighteenth Century. 17. Heat during the
Eighteenth Century. 18. Light during the Eighteenth Century. 19.
Electricity during the Eighteenth Century. 20. Close of the Second
Period.

THIRD PERIOD (1800–1890 A.D.): THE RISE OF CLASSICAL PHYSICS . . .   31

21. The Nineteenth Century in Physics. 22. Heat and Energy. 23. Light.
24. Electricity and Magnetism. 25. Michael Faraday. 26. Joseph Henry.
27. James Clerk Maxwell. 28. The Completion of the Electromagnetic
Theory.

CHAPTER 2.   THE THEORY OF RELATIVITY   49

29. Newtonian Relativity. 30. Relativity and the Propagation of Light.
31. The Michelson-Morley Experiment. 32. The New Relativity of Einstein. 33. Simultaneity and Time Order. 34. The Lorentz Transformation. 35. Contractions in Space and Time. 36. The Transformation of
Velocities. 37. Relativistic Mechanics, the Variation of Mass. 38. Force
and Kinetic Energy. 39. A Relation between Mass and Energy. 40.
Relativity and Electromagnetism. 41. General Theory of Relativity.
42. Einstein's Law of Gravitation.

CHAPTER 3.   ELECTRONS AND THE PHOTOELECTRIC EFFECT .   77

43. Discovery of the Photoelectric Effect. 44. A Problem. 45. Electricity
in Matter. 46. The Zeeman Effect. 47. The Discovery of the Electron.
48. Electronic Magnitudes. 49. Photoelectrons. 50. Relation between

Photoelectric Current and Intensity of Illumination. 51. Energy Distribution of Photoelectrons. 52. Relation between the Velocities of Photoelectrons and the Frequency of the Light. 53. Other Properties of Photoelectric Emission. 54. Thermionic Emission. 55. What Is the Photoelectric Mechanism? 56. The Free-electron Theory of Metals. 57. Origin of Photoelectrons.

CHAPTER 4.   THE ORIGIN OF THE QUANTUM THEORY   106

58. Thermal Radiation. 59. The Isothermal Enclosure and Black-body Radiation. 60. Pressure and Energy Flux Due to Isotropic Radiation. 61. The Stefan-Boltzmann Law. 62. Reflection from a Moving Mirror. 63. Effect of an Adiabatic Expansion upon Black-body Radiation. 64. The Wien Displacement Law. 65. The Formula for Black-body Radiation. 66. The Principle of the Equipartition of Energy. 67. Degrees of Freedom in an Enclosure. 68. The Rayleigh-Jeans Formula. 69. Planck's Investigation of Black-body Radiation. 70. Distribution of Energy among Oscillators in Thermal Equilibrium. 71. Planck's Quantum Hypothesis. 72. Planck's Radiation Law.

CHAPTER 5.   THE NUCLEAR ATOM AND THE ORIGIN OF SPECTRAL LINES   133

73. Spectroscopic Units. 74. Early Search for Regularities in Spectra. 75. Spectral Series and Their Interrelations. 76. Further Relations between Series. Spectral Terms. 77. Early Views on Atomic Structure. 78. The Scattering of Alpha-particles by Atoms. 79. The Nuclear Atom. 80. The Bohr Theory of Atomic Hydrogen. 81. Quantum States of One Electron in an Atom. 82. Spectrum of a One-electron Atom. 83. The Spectrum of Atomic Hydrogen. 84. Ionized Helium. 85. Energy Levels and Series Relations for Sodium. 86. Excitation and Ionization of Atoms by Electrons. 87. Absorption and Reemission of Radiation. 88. The Boltzmann Distribution Law. 89. The Extension of Bohr's Theory.

CHAPTER 6.   WAVE MECHANICS   172

90. Matter Waves. 91. Mechanics as Geometrical Optics of the Waves. 92. Refraction of Matter Waves. 93. The de Broglie Wavelength. 94. Experiments on Electron Waves. 95. Diffraction of Molecule Waves. 96. The Schrödinger Wave Equation. 97. The Physical Significance of Ψ. 98. The Probability Stream Density. 99. The Indeterminacy Principle. 100. Stationary or Quantum States. 101. Physical Magnitudes as Operators. 102. Particle in a Box; the Harmonic Oscillator. 103. Perturbation Theory. 104. The One-electron Atom. 105. Relativistic Effects and Electron Spin. 106. Two Noninteracting Particles in a Box. 107. Electron Spin. The Exclusion Principle. 108. Emission and Absorption of Radiation.

CHAPTER 7.   ATOMIC STRUCTURE AND OPTICAL SPECTRA   . .   224

COMPLEX ATOMS   224

109. The Central-field Approximation for a Many-electron Atom. 110. Shells and Subshells.

THE PERIODIC TABLE OF THE ELEMENTS 228

111. General Features of the Periodic Table. 112. The First Two Periods. 113. Valence Bonds. 114. Remainder of the Periodic Table.

OPTICAL SPECTRA. 240

115. Angular Momentum and Its Selection Rules. 116. Alkali-type Spectra. 117. Term Energies of the Alkali Metals. 118. The Spin-orbit Effect in a Central Field. 119. Fine Structure in Alkali-type Spectra. 120. Multiplet Levels for One-electron Atoms. 121. Fine Structure of Spectral Lines from One-electron Atoms. 122. Many-electron Wave Theory. 123. LS or Russell-Saunders Coupling. 124. LS Multiplets of Levels. 125. Spacing of the LS Multiplet Levels. 126. The Arc Spectrum of Mercury. 127. Equivalent Electrons. 128. Coupling of the jj Type. 129. Effects of a Magnetic Field on an Atom. 130. Zeeman Effect in a Huge Field. 131. Zeeman Effect in a Weak Field. 132. Zeeman Patterns of LS Multiplets in a Weak Field. 133. The Paschen-Back Effect. 134. The Stern-Gerlach Experiment. 135. Isotope Structure and Hyperfine Structure. 136. Magnetic Beam Measurement of Nuclear Spins and Moments. 137. The Breadth of Spectral Lines. 138. Molecular Spectra. 139. Rotation Spectra. 140. Vibration-rotation Spectra. 141. General Theory of Molecular Quantum States. 142. Electronic Bands. 143. The Raman Effect. 144. Homonuclear Molecules. 145. The Ammonia Inversion Spectrum.

CHAPTER 8. X-RAYS 345

EARLY, MOSTLY QUALITATIVE DEVELOPMENTS (1895–1912). 345

146. The Discovery of X-rays. 147. Production and Measurement of X-rays. 148. The Classical Pulse Theory of X-rays. 149. Polarization, Absorption, and Fluorescence of X-rays.

X-RAY SPECTRA 355

150. The Crystal Diffraction Grating. 151. The X-ray Spectrometer. 152. Monochromatic Characteristic Radiations. 153. Moseley's Law. 154. The Origin of X-ray Lines. 155. X-ray Energy Levels and Selection Rules. 156. The Continuous X-ray Spectrum.

INTERACTIONS OF X-RAYS WITH ATOMS 377

157. The Absorption of X-rays. 158. The Photoelectric Effect of X-rays. 159. The Scattering of X-rays. 160. The Compton Effect. 161. Refraction and Reflection of X-rays. 162. The Nature of Electromagnetic Radiation.

SOME LATER DEVELOPMENTS IN X-RAY SPECTROSCOPY 396

163. Multiple Ionization of Inner Shells. 164. X-ray Spectra and the Outer Part of the Atom. 165. X-ray Spectroscopy of Solids.

CHAPTER 9. WAVE MECHANICS OF MATTER IN BULK 405

THE QUANTUM THEORY OF SPECIFIC HEATS 405

166. The Specific Heats of Ideal Gases. 167. The Specific Heats of Simple Solids.

THE WAVE MECHANICS OF IDEAL GASES 414

168. The Ideal Gas.   169. Gaseous Pressure.   170. The Fermi-Dirac Gas.

CRYSTALLINE SOLIDS. 420

171. The Atomic Approach in the Wave Mechanics of Crystals.   172.
Conductors and Insulators.   173. The Collective-electron Approach.
174. Metals and Nonmetals.

CHAPTER 10.   THE NUCLEUS 431

NATURAL RADIOACTIVITY 431

175. The Discovery of Radioactivity.   176. Radiations from Radioactive
Substances.   177. Radioactive Transformations.   178. Detection of
Individual Charged Particles.   179. Nuclear Spectra of the Radioelements.

MASSES OF ATOMS 455

180. Positive Rays.   181. Isotopes of Stable Elements.

ARTIFICIAL TRANSMUTATIONS BY ALPHA-PARTICLES 463

182. Discovery of Artificial Transmutation.   183. Discovery of the Neutron.

NUCLEAR BINDING ENERGIES AND NUCLEAR FORCES 470

184. Properties of Nuclei.   185. Constituents of Nuclei.   186. Masses
and Binding Energies.   187. Nuclear Forces.

POSITRONS, ARTIFICIAL RADIOACTIVITY, ARTIFICIALLY ACCELERATED PAR-
TICLES. 490

188. The Positron.   189. Induced Radioactivity.   190. Nuclear Transformations with Artificially Accelerated Particles.   191. Accelerators.

NUCLEAR REACTIONS AND NUCLEAR MODELS. 504

192. General Features of Nuclear Reactions.   193. Masses of Mirror
Nuclides.   194. Particle Groups.   195. Nuclear Resonances.   196. Liquid-
drop Model.   197. Neutron Reactions.   198. Energy Levels of Nuclei.
199. The Shell Model.

NUCLEAR FISSION AND NUCLEAR ENERGY. 540

200. Discovery of Fission.   201. Theory of Fission.   202. Prompt Neutrons
—Chain Reactions.   203. Fast Fission—Explosive Reactors.   204. Fusion:
Energy from the Light Elements.

CHAPTER 11.   COSMIC RAYS AND FUNDAMENTAL PARTICLES . 555

205. Early Work on Cosmic Rays.   206. Measurement of Cosmic-ray
Ionization.   207. The Altitude-depth Curve.   208. Discovery of the
Latitude Effect.   209. Theory of Geomagnetic Effects.   210. Primary
Momentum Spectrum.   211. Observations on Single Cosmic-ray Particles.
212. Showers and Bursts.   213. Theory of the Shower Phenomenon.   214.
Discovery of the Mu Meson.   215. Properties of Mu Mesons.   216. The
Pi Meson.   217. Artificial Production of Pi Mesons.   218. Heavy Mesons
and Hyperons.   219. Nuclear Interactions of Cosmic Rays.   220. Cosmic-
ray Primaries.   221. Development of the Cosmic Radiation in the Atmosphere.   222. Origin of Cosmic Rays.

APPENDIX I.   ELECTROMAGNETIC ENERGY, MOMENTUM, AND RADIATION .   633

  223. Electromagnetic Units. 224. Electromagnetic Energy. 225.
  Electromagnetic Momentum. 226. Electromagnetic Waves. 227. Field
  of a Moving Point Charge. 228. Energy Radiated by Accelerated Point
  Charges.

APPENDIX II.   COMPOSITION OF THE ELEMENTS AND MASSES OF ISOTOPES .   639

APPENDIX III.   FIRST IONIZATION POTENTIAL V, LOWEST SPECTRAL TERM T,
                 AND ELECTRON CONFIGURATION OF THE ELEMENTS .   .   .   648

Some Useful Constants and Relations   651

Index   653

INTRODUCTION

The term "modern physics," taken literally, means, of course, the *sum total* of knowledge included under the head of present-day physics. In this sense, the physics of 1890 is still modern; very few statements made in a good physics text of 1890 would need to be deleted today as untrue. The principal changes required would be in a few generalizations, perhaps, to which exceptions have since been discovered, and in certain speculative theories, such as that concerning the ether, which any good physicist of 1890 would have recognized to be open to possible doubt.

On the other hand, since 1890, there have been enormous advances in physics, and some of these advances have brought into question, or have directly contradicted, certain theories that had seemed to be strongly supported by the experimental evidence.

For example, few, if any, physicists in 1890 questioned the wave theory of light. Its triumphs over the old corpuscular theory seemed to be final and complete, particularly after the brilliant experiments of Hertz, in 1887, which demonstrated, beyond doubt, the fundamental soundness of Maxwell's electromagnetic theory of light. And yet, by an irony of fate which makes the story of modern physics full of the most interesting and dramatic situations, these very experiments of Hertz brought to light a new phenomenon—the photoelectric effect—which played an important part in establishing the quantum theory. The latter theory, in many of its aspects, is diametrically opposed to the wave theory of light; indeed, the reconciliation of these two theories, each based on incontrovertible evidence, was one of the great problems of the first quarter of the twentieth century.

It will be the purpose of the following pages to give an outline of the origin, development, and present status of these parts of physics which have developed during the last half-century. But a history of the United States cannot begin abruptly with July 4, 1776. In like manner, if we would understand the full meaning of the growth of physics since 1900, we must have clearly in mind at least the main events in the development of the subject up to that time. Accordingly, we shall begin

1

our study with a brief account of the history of physics up to a half-century ago.

In presenting this brief historical survey, a further purpose has been kept in mind toward which it is hoped that the reader will be, ultimately at least, sympathetic. Modern scientists, with few exceptions, have grossly neglected to cultivate the history of their respective sciences. How many physicists can answer the questions: When was the law of the conservation of energy first enunciated? Who was Count Rumford? Did the concept of universal gravitation spring full grown from the head of that genius, Newton? Indeed, when did Newton live?

Just as any good American should know the essential outline of the history of his country, so any good physicist should know the principal facts in the history of physics. For, in that history, in the lives of those men whose labors have given us our subject, and in the part that physics has played in molding human thought and in contributing to modern civilization, the student will find a story which is as full of human interest and inspiration as any subject of the curriculum. What can be more inspiring than the life of Michael Faraday and his whole-souled devotion to his work? The physicist owes it to his science to possess such a knowledge of the history of physics as gives *him* a correct perspective of the development and present-day importance of the subject and, in turn, enables him to acquaint his contemporaries in other fields with these essential facts. It is hoped, therefore, that the student who proposes to follow physics as a profession, as well as the student whose interest is largely cultural, will extend the following all too brief historical sketch by independent study, particularly of biography.

The history of physics may be somewhat arbitrarily divided into four periods.

The First Period extends from the earliest times up to about 1550 A.D., this date marking approximately the beginning of the experimental method. During this long era, there was some advance in the accumulation of the *facts* of physics as a result of the observation of natural phenomena, but the development of physical *theories* was rendered impossible, partly by the speculative, metaphysical nature of the reasoning employed, but more particularly by the almost complete absence of experiment to test the correctness of such theories as were proposed. The main characteristic of this period, therefore, is *the absence of systematic experiment.*

The Second Period extends from 1550 to 1800 A.D. Numerous basic advances were made during this period—by such men as Gilbert, Galileo, Newton, Huygens, Boyle—but its most important characteristic is *the development and the firm establishment of the experimental method* as a recognized and accepted means of scientific inquiry. This period was inaugurated by the classic work of Galileo (1564–1642); but it took nearly two centuries more to overcome prejudice, dogma, and religious intolerance and to bring universal recognition, even among scientific men, of the basic principle that

. . . science can advance only so far as theories, themselves based upon experiment, are accepted or rejected according as they either agree with or are contrary to other experiments devised to check the theory.

The Third Period, 1800–1890, is characterized by the development of what is now called "classical physics" in contrast with the "quantum physics" of the present century. The experiments of Count Rumford and Joule led to our present kinetic theory of heat. The observations of Thomas Young (1802) and his proposal of the principle of interference (of two beams of light) resulted ultimately in the triumph of Huygens's wave theory of light over the corpuscular theory. And the researches of Faraday and others gave Maxwell the material for the crowning achievement of this period, the electromagnetic theory.

So profound were these and other developments that, by 1880, not a few physicists of note believed that all the important laws of physics had been discovered and that, henceforth, research would be concerned with clearing up minor problems and, particularly, with improvements of methods of measurement so as "to investigate the next decimal place." They could not foresee that the world of physics was on the eve of a series of epoch-making discoveries destined, on the one hand, to stimulate research as never before and, on the other, to usher in an era of the application of physics to industry on a scale previously unknown.

The Fourth Period may be said to begin with the discovery of the photoelectric effect (1887). In the first decade of this period there were discovered, in rapid succession: x-rays, in 1895; radioactivity, in 1896; the electron, in 1897. The beginnings of the quantum theory date from 1900. From 1900 to 1925 the older form of the quantum theory grew to occupy a commanding position in almost every field of physics; the nuclear type of atom and its relation to the emission and absorption of radiation were developed to a high degree; research in physics, stimulated in part by these outstanding discoveries and in part by extensive industrial applications, increased to almost a new order of magnitude. Then, when physicists were just beginning to grow accustomed to the use of either the classical theory or the quantum theory, according to the problem in hand, the theoretical papers of de Broglie, Heisenberg and Schrödinger, and the experimental work of Davisson and Germer and of G. P. Thomson, beginning about 1925, initiated the new form of quantum theory known as wave mechanics. This new theory has effected, in a radical and remarkable way, a synthesis of classical and quantum physics and has exerted as profound an influence on physics as did the discoveries of Newton over two and a half centuries ago.   Perhaps 1925 should be regarded as marking the beginning of a *fifth* period in the history of physics.

It is obviously far beyond the scope of this book to give a detailed account of the history of physics during each of these periods.   Instead, in the first chapter we shall discuss briefly the history of physics up to the establishment of the electromagnetic theory of light.   Thereafter we shall not adhere strictly to the historical method.   In the first chapter, furthermore, we shall make no attempt to give a complete outline of the history of physics, but we shall select such material for presentation as best illustrates general trends and viewpoints.   No mention at all will be made of the work of many distinguished physicists of the past.   It is hoped that the student will fill in the gaps by supplementary reading.

It should be emphasized that this book is an *introduction* to the subject and is in no sense a compendium.   If no mention is made of certain important branches of physics, it is because of the feeling that the student's interests will be served best by discussing relatively few subjects more thoroughly.   It is desirable, of course, that a book dealing with modern physics should be up to date.   The subject is growing at such an astonishing rate, however, that any book, even if up to date when published, would be out of date within a few months.   Accordingly, those topics have been selected for discussion which seem most likely to remain permanently important and to provide the student with the most effective starting point for further study.

CHAPTER 1

HISTORICAL SKETCH

FIRST PERIOD: EARLIEST TIMES TO 1550 A.D.

1. The Greeks. Relatively speaking, the contributions made by the Greeks to the natural sciences were far less than their contributions to mathematics, literature, art, and metaphysics. Nevertheless, in spite of their vague and misty philosophizing concerning natural phenomena and in spite of their general failure to test theory by experiment, the Greeks gave to the world much of the physics that was known up to 1400 A.D. In their writings, one finds, here and there, the germ of such fundamental modern principles as the conservation of matter, inertia, atomic theory, the finite velocity of light, and the like.

2. Thales of Miletus (624–547 B.C.), according to Aristotle, was acquainted with the attractive power of magnets and of rubbed amber. He is often said to have discovered the inclination of the ecliptic and the spherical shape of the earth,[1] but Aristotle credited him with the doctrine that the earth was cylindrical in shape and rested on water.

3. Pythagoras (580–500 B.C.) was one of the greatest of the early Greek philosophers and the founder of the Pythagorean school. He held that the earth is spherical, although the basis of this belief is not known. According to Heath,[2] his argument was probably a "mathematico-esthetic" one based on the idea that "the sphere is the most perfect of all figures." Pythagoras himself, and probably his immediate successors among the Pythagoreans, believed that the entire universe was spherical in shape with the earth at its center and that the sun, stars, and planets moved in independent circles around the earth as a center.

4. Anaxagoras (500–428 B.C.) **and Empedocles** (484–424 B.C.). According to Plato, Anaxagoras neglected his possessions in order to devote himself to science. He is credited with the view that the moon does not shine by its own light but that "the sun places the brightness in the moon" and "the moon is eclipsed through the interposition of the earth." Also, "The sun is eclipsed at new moon through the interposition of the

---

[1] F. Rosenberger, "Geschichte der Physik," vol. I, p. 6.
[2] T. L. Heath, "Aristarchus of Samos."

5

moon."[1] Anaxagoras was accused of impiety, however, because he taught that the sun was a red-hot stone and that the moon was simply earth, and for holding this doctrine he was banished from Athens.

To Anaxagoras is due the germ of the idea of the atomic hypothesis of Democritus, who lived in the next generation. Anaxagoras denied the contention of the earlier Greeks regarding the creation or destruction of matter. He taught that changes in matter are due to combinations or separations of small, invisible particles (spermata). These particles themselves were conceived to be unchangeable and imperishable but different from each other in form, color, and taste. This doctrine foreshadowed the law of the conservation of matter.

Empedocles, on the other hand, reduced the elements to four—earth, water, air, and fire—through combinations and separations of which the All exists. He also held definite views concerning the phenomena of light. According to him, light is due to the emission by the luminous or visible body of small particles that enter the eye and are then returned from the eye to the body, the two "streams" giving rise to the sense of form, color, etc.

According to Aristotle, Empedocles believed that light "takes time to travel from one point to another." This idea was rejected by Aristotle, who stated that "though a movement of light might elude our observation within a short distance, that it should do so all the way from east to west is too much to assume."[2]

5. Democritus (460–370 B.C.) gave more definite form to the atomic hypothesis of Anaxagoras by postulating that *the universe consists of empty space and an (almost) infinite number of indivisible and invisible particles* which differ from each other in *form, position, and arrangement*. In support of this hypothesis, Democritus argues that the creation of matter is impossible, since *nothing* can come from *nothing* and, further, nothing which is can cease to exist. Aristotle[3] puts the argument in this form: "If, then, some one of the things which are is constantly disappearing, why has not the whole of what is been used up long ago and vanished away?" But Aristotle rejects the atomic hypothesis which, indeed, on the basis of speculative reasoning alone, could not evolve beyond the point where Democritus left it.

6. Aristotle (384–332 B.C.), a pupil of the philosopher Plato, contributed so much to all branches of knowledge—logic, rhetoric, ethics, metaphysics, psychology, natural science—that it is difficult to sift out that which is germane to a brief history of physics. Perhaps the most

---

[1] *Ibid.*, p. 78. Quotations cited from later Greek writers.

[2] Quoted by Heath, *op. cit.*, p. 93.

[3] "De Generatione et Corruptione," bk. I, cap. III, H. H. Joachim (tr.), Clarendon Press, Oxford, 1922.

important single fact is the tremendous influence which, as a result of his intellectual brilliance and achievements in *many* branches of learning, he exerted for many succeeding centuries in *all* branches, physics included. Viewed from our twentieth-century vantage point, however, not a little of his reasoning concerning the physical universe sounds like piffle. For example, in "De Generatione et Corruptione," he discusses the "coming-to-be" and the "passing-away" of things, and argues for the indestructibility of matter by saying that (Book II, Cap. X) "it is far more reasonable (to assume) that *what is* should cause the coming-to-be of *what is not* than that *what is not* should cause the being of *what is*," which is understandable. But then follows the curious argument: "Now that which is being moved *is*, but that which is coming to be *is not;* hence, also, motion is prior to coming-to-be . . . and we assert that motion causes *coming-to-be*." But *coming-to-be* and *passing-away* are two processes contrary to one another. Therefore, says Aristotle, we must look for *two motions*, likewise contrary, as the cause of both *coming-to-be* and *passing-away*. Since these processes go on continuously, we must look for continuous motion. Only motion in a circle is continuous, and motion in an inclined circle has the necessary duality of opposing movements. Such a motion is that of the sun along the ecliptic, which, as it approaches (spring), causes coming-to-be and, as it retreats (autumn), causes decay.

And yet Aristotle frequently calls in observed facts to substantiate his speculations. For example, in "De Caelo" (Book II, Cap. XIV), after proving, by a more or less abstract argument, that the earth is spherical, he says:

The evidence of all the senses further corroborates this. How else would eclipses of the moon show segments as we see them? . . . since it is the interposition of the earth that makes the eclipse, the form of this line (*i.e.*, the earth's shadow on the moon) will be caused by the form of the earth's surface, which is therefore spherical.

He also points to the apparent change in altitude of the stars as one travels north or south and concludes that "not only is the earth circular, but it is a circle of no great size."

Indeed, in theory if not in his own practice, Aristotle places great emphasis on the importance of facts in connection with scientific development. In a paragraph in "De Generatione et Corruptione" (Book I, Cap. II), he says:

Lack of experience diminishes our power of taking a comprehensive view of the admitted facts. Hence, those who dwell in intimate association with nature and its phenomena grow more and more able to formulate, as the foundation of their theories, principles such as to admit of a wide and coherent development; while those whom devotion to abstract discussions has rendered unobservant of the facts are too ready to dogmatize on the basis of a few observations.

This is surely good doctrine even for twentieth-century scientists!

An attempt to summarize Aristotle's views on physics is beyond the scope of this book, but reference may be made to two of his doctrines because of their bearing upon subsequent history.

The first is his supposed views on falling bodies. The statement is commonly made that Aristotle held that a heavy body would fall from a given height with greater velocity than a light body. It is difficult, however, to be sure from Aristotle's extant writings just what he actually held in regard to this point. The passages that seem to refer to it occur in the course of his arguments against the possibility of the existence of a void. For example, he states:[1]

. . . We see the same weight or body moving faster than another for two reasons, either because there is a difference in what it moves through, as between water, air, and earth, or because, other things being equal, the moving body differs from the other owing to excess of weight or lightness. . . . And always, by so much as the medium is more incorporeal and less resistant and more easily divided, the faster will be the movement.

Here, as elsewhere, Aristotle speaks always of movement of a body through a medium. It has been suggested by Greenhill[2] that he may have meant *terminal* velocity, such as the constant velocity of rain drops as they approach the ground. The *heavier* drops *do* fall faster. It seems perhaps more probable that Aristotle, believing that a medium of some sort must always be present, was unaware of such distinctions as that between terminal and nonterminal velocity and actually did believe that in all stages of its motion the heavier body falls faster.[3]

The second doctrine referred to is that of the motion of the earth, sun, and planets. In his "De Caelo" (Book II, Cap. XIV), after a series of abstract arguments, in the course of which he states that "heavy bodies forcibly thrown quite straight upward return to the point from which they started even if they be thrown to an infinite (!) distance," Aristotle concludes "that the earth does not move and does not lie elsewhere than at the center." He supposed that the sun, planets, and stars are carried by a series of concentric spheres which revolve around the earth as a center. The authority of Aristotle was so great as to render sterile the brilliant work of Aristarchus in the next century.

[1] This and the following quotation from Aristotle are taken from "The Works of Aristotle translated into English," vol. II, Clarendon Press, Oxford, 1930.

[2] Greenhill, *Nature*, vol. 92, p. 584.

[3] Cf. L. Cooper, "Aristotle, Galileo, and the Tower of Pisa," 1935.

7. Aristarchus (about 310–230 B.C.) enunciated a cosmogony identical with that proposed by Copernicus nearly 2,000 years later. No mention of this hypothesis is made in his only extant work, "On the Sizes and Distances of the Sun and Moon," but Archimedes tells us, in a book called "The Sand-reckoner," that "Aristarchus of Samos brought out a book" containing the hypothesis "that the fixed stars and the sun remained unmoved; that the earth revolves around the sun in the circumference of a circle, the sun lying in the middle of the orbit"; and that "the sphere of the fixed stars" is very great compared with the circle in which the earth revolves. The prestige of Aristotle was too great, however, and the geocentric hypothesis that he supported was so completely satisfactory to the ancient mind that Aristarchus' theory was practically lost for nearly 2,000 years.[1]

8. Archimedes (287–212 B.C.), whose name is known to every student of elementary physics because of the famous principle of hydrostatics that bears his name, was one of the most noted physicists of antiquity. He was a man of great ability in what would now be called "theoretical (or mathematical) physics" as well as a practical engineer—a sort of ancient Lord Kelvin. In one of his books already mentioned, "The Sand-reckoner," he computes that 10^{63} grains of sand would fill the sphere of the universe as fixed by Aristarchus. In another, "On Floating Bodies," he lays the foundations of hydrostatics. His Proposition 7, in this book, enunciates the famous principle: "A solid heavier than a fluid will, if placed in it, descend to the bottom of the fluid, and the solid will, when weighed in the fluid, be lighter than its true weight by the weight of the fluid displaced."

9. From the Greeks to Copernicus. To give but a passing comment to the 17 centuries between Archimedes and Copernicus would seem to give the reader the impression that no developments of moment occurred during that long period. This impression is almost correct. During ancient times Ptolemy of Alexandria (70–147 A.D.) collected the optical knowledge of his time in a book in which he discusses, among other things, reflection from mirrors—plane, convex, concave—and, particularly, refraction, which Ptolemy evidently studied experimentally. He gives, in degrees, relative values of angles of incidence and of refraction for air-water, air-glass, and water-glass surfaces and describes an apparatus by which he determined these quantities; he states that for a given interface these two angles are proportional. He also mentions atmospheric refraction as affecting the apparent position of stars. He invented

[1] Heath's "Aristarchus of Samos" is an exceedingly interesting and valuable book. It contains a review of early Greek astronomy up to the time of Aristarchus, a discussion of his work, and a translation of his only extant book, "On the Sizes and Distances of the Sun and Moon."

a complicated theory of the motions of the planets in their orbits about the earth in order to explain their apparent motions among the stars.

From Ptolemy to the Arabian Alhazen is a span of nine centuries—twice the total lapse of time from the discovery of America to the present—during which there was stagnation in almost all lines of intellectual pursuits. But about the eighth century A.D., as an indirect result of religious activity, the Arabs began to cultivate chemistry, mathematics, and astronomy, in large part by translating into Arabic the works of the Greeks but also, in a few instances, by making original contributions. About the year 1000, Alhazen produced a work on optics in seven books. This treatise sets forth a clear description of the optical system of the eye, discusses the laws of concave and convex mirrors, both spherical and cylindrical, and carries the subject of refraction a little further by recognizing that the proportionality between the angles of incidence and refraction holds only for small angles.

During the next 500 years, a very few advances in physics were made. Roger Bacon (1214–1294), British philosopher and scientist and a monk of the Franciscan Order, taught that in order to learn the secrets of nature *we must first observe.* He believed in mathematics and in deductive science, but he clearly realized that only as scientific conclusions are based on observed phenomena and tested by experiment can useful knowledge result.

About the same time Petrus Peregrinus recognized that magnetic poles are of two kinds, like poles repelling and unlike attracting each other.

Then there was Leonardo da Vinci (1452–1519), Italian painter, architect, sculptor, engineer, and philosopher, whose greatness as a scientist has come to be appreciated only in recent years, for his works were left in manuscript form and were probably not widely known among his contemporaries—for which reason his influence on early science is comparatively insignificant.   His belief in the value of experiment is worthy of the twentieth century: "Before making this case a general rule, test it by experiment two or three times and see if the experiment produces the same effect."   Although expressed in the vague language of his time, some of his ideas concerning what we now refer to as "force," "inertia," "acceleration," the "laws of motion," etc., were qualitatively correct. Concerning perpetual motion, he wrote: "Oh, speculators on perpetual motion, how many vain projects of the like character you have created! Go and be the companions of the searchers after gold."   Rejecting the Ptolemaic theory, he held that "the sun does not move."   That he was not persecuted or even burned at the stake, as was Bruno a century later, for holding such revolutionary and, therefore (!), heretical views is probably due to the fact that his doctrines were given little publicity; for, holding no academic position, he did not teach, and he published nothing.

Finally, in the sixteenth century, the full force of that period of intense intellectual activity known as the Renaissance began to be felt in the field of physics. Then were produced such men as Copernicus, Tycho, Kepler, Galileo, Newton, who with their contemporaries and colleagues, in a space of hardly more than a century, completely broke the "spell" of Aristotle and made possible the beginnings of modern experimental science. In so far as the heliocentric theory completely revolutionized man's conception of the universe and his place in it, it is quite correct to regard the work of Copernicus as beginning a new era in scientific thought. But had it not been for other discoveries coming immediately after Copernicus, such as the telescope, Kepler's laws, Galileo's famous experiments on falling bodies, and many others, it is quite possible that the theory of Copernicus would have had the same fate as that of Aristarchus centuries earlier. It is, therefore, fitting to regard the birth of the Copernican theory as *closing* the first period in the history of physics.

10. The Copernican System. Copernicus (1473–1543), a younger contemporary of Columbus, spent most of his life as one of the leading canons in the monastery at Frauenburg, near the mouth of the Vistula. As a student, however, he had studied, among other subjects, mathematics and astronomy; at the University of Bologna, he was a pupil of a famous astronomer, Novara, who supported the Pythagorean system of the universe as against the Ptolemaic. Copernicus's new theory of the universe is set forth in his "De Revolutionibus Orbium Coelestium," which he allowed to be printed near the close of his life. The new theory appears to have been the result of long reflection upon the difficulties of the current astronomical theory of his day, and upon the various speculations of ancient philosophers.

Copernicus perceived that, by assuming that the earth is a planet like the others and that all the planets move in circles around the sun, a great simplification, both philosophical and mathematical, could be made with regard to the world system. He could thus easily account for the seasons and for the apparent retrograde motion, at times, of the planets. The rotation of the earth on its axis causes the *apparent* daily motion of the sun, moon, and stars; and he pointed out that, probably, the stars are too far away for any motion of the earth to affect their apparent positions. He gave the correct order of the planets from the sun outward.

Whatever the system as proposed by Copernicus lacked quantitatively, it was correct, in its main outline, qualitatively. Its reasonableness set a few men thinking and did much to usher in a new era in science, an era that could come only when truth could have the opportunity of standing alone, *unaided* or *unhindered* by the "authority" of 2,000 years.

SECOND PERIOD (1550–1800 A.D.): RISE OF
THE EXPERIMENTAL METHOD

11. Galileo Galilei (1564–1642).   Galileo is widely, and quite correctly, regarded as the father of modern physics.   To be sure, modern physics has grandfathers and still more remote ancestors, but none of them gave to experimental physics so much as Galileo.   Physicists should be acquainted with the main details not only of his scientific work but also of his life.   The student is urged, therefore, to peruse one of the several biographies and to read some of Galileo's writings, at least in translation. Even a short time spent in following his deductions and in reading *first-hand* something he wrote will prove both interesting and instructive.

Galileo was descended from a noble family, and it is quite probable that he inherited from his father the spirit of free inquiry which characterized his life.   For, in the writings of the elder Galileo, who was well educated and was an accomplished musician, is the statement: "It appears to me that they who in proof of any assertion rely simply on the weight of authority, without adducing any argument in support of it, act very absurdly."

As a student in the monastery of Vallombrosa, near Florence, the young Galileo excelled in the classics and literature and was something of a poet, musician, and art critic.   He also showed an aptitude for science and exhibited considerable mechanical inventiveness.   At the age of seventeen he was sent to the University of Pisa to study medicine.   It was here that he made his first discovery and invention.   One day, in 1581, he noticed the regular oscillations of the great hanging lamp in the cathedral at Pisa.   Although the amplitude of these oscillations became less and less, they were all performed in the same time, as he determined by counting his pulse.   Turning the process around, he invented a "pulsometer," a ball-and-string (i.e., simple pendulum) device, whose length, when adjusted to synchronism with the pulse, was a measure of its frequency.

But the urge toward mathematics and science overcame the pecuniary advantages of a medical career.   At the age of twenty-six, Galileo became professor of mathematics at Pisa.   Here he began a systematic investigation of the mechanical doctrines of Aristotle.   He soon demonstrated by experiment to his own satisfaction that Aristotle was in error in many of his assertions, and these errors he proclaimed energetically from his professorial chair.

It will be recalled that Aristotle was commonly understood to teach that a heavy body falls faster than a light one.   This doctrine had been questioned, on the basis of actual test, by various writers, e.g., by Philoponus in the fifth century and by Benedetto Varchi in the genera-

PLATE 1. Galileo.

tion before Galileo. Nevertheless the authority of Aristotle had continued to be accepted. To test the point, Galileo apparently tried the famous experiment of dropping bodies of unequal weight from the leaning tower of Pisa and found that they all fell with practically equal velocities. We know nothing of the details of the experiment; indeed it is not even certain that he performed it at all.[1] It is certain, however, that Galileo and a few of his friends were convinced of Aristotle's error; and it seems equally certain that the majority maintained, in spite of all experiments and arguments to the contrary, that Aristotle must be right.

And then began a persecution which was to last Galileo's lifetime, increasing in severity as he grew older and, finally, resulting in imprisonment. To present the full details of his stormy life is far beyond the scope of this book. The reader is referred to his biographers.[2]

He was soon forced to quit Pisa, and, in 1592, he became professor of mathematics at the University of Padua, where he remained 18 years, enjoying comparative liberty of thought and teaching. His fame as a teacher spread all over Europe, and his lectures were crowded.

In 1608, a Dutch optician, Lipperhey, as a result of a chance observation of an apprentice, had succeeded in "making distant objects appear nearer but inverted" by looking through a tube in which were mounted two spectacle lenses. News of this invention reached Galileo in June, 1609. Immediately grasping the principle involved, he made a telescope and exhibited it in Venice "for more than a month, to the astonishment of the chiefs of the republic." By January, 1610, Galileo had made a telescope with a power of 30 diameters,[3] and with this instrument he made a number of fundamental discoveries. He saw that the number of fixed stars was vastly greater than could be seen by the unaided eye, and thus he was able to explain the agelong puzzle of the Milky Way. He saw that the planets appeared in his telescope as luminous disks while the stars still remained points of light, and he discovered the satellites of Jupiter. These discoveries naturally made Galileo famous, and he soon accepted an invitation to return to Pisa as "First Mathematician and Philosopher," at a very substantial increase in salary, but at a sacrifice, unfortunately, of his "academic freedom" in Padua. Continuing his astronomical investigations, he discovered the crescent phases of Venus, sunspots and the rotation of the sun, the faculae of the solar atmosphere,

[1] Recently there has been a tendency to question the historical accuracy of the various accounts of this experiment. For an excellent discussion of the whole subject see L. Cooper, "Aristotle, Galileo and the Tower of Pisa," 1935.

[2] J. J. Fahie, "Galileo: His Life and Work," 1903; Sir David Brewster, "Martyrs of Science," 1870; Oliver Lodge, "Pioneers of Science."

[3] Galileo's telescopes were similar to the modern opera glass—a double-convex (or plano-convex) object glass and a double-concave eyepiece. Thus, they had an erect image.

and the libration of the moon.   In 1612, he published his "Discourse on Floating Bodies."

At first, it seemed as if his fame had silenced all opposition from the church.   But the support that his discoveries gave to the hated Copernican theory and his vigorous attacks on Aristotelian philosophy roused his enemies to fury, with the result that in 1615 he was hauled before the Pope and, under threat of imprisonment and torture, was "enjoined . . . to relinquish altogether the said opinion that the sun is the center of the world and immovable . . . nor henceforth to hold, teach, or defend it in any way . . . ."   Simultaneously, it was decreed that the works of Copernicus "be suspended until they be corrected."   Galileo acquiesced in these decrees and was allowed to return to Pisa, where he continued his researches along such lines as would not give offense.

In 1623, one of Galileo's friends, Barberini, became Pope Urban VIII, from whom Galileo received assurances of "pontifical good will."   Thereupon, thinking that the decree of 1615 would no longer be enforced, he began the writing of his great book, "Dialogues on the Ptolemaic and Copernican Systems."   This was published in 1632, under formal permission from the censor.   The form of these dialogues is ingeniously contrived to abide by the *letter* of the decree of 1615.   Three "characters" carry on the discussion: Salviati, a Copernican; Simplicio, an Aristotelian; and Sagredo, a witty, impartial, good-natured chairman.   The dialogues cover four "Days," during which the arguments for and against each system are set forth with apparent impartiality and without reaching any *stated* conclusion.   Nevertheless, the general effect of the book was "a powerful plea for Copernicanism."[1]

In spite of its enthusiastic reception by the public, the form of the book did not deceive his enemies, who were now determined that he must be silenced.   This was effectually accomplished by representing to the Pope that the Simplicio of the dialogues, whose ignorance was very apparent, was simply a caricature of the Pope himself.   In spite of the absurdity of the argument—for Galileo would hardly have risked offending Urban VIII, his one friend in the church—the Pope, who seems to have been both ambitious and vain, became convinced that Galileo "had made game of him."   Whereupon he was ready to join Galileo's enemies in persecuting that great scientist, ostensibly for "the safety of the church and the vindication of its decrees."

This tragic incident is illustrative of the fact that, in the seventeenth just as in the twentieth century, much of the "warfare between science and theology"—as Andrew D. White calls it[2]—has been based upon personal motives rather than upon a sincere wish to uphold theological doc-

[1] Fahie, *op. cit.*

[2] Andrew D. White, "The History of the Warfare between Science and Theology."

trines.   Intolerance, even when it is sincere, is to be condemned; but *insincere* intolerance is to be despised.   Yet, one cannot fully comprehend the forward march of science unless one recognizes the seriousness of the obstacles of this kind that have had to be overcome.   Great as is the fame of Galileo, how much more might he have accomplished if the energy that he was forced to spend in overcoming opposition could have been directed toward his researches.

Galileo was presently called before the Inquisition.   He was sixty-seven years old, impaired in health and in spirit.   Bowing to the inevitable because of the magnitude of the forces arrayed against him, he followed the advice of his friends and indicated his "free and unbiased" willingness to recant, to "abjure, curse, and detest the said heresies and errors and every other error and sect contrary to the Holy Church," and he further agreed "never more in future to say or assert anything, verbally or in writing, which may give rise to a similar suspicion."   Thereafter Galileo was kept a prisoner under suspended sentence, first at Rome, then at his home in Arcetri.   Here, during the last years of his life, he prepared and, in 1636, published his "Dialogues on Two New Sciences"[1] (i.e., Cohesion and Motion).

The dialogues on "Motion" sum up Galileo's earlier experiments and his more mature deliberations.   He states that "if the resistance of the media be taken away, all matter would descend with equal velocity." He deduces the formulas of uniformly accelerated motion.   He shows that the path of a projectile is parabolic under suitable limiting conditions and states that, if all resistance were removed, a body projected along a horizontal plane would continue to move forever.   His work on mechanics paved the way for the enunciation by Newton of the famous three laws of motion, which form the foundation of mechanics.

12. Tycho Brahe (1546–1601) **and Kepler** (1571–1630).   The work of Tycho and Kepler is particularly interesting not only because of its direct bearing on the development of physics but more particularly because of the mutual dependence of the work of each one upon that of the other, a relation very common in present-day science.   Tycho was the experimentalist, the observer, who supplied the accurate data upon which Kepler, the theorist, built a new theory of planetary motion.   Without a Kepler to build a theory from them, Tycho's observations would have attracted

---

[1] See the excellent translation by Crew and de Salvio.

Some writers have severely censured Galileo for yielding to the Inquisition.   They say that "had Galileo added the courage of a martyr to the wisdom of a sage . . . science would have achieved a memorable triumph" (see Brewster, "Life of Newton"). Whatever opinions on this question one may hold, one fact stands out indisputable: Had Galileo *not* yielded he would surely have been cast into the dungeon and would probably have been burned at the stake.   We should not then have had handed down to us these dialogues on Motion, so fundamental to our modern physics.

hardly more than passing notice.   Kepler, in turn, might have theorized to his heart's content, but, without the accurate data of a Tycho, those theories would ultimately have shared the fate of Aristotle's.   Sometimes theory precedes, sometimes experiment.   But neither can get far without the other.

Tycho Brahe, born of a noble family in Sweden, was educated for a career as a statesman, but he developed a consuming interest in astronomy.   By means of observations of his own, he soon found that the current astronomical tables were incorrect.   In 1575, he was put in charge of the observatory of Uraniborg by King Frederick II of Denmark, one of his duties being to make *astrological* calculations for the royal family. Here he spent 20 years making systematic observations of the planets, constructing a star catalogue, and accumulating other astronomical data, always with the highest possible order of accuracy that could be attained without a telescope.   In 1599, Tycho undertook to establish a new observatory at Prague for the German emperor, Rudolph the Second, but in the midst of this work he suddenly died (1601).

Now among Tycho's assistants at Prague had been, during the last few months, a brilliant young mathematician, Johann Kepler.   He succeeded Tycho as principal mathematician to the emperor and undertook to carry to completion the new set of astronomical tables based on elaborate observations, which Tycho had begun.   Kepler remained at Prague until 1612; from then until his death in 1630, he held a professorship at Linz.

Kepler believed thoroughly in the Copernican system, which Tycho had rejected for a geocentric system of his own.   It is one of the dramatic situations in science that Tycho's data on planetary motions, taken in support of his own theory, became, in the hands of Kepler, the clinching argument for the Copernican system.   Using Tycho's observations, Kepler made a special study of the motion of Mars.   He tried to reconcile the various recorded positions of the planet by assuming circular orbits for Mars and for the earth, trying various positions of these orbits relative to the sun.   None worked.   By resorting to the Ptolemaic notion of epicycles and deferents, some improvement resulted, but still the observed positions differed from the computed, in some cases by as much as 8 minutes of arc.   Kepler knew that Tycho's observations could not be in error by that amount.   Some new concept regarding planetary motion was necessary.

Then Kepler gave up *uniform* circular motion and assumed that the speed varied inversely as the planet's distance from the sun.   This assumption is his famous "second law," that *the radius vector from the sun to the planet describes equal areas in equal times.*   It worked approximately, but still there were systematic errors which exceeded the possible errors of observation.   Finally, he cast aside the last traditions of the Ptolemaic system and tried orbits of other forms, first, an oval path, and, then, an ellipse, with the sun at one focus.   At last, his years of computation bore fruit.   The path *was* an ellipse.   Theory and observation agreed!   And one of the most important and far-reaching laws in all science had been discovered, all because of a discrepancy of 8 minutes of arc between observation and theory!   In fact, one of the striking things in the growth of science, particularly physical science, is the fact that many fundamental advances have come about because of just such discrepancies, frequently very small ones, between observation and theory. Studying Tycho's observations further, Kepler finally hit upon the true relation between the periods of the planets and the radii of their orbits, a relation now known as Kepler's "third law," that *the squares of the times of revolution around the sun are as the cubes of the mean orbital radii.*

Thus were completed the three laws of planetary motion that Kepler handed down to posterity and which, sweeping away all remnants of the Ptolemaic system, paved the way for modern astronomy:

1. The planets move around the sun in orbits which are ellipses, with the sun at one focus.

2. The radius vector (from sun to planet) sweeps over equal areas in equal times.

3. The squares of the periods of revolution of the planets around the sun are proportional to the cubes of the (mean) radii of their respective orbits.

But what makes the planets move?   *Why* do the outer ones go more slowly?   Is there "one moving intelligence in the sun, the common center, forcing them all around, but those most violently which are nearest?" Kepler speculated long on this question and actually arrived at the idea of an attraction acting between any two material bodies.   This *qualitative* idea of Kepler's was later developed by Newton into his *quantitative* theory of universal gravitation.   Kepler himself, however, seems to have had no idea that it is this very attractive force which keeps the planets themselves in their orbits.

In passing, it may be mentioned that Kepler also made substantial contributions in the field of optics.   He understood clearly the principle of total reflection and how to determine what we now call the "critical angle."   He studied atmospheric refraction as affecting the apparent position of the heavenly bodies and worked out an approximate formula to allow for this error for all positions, from zenith to horizon.   He was the first to propose the meniscus type of lens.   And he proposed the Keplerian or astronomical type of telescope, in which a *real* image is formed, thus making possible accurate measurements by means of cross hairs in the focal plane of the objective.

13. The Experimental Method Spreads. The impetus given to science by that great trio, Galileo, Tycho, and Kepler, resulted in an ever increasing number of investigators in the generations that followed. We can mention only a few of them. Of great significance, too, is the fact that at about this time there were formed in several European centers various learned societies which brought together, for argument and discussion, men of kindred interests. The Lincean Society was founded in Italy, in 1603; the Royal Academy of Sciences, in France, in 1666; and the Royal Society for the Advancement of Learning, in England, in 1662. The continued improvement of the art of printing enormously facilitated the diffusion of scientific knowledge.

In 1600, Gilbert, an English physician, published his famous work, "De Magnete," based largely upon his own experiments, in which he showed the fallacy of such popular fancies as the belief that lodestones lost their magnetic power when rubbed with garlic and regained it again when smeared with goat's blood. He was the first to recognize that the earth is a great spherical magnet, and he actually magnetized a small sphere of iron and showed that it produced a magnetic field similar to that of the earth.

Among other workers in magnetism may be mentioned Kircher (1601–1680), who, by measuring the force required to pull a piece of iron from either pole of a magnet, demonstrated the equality of the two poles; Cabeo (1585–1650), who showed that an *unmagnetized* iron needle floated freely on water would place itself along the earth's magnetic meridian; and Gellibrand (1597–1637), who discovered the secular variation of the magnetic declination.

In the field of optics, there was Scheiner (1575–1650), who studied the optics of the eye; Snell (1591–1626), who discovered the true law of refraction; and Cavalieri (1598–1647), who gave the correct formula for the focal length of a thin glass lens in terms of the radii of curvature of the two sides. Studies in acoustics, also, were not wanting. For example, Mersenne (1588–1648), after having investigated the laws of vibrating strings, determined, in absolute measure, the frequency of a tone. He also measured the velocity of sound by observing the time interval between the flash of a gun and the arrival of the report.

In the field of fluid mechanics, there was Torricelli (1608–1647), who studied the flow of liquids from orifices, discovered the principle of the barometer, and observed variation in barometric height with altitude. Working independently, Guericke (1602–1686) invented the air pump. Pascal (1623–1662) measured the difference in barometric height between the base and the top of a mountain, correctly explaining the reason for the difference, and, later, announced the famous principle of hydrostatics that bears his name.

Not only was physics, as a subject, beginning to assume definite form, but even the usual subdivisions such as mechanics, light, sound, etc., were beginning to crystallize out.

Then came a man

. . . towering head and shoulders above all his contemporaries, a veritable giant among the giants, a man whose intellect and whose contributions to knowledge are incomparably greater than those of any other scientist of the past, that prince of philosophers, Sir Isaac Newton.[1]

The other "giants" referred to, contemporaries of Newton, are such men as Boyle, Huygens, and Hooke.

14. Sir Isaac Newton (1642–1727). Newton was born in the little hamlet of Woolsthorpe, England, in 1642, less than a year after the death of Galileo. In the public school at Grantham, he showed at first no exceptional aptitude for his studies, but ultimately he rose to the highest place in the class. Then, at the age of fifteen, he was removed from school to assist his widowed mother in running the family estate at Woolsthorpe. But he had little taste for farming. Rather, he was interested in studying and in devising various mechanisms. He made a water clock, water wheels, sundials, and a working model of a windmill. And one morning his uncle found him under a hedge studying mathematics when he should have been farming. Thereupon Newton's mother wisely decided that an educational career was more suitable for her son, and he was sent back to school and, ultimately, to Cambridge, which he entered in 1661. Here his fondness for mathematics continued, and soon his creative genius began to appear. While still a student, he discovered the binomial theorem, developed the methods of infinite series, and discovered "fluxions," or the differential calculus.

Soon thereafter, an outbreak of the plague closed the University for some months, during which time Newton, at the family estate at Woolsthorpe, began his speculations on the subject of gravity, which later led to his enunciation of the inverse-square law. It was here that the much-quoted "falling apple" episode is said to have occurred, which is supposed to have given Newton the basic idea of *universal* gravitation. But Newton himself makes no mention of the incident, and it seems far more probable that at Cambridge he had read Kepler's qualitative proposal of a general principle of gravitation. Certainly, Newton was familiar with the three laws of planetary motion that Kepler had discovered.

In 1667, Newton returned to Cambridge as Fellow of Trinity. Two years later, at the age of twenty-six, he was appointed Lucasian Professor of Mathematics, a chair which he held for nearly 30 years. In 1703, he resigned his professorship to devote himself to his duties as Master of the

[1] Hart, "Makers of Science."

PLATE 2. Newton.

Mint, to the scientific work of his contemporaries, and to defending his own work against the attacks of jealous rivals. In this same year, he was elected President of the Royal Society, an office which he held until his death. In 1705, he was knighted by Queen Anne.

Most of Newton's important scientific work was done before he vacated the professorship, although he remained thereafter "a power of the first magnitude in the world of science." In his later years, he devoted much time to theological studies. He died Mar. 20, 1727, at the ripe old age of eighty-five. Throughout his life, he shunned publicity and retained a modesty and simplicity which are indicated by a sentiment uttered shortly before his death:

I do not know what I may appear to the world, but to myself I seem to have been only like a boy playing on the seashore, and diverting myself in now and then finding a smoother pebble or a prettier shell than ordinary, whilst the great ocean of truth lay all undiscovered before me.

Any brief account of Newton's work must inevitably give a very inadequate impression of his contributions to science. The student is urged to read some of his writings firsthand or, at least, some extensive biographical discussion of his life and work. We can here refer only to a very few of his researches on optics and on mechanics.

Newton's work on *optics* arose out of an attempt to improve lenses. The inability of a lens with spherical surfaces to bring parallel rays to a point focus was early recognized. In 1629, Descartes had shown that lenses with hyperbolic or, under certain conditions, parabolic surfaces should be free from the defect which we now call "spherical aberration." Newton found, however, that such lenses produced only a very slight improvement in the image, and he conjectured that, perhaps, the trouble lay not in the lens but in the light itself.

Accordingly, he procured a prism of glass and, placing it over a hole $\frac{1}{4}$ in. in diameter through which sunlight was shining into a darkened room, he observed the "very vivid and intense colors" produced on a wall some 20 ft distant. Newton was surprised to find that this "spectrum," as we now call it, was so much longer than it was wide ($13\frac{1}{4}$ by $2\frac{5}{8}$ in.). The *width* subtended at the hole an angle corresponding *exactly* to the sun's angular diameter, but the length could not be so explained. He made various surmises as to the origin of the colors, such as the varying thickness of the prism from apex to base, the unevenness of the glass, a curvilinear motion of the light after leaving the prism, etc. One by one, experiment proved these hypotheses wrong. Finally, he isolated one ray, or "color," by suitable screens and caused it to pass through a second prism. In this way, he could measure the refrangibility of a single ray. And he found that the refrangibility increased from red to violet, that, therefore, the first prism simply "sorted out" the colors, which, in combination, made "white" light. In other words, he discovered that so-called "white light" is made up of the spectral colors—a very elementary concept to us of the twentieth century but very new and of far-reaching importance in 1666.

Newton at once saw that this dispersion of light was the cause of his failure to effect any substantial improvement in telescopes by use of paraboloidal lenses. Furthermore, he concluded, on the basis of a hurried experiment, that, in different mediums, dispersion was always proportional to refracting power. If this were so, it would follow that by no combination of lenses of different materials could chromatic aberration be eliminated. This singular error of Newton's retarded the development of refracting telescopes for many years. In 1730, Hall made several achromatic combinations of crown and flint glasses, but he published no account of his work, so that, when Dolland, about 1757, rediscovered the method of making such combinations, he was able to secure a patent on it—an invention that had been within the grasp of Newton three-quarters of a century before.

Newton's theories concerning the nature of light are of great historical interest. And much has been written concerning the extent to which he is supposed by some to have retarded the development of optics by espousing the corpuscular theory as against the wave theory of his contemporaries, Huygens (1629–1695) and Hooke (1635–1703). Accordingly, it may be of interest to point out, by a quotation or two, that Newton was by no means dogmatic in his support of the corpuscular theory and that later writers may have taken him, in this regard, more seriously than he intended.

In a communication to the Royal Society, in 1675, concerning "An Hypothesis Explaining the Properties of Light," Newton states:

. . . I have here thought fit to send you a description . . . of this hypothesis . . . though I shall not assume either this or any other hypothesis, not thinking it necessary to concern myself whether the properties of light discovered by men be explained by this or any other hypothesis capable of explaining them; yet while I am describing this, I shall sometimes, to avoid circumlocutation . . . speak of it as if I assumed it.

He then proceeds to describe "an ætherial medium, much of the same constitution with air but far rarer, subtiler and more strongly elastic" and supposes that

. . . light is neither æther, nor its vibrating motion, but something of a different kind propagated from lucid bodies. They that will may suppose it an aggregate of various peripatetic qualities. Others may suppose it multitudes of unimaginable small and swift corpuscles of various sizes springing from shining bodies

. . . and continually urged forward by a principle of motion which in the beginning accelerates them, till the resistance of the aetherial medium equals the force of that principle much after the manner that bodies let fall in water are accelerated till the resistance of the water equals the force of gravity.

Nearly 33 years later (1704), Newton published his optical researches in book form in his well-known "Opticks," bringing out a third edition in 1721. His first sentence reads: "My Design in this Book is not to explain the Properties of Light by Hypotheses, but to propose and prove them by Reason and Experiment." He then, in some 300 pages, gives his researches on refraction, reflection, colors of thin plates, etc., and he concludes the book by "proposing only some queries in order to further search to be made by others." One of these queries expresses his objections to the wave theory of light:

28. Are not all hypotheses erroneous in which light is supposed to consist in pression or motion propagated through a fluid medium? If light consists only in pression propagated without actual motion, it would not be able to agitate and heat the bodies which refract and reflect it, and . . . it would bend into the shadow. For pression or motion cannot be propagated in a fluid in right lines beyond an obstacle . . . but will bend and spread every way into the quiescent medium which lies beyond the obstacle.

In order to account for the colors of thin films, which are now regarded as strong evidence for the wave nature of light, he supposes that "every ray of light in its passage through any refracting surface is put into a certain transient constitution or state, which in the progress of the ray returns at equal intervals and disposes the ray at every return to be easily refracted through the next refracting surface and between the returns to be easily reflected by it." He even suggests that the effect might be due to vibrations excited by the "rays" in the material medium which vibrations "move faster than the rays so as to overtake them; and that when any ray is in that part of the vibration which conspires with its motion, it easily breaks through a refracting surface, but when it is in the contrary part of the vibration which impedes its motion, it is easily reflected. . . . But whether this hypothesis be true or false, I do not here consider."[1]

It is clear that Newton regarded his corpuscular theory as a tentative one, subject to confirmation or rejection on the basis of further experiments. If his theory really did retard progress in optics, the fault lay rather with those who attached too great weight to his opinions, perhaps because they retained something of that medieval respect for authority which had kept Aristotle enthroned so long.

Newton's speculations may also serve as an example to illustrate the rule that even the greatest intellect works on the basis of the knowledge

[1] Quoted in Preston's "Light," p. 22.

and viewpoints of its age.   Had Newton lived a century later, he would probably have been one of the first believers in the wave theory.   The fact that great scientists share the limitations of their age is an added reason for treating their speculative opinions chiefly as sources of inspiration for further experiment.

Newton's researches on optics alone would have given him a high rank among the scientists of his time.   But of still greater value was his work in *mechanics*.   In announcing that "every particle of matter in the universe attracts every other particle with a force inversely proportional to the square of the distance between the two particles," in showing that this one universal and comparatively simple law governs not only the motions of the planets around the sun and of the satellites round their planets but, probably, also the relative motions of all the heavenly bodies, he gave to the world a truth which exercised an enormous influence upon thought.   This achievement of Newton's played a large part in bringing about the general conviction that the physical universe in its entirety is governed by law, not by caprice.

Newton himself has told us how he came to discover the law of gravitation.   First he attacked the problem of finding a law of attraction between two bodies, such as the sun and a planet, which would result in Kepler's third law, viz., that squares of the periods of rotation of the planets around the sun are proportional to the cubes of their mean distances from the sun.   He found that a gravitational attraction varying as the inverse square of the distance gives this law of planetary motion.

Then he saw that a test of this inverse-square law could easily be made by comparing the acceleration of the moon toward the earth with the acceleration of falling bodies at the surface of the earth.   It was known that the distance between the moon and the earth's center is about sixty times the earth's radius.   By the inverse-square law, therefore, the moon should "drop" toward the earth, in 1 sec, $\frac{1}{60^2}$ as far as a body at the surface of the earth drops in 1 sec.   The latter distance being, from observations on falling bodies, 16 ft, the former should be $\frac{16}{60^2}$ ft, or 16 ft in 1 min.   But the acceleration of the moon could be determined directly by applying to the moon the expression he had used for the motion of the planets in their orbits, viz.,

$$a = \frac{v^2}{r} = 4\pi^2 \frac{r}{T^2}$$

where v is the velocity of the moon in its orbit or T is the period of its motion around the earth and r is the radius of the orbit.   Now r is equal to sixty times the earth's radius, which was taken as 3,436 miles, on the then common assumption that a degree of latitude is 60 miles.   On this basis, the moon is found to "drop" 13.9 ft toward the earth in a minute, instead of 16 ft, as should be the case if the inverse-square law were obeyed. Thus the two results did not agree.

Newton was twenty-three years old at the time, and he laid this calculation aside, not mentioning it to anyone. Some years later, however, he learned of a new and more accurate determination of the length of a degree which had been made by Picard, who found not 60 but more nearly 70 miles. In the meantime Newton had also succeeded in proving that a homogeneous sphere attracts an external body as if all its mass were concentrated at its center, thereby removing one uncertainty in the calculation. Therefore, on the basis of Picard's new value for the length of a degree, Newton revised his computations on the moon's acceleration and, to his great joy, found that it falls toward the earth 16 ft in a minute, just as predicted by the inverse-square law. At last, he had discovered the true law of gravitation. On the basis of this law, he could now *derive* all three of Kepler's laws. Theory and observation checked perfectly.

These results, together with some propositions on the motion of the planets, were communicated in 1683 to the Royal Society, which requested permission to publish Newton's complete researches on the subject of motion and gravitation. In 1687, there appeared the first edition of his "Principia" or, in full, "Philosophiae Naturalis Principia Mathematica" (Mathematical Principles of Natural Philosophy), "without exception the most important work in natural philosophy extant."[1] The original is in Latin, but English translations are available. The treatise is divided into three books, the subject matter of each being presented by propositions, theorems, and corollaries. The first two books deal with general theorems concerning the motions of bodies, whereas the third contains applications to the solar system. The entire treatise is characterized by the exposition of the principle of universal gravitation and its ramifications but, as the author carefully points out, without attempting any hypothesis as to the *cause* of gravitation.

In this treatise the famous three laws of motion are assumed as axioms. Their greatest merit lies in the fact that they contain just enough to constitute a complete basis for the science of mechanics and no more. The laws can be expressed with greater clarity in modern terminology, and we now realize that in part they express definitions rather than experimental facts, but it is commonly felt that no more *convenient* basis for mechanics has been proposed.

In addition to the formulation of the laws, Newton's treatise makes several other important contributions to mechanics. He was the first to give precision to the concept of mass; and he describes a series of experiments showing that the period of a pendulum is independent of the mate-

[1] Hart, *op. cit.*

rial of which it is made, from which he concluded that, for different bodies, mass and weight are proportional to each other. He also gave precision to the idea of force, and formulated in general terms the principle of the parallelogram of forces.

Of Newton's invention of the method of fluxions (i.e., the calculus), of his very interesting miscellaneous writings, of the many controversies with his contemporaries into which he was unwillingly drawn in defense of his scientific work, we cannot take space to write. We can only urge our readers to make further study of the life and works of this renowned physicist.

15. Newton's Contemporaries. The true productive period of Newton's life ended about 1700. His biography is so full of interest and inspiration that it is a temptation to discuss, similarly, the work of his contemporaries, themselves eminent scientists—the Honorable Robert Boyle (1627–1691), the discoverer of "Boyle's law"; Huygens (1629–1695), whose wave theory of light was to triumph a century and a half later; Robert Hooke (1635–1703), proponent of the undulatory theory and originator of "Hooke's law" of elasticity; Leibnitz (1646–1716), whose calculus ultimately replaced Newton's fluxions. But, remembering that the main business of this book is "modern" physics, we must pass on to a rapid review of the developments of physics during the *eighteenth* century.

16. Mechanics during the Eighteenth Century.[1] The subsequent history of mechanics has consisted of the derivation, from Newton's three laws, of various secondary principles which are convenient for special purposes, and of the solution of all sorts of problems. Among the prominent workers during the eighteenth century, we find such names as Daniel Bernoulli (1700–1782), who worked on hydrodynamics, the kinetic theory of gases, and the transverse vibrations of rods; Euler (1707–1783), who shares with Bernoulli the honor of discovering the general law of the conservation of angular momentum (1746); and Lagrange (1736–1813), who gave, in the equations that bear his name, a general method of attacking any problem, using any sort of coordinates that may be convenient.

17. Heat during the Eighteenth Century. Galileo had invented an air thermometer in 1597, but the first mercury thermometer was used by Kircher in 1643. About 1724, Fahrenheit proposed the temperature scale now known by his name; this was followed by the Réaumur scale and, in 1742, by the Celsius scale. James Black (1728–1799), a professor of chemistry at Glasgow and Edinburgh, made measurements of the heat of fusion and of vaporization of water, which led to modern calorim-

[1] The reader will find in Mach's "The Science of Mechanics" a valuable discussion of the history and the fundamentals of the subject of mechanics.

etry, and gave definite form to the previously hazy distinctions between temperature and heat.

With regard to theories of heat, however, there was retrogression during the eighteenth century. From his writings, it is clear that Newton regarded heat as intimately connected with the motion of the small particles of which bodies are composed, and this view seems to have been shared by his contemporaries. But, early in the eighteenth century, there was a return to the "caloric" theory, which held heat to be a fluid that could be extracted from or added to a body, thereby causing its changes of temperature. This heat fluid was indestructible, its particles were self-repellent but were attracted by ordinary matter, and it was all-pervading. The expansion of bodies when heated was the natural result of "swelling" due to forcing caloric into matter. The production of heat by percussion was due to the releasing or "pounding loose" of some of the caloric naturally condensed in or absorbed by the body, thereby increasing the amount of free caloric. Black explained latent heats and specific heats on the basis of this theory. Indeed, by the end of the eighteenth century, the caloric theory of heat was generally accepted.

18. Light during the Eighteenth Century. An event of special importance in the history of science was the discovery of the aberration of light by Bradley in 1728. The absence of any measurable stellar parallax had been one of the stumbling blocks in the way of the Copernican system and was, therefore, one of the outstanding problems of astronomy. Tycho had recognized that, viewed from opposite sides of the earth's orbit, the stars should show a perspective displacement, but his careful observations convinced him that no such displacement so great as 1 minute of arc existed. Later observers, likewise, sought such an effect in vain.

In hopes of being able to measure stellar distances, Bradley began, in 1725, systematic observations on the position of a zenith star, γ Draconis. If stellar parallax existed, this star should be farthest south in December and should then move north, reaching its maximum northerly position 6 months later. The position of the star was found to change, but not in the manner expected. It reached farthest south in *March* and farthest north in *September*, the angular distance between the two positions being about 40 seconds of arc. Bradley continued his observations on other stars, and, in 1728, he came to the conclusion that the observed displacement was not due to parallax at all but to an apparent shift in the star's position due to a combination of the velocity of light with that of the earth in its orbit.[1] He was thus enabled to deduce a value for the velocity of light. The value so found was in substantial agreement with that determined by Römer a half-century earlier, from a study of the motion

---

[1] See any text on astronomy for further explanation of aberration.

of Jupiter's moons, which constituted the first determination of the velocity of light. This discovery of Bradley's was the first in the series that formed the basis for the modern theory of relativity.

Theories as to the nature of light made no material progress during the eighteenth century. Some writers are inclined to ascribe this to the prestige given to the corpuscular theory by the fact that it was supported by Newton, whose preeminence "seemed to act like a spell," as had Aristotle's centuries before. But if so, then, likewise, the kinetic theory of heat held by Newton should have been uppermost during the eighteenth century, whereas, as has already been pointed out, the reigning theory of heat during this period was the caloric theory. Lack of progress in the theory of light was more likely due to the lack of any crucial experiment, just as was the case with theories of heat. Science has never progressed on the basis of speculation only.

19. Electricity during the Eighteenth Century. Electricity received a great deal of attention during the eighteenth century, but research was concerned principally with electrostatics. Stephen Gray (1670–1736) distinguished clearly between conductors and nonconductors of electricity and showed that even conducting bodies may be electrified provided they are insulated. Du Fay (1698–1739) showed that flames exercise a discharging power and that there are two kinds of electricity, which he called "vitreous" and "resinous." He was thus led to propose the two-fluid theory of electricity. During the first half of the eighteenth century, the electroscope was invented (by Hawksbee, in 1705), frictional electric machines were developed, the Leyden jar was discovered (1745), and there was considerable popular interest in electrical phenomena. During the latter half of the century, three names stand out preeminent: Benjamin Franklin (1706–1790), Henry Cavendish (1731–1810), and Charles A. Coulomb (1736–1806).

Franklin's experiments began about 1745. One of his first observations was the effect of points "in drawing off and throwing off the electrical fire." He proposed the one-fluid theory of electricity, somewhat similar to the caloric theory of heat. This theory supposed that all bodies contained naturally a certain amount of the electric fluid. When a body had an excess of the fluid, it exhibited one of the two kinds of electrification, which Franklin chose to call for this reason *positive;* when it had a deficit, it exhibited the other kind, which he called *negative.* Certain features in the appearance of electric sparks led him to identify his positive electrification with that which had been called vitreous. (In the light of the modern electron theory, we should prefer that he had applied the signs in the opposite order!)

About 1750, Franklin began to speculate on the identity of electricity and lightning, pointing out many similarities and proposing, by means of a pointed iron rod, to "draw off the fire from a cloud." Franklin's writings were published in Europe, and in 1752 Dalibard tried the experiment in Paris, confirming Franklin's prediction. A short time later, Franklin performed the famous kite experiment, so well known to every schoolboy; this led to his study of atmospheric electricity and to his invention of the lightning rod. Franklin's researches occupied but a small portion of his long and busy life, but they were sufficient to give him a high standing among the scientists of the world.

Quantitative researches in electricity began with Cavendish and Coulomb. Cavendish is known not only for his work in electrostatics but also for his researches in chemistry and for the well-known "Cavendish experiment," in 1798, in which he determined the constant of gravitation. His electrical researches were very extensive, but most of his work remained unknown, for he published only one paper of importance. He left behind a large amount of material, however, in the form of manuscript notes, and these were edited and published in 1879 by Maxwell. In these experiments, Cavendish proved the inverse-square law of electrostatic force; measured capacity, recognized the principle of the condenser, and measured the specific inductive capacity of several substances; arrived at a reasonably clear idea of the quantity which we now call "potential"; and anticipated Ohm's law by 50 years. Had these important measurements been communicated to his scientific contemporaries, the history of electricity might have been substantially modified. As it is, the credit of *discovery* seems fairly to belong to others, for a discovery is of no importance to any one else if it is kept secret.

Coulomb's work in electricity grew out of his development of the torsion balance, originally used for studying the torsional elasticity of wires. In the period 1785–1789, he published seven papers on electricity and magnetism in the *Mémoires de l'Académie Royale des Sciences*. In these papers, he showed by means of the torsion balance that electrostatic forces obey the inverse-square law; that, on conducting bodies, the charge exists only on the surface; and that the capacity of a body is independent of the nature of the material of which it is composed. He advocated the two-fluid theory of electricity.

20. Close of the Second Period. The end of the eighteenth century found rival theories contending in each of three of the subdivisions of physics: the caloric vs. the kinetic theory in heat; the corpuscular vs. the undulatory theory in light; and the one-fluid vs. the two-fluid theory in electricity. The very fact that these issues were raised in rather clean-cut fashion is an indication of the tremendous strides that had been taken since Galileo. But most important of all, men had learned the value of experiment and observation and the fallacy of blindly following "authority."

During the next century the caloric theory was definitely ruled out, apparently never to return. The corpuscular theory of light seemed likewise to be effectively disproved by many new experiments. But further progress in regard to the nature of electrification waited, for the most part, until the twentieth century.

THIRD PERIOD (1800–1890 A.D.): THE RISE OF CLASSICAL PHYSICS

21. The Nineteenth Century in Physics. So much was added to physical knowledge during the nineteenth century that an adequate history of this period would almost constitute a textbook of physics. We can only comment briefly upon the principal lines of advance and a few of the most important discoveries, selecting especially those that form the background for the characteristic advances of the present century.

In mechanics, there was Hamilton, who discovered in the "Hamiltonian equations" a new form of the equations of motion which is especially convenient in attacking theoretical questions. The theory of the motion of rigid bodies, including the gyroscope, was worked out, as well as the mathematical theory of elasticity. The subject of hydrodynamics, dealing with the motion of fluid of all sorts, was developed. In dealing with the flow of viscous fluids, however, only simple problems could be solved; extensive study of such fluids, by half-empirical methods, was not made until during the present century, after the invention of the airplane.

The work in other fields was more striking. The most significant discoveries and advances were: the establishment of the kinetic theory of heat, and the development of the kinetic theory of gases; the victory(?) of the wave theory of light over the corpuscular theory; the formulation of the general law of the conservation of energy; the discovery of the second law of thermodynamics; and, above all, the discovery, by Faraday and others, of the whole range of electromagnetic phenomena, culminating in Maxwell's theory of the electromagnetic field and of light.

Of these lines of advance we shall select three for detailed presentation, choosing those which bear more or less directly upon modern developments in physics; and, as typical scientists of the period, we shall discuss especially Faraday and Maxwell.

22. Heat and Energy. The law of the conservation of energy is one of the most fundamental and far-reaching of all physical laws, and yet, curiously enough, it is of comparatively recent origin, for it was not announced until the middle of the nineteenth century. As exemplified in mechanics, it had been recognized during the eighteenth century, in the theory of the "vis viva"; but its announcement as a law of universal application awaited experimental work demonstrating the definite equivalence of heat and mechanical work.

The first *qualitative* experiment bearing on the nature of heat was performed in 1798 by Count Rumford, an American who had fled to England in 1775 and eventually became a sort of military engineer to the Bavarian government. He became impressed by the large amount of heat that was developed in boring cannon, and he performed experiments indicating that this heat was too great to be accounted for plausibly by the caloric theory. He could find no loss of weight, when the chips made by boring were included, and showed that the specific heat of the chips was the same as that of the block from which they had come. He concluded that heat "cannot possibly be a material substance" such as caloric but must be a form of "motion."

A still more difficult experiment for the caloric theory to explain was one performed by Sir Humphry Davy, Director of the Royal Institution, which had been founded by Count Rumford. Davy rubbed together two pieces of ice in a vacuum surrounded by walls kept below the freezing point and found that the ice was melted. Here the mechanical work of rubbing accomplished exactly the same effects that could have been produced by the addition of a certain quantity of heat from the outside, yet there was no way in which caloric could have entered the ice.

The majority of the supporters of the caloric theory were, however, unconvinced. Even Carnot (1796–1832), the founder of the modern science of thermodynamics, when he proposed the now famous Carnot's cycle in 1824, based his reasoning on the caloric theory. A given quantity of caloric "falling" from a higher to a lower temperature was analogous to a given quantity of water falling from a higher to a lower level; each was capable of producing motive power. The kinetic theory had to wait for a *quantitative* experiment.

In 1842, R. J. Mayer (1814–1878) published a paper[1] in which, partly on philosophical grounds, he announced the equivalence of heat and energy, and from data on the specific heats of a gas he deduced a value for the mechanical equivalent of heat. Meanwhile, Joule (1818–1889), in England, unacquainted with Mayer's work, was carrying on a very careful series of experiments in which he converted the mechanical energy of a falling weight into heat by a paddle wheel revolving in water and thus determined that 778 ft-lb of work would raise 1 lb of water 1°F. Joule announced his results at a meeting of the British Association for the Advancement of Science in 1847. The paper would have passed almost unnoticed, had it not been for William Thomson, later Lord Kelvin, who, grasping the real significance of the proposed theory, by his discussion made the paper the event of the meeting.

Quite independently of the work of Mayer and of Joule, Helmholtz (1821–1894) in 1847 read a paper before the Physical Society in Berlin

[1] *Ann. Chem. u. Pharmacie*, May, 1842.

on "Die Erhaltung der Kraft," in which, on the basis of the impossibility of perpetual-motion machines, he announced the law of the conservation of energy. The paper was rejected for publication by the editor of the *Annalen der Physik!* It was later published in pamphlet form.

The caloric theory could not withstand these attacks, and by 1850 the mechanical theory of heat and the doctrine of the conservation of energy were generally accepted. The science of heat then proceeded to grow apace. The second law of thermodynamics was announced by Clausius (1850) and, in another form, by Kelvin (1851), and in 1854 Kelvin proposed the thermodynamic scale of temperature. Thus was developed the highly successful "classical theory" of heat. We shall discuss later the facts that this theory, in turn, was unable to explain and the way in which the study of these facts led to the development of the quantum theory.

23. Light. The revival of the wave theory of light, begun by Thomas Young (1773–1829), is one of the most important features of the history of the nineteenth century. Young pointed out that the dividing of a beam of light into a refracted ray at the interface between two mediums was to be expected from the wave theory but had not been satisfactorily explained on the corpuscular theory. In 1801, he presented to the Royal Society a paper "On the Theory of Light and Colors," in which he proposed the principle of the interference of two wave trains as an explanation of Newton's rings and the colors of thin plates. From Newton's measurements of the thickness of the air layers necessary to produce the several colors, Young was enabled to compute wavelengths. In subsequent papers, he described the interference fringes which he had observed by placing hairs or silk threads in front of a narrow slit illuminated from the rear; he announced the change of phase on reflection; he explained diffraction bands by the principle of interference, and he showed that the spacing of these bands gave values of the wavelength agreeing with those obtained from Newton's rings and that, therefore, both phenomena must be due to a common cause. Again, *quantitative* measurements became an indispensable link in the chain of reasoning.

But the dogmatic spirit in regard to scientific matters was not yet dead. Young's paper aroused a storm of protest, even of derision and abuse. He was attacked not by the church, as was Galileo, but by some of his scientific, or, more probably, pseudoscientific, contemporaries. His chief assailant was Henry Brougham, afterward Lord Chancellor of England, who "reviewed" Young's papers in the *Edinburgh Review*. The nature of Brougham's attack is indicated by the following quotation:

We wish to raise our feeble voice against innovations that can have no other effect than to check the progress of science and renew all those wild phantoms of the imagination which Bacon and Newton put to flight from her temple. We wish to recall philosophers to the strict and severe methods of investigation . . .

Although Young replied at length in a privately published pamphlet, it was a long time before public opinion was willing to receive his theories with an open mind.

In 1815, a Frenchman, Fresnel (1788–1827), rediscovered the phenomenon of interference, performing the famous experiment with the two mirrors. A few years later he developed a mathematical theory of such phenomena (1818–1819). He also explained the polarization of light by assuming that the light vibrations in the ether are *transverse* to the direction of propagation of the light rather than longitudinal. He did not know that this suggestion had already been made by Young in a letter to Arago written in 1817. Fresnel supported the explanation by showing experimentally that two plane-polarized beams of light cannot interfere at all if their planes of polarization are perpendicular to each other. Phenomena of polarization had been known to Newton, the polarization of light by Iceland spar being discovered by Bartholinus in 1669. Newton had tried to fit these phenomena into the corpuscular theory by assuming a sort of structure in the corpuscles, but the explanation was not convincing, and polarization had remained an enigma to both theories of light. Even Fresnel's explanation seemed almost to demand the impossible, for it required the ether to be a solid, or at least to have such properties of a solid as are necessary for the transmission of transverse waves, i.e., the properties of rigidity and density. And yet the planets must move through this "solid" pervading all space, with no measurable changes in their periods of revolution!

Experimental evidence for the wave theory continued to accumulate. Finally, in 1850, Foucault performed a crucial experiment in its favor by showing, with his well-known revolving-mirror apparatus for measuring the velocity,[1] that light travels more slowly in water than in air, as it should on the wave theory, in order to account for the relative refractive index of these two mediums, whereas, on the corpuscular theory, the reverse should be the case.[2]

From 1850 until the end of the Third Period (1890), the wave theory held the field undisputed. The frequent assertions that the corpuscular theory was finally disposed of certainly seemed justified, particularly after the development of Maxwell's electromagnetic theory of light and its experimental verification. Yet the corpuscular theory was not actually dead. It was only sleeping.

[1] See Edser, "Light for Students," Macmillan.
[2] See any textbook on optics.

Some important discoveries in light from 1800 to 1890 not previously mentioned are:

	Discoverer
Dark lines in the solar spectrum........................	Fraunhofer
Three-color theory of vision (1807)......................	Young
Rotary polarization of quartz (1811).....................	Arago
Polarization of scattered light (1813)...................	Arago
Rotary polarization by liquids (1815)....................	Biot
Light sensitivity of silver bromide (1826)................	Balard
Change of conductivity of selenium on illumination (1837)...	Knox
Doppler effect (1842)...................................	Doppler
Foundation of spectral analysis (1859)...................	Kirchhoff and Bunsen

24. Electricity and Magnetism. The history of electricity during the nineteenth century is so extensive that even a sketchy outline would fill a small volume. We shall, therefore, discuss little besides the fundamental discoveries of the opening decades and then the work of Faraday and that of Maxwell, which are so closely related to each other and to recent developments in physics that we can best present the part of electricity and magnetism in which we are particularly interested by giving an account of the contributions of these two men.

While the mathematical theory of electrostatics and of magnetism was being elaborated by Laplace, Green, and Poisson, fundamental discoveries were made in regard to electric *currents*. Galvani, in 1786, as a result of a chance observation that a frog's leg kicked convulsively when connected with the terminal of an electric machine, was led to an extensive study of "animal electricity." In the course of these experiments he observed that if the frog's leg was so suspended that the exposed nerves touched a metal plate, say silver, then, a contraction of the muscle occurred whenever the foot touched another metal, say iron. He even observed slight muscular contraction when both plates were of the same kind of metal. This led him to believe that the nerve was the source of electricity and that the metal served simply as conductor. Volta later found that potentials could also be produced using inorganic materials and, in 1800, he described the first battery for producing an electric current—the historically famous voltaic "pile," consisting of zinc and copper plates placed alternately and separated by blotting paper moistened with brine. He also described a battery consisting of cups containing brine or dilute acid connected by copper and zinc strips joined together.

Volta ascribed the effect to the contact of two dissimilar metals. We now know, however, that the current that can be caused in this manner to flow in a closed circuit is due to chemical action at the contacts of the metals with the electrolyte; the effect at the junction of the metals gives rise to potential differences of a different nature, the "contact difference of potential" or "Volta effect," which adds up to a total of zero in any closed circuit.

This new source of electricity was received with a great deal of interest. A few weeks after hearing of Volta's work, Nicholson and Carlisle accidentally discovered the decomposition of water by the electric current. Thinking to secure better contact between two wires forming part of the circuit, they had joined the ends of the wires by a drop of water. At once they observed the formation of a gas, which they recognized as hydrogen. This was the beginning of the study of electrolysis. During this same period the heating effect of the current and the arc light were discovered.

It was early suspected that there was some relation between electricity and magnetism, but the first significant discovery was made in 1820 by Oersted, who found that a magnetic needle tends to set itself at right angles to a wire through which an electric current is flowing. Soon after, Biot and Savart discovered the law for the field of a long straight current, and, toward the end of 1820, Biot proposed, on the basis of a special experiment, the formula for the field due to a current element that is commonly used today and is often miscalled "Ampère's formula."[1] Soon after, the brilliant French physicist, Ampère (1775–1836), on the basis of just enough crucial experiments, showed that a closed current is equivalent in its magnetic effects to a magnetic shell. Then, reversing his line of thought, he suggested that magnetism itself might be due to currents circulating in the molecule. He also discovered the action of a magnetic field on a current. Thus, within 5 years of the first discovery, the foundations of electromagnetism had been completely laid.

25. Michael Faraday.[2] *a. Biographical Sketch.* Michael Faraday was born in 1791, in a small village near London. He was the son of a blacksmith, James Faraday. Being required to assist his mother in providing for the family, he was engaged in 1804 as errand boy to a bookseller and stationer, and in the following year he was formally apprenticed to his employer to learn the art of bookbinding. During this apprenticeship, Faraday made good use of his spare time by reading some of the books that passed through the shop. He was particularly interested in works on science, and in connection with his reading he showed one of the important characteristics[3] of the great investigator-to-be by performing

---

[1] That is, $dH = i\, ds \sin \theta / r^2$. Cf. J. B. Biot, "Précis élémentaire de Physique expérimentale," 1824. Ampère appears to have assumed that the force-action between two current elements must necessarily lie along a line drawn through the elements, which is not the case if Biot's formula is used for the magnetic field.

[2] See Sylvanus P. Thompson, "Michael Faraday: His Life and Work."

[3] In later life, he wrote: "I was never able to make a fact my own without seeing it."

PLATE 3. Faraday.

such of the simple experiments described "as could be defrayed in their expense by a few pence per week."

Aside from his own reading, *Faraday's only scientific education consisted in a dozen lectures on natural philosophy by a Mr. Tatum and four lectures on chemistry by Sir Humphry Davy, in the winter of 1812.* Submitting the very careful and neatly written notes which he made of these lectures "as proof of his earnestness," he made bold to apply to Sir Humphry Davy for a position, however menial, at the Royal Institution of which Davy was then director. Davy was so pleased with the letter and the notes that in March, 1813, Faraday was engaged as apparatus and lecture assistant at 25 shillings per week. In October, 1813, he accompanied Sir Humphry and Lady Davy on a trip to the Continent, which took them to many of the important scientific centers of Europe. Assistant though he was, Faraday impressed others because of his modesty, amiability, and intelligence; said one writer, "We admired Davy, we *loved* Faraday."

On returning to England, under Davy's encouragement, Faraday soon began original investigations, initially in chemistry. From 1816 to 1819 he published 37 papers. These were concerned with such subjects as the escape of gases through capillary tubes, the production of sound in tubes by flames, the combustion of the diamond, and the separation of manganese from iron. About 1820, he began his electrical researches. These, and others growing out of them, continued for nearly 40 years.

Almost his entire scientific life was spent at the Royal Institution. In 1825, he was made Director of the Laboratory. Declining offers of positions elsewhere, turning away professional occupations which might have made him wealthy, he gave to his science and to the institution he served a devotion seldom if ever equaled. The secret of his success, which brought him, during his lifetime, honors from all over the scientific world and which immortalized his name by the long list of scientific discoveries ascribed to him, is, perhaps, to be found in some excerpts from his many notes:

Aim at high things, but not presumptuously.
Endeavor to succeed—expect not to succeed.
It puzzles me greatly to know what makes the successful philosopher. Is it industry and perseverance with a moderate proportion of good sense and intelligence? Is not a modest assurance or earnestness a requisite? Do not many fail because they look rather to the renown to be acquired than to the pure acquisition of knowledge . . . ? I am sure I have seen many who would have been good and successful pursuers of science, and have gained themselves a high name, but that it was the name and the reward they were always looking forward to—the reward of the world's praise. In such there is always a shade of envy or regret over their minds and I cannot imagine a man making discoveries in science under these feelings.

The reader is urged to study carefully Faraday's life and works, particularly to read, as unexcelled examples of scientific expositions, portions of his "Experimental Researches in Electricity and Magnetism." We can mention here only a few of his most important discoveries.

b. The Principle of the Motor. Faraday had been interested in electromagnetism since April, 1821, when Wollaston attempted, at the Royal Institution, to make a wire carrying an electric current revolve around its own axis when the pole of a magnet was brought near. The experiment was unsuccessful, but the phenomenon excited Faraday's interest, and he determined to make a study of it. First, he read what had been done by others and repeated many of their experiments. In the course of these experiments, he observed that, when the magnetic pole was brought near the wire, "the effort of the wire is always to pass off at right angles from the pole, indeed to go in a circle around it. . . . "[1]

The following day he wrote in his laboratory notebook:

Apparatus for revolution of wire and magnet. A deep basin with a bit of wax at bottom and then filled with mercury. A magnet stuck upright in wax so that pole [is] just above surface of mercury. Then piece of wire, floated by cork, at lower end dipping into mercury and above into silver cup.

When a current passed through the wire, it revolved *continuously* around the magnet. This was the first electric motor!

c. Electromagnetic Induction. Oersted's experiment and subsequent developments had clearly shown how "to produce magnetism by electricity." Faraday seems to have held it as one of the tenets of his scientific philosophy that every physical relation (of cause and effect) has its converse. If electricity can produce magnetism, then magnetism should produce electricity. His repeated attempts to accomplish this failed. For example, in 1825, he tried what seemed to be the obvious converse by looking for an electric current in a helix of wire coiled around a magnet. Later, he tried to find a current in a wire placed near another wire carrying current. Other scientists were looking for similar effects but without success. They were all looking for the production of a *steady* current.

But several times investigators were very near to the discovery of induced currents. In 1824, Arago observed the damping of the vibrations of a magnetic needle suspended over a copper plate. This observation was extended by causing the needle to revolve by revolving the copper plate underneath it, air disturbances being, of course, eliminated. It was shown that this "dragging" effect was greater, the greater the electrical conductivity of the spinning plate. Even the effect of radial slits in the copper disk, in reducing the dragging action on the magnet,

[1] Quotation from Faraday's laboratory notebook, Sept. 3, 1821.

was observed.   Suggestive as these experiments were, however, the true explanation remained undiscovered.

In the summer of 1831, Faraday attacked the problem for a fifth time. This time, instead of placing a *permanent* magnet inside a helix, he procured a soft iron ring 6 in. in external diameter, on which he wound two coils of copper, *A* and *B*, "separated by twine and calico."   To detect a possible current in coil *B*, he "connected its extremities by a copper wire passing to a distance and just over a magnetic needle."   When coil *A* was connected to a battery, there was "a sensible effect on the needle. It *oscillated* and settled at last in *original position*.   On breaking connection of side *A* with battery, again a disturbance of the needle."   Slight as these momentary effects were, Faraday recognized their importance, although he too had been looking for a *continuous* effect.   On Aug. 30, he writes, "May not these transient effects be connected with causes of difference between power of metals at rest and in motion in Arago's experiments?"

From this slender clue, Faraday proceeded rapidly to the discovery of the real effect.   On the "third day" of his experiments, he wound a coil of wire around an iron cylinder and placed the cylinder so as to join the *N* pole of one permanent magnet with the *S* pole of another.   The coil was connected to a galvanometer:

Every time the magnetic contact at *N* or *S* was made or broken there was a magnetic action at the indicating helix [i.e., galvanometer]—the effect being, as in former cases, not permanent but a mere momentary push or pull.

On the fourth day, he showed that the presence of iron was not necessary; that the effect could be produced by the action of one helix on another.   On the fifth day:

A cylindrical bar magnet . . . had one end just inserted into the end of the helix cylinder, then it was quickly thrust in the whole length and the galvanometer needle moved; then pulled out and again the needle moved, but in the opposite direction.   The effect was repeated every time the magnet was put in or out, and therefore a wave of electricity was so produced from mere *approximation* of a magnet and not from its formation *in situ*.

At last!   He had "converted magnetism into electricity."   The essential requisite was *relative motion*, or a *change* of condition.   On the ninth day, he produced a continuous current by turning a copper disk between the poles of a powerful electromagnet, the periphery of the disk being connected to its axis through an indicating galvanometer.   This was the now well-known Faraday disk dynamo, the *very first* dynamoelectric machine.

Thus, after only a few days' work in his laboratory, following, however, years of patient and persistent experiment, Faraday had discovered a phenomenon for which the greatest scientists of his time had sought in vain—electromagnetic induction.

Following this discovery, Faraday devised and tried various electric machines to test and extend his newly discovered principle. One of these machines, consisting of a rotating rectangle of wire *with a commutator attached,* is the prototype of the modern dynamo. But his interest was always in pure science, for he writes:

I have rather, however, been desirous of discovering new facts and relations dependent on magnetoelectric induction, than of exalting the force of those already obtained; being assured that the latter would find their full development hereafter.

Being unacquainted with mathematical symbols and methods, Faraday always sought to explain his discoveries and to extend his researches by purely physical reasoning. To the mathematician, the law of magnetic attraction

$$F = \frac{m_1 m_2}{r^2}$$

may have been a sufficient explanation of the phenomenon. To Faraday, this gave a statement only of the *magnitude* of the magnetic forces; *it left the phenomenon itself quite unexplained.* Accordingly, he insisted that two magnetic poles, or two electric charges, could act on each other *only if the medium between the two played some important part in the phenomenon.* This insistence on the importance of the medium ultimately led him to the very fruitful concept of lines of force and of the "cutting" of these lines as essential to electromagnetic induction. At first qualitative, this concept was developed by Faraday into an essentially quantitative form, although it was first stated in mathematical language by F. Neumann in 1845. Commenting on Faraday's laws of electromagnetic induction, Maxwell wrote:

After nearly a half-century . . . , we may say that, though the practical applications of Faraday's discoveries have increased and are increasing in number and value every year, no exception to the statement of these laws as given by Faraday has been discovered, no new law has been added to them, and Faraday's original statement remains to this day the only one which asserts no more than can be verified by experiment, and the only one by which the theory of the phenomena can be expressed in a manner which is exactly and numerically accurate, and at the same time within the range of elementary methods of exposition.

d. The Laws of Electrolysis. Faraday next turned his attention to proving that "Electricity, whatever may be its source, is identical in its nature." He found, for example, that electricity from a friction machine would deflect a galvanometer and would cause chemical decomposition

just as would electricity produced by chemical action.   This led him into
the field of electrolysis.   He found that many substances, such as certain chlorides and sulfates, are nonconductors when solid but are good
conductors when melted, and that in the molten state they are decom-
posed by the passage of current.   This showed that water was *not* essential to electrolysis.   To clarify description of his experiments, he introduced the terms "electrode," "anode," "cathode," "ion," "anion,"
"cation," "electrolyte," "electrochemical equivalent," etc.   A quantitative study of the phenomena resulted in his discovery of the laws of electrolysis that bear his name and which are the basis of all present-day
work in that field.

Further, Faraday clearly recognized that a definite quantity of electricity is associated with each atom or ion in electrolysis.   Had he been
able to determine the number of atoms in unit mass of any substance, he
would have anticipated, by 60 years, the determination of the fundamental charge e.   For he says:

Equivalent weights of bodies are simply those quantities of them which contain
equal quantities of electricity; . . . it being the *electricity* which determines the
combining force.   Or, if we adopt the atomic theory or phraseology, then the
atoms of bodies which are equivalent to each other in their ordinary chemical
action, have equal quantities of electricity naturally associated with them.

e. The Conservation of Energy.   In connection with a proof of the fact
that the electricity from the voltaic pile results from chemical action and
not from mere contact of one substance with another, Faraday stated
clearly the doctrine of the conservation of energy several years before
the statement of Helmholtz.   In 1840, he wrote:

The contact theory assumes that a force which is able to overcome a powerful
resistance . . . can arise out of nothing. . . . This would indeed be a creation
of power, and is like no other force in nature.   We have many processes by
which the form of the power is so changed that an apparent conversion of one
into the other takes place. . . . But in no case is there a pure creation or a
production of power *without a corresponding exhaustion of something to supply it.*

f. The "Faraday" Effect.   Reference has already been made to Faraday's abhorrence of the doctrine of "action at a distance."   He believed
that, if two electric charges attract each other, the medium between the
two plays some important role.   Presumably, therefore, the medium
between two such charges is in a different state than it would be if the
charges were not present; and if so, such an altered state should be detectable by observing the alteration in some physical property of the medium.
As early as 1822, Faraday had experimented with a beam of polarized
light passing through a transparent solution carrying a current, to see
whether the current caused any "depolarizing" action.   Although he

repeated the experiment several times in subsequent years, the results were all negative. In 1845, he returned to the problem, but still with negative results. He then tried solid dielectrics between plates of metal foil connected to a powerful electric machine to see whether, under electric strains, they would show any optical effects. No results![1]

Faraday then substituted a magnetic field for the electrostatic field to see whether the former would cause any depolarizing action on the beam of light. Various substances were tried but still with negative results. Finally, he placed in the magnetic field a very dense piece of lead glass, which he had made many years earlier. When the magnetic lines were parallel to the direction of the beam of polarized light, he observed that the plane of polarization was rotated. At last, he had found a relation between magnetism and light. This magnetic rotation is now known as the "Faraday effect." Again, his persistent search, maintained during 20 years of repeated failures, was rewarded by the discovery of an effect in the existence of which he had the most sublime confidence.

g. Miscellaneous. Among Faraday's other researches may be mentioned: numerous investigations in chemistry; the liquefaction of several gases formerly thought "permanent"; the diffusion of gases through solids; self-induction; certain fundamental properties of dielectrics; diamagnetism; distinction between anode and cathode in the electric discharge through gases at low pressure; vibration of plates; regelation of ice; alloys of steel; and optical glass.

Well may this simple, modest, self-taught philosopher be given a conspicuous place among the great benefactors of mankind.

26. Joseph Henry (1799–1878). Any account of Faraday's work, however brief, should be accompanied by at least a mention of the researches of the American physicist, Joseph Henry, whose memory is honored by the name of the unit of inductance, the henry, which bears to electrokinetics a relation identical with that of the farad to electrostatics. Had Henry been able to experiment continuously, and with more resources, instead of only during a summer vacation of 1 month while teaching mathematics at Albany Academy, and then only with such apparatus as he could make with his own hands, he would undoubtedly have anticipated Faraday in the discovery of electromagnetic induction, including the phenomena of self-induction. In all his work, furthermore, he was greatly hampered by his isolation from the scientific atmosphere of Europe.

Henry was interested especially in the design and use of electromagnets. He constructed the first electric motor operating by an electromagnet, which rocked back and forth between two permanent magnets. He found that, for maximum tractive effect, the cells of the battery and

[1] Years later (1875) this effect was found by Kerr (*Phil. Mag.*, vol. 1, p. 337, 1875).

also the "spools" of the electromagnet should be connected in series if the magnet were a long distance from the battery, but they should be connected in parallel if the wires joining the magnet to the battery were short.   His work on electromagnets led *directly* to the commercial development of the telegraph.

27. James Clerk Maxwell (1831–1879).   It would be difficult to pick out two eminent scientists whose beginnings differed from each other more than did Maxwell's and Faraday's.   Faraday came of very humble parentage; Maxwell, from a long line of distinguished ancestors.   Faraday's early life was lived almost in poverty; Maxwell's family had abundant means.   Faraday received only the most rudimentary education; Maxwell was given every advantage of school and university.   They differed also in their aptitude for scientific work.   Faraday was one of the greatest exponents of experimental science that the world has ever seen; whereas Maxwell, although likewise an able experimenter, is one of the greatest figures in the history of theoretical physics.   And yet both made indispensable and mutually supplementary contributions to the classical theory of electromagnetics.

Maxwell was born in Edinburgh in 1831.   At the age of ten he was sent to the Edinburgh Academy, where he was a friendly boy, though never quite amalgamating with the rest.   But, however strange he sometimes seemed to his companions, he had three qualities which they could not fail to understand: agile strength of limb, imperturbable courage, and profound good nature.[1]

When he left the Academy in 1847, he was "first in mathematics and in English and nearly first in Latin."   Then, after 3 years in the University of Edinburgh, he entered Trinity College, Cambridge, from which he graduated in 1854 with high honors.

Maxwell early showed extraordinary interest in both theoretical and experimental research in physics.   At the academy, he invented a means of drawing certain types of oval curves, and a few years later he published a paper on "The Theory of Rolling Curves" and another on "The Equilibrium of Elastic Solids"—all this before he was nineteen years old! During these same years he was also busy with experiments of many sorts, especially in his little laboratory in a garret on the family estate at Glenlair, where he spent his vacations.

After 4 years at Aberdeen, he was Professor for 5 years at King's College, London (1860–1865); from here some of his most important papers were published, such as "Physical Lines of Force" (1862) and his greatest paper, "A Dynamical Theory of the Electromagnetic Field."   After a retirement of several years, he was elected in 1870 to the newly founded professorship of experimental physics at Cambridge.   In this capacity,

[1] Glazebrook, "James Clerk Maxwell and Modern Physics."

PLATE 4. Maxwell.

he superintended the planning and equipment of the now famous Cavendish Laboratory, of which he was director until his untimely death in 1879.

A large proportion of Maxwell's papers, over 100 in number, may be grouped under three headings: color vision; molecular theory; and electromagnetic theory.

The work on color vision was undertaken to make a quantitative study of the physical facts pertinent to the theory of color sensations proposed by Thomas Young, according to which any luminous sensation is the result of exciting in the eye three primary sensations, red, green, and violet. For this purpose Maxwell invented a "color box," by means of which he could mix spectral colors.

Maxwell's work on molecular physics is very extensive. He discovered and, in part, established theoretically the law of the distribution of velocities among the molecules of a gas ("Maxwell's law"). He showed that when two gases are at the same temperature, the mean kinetic energy of translatory motion of their individual molecules is the same in both gases. From the kinetic theory of viscosity, he drew the surprising conclusion that the viscosity of a gas should be independent of its density so long as the mean free path is not too large, and he verified this conclusion by experiment. He brought to bear upon the whole subject mathematical methods "far in advance of anything previously attempted on the subject"; indeed, he is the co-founder with Clausius (1822–1888) of the kinetic theory of matter.

In the electromagnetic theory, Maxwell's great contributions were the "displacement currents" and the formulation of the general equations of the electromagnetic field, which led to the electromagnetic theory of light. In the preface to his treatise "Electricity and Magnetism," he makes the interesting remark:

Before I began the study of electricity I resolved to read no mathematics on the subject till I had first read through Faraday's "Experimental Researches on Electricity."

He became convinced that Faraday was right in regarding the dielectric as the true seat of electrical phenomena and in supposing that it acted by becoming electrically polarized, the positive ends of its molecules pointing on the whole with the field and the negative ends in the opposite direction. The term "dielectric," as used here, must be understood to include a tenuous medium or ether filling all space, even in what we call a vacuum. He drew the conclusion that when the polarization changes, this change must involve a displacement of electricity, and so there must exist in the dielectric, while the change is going on, a current having the same magnetic properties as the current in a conductor.

This assumption of displacement currents opened the way for the deduction of Maxwell's famous equations of the electromagnetic field. It is interesting, however, that he was first led to these equations through a mechanical analogy, i.e., in studying the behavior of a *mechanical system* filling all space, which would be capable of causing the observed electrical and magnetic phenomena. He showed (1862) that his hypothetical medium would be capable of transmitting transverse vibrations with a speed equal to the ratio of the electromagnetic to the electrostatic unit of charge. Although he did not take his model too seriously, he nevertheless remarks that the ratio of the units

. . . agrees so exactly with the velocity of light calculated from the optical experiments of M. Fizeau, that we can scarcely avoid the inference that *light consists in the transverse undulations of the same medium, which is the cause of electric and magnetic phenomena.*

The theory was restated, without reference to any particular model, in his great paper of 1864, in which he says:

The theory which I propose may therefore be called a theory of the *Electromagnetic Field,* because it has to do with the space in the neighborhood of the electric or magnetic bodies, and it may be called a *Dynamical Theory,* because it assumes that in that space there is matter in motion by which the observed phenomena are produced.

In 1873, Maxwell published his "Treatise on Electricity and Magnetism," which ranks with Newton's "Principia" as one of the most important books in all science.

28. The Completion of Electromagnetic Theory. The *physical ideas* underlying Maxwell's new theory were left none too clear by him. In his treatise, we find the assumption that all space is full of incompressible "electricity"; in a conductor this electricity can move freely (except for ohmic resistance), thus constituting an electric current, but in a dielectric "there is a force which we have called electric elasticity which acts against the electric displacement and forces the electricity back when the electromotive force is removed." This is clear enough. But what is the origin of this "electromotive force" in empty space? And in what does electrification consist? Maxwell appears to have supposed that, when a conductor is charged by allowing a current to flow onto it through a wire, what really happens is that electricity flows into the conductor along the wire and displaces some of the electricity out of the conductor into the space surrounding it; or, if the electrification has the opposite sign, electricity enters the conductor from the surrounding space and forces an equal quantity of electricity out of it along the wire. Thus a charged conductor would contain neither more nor less electricity than an uncharged one. Such a hypothesis concerning electrification became very improbable when in 1876 the American physicist Rowland showed that a moving charged conductor is surrounded by a magnetic field, the moving electrification evidently constituting a current. Evidence obtained since Maxwell's time supports a different assumption, that electricity does not occur in empty space but only in the form of charges upon small particles such as electrons or atomic nuclei.

The new *mathematical theory*, on the other hand, was slowly developed by others, especially by H. A. Lorentz, and was eventually shown to give a good account of all electric and magnetic phenomena and of the principal properties of light. In Germany, stimulated by Helmholtz, Hertz set out to search experimentally for the magnetic effects of Maxwell's displacement currents and in 1887 discovered waves that were undoubtedly of electrical nature. Later, it was shown that the speed of propagation of these waves is the same as that of light. Speculation as to the nature of the displacement currents in a vacuum then gradually died out, until today it is usual to speak only of electric and magnetic "fields" governed by the Maxwell-Lorentz equations. This development in electromagnetic theory illustrates a general tendency, notable during the last half-century but regretted by many, for the fundamentals of physics to become an abstract mathematical theory unsupported by underlying concrete ideas. Further examples are afforded by Einstein's principle of relativity, to be described in the next chapter, and in the foundations of wave mechanics.

A few conclusions from the Maxwell-Lorentz theory which will be especially useful in understanding this book are summarized in Appendix I.

CHAPTER 2

THE THEORY OF RELATIVITY

The first revolution in physical thought during the twentieth century is represented by the new theory of relativity put forward by Einstein in 1905. Relativity touches all branches of atomic physics here and there, but in itself it occupies a detached and fundamental position. A short account of the theory will be given in this chapter.

29. Newtonian Relativity. The phenomenon of *motion* has been a subject of speculation since ancient times. It was early recognized that all motion involves displacement *relative* to something or other; but ideas have varied in regard to the entity relative to which the displacement occurs. In his treatise on mechanics, Newton says that "absolute motion is the translation of a body from one absolute place to another absolute place."[1] But he does not explain what he means by "absolute place." He states explicitly that translatory motion can be detected only in the form of motion *relative to other material bodies.*

Motion involves, also, the passage of time. Until recently, time was regarded as something entirely distinct from space or from the behavior of material bodies. Newton says, "Absolute, true, and mathematical time, of itself, and by its own nature, flows uniformly on, without regard to anything external."[2] Thus there was supposed to be a single time scale valid everywhere.

The kind of relativity embodied in these views has been called "Newtonian relativity." For purposes of comparison, it will be worth while to formulate it in mathematical terms. Let us represent position by means of cartesian coordinates x, y, z, and let t denote the time. Then a set of four numbers representing values of x, y, z, and t specifies the position and the time at which an *event* of some sort occurs. All physical phenomena, in so far as they involve positions and times, can be resolved into sequences of events.

In order to specify the location of an event, we must have some material reference body from which distances can be measured. Similarly, in

---

[1] Cf. E. Mach, "Science of Mechanics," 4th ed., p. 226, 1919.
[2] *Ibid.*, p. 222.

order to define a time, we must have available some reference process, such as the rotation of the earth, in order that times may be specified by stating the stage to which the reference process has advanced. These material means of fixing positions and times, together with the methods adopted for using them, are said to constitute a *space-time frame of reference.*

Now suppose we have *two different* frames of reference, each in *uniform translatory motion* relative to the other. Let us call the two frames S and S'; and let the velocity of S' relative to S be u. Let coordinates and times of any event as obtained when the frame S is used be denoted by x, y, z, t and those obtained for the same event when S' is used, by x', y', z', t'. In order to make the relation between these variables as simple as possible, let us choose our axes so that the x and x' axes are both parallel to the velocity u and, in fact, slide along each other; and let the

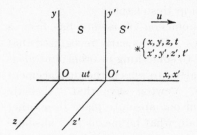
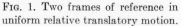

y' and z' axes be parallel to y and z, respectively (Fig. 1). Let us also count time from the instant at which the two origins of coordinates, O and O', momentarily coincide. Then the coordinates of O', the origin of S', as measured in the first frame S, will be $x = ut$, $y = 0$, $z = 0$; and, if any event occurs at a position and time specified by certain values of x, y, z, t, then, according to Newton, its position and

FIG. 1. Two frames of reference in uniform relative translatory motion.

time as measured using S' will be represented by x', y', z', t', where

$$x' = x - ut \qquad t' = t$$
$$y' = y$$
$$z' = z$$

These equations may be called the *equations of space-time transformation* for Newtonian relativity. They enable us to pass from coordinates and times of events referred to one frame of reference to coordinates and times referred to another, when all relations are assumed to be Newtonian. The superfluous equation, $t' = t$, is included with an eye to the future.

30. Relativity and the Propagation of Light. With the adoption of the wave theory of light, a new element, unknown to Newton, was brought into the problem of motion. For, if light consists of "waves" in an ether, these waves should move with a definite velocity *relative to the ether*, and their velocity *relative to material bodies* should change when the motion of these bodies through the ether changes. Analogous statements made about waves in material mediums are certainly true. Water waves of a given length, for example, move with a certain speed over the water; as seen from a moving ship, they move past the ship faster when the ship is moving over the water against the waves than when the ship is moving in the same direction as the waves themselves. Now, in accordance with Huygens' principle, many optical phenomena depend in a very simple way upon the velocity of light relative to material objects. It might be anticipated, therefore, that such phenomena would be influenced by a motion of the optical apparatus through the ether. The velocities that can be given to a material body in the laboratory are extremely small as compared with the velocity of light; but this is less true of the velocity of the earth in its orbital motion about the sun, which is one ten-thousandth of the velocity of light in free space.

An interesting case to consider is the formation of images by the object lens of a telescope. Suppose a light wave from a star enters the telescope sketched in Fig. 2; when the telescope is at rest in the ether, let the wave come to a focus so as to form a star image on the cross hairs at P. Then, if the telescope, instead of being at rest, is moving toward the star, the wave might be expected to focus on the same point P *in the ether* as before. While the wave is passing from the lens to this point, however, the telescope will move forward, carrying the cross hair to some other point P'. The eyepiece would therefore have to be drawn out farther in order to focus on the image of the star. Thus the focal

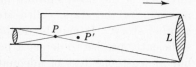

Fig. 2. Effect of motion of a telescope through the ether.

length of the telescope would appear to the observer to be increased. Similarly, if the telescope were moving in the same direction as the light, its effective focal length would be shortened. Thus, as an astronomical telescope is pointed at stars in different directions, its apparent focal length might be expected to vary slightly because of the earth's orbital motion. This effect was looked for long ago by Arago but in vain.

This and other negative results led Fresnel in 1818 to propose a simple possible explanation. He suggested that moving transparent bodies may partially drag the light waves along with them. In the case just considered, if the lens L were to drag the light with it in its motion (toward the right in Fig. 2), the part of the wave that goes through the center of the lens would spend a longer time in the lens, and hence would be retarded more than it would be if there were no motion. Consequently the wave would emerge from the lens more concave in shape and would focus on a point nearer the lens. If the amount of the drag were just right, there would be no effect at all on the apparent focal length, the star image falling on the cross hair however the telescope might be moving. Fresnel showed[1] that all effects on phenomena of refraction would be prevented if it were a law of optics that any moving transparent medium of refractive index n changes the velocity of light in such a way as to add vectorially to its velocity in the stationary medium the fraction

$$1 - \frac{1}{n^2}$$

of the velocity of the medium.   That is, in a medium moving with vector velocity $\mathbf{u}$, the vector velocity of light in any given direction is the sum of a vector of magnitude $(1 - 1/n^2)\mathbf{u}$ and a vector of magnitude c/n.

In 1851 Fizeau showed, by an interference method, that a moving column of water *does* drag the light waves with it to the extent required by Fresnel's hypothesis!   The cause of the drag was assumed by Fresnel to lie in an actual partial dragging of the ether itself along with the moving medium.   When Lorentz worked out his electromagnetic theory, however, about 1895, on the assumption of a stationary ether, he found that the theory led automatically to Fresnel's formula for the light drag.

No effect of the earth's orbital velocity on terrestrial optical phenomena has ever been observed.   It is well known that annual *changes* in the direction of the earth's orbital motion cause a variation in the apparent positions of the stars, called stellar aberration (Sec. 18); but that is another story.   It may be doubted whether the *early* experiments were sufficiently precise to detect a possible effect due to the earth's motion, but at least one test of adequate delicacy was that made in 1871 by Airy, who filled a telescope tube with water and observed that star images were formed in the same position with or without the water, in spite of the longer time required for the light to reach the focal plane when traveling through water instead of air.

It was shown by Fresnel and Lorentz that there should never be any effect on optical phenomena that is of the *first order* in the velocity of the apparatus through the ether.   There might, however, be second-order effects.   Since the square of the earth's orbital velocity is only a hundred-millionth of the square of the velocity of light, such effects would be difficult to detect.   In seeking a sufficiently delicate means of observation, Michelson was led to invent his interferometer, and with this instrument, in conjunction with Morley, he performed in 1887 a famous experiment in which a second-order effect could surely have been detected if it had been present.

31. The Michelson-Morley Experiment.   The interferometer arrangement that was used in this experiment is sketched in Fig. 3.   A beam of

[1] For an excellent discussion of relativity see M. Born, "Einstein's Theory of Relativity," H. L. Brose (tr.), Methuen, London, 1924; also, P. G. Bergmann, "Introduction to the Theory of Relativity," 1942.

light from a lamp S falls upon a half-silvered glass plate P placed at 45°
to the beam, which divides each wave into two parts. One partial wave,
reflected from P, travels off sideways to a mirror M_1, by which it is
reflected back to P; part of it is then transmitted through P and enters
the telescope T. The other part of the original wave, transmitted at
once through P, travels ahead and is reflected back by a second mirror
M_2; upon returning to P, it is partially reflected into the telescope on top
of the first part of the wave, with which it forms an interference pattern.

Let both mirrors be at the same distance from the plate P. Then, if
the apparatus is at rest in the ether, the two waves take the same time
to return to P and meet in phase both there and in the telescope. Suppose, however, that the apparatus is moving with speed v through the
ether in the direction of the initial beam of light. Then, if the initial
wave strikes the plate P when it has the position shown in the figure, the

paths of the waves and the subsequent
positions of reflection from mirrors
and plate will be as shown by the
dotted lines. The necessary change
in the direction of the transverse beam
is produced automatically, as an aberration effect, through the operation of
Huygens' principle. But now the
times taken by the two waves on their
journeys are no longer equal. The
wave moving longitudinally toward
M_2 has a velocity *relative to the apparatus* of $c - v$ on the outgoing trip, c

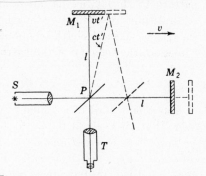

FIG. 3. Diagram illustrating the
Michelson-Morley experiment.

being the speed of light through the ether, and $c + v$ on the return trip;
hence the time required by this wave is

$$t_2 = \frac{l}{c - v} + \frac{l}{c + v} = \frac{2lc}{c^2 - v^2}$$

l being the distance from the plate to either mirror. If we keep small
terms only as far as v^2/c^2, we can write, by the binomial theorem,

$$\frac{1}{c^2 - v^2} = (c^2 - v^2)^{-1} = c^{-2} + v^2 c^{-4}$$

$$t_2 = 2l\left(\frac{1}{c} + \frac{v^2}{c^3}\right)$$

The wave moving transversely, on the other hand, travels along the
hypotenuse of a right-angled triangle having a side of length l. Let it
take a time t' to go from P to M_1, traveling a distance ct'. Then in the
same time the mirror M_1 advances a distance vt'. Hence

$$c^2 t'^2 = v^2 t'^2 + l^2 \qquad t' = \frac{l}{(c^2 - v^2)^{1/2}} = l \left(\frac{1}{c} + \frac{1}{2} \frac{v^2}{c^3} \right)$$

approximately.   Hence this wave returns to P after a time

$$t_1 = 2t' = 2l \left(\frac{1}{c} + \frac{v^2}{2c^3} \right) = \frac{2\ell}{c} \left(1 + \frac{v^2}{2c^2} \right)$$

Thus the two waves interfere in the telescope with a phase difference of $t_2 - t_1 = lv^2/c^3$ sec, or $c(t_2 - t_1)/\lambda = lv^2/(c^2\lambda)$ wavelengths, λ being the wavelength of the light, and the fringe pattern is shifted by the motion through $v^2 l / c^2 \lambda$ fringes.[1]

In performing the experiment, the whole apparatus, floated on mercury, was rotated repeatedly through $90°$.   Since the two light paths are caused to exchange roles by such a rotation, it should cause the fringe pattern to shift twice as much; by reflecting the beam back and forth several times, the effective length l was brought up to 11 meters.   Even then, with a wavelength of about 5.9×10^{-5} cm, if we insert for v the whole orbital velocity of the earth so that $v/c = 10^{-4}$, we find only

$$N = 2 \times 10^{-8} \times \frac{11 \times 10^2}{5.9 \times 10^{-5}} = 0.37 \qquad 2 \times 10^{-8} \frac{\ell}{\lambda}$$

or about one-third of a fringe.   Michelson and Morley were sure, however, that they could detect a shift of a hundredth of a fringe. *Such shifts as were observed amounted only to a small fraction of the theoretical value, and were not consistent.*   Thus the result of the experiment was negative; the expected effects of motion through the ether did not appear.

It might happen, to be sure, that at a given moment the earth by accident had no resultant component of velocity parallel to the surface of the earth; for upon its orbital motion there would probably be superposed a motion of the entire solar system through the ether.   But, if this happened at a certain time, then 6 months later the earth's orbital velocity about the sun would be reversed, and its velocity through the ether should then be twice its orbital velocity.   Michelson and Morley made observations both at various times of day and at different seasons of the year, always with the same negative result.[2]

From the theoretical point of view, Michelson and Morley's failure to detect the anticipated motion of the earth through the ether was one of the most important experimental results ever obtained.   This result was very hard to bring into harmony with current theories of light and mat-

[1] For the formation of the fringes in the interferometer see C. R. Mann, "Manual of Advanced Optics."

[2] Michelson and Morley, *Silliman J.*, vol. 34, pp. 333, 427, 1887; Morley and Michelson, *Phil. Mag.*, vol. 24, p. 449, 1887.   Cf. Miller, *Revs. Mod. Phys.*, vol. 5, p. 203, 1933.

ter.   The theoretical calculation rests on a peculiarly simple foundation, for the only properties of light that are made use of are the constancy of its velocity in space and Huygens' principle.   Neither of these principles can be given up if we are to retain the idea of waves in a mechanical ether.   Only three possible explanations of the negative result seem to offer themselves.

1. Perhaps the student will have wondered why we cannot simply assume that the earth drags the ether with it, much as a moving baseball carries along the air next to it.   On this assumption there would never be any motion of the earth through the ether at all, and no difficulties could arise.   One objection to this explanation is that the ether next to the earth would then be in motion relative to the ether farther away; and this relative motion between different parts of the ether would cause a deflection of the light rays coming from the stars, just as wind is observed to deflect sound waves.   This deflection would alter the amount of the stellar aberration.   It was found very difficult to devise a plausible type of motion for the ether which would give a value of the aberration agreeing with observation and yet at the same time preserve the negative result of the Michelson-Morley experiment.   A second objection arises from the fact that, as has already been stated, experiments show that a transparent object of laboratory size does not drag the light waves with the full velocity of the moving matter, as it necessarily would do if it *completely* dragged the ether along with it; and the observed *partial* drag is fully accounted for by current electromagnetic theory.

2. As an alternative, the negative result would at once be accounted for if we could assume that light projected from a moving source has added to its own natural velocity the velocity of the source, just as the velocity of a projectile fired from a moving ship is equal to the vector sum of its velocity of projection from the gun and the velocity of the ship.   If this were true, the negative result obtained by Michelson and Morley would at once be explained, for the light from their lamp would have always the same constant velocity relative to the lamp and to the interferometer.   Such an assumption, however, is in gross conflict with the wave theory of light.   It is of the essence of waves in a medium that they have a definite velocity *relative to the medium*, just as sound waves have a definite velocity relative to the air.   Furthermore, there is strong *experimental evidence against* the assumption in question, which we have not space to describe.

3. The third possible explanation of Michelson and Morley's negative result, put forward independently by Fitzgerald and by Lorentz, is that motion through the ether might in some manner cause the material composing the interferometer to *shorten in a direction parallel to the motion*. It is easily seen that such a contraction in the ratio $\sqrt{1 - v^2/c^2}$ would

serve to equalize the light paths and thus to prevent a displacement of the fringes.   Lorentz endeavored to make the occurrence of such a contraction plausible on the basis of his electrical theory of matter, but he was never quite able to show that it *must* occur.   This explanation, however was never felt to be very satisfactory because of its *ad hoc*[1] nature.

32. The New Relativity of Einstein.   From the situation just described one easily gains the impression that there exists something like a conspiracy in nature to prevent us from detecting motion through the ether. A similar situation can be shown to exist in the field of electromagnetism as well as in optics.   A number of electrical or magnetic experiments can be invented which, at first sight, offer promise of revealing motion through the ether; but always there occurs some other effect which just cancels the effect sought.

In reflecting upon this extraordinary situation, Einstein arrived in 1905 at a radically new idea.[2]   He proposed the view that, for some unspecified reason, motion through an ether filling empty space is a *meaningless concept;* only motion *relative to material bodies* has physical significance.   He then considered how this assumption could be made to harmonize with the known laws of optics.   Possibilities of conflict arise in any argument involving the velocity of light.   Consider, for example, a frame of reference S' (say on the earth) moving relative to another frame S (say on the sun), and suppose that S' carries a source of light. Then light from this source must move with the same velocity relative to S as light from a source on S itself, since, as explained above, we cannot suppose that the velocity of light is influenced by motion of its source.   But this light must also move *with the same velocity relative to S'*; otherwise the laws of nature would not be the same on S' as on S, and no reason could be assigned for their being different.   Yet it seems quite impossible that light should move with the same velocity relative to *each* of *two* frames that are *moving relatively to each other!*

Einstein accordingly put the laws of the propagation of light in the forefront of the discussion.   He based his new theory, which is known as the *special* or *restricted theory of relativity*, upon two postulates which may be stated as follows:

1. *The laws of physical phenomena are the same when stated in terms of either of two inertial frames of reference (and can involve no reference to motion through an ether).*
2. *The velocity of light is independent of the motion of its source.*

---

[1] An *ad hoc* hypothesis is one that is proposed in order to explain a single fact as distinguished from a hypothesis that explains simultaneously several distinct facts. "*Ad hoc*" translated from the Latin means "to this" or "for this."

[2] Einstein, *Ann. Physik.* vol. 17. p. 891, 1905.

By an "inertial" frame is meant one in which the law of inertia is true, i.e., relative to which a body that is free from external influence and at rest remains at rest.   An inertial frame is thus what is usually called an "unaccelerated" one; and the relative motion of two inertial frames can consist only of a uniform translation.   Thus, in the special theory of relativity, we compare statements of physical laws expressed alternatively in terms of two frames of reference which are in *uniform translation* relative to each other.

Of these two "postulates," the second is believed to represent a rather simple experimental fact, whereas the first is a generalization from a wide range of physical experience.   There is no implication that the first postulate is in any way self-evident; like the assumptions made in all physical theories, it is intended as a hypothesis to be tested by comparing deductions from it with experimental observation.

33. Simultaneity and Time Order.   Einstein found the key by which these two postulates could be brought into harmony in a modification of our ideas concerning time.   He showed that it is necessary to give up the Newtonian conception of absolute time.   Newton had undoubtedly supposed that it is always possible to say unambiguously which of two events precedes the other, or that they occur simultaneously.   But how can this be done if the two events occur in widely separated locations?

In practice, times at two different places are compared by reference to a clock at each place.   It is necessary to set these clocks into synchronism; and in modern practice this is done by means of radio signals, which are a form of light signal.   For precision, however, it is necessary to correct for the time required for light to travel from one place to the other; and making this correction requires a knowledge of the velocity of light *in one direction*.   Ordinary measurements of the velocity of light furnish only its *average velocity in two opposite directions*. We could measure its velocity in one direction if we had our clocks already synchronized, of course; but this thought leads into a logical circle.

As an alternative, we might think of carrying a chronometer from one place to the other and setting both clocks by comparison with this chronometer.   But how could we prove experimentally that the chronometer runs at a constant rate while moving in various directions?   Every method that can be devised to prove this or to measure the velocity of light in one direction turns out to rest upon some fresh assumption that cannot be tested in advance.   Finally, one might think of hurling a ball from one location to the other with infinitely great speed, so that no correction for its time of flight would be necessary.   This would, in fact, do the trick.   But, if all masses increase with velocity as the mass of the electron is known to do, a ball could not possibly be projected with a speed exceeding that of light.   From the standpoint of existing knowledge, it is entirely possible, and it is a consequence of Einstein's new theory of relativity, that no signal of any sort can be transmitted faster than a light signal.

It follows, then, that a general time scale can be set up only on the basis of an artificial convention of some sort. The simplest procedure is the usual one of *assuming* the velocity of light to be the same in any one direction as in the opposite direction. We shall see, however, that a time scale set up on this basis varies somewhat according to the frame of reference that is used in measuring velocities; even the time order of two events may be different.

Before developing the mathematical theory further, the following additional remarks may be of interest. Consider only events that happen at various points along a straight track, so that the situation can be diagramed in two dimensions. On a plot (Fig. 4) let roughly horizontal distances represent displacements along the track and roughly vertical distances lapses of time. Consider a certain mark M on the track and let P_0 represent M when in a certain position at time t_0. Through P_0 draw two lines representing the progress of two light signals which are traveling in opposite directions along the track and which pass P_0 at time t_0.

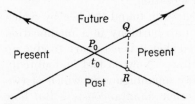

FIG. 4. Diagram illustrating a classification of space-time relations.

Then points on the plot in the area above these two lines will represent possible events which, at time t_0, certainly lie in the *future* for *any* observer at P_0. These events occur late enough so that the observer still has an opportunity to influence them causally, perhaps by sending a radio signal. Below both lines, on the other hand, lies the observer's definite *past*. This area consists of events on the track which may have had a causal influence on events in his neighborhood at time t_0, and of which he may have already acquired knowledge at that time by means of radio signals or other means of communication. Between the lines, however, lies also a third region, representing what might be called the observer's *physical present*. At time t_0 it is too late for him to influence events plotted in this region, but, on the other hand, it is also too early for him to have any observational knowledge of them. For events located at a given point of the track, the observer's physical present covers a range of time such as QR that increases with increasing distance from M. If the observer is in New York, this interval is about $\frac{1}{30}$ sec for events in San Francisco (the time required for light to make the double journey); it is about 16 min for events on the sun. Here we have an essential difference between Einstein's relativity and Newton's;

for in the older theory the physical present was reduced to a single line.

34. The Lorentz Transformation.   If the postulates of Einstein's relativity are accepted, it becomes important to inquire whether or not the accepted laws of physics are all in harmony with the theory.   Furthermore, on the basis of this theory, it may be possible to predict new phenomena, which can be looked for experimentally.   In any case, like all physical theories, the theory of relativity must stand or fall according to whether or not the deductions that can be drawn from it agree with the experimental facts.

In order to make deductions from relativity, we must compare the descriptions of some phenomenon in terms of two inertial frames which are moving relatively to each other.   It is important to know, first of all, how measurements of space and time compare.   In discussing these, for the sake of vividness, we shall sometimes speak of an *observer* who is supposed to make the measurements referred to a particular frame.   This must not be understood to imply, however, that relativity has any closer connection than the rest of physics with human psychology.

The assumption already mentioned will be made, that the velocity of light in a vacuum must measure the same in any two opposite directions. The velocity of light is then the same in all directions and becomes a universal constant c; and, as a further consequence, it is believed that all laws of nature involving velocities become isotropic in space.   On the basis of this assumption, with velocities measured relative to any chosen inertial frame of reference, a general time scale can be set up.   The time at any point may be supposed to be shown by a clock fixed in the frame of reference, clocks at different points being set into synchronism by means of radio signals.   It is found that time scales so established may vary from one frame of reference to another.

Let us use the same units with all frames of reference; to make sure of doing this, we may select such units of length and time that certain natural constants have the same values for both frames.   For example, we may make the wavelengths of spectral lines and the velocity of light measure the same in all frames.   When this has been done, the equations expressing all physical laws must take the same form, according to the first postulate of relativity.

In order to find the relation between measurements made with different frames, consider again the two inertial frames S and S' described in Sec. 29.   It is fairly obvious without proof that the equations $y' = y$ and $z' = z$ must still hold, since there is nothing in the situation to determine which measurement of a length perpendicular to the direction of relative motion should be the greater; the motion of S relative to S' is, to be sure, opposite in direction to the motion of S' relative to S, but this fact cannot determine a difference in the measurements named because that would violate the isotropy of space. For a similar reason it may be assumed that events occurring at different values of y or z but at the same x and t will be found by the S' observer to occur at the same x' and t'.

There remain to be found, therefore, only the relations between x', t' and x, t. At the origins, as these points pass each other, we have $x' = x = 0$ and $t' = t = 0$. If, for another event, x' differs from x or t' from t, it may safely be assumed that these differences will increase in direct proportion to x and t, because of the homogeneity of space and the uniformity of natural laws in time. For example, at a given time t, any discrepancies $x' - x$ and $t' - t$ should increase as much over the second mile from the origin as they do over the first mile; or, at a given point x, they should increase by the same amount in each second. Hence we may safely assume that for any event

$$x' = \alpha x + \beta t \qquad t' = \epsilon x + \gamma t \qquad (1a,b)$$

where α, β, γ, ϵ are constants that remain to be found.

Now at the origin of S' we have always $x' = 0$ and $x = ut$. Hence $0 = (\alpha u + \beta)t$, whence

$$\beta = -\alpha u$$

Next, let a light signal, starting from the coincident origins at time $t = t' = 0$, travel toward positive x. After time t it will be at $x = ct$, and also at $x' = ct'$, since the speed of light c is the same in all frames. Substituting these values of x and x' in $(1a,b)$ and eliminating t and t', we find $0 = \alpha c + \beta - \epsilon c^2 - \gamma c$. If the signal travels toward negative x, on the other hand, we have $x = -ct$, $x' = -ct'$, and

$$0 = -\alpha c + \beta - \epsilon c^2 + \gamma c$$

Hence

$$\alpha = \gamma \qquad \beta = \epsilon c^2$$

Finally, let the signal follow the y' axis. Then, relatively to S it travels obliquely; for, while the signal goes a distance ct, the y' axis advances a distance $x = ut$. Thus $c^2 t^2 = u^2 t^2 + y^2$, whence $y = (c^2 - u^2)^{\frac{1}{2}}t$. But, also, $y' = ct' = c(\epsilon u + \gamma)t$. Equating y' to y, we have

$$c(\epsilon u + \gamma) = (c^2 - u^2)^{\frac{1}{2}}$$

Since, by prior results, $\epsilon = \beta/c^2 = -\alpha u/c^2 = -\gamma u/c^2$, it follows that $c\gamma(1 - u^2/c^2) = (c^2 - u^2)^{\frac{1}{2}}$ and $\gamma = (1 - u^2/c^2)^{-\frac{1}{2}}$.

All constants are now determined, and the equations expressing x', y', z', t' in terms of x, y, z, t can be written down as follows:

i.e., $x' = (x - vt')\left(\sqrt{1 - \frac{v^2}{c^2}}\right)$

$$x' = \gamma(x - ut) \qquad y' = y \qquad \gamma = \frac{1}{(1 - u^2/c^2)^{\frac{1}{2}}}$$

$$t' = \gamma\left(t - \frac{ux}{c^2}\right) \qquad z' = z$$

(2)

$t' = \left(t - \frac{v}{c^2}x\right)\left(\sqrt{1 - v^2/c^2}\right)$

These equations, known as the "Lorentz transformation," were discovered by H. A. Lorentz in the course of his study of matter moving in an electromagnetic field; but he assumed one frame of reference to be at rest in the ether and attached an immediate physical meaning only to measurements made with this frame. The new principle embodied in the theory of relativity implies that all inertial frames are to be treated on an equal footing.

By solving the equations for x, y, z, t, we obtain the inverse transformation:

$$x = \gamma(x' + ut') \qquad y = y'$$

$$t = \gamma\left(t' + \frac{ux'}{c^2}\right) \qquad z = z'$$

(3)

From these equations, we can easily confirm the statement, made previously, that, according to the new relativity, events which happen at the same place at different times, as viewed from one frame, may be seen from another frame to happen at different places as well. Similarly, a difference in spatial position with respect to one frame may correspond to a difference in both space and time with respect to another. Thus a space difference can be converted partly into a time difference, or vice versa, merely by changing the frame of reference that is being used. For this reason it has become customary to speak of space and time as aspects of a four-dimensional continuum known as "space time."

35. Contractions in Space and Time. There are two famous cases in which the Lorentz transformation leads immediately to results of special interest.

Consider a body which, when at rest in S, has a length L_0 in the direction of the x axis. Let it be set moving relative to S at such speed that it is at rest in S'. Its length as measured in S' will now be L_0; for its length is determined by certain natural laws and hence must have a certain fixed value in any frame in which the body is at rest. Let us see how the length now measures in S, relative to which the body is moving with speed u. To do this, we must first consider what we mean by the *length* of a *moving* object. It seems reasonable to define the length as the distance between two points fixed in S which are occupied by the ends of the object simultaneously, i.e., at the same time t. If the coordinates of these points are x_1 and x_2, the length is then $L = x_2 - x_1$. By the same definition, since the body is at rest in S', its ends have fixed coordinates x_1', x_2' such that

$$L_0 = x_2' - x_1'$$

If we substitute in this last equation values of x_2' and x_1' calculated from the first of Eqs. (2) for a given value of t, we obtain

$$L_0 = \gamma(x_2 - x_1) = \gamma L \qquad L = \frac{1}{\gamma} L_0 \qquad (4a,b)$$

From this equation we may draw two distinct conclusions. In the first place, any body measures shorter in terms of a frame relative to which it is moving with speed u than it does as measured in a frame relative to which it is at rest, the ratio of shortening being $\sqrt{1 - u^2/c^2}$. This is a relation between *measurements* referred to different frames.

In the second place, relative to a single frame, any physical body set into motion with speed u shortens in the direction of its motion, as was postulated by Fitzgerald and Lorentz, in the ratio $\sqrt{1 - u^2/c^2}$. In one sense, the contraction is perhaps not a "real" one, since in a frame in which it is at rest the body measures the same as before; but, as far as effects on surrounding bodies are concerned, the contraction is as real as if it were due to a drop in temperature. For example, a row of similar crystals placed in contact and at rest in a certain frame, and then accelerated simultaneously and equally so as to preserve the spacing of their centers as measured in that frame, would separate because of the contraction under discussion and would allow light to pass through between them.[1] Perhaps we might say that we have here a sort of *kinematical perspective*, analogous in a way to the ordinary experience that an object appears to change in size as it recedes into the distance. Unfortunately, these effects are too small to observe on the laboratory scale. It can be said, however, that the negative result of the Michelson-Morley experiment, when considered by an observer relative to whose frame of reference the apparatus is in motion, is due to the contraction in question.

There is a somewhat similar effect in *time*. Consider a vibrator, such as a good crystal clock or a radiating atom, whose frequency is determined by natural laws and hence is the same in any frame in which the vibrator is at rest. Let the vibrator be stationary in S'. Then the time for one vibration as measured in S can be written $t_2 - t_1$ where, using Eqs. (3) for t_2 and t_1 with x' held constant,

---

[1] Let each crystal have a length L_0 when at rest in S, and let their centers have respective coordinates $x_1 = \frac{1}{2}at^2$, $x_2 = L_0 + \frac{1}{2}at^2$, $x_3 = 2L_0 + \frac{1}{2}at^2$, etc., as measured in S, where a is their constant acceleration. The centers have thus the same velocity at at time t. The coordinate of the leading end of the first crystal is, therefore, by Eq. (4b), $x_1' = \frac{1}{2}at^2 + \frac{1}{2}L_0 \sqrt{1 - a^2t^2/c^2}$, whereas that of the trailing end of the second crystal is $x_2'' = L_0 + \frac{1}{2}at^2 - \frac{1}{2}L_0 \sqrt{1 - a^2t^2/c^2}$; the length of the gap between them is thus $x_2'' - x_1' = L_0(1 - \sqrt{1 - a^2t^2/c^2})$.

$$t_2 - t_1 = \gamma(t_2' - t_1')$$

$t_2' - t_1'$ representing the period as measured in S'. This result has again a meaning beyond a mere relation between measurements. For $t_2' - t_1'$ is also the period that the vibrator would have in S if it were stationary in that frame. Thus, relatively to S, setting it in motion has lengthened its period of vibration in the ratio γ. More generally, when any two physical systems are in uniform relative translation at speed u, the effects produced by system A on system B are modified just as if all natural processes on A were slowed down in the ratio $(1 - u^2/c^2)^{1/2}$, and similarly for the effects of B on A. Spectral lines from moving atoms, for example, should show a slight displacement toward the red, superposed upon any Doppler shift that may also be present. Such an effect appears to have been observed by Ives, working with canal rays in hydrogen.[1] Again, certain observations on mesons can be brought into agreement only if the apparent mean life of the mesons is assumed to be increased by motion in the ratio γ (Sec. 215).

Here, also, the effects seem to be as real as those due to a slowing down of any other sort. As a further example, suppose a good crystal clock were subjected to steady translation for some time, first in one direction and then in the opposite, until it returned to the starting point. As judged by clocks that did not share its variable motion, it would lose time, and, after its return, it would be behind a similar clock that had remained at rest. Since clocks at the same location can be compared directly, no comparison of measurements is involved in this difference, which is essentially qualitative.

36. The Transformation of Velocities. The Lorentz transformation leads to important formulas for the transformation of *velocities* from one frame of reference to another. These formulas are easily obtained by noting that, if any moving entity has a velocity v relative to S as measured by the observer who uses S, or v' relative to S' when measured by the S' observer, with corresponding cartesian components v_x, v_y, v_z and v_x', v_y', v_z', then

$$v_x = \frac{dx}{dt} \qquad v_y = \frac{dy}{dt} \qquad v_z = \frac{dz}{dt} \qquad v_x' = \frac{dx'}{dt'} \qquad v_y' = \frac{dy'}{dt'} \qquad v_z' = \frac{dz'}{dt'}$$

On the other hand, from (2), $dy' = dy$, $dz' = dz$, and

$$dx' = \gamma(dx - u\,dt) \qquad dt' = \gamma\left(dt - \frac{u}{c^2}dx\right)$$

From these expressions, one finds by substitution that

$$v_x' = \frac{v_x - u}{1 - uv_x/c^2} \qquad v_y' = \frac{v_y}{\gamma(1 - uv_x/c^2)} \qquad v_z' = \frac{v_z}{\gamma(1 - uv_x/c^2)} \qquad (5a,b,c)$$

[1] Ives and Stilwell, *J. Opt. Soc. Amer.*, vol. 28, p. 215, 1938.

As an example illustrating the mode of deduction,

$$v'_x = \frac{dx'}{dt'} = \frac{\gamma(dx - u\,dt)}{\gamma(dt - u\,dx/c^2)} = \frac{dx/dt - u}{1 - u\,dx/c^2\,dt} = \frac{v_x - u}{1 - uv_x/c^2}$$

The equations just given for the transformation of velocities as measured in *different frames* should not be confused with the ordinary rules for the composition of two velocities measured in the *same frame*, which remain valid. To take a numerical example, let two electrons, ejected from a filament stationary in S, move off with equal speeds of magnitude $0.9c$, one toward $-x$ and the other toward $+x$. Then their speed relative to each other, measured in S, is $1.8c$, by the usual rule. This exceeds c. But, if we make $u = -0.9c$, so that the S' frame keeps up with the electron going toward $-x$, by (5a) the velocity of the second electron relative to the first, *measured now in S'*, is

$$\frac{[0.9c - (-0.9c)]}{(1 + 0.9^2c^2/c^2)} = \frac{1.8c}{1.81}$$

which is a little less than c.

If in Eqs. (5a,b,c) we let $c \to \infty$, so that $\gamma \to 1$, the equations approach the form that is familiar in Newtonian kinematics:

$$v'_x = v_x - u \qquad v'_y = v_y \qquad v'_z = v_z$$

At the same time the equations of the Lorentz transformation, Eqs. (2), pass over into the Newtonian ones as given in Sec. 29. Thus the Newtonian relations constitute an approximation that is valid as long as we are dealing with velocities much below that of light.

37. Relativistic Mechanics. The Variation of Mass. The laws of mechanics as they left the hands of Newton are found upon examination to be not quite in harmony with the new theory of relativity. The necessary corrections to them were discovered originally in studying the motion of charged particles in electromagnetic fields, but they can also be inferred without difficulty from a study of ordinary mechanical phenomena.

For this purpose, we select for study a phenomenon the outcome of which can be inferred from considerations of symmetry, so that it cannot be in doubt. Let two exactly similar elastic balls approach each other along parallel lines and at equal speeds relative to a frame of reference S', and let them collide with each other elastically. Then, by the law of conservation of energy, their total kinetic energy must be the same after the impact as before; and, because of the symmetry, this requires that the balls rebound with their speeds unaltered and with their directions of motion deflected through the same angle (Fig. 5). In describing the collision, let cartesian axes be drawn so that all lines of motion make equal angles with the x axis and are parallel to the xy plane. Let the x' component of velocity of the two balls relative to S' be $-v_x'$ and $+v_x'$, respectively, where $v_x' > 0$.

Now consider the description of this same collision in terms of another frame of reference, S, which is moving toward $-x$ relative to S' at velocity $-u$, where $u = v_x'$, and let the axes in S be drawn in the usual manner. Then one ball, which we may call A, as viewed from frame S, moves up in a direction parallel to the y axis and rebounds with a simple reversal of its motion, whereas the other, which we may call B, rebounds obliquely.

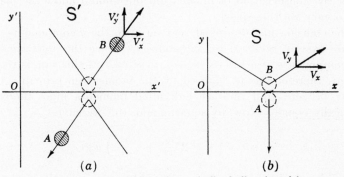

Fig. 5. Diagram of a symmetric collision of two similar balls, viewed from two frames of reference.

In terms of either frame, the x component of the velocity of both balls remains constant; the y component, on the other hand, becomes exactly reversed by the collision. As measured in S', let the y component of the velocity of A before the collision be v_y'; then, because of the assumed symmetry, the corresponding component of B is $-v_y'$. According to Newtonian mechanics, these components would also have the same values when measured in the S frame. The requirements of relativity, however, make this impossible. In terms of S, let the y velocity of A before the collision be w_y, that of B, $-v_y$. Then, by applying (5b) to the y velocity first of A and then of B, we obtain the two equations

$$v_y' = \frac{w_y}{\gamma} \qquad v_y' = \frac{v_y}{\gamma(1 - uv_x/c^2)}$$

v_x being the x component of the velocity of B referred to S.
Dividing these two equations, we find that

$$\frac{v_y}{w_y} = 1 - \frac{uv_x}{c^2} \tag{6}$$

Thus $v_y < w_y$, so that, as viewed from S, ball B suffers a smaller change in its y component of velocity than does A.

This result shows beyond a doubt that the mechanics of Newton cannot be quite correct. The form of the necessary correction cannot be inferred from the theory of relativity alone; but a useful hint is furnished by the theory of the electromagnetic field. It is shown in that theory that momentum is conserved provided electromagnetic momentum of the proper magnitude is assumed to exist in the field (see Sec. 225 in Appendix I). A consequence of this assumption is that the mass of a *charged* body varies with its speed because of the electromagnetic momentum that exists in the field surrounding it. These results suggest that in revising the laws of mechanics we should endeavor to preserve the principle of the conservation of momentum but should allow the mass of a body to vary with its speed.

In the collision just described, as seen in S, the y components of both balls are exactly reversed by the collision; hence the algebraic sum of these components, if not zero, is also reversed. If this sum is to remain constant, therefore, as is required by the momentum principle, it must actually be zero, and the two individual momenta must therefore be numerically equal. Now, by squaring Eq. (6), we have

$$v_y{}^2 = \left(1 - 2\frac{uv_x}{c^2} + \frac{u^2 v_x{}^2}{c^4}\right) w_y{}^2 \tag{7}$$

But $u = v_x'$, which is the x component of the velocity of B referred to S'. Hence, by (5a)

$$u = \frac{v_x - u}{1 - uv_x/c^2}$$

Multiplying through by $-v_x(1 - uv_x/c^2)/c^2$ and rearranging, we have

$$-2\frac{uv_x}{c^2} + \frac{u^2 v_x{}^2}{c^4} = -\frac{v_x{}^2}{c^2}$$

Substituting in (7) and adding $-v_y{}^2 w_y{}^2/c^2$ on both sides,

$$v_y{}^2 - \frac{v_y{}^2 w_y{}^2}{c^2} = \left(1 - \frac{v_x{}^2 + v_y{}^2}{c^2}\right) w_y{}^2$$

$$\therefore v_y \left(1 - \frac{v_x{}^2 + v_y{}^2}{c^2}\right)^{-\frac{1}{2}} = w_y \left(1 - \frac{w_y{}^2}{c^2}\right)^{-\frac{1}{2}}$$

Now $v_x{}^2 + v_y{}^2$ is the square of the speed of B, whose y velocity is v_y, whereas $w_y{}^2$ is the square of the speed of A, with y velocity w_y. Suppose that the mass m of each ball varies with its speed v according to the formula

$$m = \frac{m_0}{(1 - v^2/c^2)^{\frac{1}{2}}} \tag{8}$$

where m_0 is a constant representing the mass when the speed is infinitesimal, called the *rest mass*. On this assumption the y momenta of the two balls will be numerically equal, as required.

The formula for m has been derived here only for a special case, but a longer investigation for which we have not space shows that this formula can be assumed to hold generally. The vector momentum **p** of a body moving with vector velocity **v** is then

$$\mathbf{p} = m\mathbf{v} = \frac{m_0\mathbf{v}}{(1 - v^2/c^2)^{1/2}} \tag{9}$$

Unfortunately the increase in mass is so small at velocities attainable in the laboratory that it has been verified experimentally only for elementary particles such as electrons or protons.

38. Force and Kinetic Energy. All other mechanical terms and principles need now to be scrutinized in order to see whether or not they require changes.

The force on a body may be defined as the *rate of change of its momentum*. This definition is certainly valid in Newtonian mechanics. If the mass varies, however, this definition of force compels us to abandon the familiar $F = ma$; for in linear motion we have then

$$F = \frac{d}{dt}(mv) = m\frac{dv}{dt} + v\frac{dm}{dt} = ma + v\frac{dm}{dt}$$

Because of this complication, it is usually best to attack problems in relativistic mechanics in terms of momentum rather than of acceleration.

The definition of *work* as *force times distance* and of *energy* as *stored work* can be retained without change. This procedure is in harmony with electromagnetic theory. The new expression for the *kinetic energy* T of a moving body can then be found in the usual way by calculating the work done in setting it into motion. This gives

$$T = \int_{v=0}^{v=v} F\, ds = \int_{v=0}^{v=v} \frac{d}{dt}(mv)\frac{ds}{dt}\, dt = \int v\frac{d}{dt}(mv)\, dt = \int v\, d(mv)$$

since $ds/dt = v$, the instantaneous velocity. Inserting the value of the mass m from Eq. (8), we have then

$$T = \int v\, d(mv) = \int v\, d\frac{m_0 v}{(1 - v^2/c^2)^{1/2}} = m_0 \int v\left[\frac{1}{(1 - v^2/c^2)^{1/2}}\right.$$
$$\left. + \frac{v^2/c^2}{(1 - v^2/c^2)^{3/2}}\right] dv = m_0 \int_0^v \frac{v\, dv}{(1 - v^2/c^2)^{3/2}} = m_0 c^2 \frac{1}{(1 - v^2/c^2)^{1/2}}\bigg|_0^v$$

Thus we find, for the *kinetic energy* of a body of which the rest mass is m_0, when moving with speed v,

$$T = m_0 c^2 \left(\frac{1}{\sqrt{1 - v^2/c^2}} - 1\right) \tag{10}$$

We can also expand in powers of v, obtaining

$$\left(1 - \frac{v^2}{c^2}\right)^{-\frac{1}{2}} = 1 + \frac{1}{2}\frac{v^2}{c^2} + \frac{3}{8}\frac{v^4}{c^4} + \cdots$$

so that

$$T = \frac{1}{2}m_0 v^2 + \frac{3}{8}m_0 \frac{v^4}{c^2} + \cdots$$

Thus, if $v \ll c$, T reduces approximately to the ordinary value, $\frac{1}{2}m_0 v^2$. Under the same circumstances, the momentum can also be written, as usual, $m_0 v$. In general, Newtonian mechanics constitutes an approximate form of mechanical theory that is valid for any motion which is slow as compared with the speed of light.

39. A Relation between Mass and Energy. Combining Eqs. (8) and (10), we can write

$$T = (m - m_0)c^2 \tag{11}$$

Thus the kinetic energy of a moving body equals c^2 times its gain in mass due to the motion. This relation suggests that we may think of the increase in energy as the actual cause of the increase in mass. It is then an attractive hypothesis to suppose that even the rest mass m_0 is due to the presence of an internal store of energy of amount $m_0 c^2$. This may be called the *rest energy* of the body.

The total energy of a moving body would then be $m_0 c^2 + T$ or

$$W = mc^2 = \frac{m_0 c^2}{(1 - v^2/c^2)^{\frac{1}{2}}} \tag{12}$$

and we can write for its inertial mass m and momentum p

$$m = \frac{W}{c^2} \qquad p = mv = \frac{Wv}{c^2} \tag{13a,b}$$

From (12) and (13b) it also follows that

$$W^2 = m_0^2 c^4 + p^2 c^2 \tag{14}$$

The foregoing relations suggest that inertial mass may be a property of *energy* rather than of matter as such, each erg of energy possessing, or having associated with it, $1/c^2$ gram of mass. The law of the conservation of mass then becomes merely another aspect of the law of the conservation of energy.

These ideas have proved very useful in dealing with nuclear phenomena, which will be described in a subsequent chapter. It appears to be possible, for instance, for a γ-ray photon, impinging upon a nucleus, to be converted into an electron and positron. Here the energy of the photon reappears in part as the kinetic energy of the particles but largely as their rest-mass energy $2m_0 c^2$. Some physicists prefer to speak of a conversion of energy into mass in such cases; they would say that neither energy by itself nor mass by itself is conserved, but only the sum total of mass times c^2 and energy. In this usage the term "mass" is restricted to "rest mass." The view stated above seems to be preferable, but the difference is scarcely more than a matter of words.

The association of mass and energy is not limited to kinetic energy or to the rest mass. It can be shown that relativity requires mass, or at least momentum, to be associated even with potential energy. Suppose, for example, that two equal masses, moving with equal and opposite velocities along the x axis as seen by an S observer, collide with each other, a spring acting as a buffer between them; just as they come to rest, let a lock snap shut and hold them thereafter combined into a single mass. In this process, the initial kinetic energy of the masses is converted by the collision into potential energy of the spring. Let us view this collision from a second frame of reference, S', that is moving with velocity u parallel to x. Then, if the velocities of the two bodies before the collision, as measured in S, are $v_1 = v_{x1} = v$, $v_2 = v_{x2} = -v$, the same velocities as measured in S' are, by Eq. (5a),

$$v'_1 = v'_{x1} = \frac{v - u}{1 - \dfrac{uv}{c^2}} = -u + \left(1 - \frac{u^2}{c^2}\right)\frac{v}{1 - \dfrac{uv}{c^2}}$$

$$v'_2 = v'_{x2} = \frac{-v - u}{1 + \dfrac{uv}{c^2}} = -u - \left(1 - \frac{u^2}{c^2}\right)\frac{v}{1 + \dfrac{uv}{c^2}}$$

Therefore,

$$\frac{v'_1}{\left(1 - \dfrac{v'^2_1}{c^2}\right)^{1/2}} = -\frac{u}{\left(1 - \dfrac{v'^2_1}{c^2}\right)^{1/2}} + \left(1 - \frac{u^2}{c^2}\right)\frac{v}{\left(1 - \dfrac{u^2 + v^2}{c^2} + \dfrac{u^2 v^2}{c^4}\right)^{1/2}}$$

the last term being obtained in this form after inserting for v'_1 under the radical the first expression given for v'_1 above. Similarly,

$$\frac{v'_2}{\left(1 - \dfrac{v'^2_2}{c^2}\right)^{1/2}} = -\frac{u}{\left(1 - \dfrac{v'^2_2}{c^2}\right)^{1/2}} - \left(1 - \frac{u^2}{c^2}\right)\frac{v}{\left(1 - \dfrac{u^2 + v^2}{c^2} + \dfrac{u^2 v^2}{c^4}\right)^{1/2}}$$

The total momentum *before* collision is, therefore,

$$\frac{m_0 v'_1}{\sqrt{1 - v'^2_1/c^2}} + \frac{m_0 v'_2}{\sqrt{1 - v'^2_2/c^2}} = -m_0 u \left(\frac{1}{\sqrt{1 - v'^2_1/c^2}} + \frac{1}{\sqrt{1 - v'^2_2/c^2}}\right) \tag{15}$$

On the other hand, if we suppose the rest mass of the combined body after collision to be merely the sum of the rest masses of the separate bodies, or $2m_0$, the total momentum *after* collision is

$$\frac{-2m_0 u}{\sqrt{1 - u^2/c^2}}$$

by Eq. (9), since the velocity of the combined body is then $-u$. This is *not equal* to the momentum *before* collision, as given by (15); this can be seen very easily in case v_1' and v_2' are both either greater or less than u.

Thus conservation of momentum fails if only the rest masses are taken into account. But now suppose we include in the mass of the combined body the mass that is to be associated, in the manner described above, with that part of the kinetic energy relative to S' which has been converted by the collision into potential energy of the spring. Then we have a total amount of mass which is proportional to the total energy; and, in consequence of the conservation of energy, this total mass is a constant. The total mass after the collision is, therefore, the same as it was before the collision, or

$$\frac{m_0}{\sqrt{1 - v_1'^2/c^2}} + \frac{m_0}{\sqrt{1 - v_2'^2/c^2}}$$

If we multiply this value of the total mass by the common velocity of the bodies after the collision, which is $-u$, we obtain for the total momentum *after* collision exactly the same expression as that given in Eq. (15) for the total momentum *before* collision. The principle of the conservation of momentum thus holds here if, and only if, we assume that the potential energy in the spring makes its proper contribution to the mass and momentum of the system.

40. Relativity and Electromagnetism. Contrary to the situation in mechanics, a review of the laws of the electromagnetic field shows that these particular laws are in harmony with relativity just as they stand. This might perhaps have been expected in view of the fact that the theory of relativity actually developed out of experiments in that part of the field of electromagnetism which is called "optics."

The distinction between the *electric* field and the *magnetic* field becomes, however, from the new point of view, *in part* a *relative* one, depending upon the frame of reference that is being employed. This conclusion, at first sight surprising, can be reached by means of elementary considerations. For example, if there is a set of electric charges at rest relative to the S frame, they will produce, as determined with the use of this frame, only an electrostatic field. But to an observer using an S' frame in motion relative to S, these same charges will constitute current elements and will be surrounded by a magnetic field as well. The general formulas for the transformation of electromagnetic fields from one frame of reference to another will not be deduced here. but they are easily stated.

As measured by the S observer, let the components of the electric field strength, in electrostatic units, be E_x, E_y, E_z, and let those of the magnetic field strength, in electromagnetic units, be H_x, H_y, H_z; let the corresponding quantities as measured by the S' observer be indicated by the same symbols with the addition of primes.   As usual, let S' have a velocity u relative to S, parallel to the x axis, and let $\gamma = 1/\sqrt{1 - u^2/c^2}$, c being the velocity of light.   Then the equations of transformation for the electromagnetic vectors are

$$E'_x = E_x \qquad\qquad H'_x = H_x \qquad\qquad \gamma = \frac{1}{\sqrt{1 - u^2/c^2}}$$

$$E'_y = \gamma\left(E_y - \frac{u}{c}H_z\right) \qquad H'_y = \gamma\left(H_y + \frac{u}{c}E_z\right) \qquad\qquad (16)$$

$$E'_z = \gamma\left(E_z + \frac{u}{c}H_y\right) \qquad H'_z = \gamma\left(H_z - \frac{u}{c}E_y\right)$$

In vector notation, if $\mathbf{E}'_2$ is the part of $\mathbf{E}'$ that is represented by the terms in H_y or H_z, and $\mathbf{H}'_2$ similarly the part of $\mathbf{H}'$ due to E_y or E_z, then

$$\mathbf{E}'_2 = \frac{\gamma}{c}\mathbf{u} \times \mathbf{H} \qquad \mathbf{H}'_2 = -\frac{\gamma}{c}\mathbf{u} \times \mathbf{E} \qquad\qquad (17a,b)$$

$\mathbf{u}$ denoting the vector velocity of S' relative to S and $\mathbf{u} \times \mathbf{E}$, etc., standing for the vector product.[1]

Isolated charges measure the same in all frames; this must be so, since the charge on an electron must be a universal constant, and the number of electrons in a body, like the number of distinct objects in any given group, must be the same in all frames of reference.   Furthermore, the usual rules for the *force* on a moving or stationary charge still hold; they furnish, in fact, the definition of what is meant by E and H.

The formulas just written may be used to ascertain the effect of uniform motion upon the field of a point charge.   Let a charge q be moving with speed v, and take the x axis through the charge and in the direction of its motion; draw the xy plane through any point P in the field (Fig. 6). First let us use an S' frame in which the charge is at rest [Fig. 6(b)].   In this frame the field is purely electrostatic and is already known; if we take the origin at the charge and let x', y', z' be the coordinates of P referred to S', the components of the field at P are, by Coulomb's law,

$$E'_x = \frac{qx'}{r'^3} \qquad E'_y = \frac{qy'}{r'^3} \qquad E'_z = 0 \qquad r'^2 = x'^2 + y'^2 \qquad (18a,b,c,d)$$

---

[1] The vector product $\mathbf{E} \times \mathbf{H}$ is a vector perpendicular to both $\mathbf{E}$ and $\mathbf{H}$, so directed that a properly oriented right-hand screw advances in the direction of $\mathbf{E} \times \mathbf{H}$ as an arrow on its head turns through the smaller angle (E,H) from the direction of $\mathbf{E}$ to that of $\mathbf{H}$, and of magnitude $EH \sin (E,H)$.

We now change to an S frame, relative to which S' has a velocity parallel to x of magnitude u.   Relative to S, the charge has a velocity $v = u$. Then, from the second set of Eqs. (16), in which $\mathbf{H'} = 0$, we find, changing u to v,

$$H_x = 0 \qquad H_y = -\frac{v}{c} E_z \qquad H_z = \frac{v}{c} E_y \qquad (19a,b,c)$$

or, in vector notation,

$$\mathbf{H} = \frac{1}{c} \mathbf{v} \times \mathbf{E} \qquad (19d)$$

Thus a moving charge is accompanied by a magnetic field proportional to its electric field.   At low velocity this formula is easily seen to agree

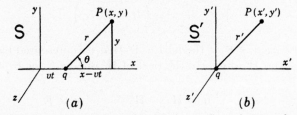

FIG. 6. Diagram of a point charge moving relative to S, stationary relative to S'.

with the familiar Biot law[1] for the field due to a current element.   Furthermore, inserting the values just found for H_y and H_z in (16) with u replaced by v, we find that

$$E'_x = E_x \qquad E'_y = \frac{1}{\gamma} E_y \qquad E'_z = \frac{1}{\gamma} E_z \qquad \gamma = \left(1 - \frac{v^2}{c^2}\right)^{-\frac{1}{2}}$$

and, by using Eqs. (18a,b,c) and also Eqs. (2),

$$E_x = \frac{\gamma q}{r'^3}(x - vt) \qquad E_y = \frac{\gamma q y}{r'^3} \qquad E_z = 0$$

But vt is the x coordinate of q, which is at the origin in S'.   Hence, if r is the distance of P from q and if θ is the angle between the line qP and the x axis [cf. Fig. 6(a)],

$$r^2 = (x - vt)^2 + y^2 \qquad x - vt = r \cos\theta \qquad y = r \sin\theta$$

Thus, using Eqs. (2),

$$r'^2 = x'^2 + y'^2 = \gamma^2(x - vt)^2 + y^2 = r^2[1 + (\gamma^2 - 1)\cos^2\theta]$$

and the expressions just found can be written

---

[1] Commonly miscalled Ampère's formula.   Cf. J. B. Biot, "Précis élémentaire de Physique expérimentale," 1824.

$$E_x = \frac{\gamma \cos \theta}{[1 + (\gamma^2 - 1) \cos^2 \theta]^{3/2}} \frac{q}{r^2}$$

$$E_y = \frac{\gamma \sin \theta}{[1 + (\gamma^2 - 1) \cos^2 \theta]^{3/2}} \frac{q}{r^2} \qquad E_z = 0 \tag{20a,b,c}$$

Thus $E_y/E_x = \tan \theta$, which shows that the electric field points radially outward from the instantaneous location of q.

Many other conclusions can be drawn by transforming fields from one frame to another; limitation of space allows only the mention of one other. The quantity $E^2 - H^2$ is an "invariant," i.e., for any field, $E'^2 - H'^2 = E^2 - H^2$, as the student can easily verify for himself. This invariance opens the possibility for plane waves in space to transform into plane waves when the frame of reference is changed; for, in such waves, $E = H$, $E^2 - H^2 = 0$. The direction of propagation and the frequency, however, are both altered by the transformation, in accordance with the phenomena of aberration and of the Doppler effect.

41. General Theory of Relativity. In considering the bearing of the special theory of relativity upon physical laws, we have said nothing about one of the simplest of physical phenomena, viz., *gravitation*. After publishing the special theory, Einstein took up the problem of harmonizing the laws of gravitation with the requirements of that theory. Since we must suppose that no physical effect can be transmitted from one place to another with a velocity exceeding that of light, it may be assumed that gravitational effects are propagated with a finite velocity. What, then, is the law of this propagation?

At the same time, another idea was active in Einstein's mind. In the special theory, only *unaccelerated* frames of reference had been compared. Why this limitation? Could not the principle of relativity be generalized somehow so that *frames of all sorts* would stand on an equal footing?

In studying these questions, Einstein was impressed by the fact that gravitational acceleration is exactly the *same for all bodies*, however much they may differ in density or in other properties. In this respect, gravitional acceleration resembles the relative acceleration which appears when a frame of reference is itself subjected to acceleration. The latter effect is a matter of common experience. Every one knows how, when riding on an elevator, he seems momentarily to become lighter whenever the elevator is accelerated downward and heavier when it is accelerated upward. This effect simulates closely an actual change in the force of gravity. By no *mechanical* experiment, indeed, can an apparent gravitational field thus produced be distinguished from a true field due to gravitational attraction.

Eventually[1] Einstein came to the conclusion that, in the neighborhood

[1] Cf. A. Einstein, "Origins of the General Theory of Relativity," Jackson, Wylie and Co., Glasgow, 1933.

of any given point, there should be *no difference of any kind* between a gravitational field due to attracting matter and the "apparent" field due to acceleration of a frame of reference. This proposition he adopted as a *postulate* called the *principle of equivalence*. If the principle is accepted, it leads to the prediction of a number of physical effects hitherto unobserved.

Light, for example, had not commonly been supposed to be subject to gravitational action. But suppose the earth's gravitational field were abolished within a laboratory by allowing the whole laboratory to fall freely. Then, relative to the laboratory, there would be no gravitational attraction; a ball thrown horizontally would travel in a straight line relative to the laboratory, not in a parabola. By the principle of equivalence, therefore, a ray of light projected horizontally would also appear to travel in a straight line; for conditions relative to the laboratory are the same as they would be out in space far from all attracting masses, and there is no doubt that in such locations rays of light are straight. Relative to the earth, however, the path of the ray of light would be slightly curved.

The principle of equivalence implies that we perceive a gravitational field on the earth only because we are using the wrong frame of reference. We ought to use a frame relative to which the earth is accelerated upward at the rate g; then we would find that the apparent gravitational field had completely disappeared. From this standpoint gravitational influence consists merely in determining what class of frames it is, relative to which there is no apparent field, and relative to which free bodies move in straight lines.

It does not follow, however, that the gravitational influence of one piece of matter on another is entirely illusory. For only a *uniform* gravitational field can be transformed away *in its entirety* by a proper choice of the frame of reference. Any field can be transformed away in the neighborhood of a single point but, in general, the choice of frame that does this varies from point to point. For example, relative to a frame falling freely in New York there is no gravitational field in New York but one of double strength in Australia.

42. Einstein's Law of Gravitation. There remains the problem as to the law according to which gravitating matter determines which frames have the inertial property. The law must be such that its consequences agree with those derived from Newton's law of gravitation as a first approximation, since this law describes the motions of the solar system with high accuracy; and it must also be in harmony with the special theory of relativity. Einstein surmised that the law could probably be stated most simply in terms of a formulation that would permit the use, not only of any frame of reference in the ordinary sense, but of any sort of generalized coordinates.   With the aid of the mathematician Grossmann, he found out how to write physical laws in a form that is valid *for any choice of space-time coordinates whatever*.   The method involves the use of general tensor analysis, which is too complicated for any example of it to be given here.   Suffice it to say that Einstein found that, among all possible guesses as to the correct law of gravitation, one stood out in contrast to all others as the simplest in mathematical form.   He adopted this law as a tentative hypothesis[1] and then proceeded to look for predictions based on it which could be tested by experiment.

From the new law of gravitation thus obtained, Einstein deduced three novel effects that might be accessible to observation:

1. Rays of light passing close to a heavy body should be bent toward it.   In the case of the sun, the deflection should be inversely proportional to the distance of closest approach of the ray to the sun's center and, for a ray just grazing the sun's surface, should amount to 1.75 seconds of arc.   Stars seen adjacent to the sun during an eclipse should appear to be displaced outward by this angular amount.

2. Physical processes in a region of low gravitational potential, when compared with similar processes at a point of high potential, should be found to take place more slowly.   Consequently, atomic vibrations on the sun should appear to be slowed down, and spectral lines observed in the spectrum of sunlight should be shifted slightly toward the red as compared with lines emitted or absorbed by the same elements on the earth.

3. The motion of the planets should be very slightly altered.   In particular, the perihelion of the orbit of Mercury should be caused to precess about the sun at the rate of 43 seconds a century.   The effect on the other planets would scarcely be detectable.

It appears that all three of these effects actually occur.   In the case of Mercury, calculation shows that perturbations by the other planets should cause an advance of the perihelion by more than 500 seconds a century, but the observed advance is about 43 seconds greater than can be accounted for in this manner.   Thus Einstein's theory removed an annoying discrepancy in astronomical theory.

The new theory of space, time, and gravitation thus arrived at is known as the *general theory of relativity*.   According to this theory, the spatial behavior of matter is not quite Euclidean.   If a triangle of astronomical size near a heavy body like the sun were surveyed by means of rigid rods, with or without the help of light signals, the angles would not quite add up to 180°; and so on.   We have no space to pursue this fascinating subject further, however, nor to discuss its astronomical applications, which

[1] Einstein, *Ann. Physik*, vol. 49, p. 769, 1916.

are connected with the question, not yet answered with certainty, as to the assumption that should be made concerning the outlying parts of space.   Is space finite or infinite?   Is it expanding, as the velocities of the nebulae suggest?

For further study of such questions, the student must be referred to other books or to the literature.

CHAPTER 3

ELECTRONS AND THE PHOTOELECTRIC EFFECT

An approach to the outstanding problem of the first quarter of the present century, viz., the nature of radiant energy, is most directly made by a study of the photoelectric effect. The term "photoelectric" might be applied with reason to a wide variety of phenomena involving the interaction between light and electricity, such as the change in the resistance of selenium under illumination or the rotation of the plane of polarization of a beam of light when passing through a medium placed in a strong electric field. This term is commonly restricted, however, to the discharge of negative electricity from bodies when illuminated by light of appropriate wavelength. In this chapter, we shall give a brief discussion of this effect, emphasizing those features which proved especially difficult of explanation in terms of the wave theory of light. The discussion naturally involves a consideration of the experiments that led to one of the most striking advances of the modern period, the discovery of the electron.

43. Discovery of the Photoelectric Effect. The electromagnetic waves whose existence was predicted by Maxwell's theory of the electromagnetic field were discovered experimentally by Heinrich Hertz. He generated the waves with an oscillating circuit containing a spark gap P and detected them by means of sparks observed at a gap S in a second suitably tuned circuit. In 1887, to facilitate observation, he happened to enclose S in a black box and then found that S must be made *shorter* to allow sparks to pass. Even a plate of glass interposed between P and S would cause this effect. Because a spark was known to emit ultraviolet light, Hertz concluded that ultraviolet light coming from spark P facilitated the passage of sparks at S when no obstacle was interposed. He found that light from another spark would be equally effective, but that in all cases the light must fall on the terminals themselves, and the terminals must be smooth and clean. This was the discovery of the photoelectric effect. It was an accidental discovery, in the sense that it was unplanned. While investigating one physical phenomenon, Hertz discovered quite a different one whose existence he had not even suspected.

The announcement of Hertz's discovery[1] at once attracted numerous investigators. Hallwachs[2] found that a freshly polished zinc plate, insulated and connected to an electroscope as an indicator, when charged *negatively* and illuminated by ultraviolet light, would lose its charge, but that there was no effect if the charge was *positive*. He concluded that, when the plate was negatively charged and illuminated, negatively electrified particles were emitted from it. He even observed, by using an electrometer instead of an electroscope, that a *neutral* insulated plate, when illuminated, could acquire a small *positive* potential, i.e., would lose a *negative* charge. Stoletow[3] devised an arrangement, shown diagrammatically in Fig. 7, for producing a continuous *photoelectric current*. P is a photoelectrically sensitive plate, say a polished zinc plate, connected to the negative terminal of a battery B of several cells. S is a wire grating or gauze connected to the positive terminal of the battery through a very sensitive galvanometer or electrometer G. When ultraviolet light falls upon P, a continuous current is observed in G, indicating that a negative charge is flowing from P to S. No current flows if the battery is reversed.

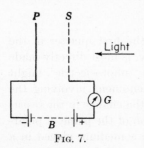

FIG. 7.

Elster and Geitel[4] showed that there is a close relation between the contact-potential series of metals and the photoelectric effect: the more electropositive the metal, the longer the wavelength to which it would respond photoelectrically. The alkali metals, sodium, potassium, and rubidium, were found to be sensitive even to light of the visible spectrum.

44. A Problem. The question then arose as to the mechanism by which negative electricity is transferred from the cathode to the anode. That the charge is carried by negatively electrified particles was clearly indicated by experiments of Elster and Geitel, who showed that a transverse magnetic field diminishes the photoelectric current if the phenomenon takes place in a vacuum. It was early found that the effect persisted even to the highest attainable vacuum and was quite independent of the "degree" of the vacuum after a certain low pressure had been reached. This seemed to indicate that the gas molecules themselves in the region between P and S could not be acting as carriers of the charge. The suggestion was made that, perhaps, under the influence of light, negatively charged particles of the cathode became detached and moved to the anode. This suggestion was rendered untenable by an experi-

[1] *Ann. Physik*, vol. 31, p. 983, 1887.
[2] *Ann. Physik*, vol. 33, p. 301, January, 1888.
[3] *J. phys.*, vol. 9, p. 486, 1890.
[4] *Ann. Physik*, vol. 38, pp. 40, 497, 1889.

ment by P. Lenard,[1] in which a clean platinum wire acted as anode and a sodium amalgam as cathode, both being in an atmosphere of hydrogen. The photoelectric current was allowed to flow until about 3×10^{-6} coulomb had passed through the circuit. If the carriers of the charge were atoms of sodium, each atom could hardly be expected to carry a larger charge than it carries in electrolysis. There should, therefore, have been deposited on the platinum wire at least 0.7×10^{-6} milligram of sodium, a quantity sufficient to be detectable by the well-known flame test. On removing the wire from the bulb, however, no trace of sodium could be detected.

If, then, the photoelectric current is carried neither by molecules of the gas surrounding the cathode nor by molecules of the cathode itself, what are the carriers? The answer to this question came through the convergence of a number of different lines of evidence, which finally culminated in the discovery of the electron by J. J. Thomson. Before continuing the discussion of the photoelectric effect we shall consider some of these other developments.[2]

45. Electricity in Matter. A certain atomicity of electricity was suggested long ago by the laws of electrolysis. Faraday found that when the same quantity of electricity deposits univalent ions of different kinds, the amounts deposited as measured by weight are proportional to the ionic weights in the chemical sense. By the ionic weight is meant here the sum of the atomic weights (ordinary oxygen = 16) of the atoms, one or more, composing the ion. It follows that the same quantity F of electricity suffices to deposit a gram-ion of any kind of univalent ion, i.e., a mass of the ions equal in number of grams to the ionic weight. The

---

[1] *Ann. Physik*, vol. 2, p. 359, 1900.

[2] Collectively these developments illustrate many characteristics of the growth of modern physics:

1. A number of seemingly unrelated lines of research frequently converge to provide an explanation of, or a theory for, a group of phenomena not hitherto understood.

2. The explanation or theory thus evolved is then found to bear directly on other branches of physics and often on other sciences.

3. Thus, the methods of physics are both (1) synthetic and (2) analytic—a fortunate circumstance, which makes it possible for the physicist to comprehend physics as a whole in spite of the vast increase, particularly in recent years, of factual knowledge.

4. These discoveries, of both fact and theory, are the *sine qua non* of applied physics and of much of industry—witness, as a single example, the wide use of the various kinds of photo- and thermionic tubes.

5. This application of science to industry very frequently reacts to provide the research man with improved tools. Electron tubes, manufactured primarily for industrial purposes, are a boon to the physicist in his research laboratory.

6. In all these developments, scientists of all nations "collaborate," the more effectively because of the very fact that they are not formally organized, *let alone directed*, but are free as individuals to follow their respective interests.

present best estimate of the value of this quantity F, which is called the faraday, is 96,493 coulombs.

Now the number of ions in a gram-ion or of atoms in a gram-atom (or of molecules in a gram-molecule) is in all cases the same. This number will be denoted by N_0. It follows that all univalent ions carry the same numerical charge, equal to F/N_0. The charge on a univalent ion thus constitutes a natural unit of charge, usually denoted by e. For this natural unit G. Johnstone Stoney proposed in 1891 the name "electron."

If the number N_0 were known, we could at once calculate e as $e = F/N_0$. In Stoney's time it was known only, from certain calculations based on the kinetic theory of gases, that N_0 is very large, perhaps of the order of 10^{23}. The most reliable modern methods of determining these numbers will be described later (Sec. 48).

An independent line of thought which likewise suggested the presence of definite electrical charges in matter was the treatment of dispersion in developing the electromagnetic theory of light. L. Lorenz suggested in 1880[1] that refractive mediums may contain small charged particles which can vibrate with a natural period ν_0 about a fixed equilibrium position. By assuming one or more sets of such particles, with different natural frequencies, it was possible to account completely for the phenomena of dispersion. But the data on dispersion could not be made to furnish any clue as to the magnitude of the charges on these particles, or even as to their sign.

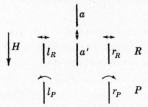

FIG. 8. Diagrammatic representation of the Zeeman effect: a is the original line; R shows the three components when viewed at right angles to the magnetic field; P shows the two components when viewed parallel to the field, which is here directed upward from the paper.

46. The Zeeman Effect. In 1862, Faraday, looking for a possible effect of a magnetic field upon a light source, placed a sodium flame between the poles of a strong electromagnet and examined the D lines by a spectroscope. He was unable to detect any change in the appearance of the lines.

Faraday's failure to observe the effect that he expected was due to the inadequate resolving power of his apparatus. For, in 1896, Zeeman,[2] repeating Faraday's experiment with the improved technique then available, discovered that spectral lines are split up into components when the source emitting the lines is placed in a very strong magnetic field; furthermore, following a suggestion by H. A. Lorentz, he found that these components are polarized. The simplest case is shown in Fig. 8, where a represents a line before the magnetic field is turned on. If the field is

[1] Lorenz, *Ann. Physik*, vol. 11, p. 70, 1880.

[2] *Phil. Mag.*, vol. 43, p. 226, 1897.

turned on and the line viewed *at right angles* (*R*) to the direction of the field, the line is seen to be triple with components l_R, a', and r_R. The central line a' has the same wavelength as the original line a but is plane-polarized with the electric vector parallel to the magnetic field *H*, the direction of polarization being indicated by the double arrow above the line. The other two components, l_R (left, shorter wavelength) and r_R (right, longer wavelength), are plane-polarized with the electric vector perpendicular to the magnetic field.

If the pole pieces of the electromagnet be drilled through longitudinally so that one may view the source in a direction parallel to the magnetic field, only two components l_P and r_P are seen, as shown at *P*. These two lines have the same respective wavelengths as the outside components in the previous case, but they are *circularly* polarized in opposite directions, as shown by the arrows above the lines. (In this latter case the magnetic field is directed toward the reader.)

In his original paper announcing his discovery, Zeeman discusses the phenomenon at first in terms of a mechanical ether, but finally he decides in favor of an explanation in terms of the electrical theory of matter, which had recently been developed more completely by Lorentz. A short description will be given of the classical Zeeman-Lorentz theory, in spite of the fact that we now believe classical theory not to be applicable to atomic phenomena. A simple, concrete picture is thus obtained which assists the memory, in contrast with the abstractness of the wave-mechanical theory. Furthermore, a motion such as Zeeman supposed to occur in the atom could actually be executed by an electron in a vacuum tube.

In order that light of a fixed frequency may be emitted by electric charges, according to classical theory, the charges must vibrate in simple harmonic motion. Assume, then, that there is within an atom a particle having a charge of *q* electromagnetic units and a mass of *m* grams (*q* being either positive or negative). When this particle is displaced a distance *r* from its normal position of equilibrium *O*, let it be acted upon by a

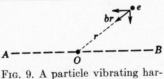

Fig. 9. A particle vibrating harmonically in two dimensions.

restoring force of *br* dynes directed toward *O*. Then the component of the force parallel to any fixed line (e.g., *AB* in Fig. 9) will also equal *b* times the component of the displacement in this direction. Hence, this component of the displacement will vary harmonically with a frequency

$$\nu_0 = \frac{1}{2\pi} \sqrt{\frac{b}{m}} \qquad (21)$$

according to the laws of simple harmonic motion. Any perpendicular component will vary in the same way but, perhaps, with different amplitude and phase. Thus, the general motion of the particle will be equivalent to three independent vibrations in mutually perpendicular directions, all executed with the same frequency.

Now let a magnetic field of B gauss be applied. Then the component of motion of the particle parallel to the field will be unaffected and the frequency of vibration of this component will remain ν_0. A velocity perpendicular to the field, however, will cause a force to act upon the particle in a direction perpendicular both to the velocity and to the field. It is clear, therefore, that vibration of the particle along a *fixed line* perpendicular to the field is impossible; the particle will be deflected sideways and a precession about the direction of the field will occur.

The effect upon the emitted radiation is most easily seen if it is first noted that simple harmonic vibration of the particle with frequency ν_0 along a fixed line through O can be resolved into two superposed circular motions about O as center, the two motions being executed with the same frequency but in opposite directions. The magnetic field then causes the frequencies of these two circular motions to be different. In addition to the elastic force of br dynes, there will be a force of qvB dynes, v denoting the constant speed of the particle in centimeters per second. If the motion is counterclockwise as viewed in the direction of the field, the total force toward O will be $br + qvB$, and the usual equation for circular motion will be

$$\frac{mv^2}{r} = br + qvB$$

Putting $v = 2\pi r\nu$ and, from (21), $b = 4\pi^2 m\nu_0{}^2$, and then solving for ν, it is found that[1]

$$\nu^2 = \nu_0{}^2 + \frac{qvB}{2\pi m}$$

$$\nu = \frac{qB}{4\pi m} + \frac{1}{2}\sqrt{4\nu_0{}^2 + \frac{q^2 B^2}{4\pi^2 m^2}}$$

In all cases of interest, however, the quantity $qB/2\pi m$ is very small as compared with $2\nu_0$, so that in the radical the term containing B^2 may be dropped in comparison with the first term. If the motion is clockwise, the force qvB is reversed and the term $qB/4\pi m$ in the equation for ν is negative. Thus the frequencies of the two circular motions are, to a sufficient approximation,

$$\nu_1 = \nu_0 + \frac{qB}{4\pi m} \qquad \text{(counterclockwise)} \qquad (22a)$$

$$\nu_2 = \nu_0 - \frac{qB}{4\pi m} \qquad \text{(clockwise)} \qquad (22b)$$

[1] The solution containing a negative radical is rejected because it makes ν and v negative.

The characteristic features of the *emitted radiation* are easily inferred now if we recall that the elec ric intensity radiated by an accelerated positive charge is directed as nearly oppositely to the acceleration as it can be, subject to the condition that it must be perpendicular to the direction of propagation of the waves (see Sec. 227). If the emitted light is viewed with a spectroscope in a direction *perpendicular* to the magnetic field, three lines will be seen. One, emitted by the component of vibration parallel to the field, will have a frequency ν_0 and will be polarized with the electric vector parallel to the applied magnetic field; the two others, emitted by the circular motions, will have frequencies ν_1 and ν_2 and will be polarized with the electric vector perpendicular to the magnetic field. If, on the other hand, the light is viewed in a direction *parallel* to the field, only the lines of frequency ν_1 and ν_2 can be seen; and they will be circularly polarized. These features agree exactly with Zeeman's observations.

For a *positive* particle, however, the slower rotation occurs in a *clockwise* direction as seen by an observer looking in the direction of the field, whereas Zeeman found counterclockwise rotation for the line of lower frequency. He concluded, therefore, that the charge on the radiating particles must be *negative*. The ratio e/m for the particles can be computed from the separation between the outer lines. Letting e stand hereafter for the *numerical* charge on a particle, so that $q = -e$, we have from Eqs. (22a,b)

$$\Delta\nu = \nu_2 - \nu_1 = \frac{Be}{2\pi m} \qquad \frac{e}{m} = \frac{2\pi}{B}\,\Delta\nu \qquad (23a,b)$$

Zeeman's first observation indicated that e/m must be "of the order of magnitude of 10^7 electromagnetic units." In a later experiment, working with much higher resolving power, he found $e/m = 1.6 \times 10^7$, which may be compared with the modern value of 1.76×10^7.

Later experiments, however, have shown the Zeeman effect to be much more complicated than Zeeman at first assumed from his observations with apparatus of relatively low resolving power. In general, many more components are observed than are shown in Fig. 8. The simple theory outlined above fails completely to explain these more complicated "patterns." The quantum theory of the Zeeman effect is discussed in Secs. 129–133.

47. The Discovery of the Electron. Previous to 1897, many studies had been made of that beautiful phenomenon, the discharge of electricity through rarefied gases. Let the discharge from an induction coil or an electrostatic machine pass between the negative terminal C (cathode) and the positive terminal A (anode) sealed into a glass tube (Fig. 10) which is being exhausted through the side tube T. At a very low pressure, there appears around the cathode a dark space, known as the

"Crookes dark space," which, with further decrease in pressure, grows
longer (i.e., extends farther toward D), until finally it reaches the glass
walls of the tube, causing them to glow.   If screens pierced with holes
S_1 and S_2 are introduced, the glow is confined to a spot on the end of the
tube, at D, thus indicating that something is proceeding from the cathode
and causing the glass to phosphoresce.   This "something" was early
called "cathode rays."   It was found that, by suitably curving the cathode, these rays could be "focused" upon a piece of platinum foil within

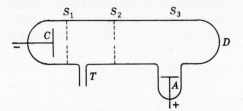

FIG. 10. Tube for electrical discharge at low pressure.

the tube, heating it to incandescence.   They could also be deflected by
a magnetic field, or by an electrostatic field, the spot at D moving upward
if a positively charged rod is brought up in the position S_3.   Finally, in
1895, Perrin caught the rays in an insulated chamber connected to an
electroscope and proved that they carry a negative charge.

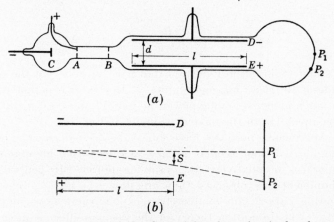

FIG. 11. (a) Thomson's apparatus for determining the ratio e/m for electrons.   (b)
Deflection of an electron by the electrostatic field.

The true nature of the cathode rays was finally established in the classical experiments[1] of J. J. Thomson, who measured the ratio of the charge
carried by the rays to their mass.   His apparatus is shown diagrammatically in Fig. 11.   The highly evacuated glass tube [Fig. 11(a)] con-

[1] *Phil. Mag.*, vol. 44, p. 293, 1897.

tains the cathode C and an anode A, which has a small rectangular slot in it through which the cathode rays may pass. B is a screen similar to A and electrically connected with it. Cathode rays, accelerated from C toward A, after passing the slot in A move with uniform velocity and emerge from the slot in B as a small bundle of rectangular cross section, which causes a small, fluorescent patch at P_1 on the far side of the bulb. But when a potential difference V is maintained between the parallel plates D and E, E being positive, the spot appears at P_2, having been deflected downward by the electrostatic field. A pair of Helmholtz coils, not shown, whose diameters are equal to the length of the plates D and E, are placed, one in front and the other behind the tube, so as to produce a magnetic field perpendicular to the plane of the paper, the strength of which can be determined from the dimensions of the coils and the current through them. If the magnetic field is directed *toward* the reader, the spot P_1 is seen to be deflected upward.

Two observations are now made. In the first observation, with a given electrostatic field E between the plates, the magnetic field B is adjusted to such a value that the spot returns to the original undeviated position P_1. If d is the distance between the plates and V the potential difference between them in electromagnetic units, then E equals V/d. The transverse force eE upon the charge e carried by one of the rays is just equal and opposite to the force evB due to the magnetic field of B gauss, e being likewise in electromagnetic units. Hence $eE = evB$ and

$$v = \frac{E}{B} \qquad \text{cm per sec} \qquad (24)$$

Thus the first observation serves to measure the velocity v of the particles, which remains constant after they emerge from screen B. The magnetic field is then removed and the deflection P_1P_2 caused by the electrostatic field alone is measured; from this, the deflection S of the particles as they pass over the distance l between the plates D and E can be determined [cf. Fig. 11(b)]. This deflection results from a uniform acceleration eE/m acting during a time l/v; hence, by the laws of uniformly accelerated motion,

$$S = \frac{1}{2} E \frac{e}{m} \left(\frac{l}{v}\right)^2 \qquad (25)$$

The value of e/m may be computed from this equation, in which all other quantities are known.

Thomson found that the value of e/m determined in this way was independent of the kind of gas in the tube (air, H_2, or CO_2) and, likewise, independent of the electrodes (Al, Fe, or Pt). His final determination was $e/m = 1.7 \times 10^7$, a value *almost identical with the value found by*

Zeeman for the particles taking part in light emission. This ratio of charge to mass is very much greater than that for hydrogen atoms in electrolysis. Its relatively great magnitude might result from either a large value of e or a small value of m, or both. It became important, therefore, to determine the magnitude of the charge carried by the particles.

Now study of the charges on gaseous ions such as are produced in a gas by x-rays had begun a few years before Thomson's work. To measure their charges, Townsend, working in Thomson's laboratory, utilized the clouds that form about the ions in saturated air. By observing the rate of fall of the cloud and applying Stokes's law for the free fall of spheres through a viscous medium, he was able to determine the size of the droplets; from a measurement of the total amount of water in the cloud, he could then calculate the number of droplets it had contained. He assumed that each droplet contained just one ion; hence, having measured also the total charge on the cloud, he was able to calculate the charge on a single ion. For this charge he obtained a value of about 3×10^{-10} electrostatic unit. A repetition of the measurements with some modifications by Thomson gave the value 6.5×10^{-10} esu.

Thomson assumed that the charge on the gaseous ions was the same as that on his cathode particles. It followed, then, that the cathode particles must be previously unknown particles of extremely small mass, which he called "corpuscles" or "primordial atoms." For many years English writers stuck to the name "corpuscle" for these particles, using the word "electron" in Stoney's original sense to denote the amount of charge carried by a corpuscle or a univalent ion; but others, including Lorentz, called the corpuscles themselves "electrons," and this usage ultimately became well established. It was generally assumed that electrons are a constituent part of all atoms and are responsible for the emission of light by them, thus accounting for the fact that the ratio e/m had been found to be the same for the vibrating particles causing the Zeeman effect as for the cathode rays. Thus was made possible the explanation of a number of more or less diverse phenomena on the basis of a single concept.

48. Electronic Magnitudes. A more reliable method of measuring ionic charges was developed by Millikan in 1909. He found that tiny droplets of oil in ionized air, viewed under a microscope, would frequently pick up charges and could then be held suspended, or accelerated upward or downward, by applying a suitable electric field. When uncharged, the droplets fall at a slow, uniform rate, their weight being balanced by the drag due to the viscosity of the surrounding air. By observing their rate of fall, Millikan was able to determine the size and weight of the droplets. According to Stokes's law, a sphere of radius a moving at a steady, slow speed v_0 through a fluid whose coefficient of viscosity is η

experiences a resisting force

$$F = 6\pi\eta a v_0 \tag{26}$$

If we equate this force to the weight of a droplet, which is $\frac{4}{3}\pi a^3 \rho g$ in terms of the density ρ of the oil, we have

$$\tfrac{4}{3}\pi a^3 \rho g = 6\pi\eta a v_0 \tag{27}$$

Now suppose the drop picks up a charge of e units and that a vertical electric field E is present, e and E both being measured in electrostatic units. Then a force eE is added to the weight and instead of (27) we have

$$\tfrac{4}{3}\pi a^3 \rho g + eE = 6\pi\eta a v_1$$

v_1 being the new velocity of steady fall. From these equations we find

$$eE = 6\pi\eta a(v_1 - v_0)$$

and, inserting in this equation the value of a given by (27) and solving for e, we find

$$e = 6\pi\eta^{3/2}(v_1 - v_0)\left(\frac{9v_0}{2\rho g}\right)^{1/2}\frac{1}{E} \tag{28}$$

All quantities in this last expression being known, e can be calculated.

Millikan found that the charges so calculated from his observations were all multiples of a smallest charge. The latter he assumed to be the charge on the electron, an assumption which is difficult to test directly but seems to be well supported by indirect evidence. For the electronic charge he found $e = 4.774 \times 10^{-10}$ esu.

This value of e was accepted for the next 20 years. In 1928, however, Bäcklin pointed out[1] that x-ray wavelengths as measured by means of a ruled grating could be made to agree with the same wavelengths measured by means of a calcite crystal provided Millikan's value of e was assumed to be 0.4 per cent too small. The discrepancy was later traced to Millikan's having used too low a value of the viscosity of air, which appears as η in Eq. (28). Improved measurements gave a value of η nearly 0.5 per cent greater than Millikan's, resulting in the value 4.804×10^{-10} for e as calculated from the oil-drop observations.

It is now recognized, however, that what is obtained directly from the x-ray measurements is actually a value of N_0, the number of atoms in a gram-atom; e is then calculated as F/N_0, where F is the value of the faraday (Sec. 45). The accuracy of the value of e obtained in this manner is actually much greater than that of the oil-drop observations.

[1] E. Bäcklin, "Absolute Wellenbestimmungen der Röntgenstrahlen," dissertation, Upsala, 1928.

Millikan's work nevertheless remains of fundamental importance. He demonstrated clearly that electric charges in ionized gases occur in multiples of a single fundamental unit, and the close agreement of his value of e with that required by the x-ray data constitutes an important confirmation of the principles underlying the calculation of e from the x-ray data themselves.

Actually, even the x-ray observations do not constitute the only accurate method of obtaining a value of e.   A considerable number of observable quantities are now available which can be measured with high precision and which can be expressed in terms of the fundamental constants of physics by formulas of apparently high reliability.   It was suggested[1] by DuMond and Cohen that the most logical procedure would be to use *all* the precise, reliable data and, making due allowance for the relative accuracy of the various experimental methods, to seek the most probable values of the fundamental constants as a group.   This is done by applying the familiar methods of least squares.   The principal data leading to values of e, m, and Planck's h are the velocity of light, the faraday F, the short-wave limit of the continuous x-ray spectrum (Sec. 156), and grating measurements of x-ray wavelengths.   The most probable values as inferred in 1953[2] for F, N_0, e, and the mass m of the electron are as follows:

$$F = 96{,}493 \pm 3 \text{ coulombs per gram-mole (chem scale)}$$
$$F = 96{,}520 \pm 3 \text{ coulombs per gram-mole (phys scale)}$$
$$N_0 = (6.02304 \pm 0.00036) \times 10^{23} \text{ (gram-mole)}^{-1} \text{ (chem scale)}$$
$$N_0 = (6.02472 \pm 0.00036) \times 10^{23} \text{ (gram-mole)}^{-1} \text{ (phys scale)}$$
$$e = (4.80288 \pm 0.00021) \times 10^{-10} \text{ electrostatic unit}$$
$$e = (1.60207 \pm 0.00007) \times 10^{-19} \text{ coulomb}$$
$$m = (9.1085 \pm 0.0006) \times 10^{-28} \text{ gram}$$

Here "chemical scale" refers to the ordinary definition of atomic weights, etc., by which a gram-mole of ordinary oxygen weighs 16 grams; on the "physical scale," a gram-mole of the oxygen isotope O^{16} weighs 16 grams and a gram-mole of ordinary oxygen, 16.00446 grams (Sec. 181c).   The values here given on the chemical scale were obtained by dividing those on the physical scale by 16.00446/16, or 1.000279.   For general use, the following approximate values are suggested:

$$N_0 = 6.023 \times 10^{23} \text{ (chem scale)}$$
$$e = 4.803 \times 10^{-10} \text{ esu}$$
$$m = 0.9108 \times 10^{-27} \text{ gram}$$

[1] J. W. M. DuMond and E. R. Cohen, *Revs. Mod. Phys.*, vol. 20, p. 82, 1948, and vol. 21, p. 651, 1949.
[2] J. W. M. DuMond and E. R. Cohen, *Revs. Mod. Phys.*, vol. 25, p. 691, 1953.

Other numbers of frequent use are

$$\frac{e}{m} = (1.75888 \pm 0.00005) \times 10^7 \text{ emu per gram}$$

$$\frac{M_\text{H}}{m} = 1837.13 \pm 0.04$$

$$\frac{M_p}{m} = 1836.13 \pm 0.04$$

Here M_H is the mass of a hydrogen atom and M_p the mass of a hydrogen nucleus, or proton.

49. Photoelectrons.   The discovery of the electron at once suggested the hypothesis that the photoelectric effect is due to the liberation, from the illuminated metal plate, of electrons which, under the influence of the electric field, pass from cathode to anode, thereby causing the photoelectric current.   This hypothesis was confirmed by Lenard,[1] who showed

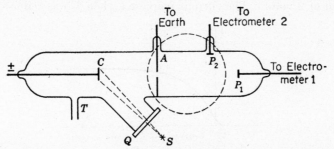

Fig. 12. Lenard's apparatus for determining the ratio e/m for electrons.

that the photoelectric discharge is deflected in a magnetic field exactly as are cathode rays.   By measuring the deflection of the "photoelectric rays" in a known magnetic field, he found a value of e/m of (about) 1.2×10^7, in qualitative agreement with Thomson's value of e/m for electrons.

Lenard's method of determining e/m for photoelectrons involves basic principles which, with ever increasing refinement, have been widely applied in "charged-particle" physics.   His apparatus is shown diagrammatically in Fig. 12.   A glass tube, which could be exhausted to the highest attainable vacuum through the side tube T, contained an aluminum cathode C, which could be illuminated by ultraviolet light from a spark S, the light passing through the quartz plate Q.   The cathode C could be charged to any potential, positive or negative.   A screen A, with a small hole at its center and connected to earth, served as anode. P_1 and P_2 were small metal electrodes connected to electrometers.   When C was illuminated and charged to a negative potential of several volts,

[1] *Ann. Physik*, vol. 2, p. 359, 1900.

photoelectrons were liberated and accelerated toward the anode A. A few electrons passed through the hole in the center of A and proceeded thereafter at uniform velocity to the electrode P_1, their reception there being indicated by the electrometer 1. But if, by means of a pair of Helmholtz coils (represented by the dotted circle), a magnetic field directed toward the reader was produced in the region between A and P_1, the electrons were deflected upward in a circular path and, with a sufficient field strength, struck the electrode P_2.

Lenard first investigated the relation between the current reaching the anode and the potential V applied to C, A being assumed to be always at zero potential. There was no photoelectric current when V was several volts positive. But, when V was dropped to about 2 volts *positive*, a small current was observed. This indicated that the photoelectrons were not simply *freed* from the cathode but that some of them at least *were ejected with sufficient velocity to enable them to overcome the retarding potential* of 2 volts. The current increased when V was reduced to zero

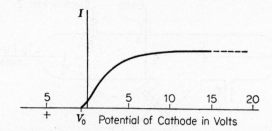

FIG. 13. Variation of photoelectric current with cathode potential.

and increased still more rapidly as V was made negative but attained a "saturation" value after V had reached some 15 or 20 volts negative. These data are shown diagrammatically in Fig. 13. I is the photoelectric current and V_0 is the positive potential that was required to prevent the escape of electrons.

The determination of e/m was made essentially as follows. Let a negative potential V, large compared with V_0, be applied to the cathode C, all potentials being in electrostatic units. The photoelectron, on reaching the anode, will have a kinetic energy given approximately by

$$eV = \tfrac{1}{2}mv^2$$

where m and e are the mass and the charge in electrostatic units of the electron and v is its velocity on reaching A (Fig. 12). Assuming that after leaving A the electron moves in a uniform magnetic field, the circular path that it follows is determined by the equation

$$\frac{evB}{c} = \frac{mv^2}{R}$$

where B is the magnetic induction in gauss just necessary to cause the electron to reach P_2, and R is the radius of the corresponding circular path, determined from the geometry of the apparatus. From the last two equations we have

$$\frac{e}{m} = \frac{2V}{B^2 R^2}$$

50. Relation between Photoelectric Current and Intensity of Illumination.

The experiments of Elster and Geitel, Lenard, and Ladenburg seemed to show that, as long as there is no change in the spectral quality of the light causing the emission of electrons, the photoelectric current is directly proportional to the intensity of illumination on the emitting surface. Subsequent experiments[1] confirmed the law of proportionality and showed that it holds rigorously over a very wide range[2] of intensities—in the experiments of Elster and Geitel, over a range of 50,000,000 to 1.

51. Energy Distribution of Photoelectrons.

In his experiments, Lenard showed, by observing the retarding potential against which these electrons could move, that for a given emitter their kinetic energy did not exceed a definite maximum, given by eV_0, where V_0 is the maximum retarding potential for which a photoelectric current was observed and e is the electronic charge. The energy of photoelectrons was the subject of many later investigations. We mention the experiments of Richardson and Compton,[3] who, by introducing important corrections and techniques, cleared up a number of previous discrepancies and gave impetus to the quantitative verification of Einstein's photoelectric equation (see next section). The apparatus used by Richardson and Compton is sketched in Fig. 14. The photoelectric emitter C, a strip 1×5 mm of the metal under investigation, was placed at the center of a spherical glass bulb B some 7.5 cm in diameter and silvered on its inner surface. The emitter C could be charged to any desired potential, read by voltmeter V. The bulb could be evacuated through the side tube T. Monochromatic light L passed through the quartz window W and fell on C. The silver coating on the inside of B, serving as anode A, was connected to the electrometer Q by which the photoelectric current was measured.

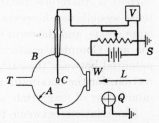

Fig. 14. Apparatus of Richardson and Compton for observations on the energy of photoelectrons.

[1] Richtmyer, *Phys. Rev.*, vol. 29, pp. 71, 404, 1909.

[2] Elster and Geitel, *Physik. Z.*, vol. 14, p. 741, 1913; vol. 15, p. 610, 1914; vol. 17, p. 268, 1916. Kunz and Stebbins, *Phys. Rev.*, vol. 7, p. 62, 1916.

[3] Richardson and Compton, *Phil. Mag.*, vol. 24, p. 575, 1912.

The large spherical anode, with the small emitter at its center, served two important purposes. First, since the electric field around C was nearly radial, it was possible to measure the energy distribution of the photoelectrons irrespective of direction of emission and thus to determine what has come to be known as the "total energy," in contradistinction to the "normal energy," which is measured when cathode and anode are a pair of parallel plates, as in Fig. 7. Second, the impact of the photoelectrons on the anode caused the diffuse emission from the latter of a certain number of secondary electrons. In the case of parallel plates, a considerable proportion of these return to the cathode, and the observed

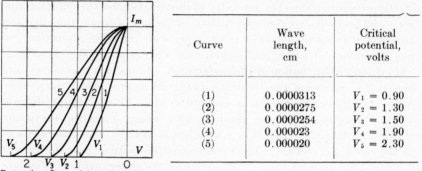

Curve	Wave length, cm	Critical potential, volts
(1)	0.0000313	$V_1 = 0.90$
(2)	0.0000275	$V_2 = 1.30$
(3)	0.0000254	$V_3 = 1.50$
(4)	0.000023	$V_4 = 1.90$
(5)	0.000020	$V_5 = 2.30$

FIG. 15. Variation of photoelectric current with retarding potential.

current is, therefore, not the true photoelectric current. Only a few of these secondaries, however, reach the small cathode C at the center of the large anode, and the error in the observed current is negligible. Richardson and Compton made careful correction for the contact difference of potential between the cathode C and the silver anode, an important correction, for the maximum retarding potentials—1 or 2 volts—were of the same order of magnitude as the contact potentials.

The relation between photoelectric current and retarding potential obtained by Richardson and Compton is shown for aluminum as emitter in Fig. 15. When the aluminum surface was illuminated by ultraviolet light of constant intensity and of wavelength 0.000020 cm, no photoelectric current was observed when the potential of C was greater than 2.3 volts—V_5, curve 5. As the retarding potential decreased from this value to zero, the current rose to a maximum I_m, beyond which there was no increase for negative potentials on the cathode. For longer wavelengths, similar curves—4,3,2,1—were obtained, but critical retarding potentials—V_4, V_3, V_2, V_1—became progressively less as the wavelength increased.[1] Curves of the same shape were obtained for other intensities of illumination.

[1] The intensity of these several monochromatic beams was adjusted to give the same value of I_m in each case.

These observations are readily interpreted on the assumption that, for a given emitter, light of wavelength λ causes the emission of photoelectrons with initial velocities v varying from zero up to a maximum v_m determined by λ. The value of the maximum velocity v_m is given in terms of the critical potential V_0 by the equation

$$eV_0 = \tfrac{1}{2}mv_m{}^2$$

e being the numerical electronic charge. When the potential V applied to the emitter is zero or negative, all electrons freed by the light reach the anode and the photoelectric current has its maximum value I_m. When $V_0 > V > 0$, only those electrons will reach the anode for which

$$\tfrac{1}{2}mv^2 > eV$$

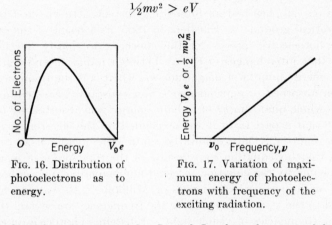

FIG. 16. Distribution of photoelectrons as to energy.

FIG. 17. Variation of maximum energy of photoelectrons with frequency of the exciting radiation.

Let the photoelectric currents be I_1 and I_2 when the potentials are V_1 and V_2, respectively. Then $(I_2 - I_1)/e$ photoelectrons per second leave the emitter with velocities between v_1 and v_2 defined by

$$V_1 e = \tfrac{1}{2}mv_1{}^2 = E_1 \qquad V_2 e = \tfrac{1}{2}mv_2{}^2 = E_2$$

E_1 and E_2 being the corresponding kinetic energies. Thus the slope of a curve such as those in Fig. 15 is proportional to the number of photoelectrons possessing energy E corresponding to the value of V at that point. A curve plotted between these slopes and V is the energy distribution curve for photoelectrons; its general form is shown in Fig. 16.

52. Relation between the Velocities of Photoelectrons and the Frequency of the Light. A very simple linear relation has been found to exist between the maximum energy of photoelectrons and the frequency ν of the light that causes their emission. As was shown by Millikan, if a curve is plotted between eV_0 and ν, a straight line results which has an intercept ν_0 on the frequency axis (Fig. 17). The experimental meaning of this intercept is that light of frequency less than ν_0 cannot cause the emission of photoelectrons from the metal concerned. The quantity ν_0

is characteristic of the emitting electrode, but *the slope of the curve is the same for all electrodes.* The equation of the curve may be written

$$\tfrac{1}{2}mv_m{}^2 = h(v - v_0) = hv - \omega_0 \tag{29}$$

where h is the slope of the curve and ω_0 is written for hv_0. If, in Fig. 17 and Eq. (29), the ordinates are expressed in ergs and the abscissas in frequencies (sec^{-1}), the numerical value of h, as found by Millikan, is 6.56×10^{-27} erg sec. (A better value is 6.63×10^{-27}.) This constant h, called "Planck's constant" for reasons which will appear in Chap. 4, is one of the fundamental constants of nature and has played an extraordinary role in modern physics. The product hv is called a quantum of energy corresponding to frequency v.

Equation (29) has had an interesting history. It was first proposed on theoretical grounds by Einstein, in 1905, as a result of the extension to the photoelectric process of the concept, previously developed by Planck, that interchanges of energy between radiation and matter take place in energy quanta of magnitude hv, where v is the frequency of the radiation absorbed or emitted and h is a constant. Einstein assumed[1] that the whole quantum hv of radiant energy was absorbed by one electron but that a part ω_0 of it was expended by the electron in escaping from the emitter. Only qualitative data were available at that time showing that his equation gave results of the right order of magnitude, but subsequently the equation received final experimental verification as a result of the precise experiments of Millikan.[2] Its validity has been extended to the x-ray region, where the frequencies are several thousand times the frequencies of visible light. Einstein's photoelectric equation played an enormous part in the development of the modern quantum theory. But in spite of its generality and of the many successful applications that have been made of it in physical theories, the equation is, as we shall see presently, based on a concept of radiation—the concept of "light quanta"—completely at variance with the most fundamental concepts of the classical electromagnetic theory of radiation.

53. Other Properties of Photoelectric Emission. It is not our purpose to give a complete account of the properties of the photoelectric effect, but a few other features of interest may be mentioned.

The critical or "threshold" frequency v_0 has been found to vary considerably with the state of the surface, as does the photoelectric current in general. Usually v_0 lies in the ultraviolet, but for the alkali metals and for barium and strontium it lies in the visible region; for potassium v_0 lies in the red, and for cesium even in the infrared. Photoelectric cells

---

[1] A. Einstein, *Ann. Physik*, vol. 17, p. 132, 1905.

[2] Millikan, *Phys. Rev.*, vol. 7, p. 355, 1916.

used for the measurement of light commonly contain either an alkali metal or barium.

Variation of temperature usually has little or no effect upon the photoelectric current, so long as the temperature does not exceed several hundred degrees centigrade and so long as no change occurs in the crystal structure or in the physical state of the metal. The alkalis, however, form an exception to this rule.

If *polarized light* is used, differences are commonly found as the plane of polarization is rotated, except, of course, at normal incidence. The effect is complicated, and its cause is in doubt. Especially interesting is the "selective effect" in the alkali metals. Over certain ranges of wavelength, the photoelectric current from these metals is much greater when the electric vector in the light has a component perpendicular to the surface than when it is parallel to the surface; in the case of certain sodium-potassium alloys, the ratio of the currents in the two cases may be 10:1 or 20:1 or even more.

For further discussion of the photoelectric effect the student is referred to other treatises.[1]

Discussion will be limited here to those fundamental problems presented by the photoelectric effect that have a bearing on quantum theory. Before continuing this discussion, however, a brief description will be given of a closely related phenomenon.

54. Thermionic Emission. It has been known for 200 years that air in the neighborhood of hot solids has the power of conducting electricity. In a systematic investigation begun about 1880, Elster and Geitel showed that, in general, at a red heat, charged bodies lose a positive charge more readily than they do a negative one, whereas at a white heat a negative charge is more readily conducted away; a few substances, however, lose a negative charge most readily at all temperatures. About the same time, Edison noticed that a current can flow in an evacuated bulb from a glowing carbon filament to another filament when the hot filament is charged negatively but not when it is positive.

The ions that carry the electricity in such cases were studied by McClelland and by J. J. Thomson. In 1899, Thomson measured e/m, the ratio of charge to mass, for the *negative* ions, using the method described in Sec. 47. He found this ratio to have about the same large value as for cathode rays and concluded that these negative ions were electrons. Later he showed that, for the positive ions, e/m was in all cases of the same order of magnitude as for electrolytic ions and concluded that the positive ions were positively charged atoms or molecules.

[1] A. L. Hughes and L. A. DuBridge, "Photoelectric Emission," 1932; V. K. Zworykin and E. G. Ramberg, "Photoelectricity and Its Applications," 1949.

The emission of electrons, called thermions, from hot bodies has been extensively studied, but mention will be made here only of a few properties of thermionic emission that are of interest in connection with the theory of the photoelectric effect.[1]

The thermionic current from a given emitter is found to increase very rapidly with increasing temperature. It depends also upon geometrical factors, which determine space-charge effects, and upon the potential of the emitter relative to its surroundings. From a given emitter operating at a given temperature, however, the thermionic current cannot be made to exceed a certain limiting value I. By means of thermodynamic reasoning it can be shown that I should vary with temperature at least approximately according to Richardson's equation[2]

$$I = AT^2\epsilon^{-e\phi/kT}$$

in which $\epsilon = 2.718$, k is the Boltzmann constant (1.380×10^{-16} erg per deg C), and ϕ and A are constants depending on the emitting substance and on the state of its surface. This equation is found to represent the experimental facts very well; the variation of the exponential factor is so rapid, however, that it is not possible to tell whether the factor T^2 is really correct.

The quantity $e\phi$ in Richardson's equation represents an energy; in the theoretical derivation it represents the "heat of emission" in ergs of the thermions at the absolute zero of temperature, that is, the amount of energy required to extract a thermion at that temperature. The energy per electrostatic unit of charge is thus ϕ. A convenient unit for the measurement of such energies is the *electron-volt*, denoted by ev and defined as the electrostatic work done on an electron when it passes between two points differing in potential by 1 volt. One electron-volt equals $e/300$ ergs, or, slightly more accurately, $(e/c) \times 10^8$ ergs; hence

$$1 \text{ ev} = 1.6021 \times 10^{-12} \text{ erg}$$

the exact value of the first factor as given recently[3] being 1.60207 ± 0.00007. It is customary to state as the value of ϕ the potential difference in volts that will change the energy of the electron by $e\phi$ ergs; the value in volts thus assigned to ϕ then also represents the energy denoted by $e\phi$ in Richardson's equation measured in electron-volts. To obtain $e\phi$ in ergs, for use with the usual value of kT, ϕ in volts must be multiplied by the value of 1 ev in ergs; alternatively, kT, which also has the dimensions of energy, might be divided by the value of 1 ev in order to

[1] Cf. A. L. Reimann, "Thermionic Emission," 1934.

[2] See O. W. Richardson, "Electron Theory of Matter," chap. XVIII, 1916; Reimann, *op. cit*

[3] J. W. M. DuMond and E. R. Cohen, *Revs. Mod. Phys.*, vol. 25, p. 691, 1953.

express kT itself in electron-volts.   As calculated from thermionic data, ϕ ranges from 2 to 6 volts.

It was early assumed that thermions and photoelectrons come from the same source inside the metal, the two types of emission differing chiefly in the mechanism by which an electron acquires sufficient energy to enable it to escape from the emitter against the action of attractive forces of some sort.   In the case of thermionic emission the electron acquires this energy from the thermal agitation incident to the high temperature of the emitter; in photoelectric emission the energy is gained by the absorption of radiant energy.   On this view, the quantity $e\phi$ in the thermionic equation ought to be at least approximately the same as the quantity ω_0 or $h\nu_0$ in the Einstein photoelectric equation, and the following relation should hold:

$$\phi = \frac{\omega_0}{e} = \frac{h\nu_0}{e} \tag{30}$$

It has not been easy to check this equation by experiment, owing to the many spurious disturbances inherent in both photoelectric and thermionic research.   Reasonably comparable measurements have, however, been accomplished on a number of the more stable metals; a few values are as follows:

Metal	$h\nu_0/e$, volts	ϕ, volts
Platinum	6.30	6.27
Tungsten	4.58	4.52
Silver	4.73	4.08
Gold	4.82	4.42

The agreement between the values of the work function determined photoelectrically and those determined thermionically seems good enough to warrant the hypothesis that the photoelectrons and the thermionic electrons have a common origin.

55. What Is the Photoelectric Mechanism?   Efforts to imagine a mechanism for photoelectric emission on the basis of the classical electromagnetic theory of light encountered great difficulties.   It was early assumed that metals contain a number of *free electrons* in the spaces between the atoms and that electric currents are due to a drift of these free electrons caused by the electric field.   Electromagnetic waves entering a metal would agitate the free electrons, and it could readily be imagined that occasionally an electron near the surface of the metal would be given enough energy to eject it entirely.

If photoelectrons originated in this way, however, it would be expected that they would emerge with smaller kinetic energies when the incident

light is faint than when it is strong, whereas the experimental fact is that
their kinetic energies are *entirely independent of the intensity* of the light.
On the other hand, their energies *do* depend on the *frequency* of the
light.

The latter two experimental facts taken together led at one time to the
proposal of an alternative hypothesis, namely, that the photoelectrons
come from inside the atoms, and that their release is of the nature of a
resonance phenomenon.   The light might function as a "trigger" releasing the electron from inside an atom in which it already possessed energy
of considerable magnitude.   Light of a given frequency would then
release only those electrons which were tuned to that frequency, and the
atomic mechanism might conceivably be such that the energy of the
expelled electron would be proportional to the frequency.   It was hard
to believe, however, that the atoms contained resonating systems of all
frequencies for which photoelectric emission was observed.   Furthermore, the fact remained to be explained that the number of the photoelectrons is rigorously proportional to the intensity of the light.

The experimental facts thus seem to demand the conclusion that the
photoelectric energy comes directly from the energy of the incident light.
Another difficulty is then encountered, however.   It is hard to understand how so much energy can be absorbed by a single electron.   According to the electromagnetic theory of light, the energy of light waves is
distributed equally over the wave front.   Let it be assumed, for purposes
of calculation, that the electron can absorb as much of this energy as
falls on the area occupied by one atom lying on the surface of the metal.
Then it can be calculated that the time required for a photoelectron to
absorb the maximum energy of emission, $\frac{1}{2}mv_m{}^2$, from faint light of
sufficient intensity to cause an easily measurable photoelectric emission
from sodium would be more than 100 days.   The situation is improved
if the electron is assumed to vibrate inside the atom in exact resonance
with monochromatic light, since it can be shown that the electron can
then manage to absorb as much of the incident energy as falls upon a
considerable fraction of a square wavelength.   Even so, however, the
calculated time exceeds 1 min.   Thus, if the electron obtains its energy
by an ordinary process of absorption, there should be an appreciable lag
between the beginning of illumination and the start of the photoelectric
current.   Precise measurements[1] showed, however, that, if such a lag
exists, it is less than 3×10^{-9} sec.

If we could return to the corpuscular theory and regard light as a rain
of corpuscles, all these difficulties would disappear.   If we could assume
(*a*) that each corpuscle, or in modern terms "quantum" or "photon,"
carries energy, and (*b*) that, under suitable circumstances, a whole pho-

[1] Lawrence and Beams, *Phys. Rev.*, vol. 29, p. 903, 1927.

ton may be absorbed by an electron, then we should at once have an explanation of the principal properties of the photoelectric effect in metals.   There could be no observable time lag in the photoelectric process; the current would be exactly proportional to the light intensity, i.e., to the number of photons striking per second; and the velocities of the photoelectrons would be entirely independent of the light intensity, since the absorption of each photon would be a process quite independent of the absorption of other photons.   The Einstein equation for the maximum velocity would also follow naturally.

The difficulties with such a radical theory of light, however, are many. For one thing, if we regard light as a "shower" of photons, what can possibly be the meaning of *frequency?*   There is nothing periodic about a falling raindrop, for example.   As a matter of fact, in order to find the frequency of a beam of light, we *measure* (a) the velocity c of the light and (b) its wavelength λ *on the assumption that light consists of waves*, and then we *compute* the frequency as

$$\nu = \frac{c}{\lambda}$$

Thus we have to rely on the wave theory of light to give us the energy value hv of a photon!   And there still remains the phenomenon of interference, which, since its discovery by Young in 1802, has defied explanation on any other basis than by assuming light to be a wave phenomenon.   However, the experimental facts of photoelectricity are equally as cogent as the phenomena of interference, and these *cannot be explained on the basis of the classical wave theory of light*.

Thus in 1920, say, the physicist could sum up the situation about like this: On one side of a seemingly impenetrable barrier, or fence, is to be found a group of phenomena—such as interference, polarization, smaller velocity of light in optically denser bodies, indeed, the whole electromagnetic theory and its ramifications—according to which we should say, without the slightest doubt, that light *must consist of waves*.   On the other side of the fence is to be found another group—the photoelectric effect, and other phenomena which we shall consider in subsequent chapters—according to which we should say, again without the slightest hesitation, if we did not know what was on the first side of the fence, that light *must be corpuscular*.   The situation thus created was perhaps the most puzzling one that has ever arisen in the whole history of physics. We cannot resolve the mystery at this time, but shall return to the question after we have become familiar with the quantum theory of atomic structure and of spectra.

The remainder of this chapter will be devoted to a short description of certain modern ideas concerning the state of the free electrons in metals and of the view of the photoelectric process to which these conceptions lead.

56. The Free-electron Theory of Metals. The classical theory of metallic conductivity was developed by Drude, Lorentz,[1] and others. They assumed that the free electrons move about and collide with each other just as do the molecules of a gas, having the usual maxwellian distribution of velocities proper to a gas of electrons at the temperature of the metal. They showed that such free electrons would account also for the high thermal conductivity of metals; because of their light mass, according to classical theory, the electrons would have much higher velocities of thermal agitation than do the atoms, and for this reason they would be, in proportion to their numbers, much more effective in the conduction of heat.

The theory had some success in accounting for the properties of the electrical and thermal conductivities of metals. A serious difficulty was encountered, however, in connection with specific heats. As will be explained in Chap. 9, the specific heat of a metal is fully accounted for by the kinetic and potential energy which the atoms themselves should possess. It was necessary to suppose, therefore, that for some reason the heat energy of the free electrons was very small, or at least independent of temperature. Several lines of evidence indicated on the contrary that the number of the free electrons should be of the order of magnitude of the number of atoms; and, according to the principle of equipartition (Sec. 66), a free electron should have the same average kinetic energy as an atom. Thus, it was hard to understand why the specific heats of good conductors were not considerably larger than the experimental values.

This difficulty disappeared when the new theory of wave mechanics, to be described in Chap. 6, was applied to electrical conductors. A brief description of the modern theory of metals will be given in Chap. 9. The wave-mechanical theory, however, has been only partially worked out and is complicated. For this reason interest still attaches to a simple form of the theory proposed by Sommerfeld in 1928, which reproduces the most important features of the conclusions derived from wave mechanics in so far as they concern photoelectric and thermionic emission.

Sommerfeld retained the artificial concept of a gas of free electrons in metals, but treated this imagined gas in terms of wave mechanics. Because of their light mass and their high density in the metal, the electrons should form a degenerate gas of the Fermi-Dirac type (Secs. 170 and 173) and should have a peculiar distribution of velocities.

According to classical theory, the free electrons should all have zero energy of translation at the absolute zero of temperature. As the tem-

[1] H. A. Lorentz, "Theory of Electrons," 2d ed., 1916.

perature rises, they should acquire thermal velocities distributed according to Maxwell's law, and at $T°K$ their average kinetic energy should be $\frac{3}{2}kT$. Even at 1500°K, this energy is equivalent only to some 0.2 ev. Some electrons would have more energy and some less, but the commonest value of the energy would be not far from the average.

In contrast, the distribution of kinetic energy given by the Fermi-Dirac theory is shown in Fig. 18 for the assumed free electrons in platinum, at three temperatures: 0, 300, and 1500°K. It will be observed that the average energy is very much greater than the classical value of $\frac{3}{2}kT$, and, furthermore, that the relative distribution of the energies of

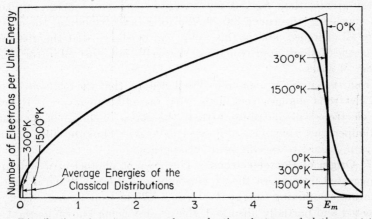

FIG. 18. Distribution of energy among the conduction electrons of platinum at three different temperatures, according to the Fermi-Dirac-Sommerfeld theory.

the individual electrons is nearly the same at the absolute zero of temperature as it is at 1500°K. The graph for absolute zero rises according to an equation of the type $y = a\sqrt{x}$ until a maximum energy E_m is reached, at which point the graph drops suddenly to zero. No electrons possess energy greater than E_m. The value of E_m is given by Eq. (240) or

$$E_m = \frac{h^2}{2m}\left(\frac{3n}{8\pi}\right)^{2/3}$$

where h is Planck's constant, m is the mass of the electron, and n is the number of electrons per unit volume. If it be assumed that the number of free electrons per unit volume is of the same magnitude as the number of atoms per unit volume, then E_m for platinum (6.6×10^{22} electrons per cubic centimeter) is approximately 6 ev. The theory shows that the mean value $\bar{E}$ of the energy per electron at absolute zero is

$$\bar{E} = \frac{3}{5}E_m = 3.6 \text{ ev for platinum}$$

These results are astonishing to any one who is used to thinking in classical terms, for they mean that even at absolute zero the free electrons in a metal have enormous energies. This energy may be thought of as kinetic in nature, but the significance of the term "kinetic" is less clear in wave mechanics than in classical theory.

The *rate of increase* of the energy with temperature, on the other hand, is much less than it is according to classical theory. Referring again to the distributions in energy for platinum at 300°K and at 1500°K as shown in Fig. 18, we note that only in the neighborhood of E_m is there any significant change in distribution with temperature. As the temperature rises, the sharp discontinuity at E_m for absolute zero becomes "rounded off" and an increasing number of electrons come to possess energy greater than E_m. A few electrons even have energies up to several times E_m; the curve has thus a long tail (extending, theoretically, up to all energies), and in this tail it can be shown that the distribution of energies follows approximately Maxwell's law, just as in the classical theory of gases.

From the curves it is obvious, furthermore, that the *total energy* of the free electrons changes very little with rise of temperature. Hence the free electrons will contribute little to the *change* in energy of the metal as its temperature rises, i.e., to its specific heat. Thus the difficulty noted above in regard to specific heats disappears.

57. Origin of Photoelectrons. The view of photoelectric action that is suggested by modern theory is briefly as follows. When a photon or quantum containing energy $h\nu$ strikes an electron in free space, it is deflected and partially absorbed, the process being known as the Compton effect (Sec. 160). It is readily seen that under such circumstances absorption of the entire quantum cannot occur. For, if the absorption were complete, the electron would acquire kinetic energy equal to $h\nu$, and also momentum equal to $h\nu/c$, since the ratio of momentum to energy in a photon is the same as the classical ratio for light waves, which is stated in Sec. 226 in Appendix I. If, however, $\frac{1}{2}mv^2 = h\nu$ and also $mv = h\nu/c$, v being the velocity imparted to the electron, it follows from these equations that $v = 2c$, which is impossible. For large values of $h\nu$ the relativistic formulas (9) and (10) must be used, with the conclusion that $v = c$, but even this is impossible.

When, however, an electron is attached to an atom or a group of atoms, an alternative process becomes possible by which the entire quantum may be absorbed. This is called *photoelectric absorption*. In such a process the momentum of the supporting atom or atomic group also undergoes a change and this change suffices to preserve the conservation of momentum.

If a free electron in the surface of a metal already has thermal kinetic energy E_i and absorbs a quantum $h\nu$, it will have total kinetic energy $h\nu + E_i$. If this energy exceeds the work Ω that must be done by any electron against attractive forces in escaping from the surface of the metal, the electron will emerge as a photoelectron with kinetic energy

$$\tfrac{1}{2}mv^2 = h\nu + E_i - \Omega$$

Since E_i cannot much exceed the limit E_m, the photoelectric energies will thus have a fairly definite maximum value given by the equation

$$\tfrac{1}{2}mv_m{}^2 = h\nu + E_m - \Omega$$

Comparison with Eq. (29) shows that the constant ω_0 in the Einstein photoelectric equation must have the approximate value

$$\omega_0 = \Omega - E_m \qquad\qquad (31)$$

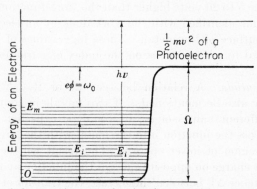

Fig. 19. Energy of electrons in a metal.   An electron with extra energy $e\phi$ can just escape as a thermion.   A photoelectron absorbs $h\nu$ and retains $\tfrac{1}{2}mv^2$ as kinetic energy.

The relation between the various electronic energies is illustrated diagrammatically in Fig. 19.   The heavy curve represents the way in which the *potential* energy of an electron varies as it traverses the surface of the metal.   The horizontal rulings represent the Fermi-Dirac thermal energy levels (actually much more closely spaced) at 0°K; at any other temperature there are a few electrons with energy above E_m.

Most of the photoelectrons, however, emerge with smaller energies than $\tfrac{1}{2}mv_m{}^2$, either because $E_i < E_m$ or because they come from deeper layers of the metal and lose energy in traveling to the surface.   Furthermore, there ought to be no absolute frequency threshold for photoelectric emission, since a *few* free electrons are present with *all* energies.   The curves in Fig. 15 ought, therefore, to be rounded off at the end, so as to meet the axis asymptotically instead of plunging into it at a finite angle.   At one time the absence of such rounding was regarded as evidence that the photoelectrons must come from inside the atoms themselves.   The effect required by wave mechanics is much smaller, however, than that implied by classical theory, for the maxwellian tail of the Fermi-Dirac distribution is extremely small. Furthermore, there is experimental evidence that a slight rounding off of the curves at this point does exist.[1]

Thermions are believed to come out of the maxwellian tail of the distribution. Since the average energy of these electrons is close to E_m, the energy lost by a thermion in emerging is sensibly equal to $\Omega - E_m$, and the thermionic work function ϕ should therefore be given by the equation

$$e\phi = \Omega - E_m \tag{32}$$

It follows that, approximately, $e\phi = \omega_0$, in agreement with the experimental result.

For platinum, ϕ is 6.3 volts and E_m/e is calculated to be at least 6 volts; hence Ω/e must be at least 12.3 volts. For the metals in general, Ω/e is calculated to be 5 to 20 volts higher than the work function ϕ, which was itself at one time identified with the work done by an electron in escaping from the surface of the metal. These high values of Ω are qualitatively confirmed by observations on the index of refraction of electrons in metals.[2]

Contact Potentials. A relation between ω_0 or $\Omega - E_m$ and contact potentials may also be mentioned. If two metals in contact with each other have different values of ω_0, it would be expected that electrons would pass across the junction into the metal with the larger ω_0, thereby moving to a region of lower energy. The result will be to develop a double layer of charge on opposite sides of the junction and an associated potential difference ΔV between the metals; the transfer of charge should continue until $e \Delta V = \Delta \omega_0$, the metal having the larger ω_0 being at the lower potential. When this condition has been established, the total energy of the uppermost electrons in the Fermi-Dirac distributions has become the same in the two metals. It is readily seen that interposition of a chain of other metals between a given pair will not affect the value of ΔV between these two, which is the algebraic sum of the ΔV's along the entire chain.

Now it is well known that conductors in electrostatic equilibrium usually appear to differ in potential by a fraction of a volt, or sometimes by several volts. All that can easily be measured, however, is the difference of potential between two points in the surrounding space, one very close to each metal. A simple way to measure this difference is to arrange two insulated parallel plates, one of each metal, connected to the terminals of an electrometer, with a bit of radioactive material so placed as to ionize the air between the plates. A zero electrometer reading is taken with the terminals connected together; then the terminals are disconnected and a second reading is taken after the accumulation of charge

[1] DuBridge, *Phys. Rev.*, vol. 43, p. 727, 1933.
[2] See G. P. Thomson, "The Wave Mechanics of Free Electrons," 1930.

on the plates has destroyed the electrostatic field between them and so stopped the flow of ions.   The difference of the two readings is the contact potential difference, the plate showing a negative charge in the second reading being the one that is positive when the plates are in contact.

The difference of surface potential thus defined depends greatly, however, upon the state of the surfaces.   The potential difference can be regarded as the algebraic sum of a potential jump between the metals themselves and other jumps, perhaps sometimes voltaic in origin, between each metal and whatever layer of oxide or other contaminating substance is present on its surface.   If thermions and photoelectrons come from the surface of such contaminations, however, the relation just stated would be expected to hold between the surface ΔV and $\Delta \omega_0$, and this is confirmed by experiment.

CHAPTER 4

THE ORIGIN OF THE QUANTUM THEORY

The quantum theory, first proposed by Planck in 1900, arose out of the inability of the classical physics to explain the experimentally observed distribution of energy in the spectrum of a black body. In the present chapter, we shall show just how far the problem of black-body radiation can be solved by classical methods, and at precisely what point these classical methods failed and the introduction of the concept of quanta seemed to offer the only solution. The phenomenon of black-body radiation is, however, of relatively minor importance in experimental physics. If the student does not wish to spend time upon it, he can without difficulty skip this chapter and proceed at once to the next.

58. Thermal Radiation. It is a matter of common observation that bodies when heated emit radiant energy—or, more simply, radiation—the *quantity* and *quality* of which depend, for any given body, on the temperature of that body. Thus, the rate at which an incandescent lamp filament emits radiation increases rapidly with increase in the temperature of the filament; and as the temperature rises, the emitted light becomes whiter. If this light is dispersed by a prism, a *continuous* spectrum is formed. Such radiation is ordinarily emitted in appreciable degree only by solids or liquids.

It is also commonly observed that radiation falling upon physical bodies is at least partially absorbed by them. The accepted view is that even at ordinary temperatures all bodies are emitting and absorbing thermal radiation; if they are neither rising nor falling in temperature, this is because as much radiant energy is being absorbed in each second as is being emitted. It is with such states of *thermal equilibrium* that we shall be concerned here. For a discussion of other properties of thermal radiation the student is referred to the standard treatises on "heat."

59. The Isothermal Enclosure and Black-body Radiation. In order to deal with the simplest possible case of thermal equilibrium, consider a cavity whose walls and contents are all at a common temperature. An *isothermal enclosure* of this sort is of special interest because the field of radiation inside it possesses some remarkably simple properties.

It can be shown that *in an isothermal enclosure the stream of radiation in any given direction must be the same as in any other direction; it must be the same at every point inside the enclosure; and it must be the same in all enclosures at a given temperature, irrespective of the materials composing them. Furthermore, all these statements hold for each spectral component of the radiation taken separately.*

The proof of these statements, which can be made rigorous, proceeds by showing that if any one of the statements were not true, a device could be constructed that would violate the second law of thermodynamics. For example, if the stream of radiation traveling west were greater than that traveling north, we could introduce two similar absorbers, one facing east and the other south. One of these absorbers would then become hotter than the other by absorbing radiant energy from the stronger stream. We could, therefore, operate a Carnot engine, using the two absorbers as source and sink, and so could convert heat continuously into work without leaving other changes in the system, in violation of the second law. Radiation of a particular wavelength can be tested similarly by using selective absorbers.

The radiation field in an enclosure has important relations with the energy emitted by the walls or other physical bodies. This relation is especially simple for an *ideal black* surface, which has the property that it absorbs completely all radiation falling upon it, none of the radiation being reflected. Such surfaces can be closely approximated by coating them with finely divided carbon such as lampblack. In an isothermal enclosure, the radiation leaving a black surface will consist entirely of radiation emitted by it, since such a surface reflects none of the incident radiation. Hence *the stream of radiation emitted by any black surface or body in any direction is the same as the stream of radiation that travels in one direction in an isothermal enclosure at the same temperature.* The total *energy density* produced just in front of a black surface by radiation emitted by that surface alone will thus be just half as great as the density of energy in an enclosure at the same temperature, since the radiation emitted by the body is confined to a hemisphere of directions, whereas in the enclosure radiation is traveling in all directions. The term, black-body radiation, is applied indiscriminately to both types of radiation.

Black-body radiation is a phenomenon of great interest from the theoretical standpoint, because its properties have a universal character, being independent of the properties of any particular material substance. Several questions press at once for an answer. How does the energy density in black-body radiation vary with the temperature? And what is the spectral distribution of the radiation? Furthermore, we wish to understand how this particular distribution is brought into existence by the atomic processes going on in matter.

Concerning the first two questions, it was found possible, during the last century, to obtain further information from thermodynamics *without making any assumption as to the atomic process.* The method consisted in considering the effect of expanding or contracting an isothermal enclosure and taking account of the work done on the walls by the radiation in consequence of *radiation pressure.* In order to follow the argument, we must ascertain the relation between the pressure and the energy density in uniformly distributed radiation.

60. Pressure and Energy Flux Due to Isotropic Radiation. Suppose a stream of radiation in a vacuum falls normally on the surface of a body. Then, if w is the mean energy density in the oncoming waves, they carry also w/c units of momentum per unit volume (Sec. 226). Thus the waves bring up to each unit area of the surface, along with cw ergs of energy, w units of momentum per second, the momentum as a vector being directed normally toward the surface. If the waves are absorbed by the surface, it receives this momentum and experiences, therefore, a pressure equal to w.[1]

Suppose, next, that the radiation is incident at an angle θ. Then the energy that crosses a unit area drawn perpendicular to the rays (PQ in

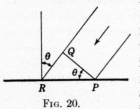
FIG. 20.

Fig. 20) is received by a larger area of magnitude $1/\cos\theta$ on the surface (PR in Fig. 20). Furthermore, the component of the momentum normal to the surface is less than in the case of normal incidence in proportion to $\cos\theta$. Thus the momentum in the direction of the normal that is delivered to unit area of the surface per second is decreased by the obliqueness of incidence in the ratio $\cos^2\theta$, and the resulting pressure, if the radiation is entirely absorbed, is

$$p = w\cos^2\theta$$

The same expression holds for the pressure caused by the *emission* of a beam at an angle θ, or for the additional pressure caused by the occurrence of a reflected beam. If an incident beam is specularly reflected from a surface at the angle of incidence θ, the total pressure on the surface is $2w\cos^2\theta$.

Finally, let radiation be streaming toward a surface and also away from it with equal intensities in all directions, as in an isothermal enclosure. Such a distribution of radiation is equivalent to a large number of beams of plane waves, all of equal intensity, with their directions of propagation distributed equally in direction. Let there be N beams in all, and let the energy density due to any one of them be w. Then the total

---

[1] Pressure and energy density are physical quantities of the same dimensions.

energy density just in front of the surface and the pressure p **on it are,**
respectively,   *N beams, each carrying energy density w*

$$\text{total energy density } \psi = Nw \qquad \text{total pressure } p = \Sigma w \cos^2 \theta = w \Sigma \cos^2 \theta \qquad (33a,b)$$

$\Sigma \cos^2 \theta$ denoting the sum of the values of $\cos^2 \theta$ for all of the beams.

To find this latter sum, imagine lines drawn outward from a point O
on the surface to represent the various directions of the beams, whether
moving toward the surface or away from it, and then about O as center
draw a hemispherical surface of unit radius with its base on the surface
(cf. Fig. 21, where only two of the lines are shown).   From the hemisphere cut out a ring-shaped element of area, QS, by means of two cones
of semiangle θ and $\theta + d\theta$, drawn from O as apex and with the normal
OP as axis.   The edge of this element is a circle of perimeter $2\pi \sin \theta$, and
its width is $d\theta$, hence its area is $2\pi \sin \theta$
$d\theta$; whereas the area of the whole hemisphere is 2π.   Now the lines of approach of the N beams of radiation, if
drawn through O, will cut the hemisphere in points equally distributed
over its surface.   Hence, if we let dN
denote the number of these lines that

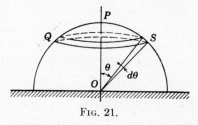

FIG. 21.

pass through the ring-shaped element, dN will be to N in the ratio of
the area of the ring to the area of the hemisphere, so that[1]

$$\frac{dN}{N} = \frac{2\pi \sin \theta \, d\theta}{2\pi} = \sin \theta \, d\theta$$

The value of $\cos^2 \theta$ is the same for all of the dN beams.   Hence their
contribution to $\Sigma \cos^2 \theta$ is $\cos^2 \theta \, dN$ or, from the last equation, $N \cos^2 \theta$
$\sin \theta \, d\theta$.   Thus

$$\sum \cos^2 \theta = \int \cos^2 \theta \, dN = N \int_0^{\pi/2} \cos^2 \theta \sin \theta \, d\theta = \tfrac{1}{3} N \qquad (34)$$

(The limit is $\pi/2$ because directions all around the normal OP are included
in the ring.)   For the pressure we thus obtain, from (33b), $p = \tfrac{1}{3} wN$,
or, by (33a),

$$\text{total pressure } p = \tfrac{1}{3} \psi \text{ radiant energy density} \qquad (35)$$

Thus the pressure on the walls of an isothermal enclosure equals one-
third of the radiant-energy density at any interior point.

It will be useful to calculate also the total *energy* brought up to the
surface.   Since half of the N waves are moving toward the surface and

---

[1] In more usual terms, $2\pi \sin \theta \, d\theta$ is an element of solid angle about O, having the
form of a conical shell, and 2π is half of the whole solid angle about O.

each wave delivers energy $cw \cos \theta$, the total energy brought up to unit area per second is

$$\tfrac{1}{2}N \int_0^{\pi/2} cw \cos \theta \sin \theta \, d\theta = \tfrac{1}{4}cwN = \tfrac{1}{4}c\psi$$

by (33a). In an isothermal enclosure an equal amount of energy is carried away from the surface. It may be shown in the same way that in an isothermal enclosure in which the energy density is ψ, energy $\tfrac{1}{4}c\psi$ per second passes in each direction across unit area of any imaginary surface drawn inside the enclosure.

Furthermore, using results of the last section, we see that the energy emitted per second by unit area of any black surface, which is called its (total) emissive power and will be denoted by E, is related to the energy density ψ in an isothermal enclosure having the same temperature by the equation

$$E = \tfrac{1}{4}c\psi \tag{36}$$

The same relation holds for each wavelength separately. Let the energy emitted from the black body with a range of wavelengths $d\lambda$ be denoted by $e_\lambda \, d\lambda$ so that $E = \int_0^\infty e_\lambda \, d\lambda$, and let the density of radiant energy in the enclosure within the same range of wavelengths be similarly represented by $\psi_\lambda \, d\lambda$, so that $\psi = \int_0^\infty \psi_\lambda \, d\lambda$. Then

$$e_\lambda = \tfrac{1}{4}c\psi_\lambda \tag{37}$$

61. The Stefan-Boltzmann Law. In 1884, Boltzmann deduced a theoretical law for the variation of the total intensity of black-body radiation with temperature. For this purpose, he applied the laws of the Carnot cycle to an engine in which the radiation played the part of the working substance.

The ideal Carnot engine consists of an evacuated cylinder with walls impervious to heat, a piston likewise impervious to heat and moving without friction, and a base through which heat may enter or leave. Let the walls, piston, and base be perfectly reflecting except for a small opening O in the base which may be covered at will by a perfectly reflecting cover. Let this cylinder be placed with the opening O uncovered and opposite an opening in an evacuated isothermal enclosure B_1, which is maintained at temperature T_1 (Fig. 22). Then the cylinder will fill up with radiation entering it through O from B_1 until there is the same density ψ_1 of radiation in the cylinder as there is in B_1, at which time radiation will be passing at the same rate from O to B_1 as from B_1 to O.

We may now consider the following cycle of events:

a. Starting with the piston in the initial position P_1 [Fig. 22(a)], the initial volume of the cylinder being v_1 and the initial pressure due to the radiation $p_1 = \frac{1}{3}\psi_1$, we cause the piston to move upward, *slowly*, until position P_2 is reached, the volume increasing to v_2. During this process the radiation density within the cylinder will

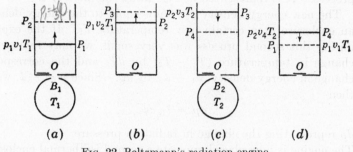

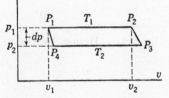

FIG. 22. Boltzmann's radiation engine.

remain constant at ψ_1. To keep it constant, additional radiation must enter the opening O from the enclosure B_1, for two reasons:

1. Work W_e is done by the radiation on the piston. If T_1 remains constant, so do ψ_1 and p_1 and

$$W_e = p_1(v_2 - v_1) = \tfrac{1}{3}\psi_1(v_2 - v_1)$$

2. The volume of the cylinder has *increased* by $v_2 - v_1$, which requires an additional influx of energy equal to $\psi_1(v_2 - v_1)$. Thus the total influx H_1 of radiation from B_1 must be

$$H_1 = \tfrac{4}{3}\psi_1(v_2 - v_1) \tag{38}$$

This isothermal process is represented on the *p-v* diagram (Fig. 23) by the horizontal line P_1P_2. The energy H_1 is equivalent to heat supplied to the space within the cylinder, just as in an ordinary Carnot cycle the first isothermal expansion is accompanied by an absorption of heat. An amount of heat equal to H_1 must also be supplied from external sources to B_1 in order to keep the temperature of B_1 constant.

FIG. 23. The *p-v* diagram for the Carnot cycle of the radiation engine.

b. When the piston has reached P_2, the perfectly reflecting cover is placed over the opening O [Fig. 22(b)], thereby effecting complete thermal isolation of the interior of the cylinder, and a further expansion to position P_3 is made. External work is done, as before, on the piston, the energy required for this external work being supplied by the radiation. Partly because of this work and partly because of the increase in volume, *the energy density of the radiation within the cylinder must decrease* from ψ_1 to some smaller value ψ_2. The pressure, likewise, has decreased. This is obviously an adiabatic process. It is represented in Fig. 23 by the line P_2P_3.

The new energy density ψ_2 is now equal to the energy density in an enclosure at a certain new temperature T_2. If the expansion during this second process was very small, we may represent the change in temperature $(T_1 - T_2)$ by dT, and the corresponding change in energy density, $\psi_1 - \psi_2$, by $d\psi$. Since $p = \frac{1}{3}\psi$, we have then

$$dp = \tfrac{1}{3}\, d\psi \tag{39}$$

dp representing the change in radiation pressure.

c. The engine is now placed opposite a second isothermal enclosure B_2 [Fig. 22(c)], at temperature T_2, the slide is removed from the opening O, and the piston is moved, by the application of suitable external force, from P_3 to P_4. On account of this compression, there is a tendency for the density of radiation within the cylinder to rise and for radiation to pass through O into B_2. The compression is supposed to take place so slowly, however, that the radiation density remains constant at a value only infinitesimally in excess of ψ_2. During this second isothermal process, radiant energy in amount H_2 leaves the engine.

d. Having reached a suitable point P_4, the opening O is closed, and the radiation is then compressed adiabatically until the initial position P_1 is reached.

The net external work done during this cycle is represented by the area $P_1P_2P_3P_4$ of Fig. 23. If we assume the change of pressure to have been very small, this area equals $(v_2 - v_1)\, dp$.[1] Calling the net external work dW, we have, therefore,

$$dW = (v_2 - v_1)\, dp = \tfrac{1}{3}(v_2 - v_1)\, d\psi$$

by (39). Hence, by the usual rule for a Carnot cycle,

$$\frac{dW}{H_1} = \frac{T_1 - T_2}{T_1} = \frac{dT}{T_1}$$

and, using the value found for dW and also Eq. (38), we have

$$\frac{d\psi}{\psi_1} = \frac{4\, dT}{T_1}$$

[1] This is the area of a rectangle of height dp and length P_1P_2. The small triangular areas at the ends will not be equal, but, as dp approaches zero, these areas become negligible *in comparison with the area* $P_1P_2P_3P_4$. Hence the difference between the latter area and the rectangle can be ignored in the limit as $dp \to 0$.

Thus, dropping the subscript,

$$\frac{d\psi}{\psi} = 4\frac{dT}{T}$$

Integrated, this equation gives $\log \psi = 4 \log T + \text{const}$ or

$$\psi = aT^4 \tag{40}$$

where a is a constant, not yet known. From Eq. (36) we have then also, for the emissive power of a black body,

Stefan-Boltzman Law

$$E = \frac{1}{4}c\psi \qquad E = \sigma T^4 \qquad \sigma = \tfrac{1}{4}ca \tag{41a,b}$$

Thus *both the energy density of the radiation within an isothermal enclosure and the total emissive power of a black body are proportional to the fourth power of the absolute temperature T.*

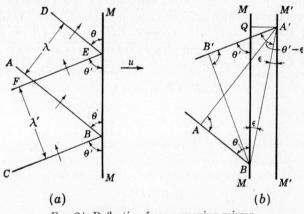

Fig. 24. Reflection from a moving mirror.

Equation (41a) is known as the "Stefan-Boltzmann law," the constant σ being called "Stefan's constant" or the "Stefan-Boltzmann constant." The law has been confirmed by numerous experimental investigations. The value of σ is 0.567×10^{-4} erg per cm^2 per deg^4 per sec.

62. Reflection from a Moving Mirror. In the preceding discussion no attention was paid to the spectral distribution of the radiation. The question presents itself, however, whether the same law can be applied also to the separate wavelengths. In order to investigate this question, we need to know what happens to the spectral distribution of a beam of radiation when it is reflected from a mirror that is in motion, such as the piston in the ideal apparatus that was described in the last section.

Let us consider first the effect of such motion upon a monochromatic beam. For this purpose we employ Huygens' principle. In Fig. 24(a), MM represents a mirror moving with a component of velocity u perpendicular to its plane, u being taken positive when the mirror is receding from the incident light. AB and DE represent parts of two incident waves which are one wavelength, or a distance λ, apart and are falling on the mirror at an angle of incidence θ; CB and FE are parts of the same waves which have been reflected and are now leaving the mirror at an angle of reflection θ', a distance λ' apart. It is obvious from the figure that $\lambda = BE \sin \theta$, $\lambda' = BE \sin \theta'$, whence

$$\frac{\lambda'}{\lambda} = \frac{\sin \theta'}{\sin \theta} \tag{42}$$

To obtain a second relation between λ' and θ', consider two successive positions of the same wave. In Fig. 24(b), the part AB of a wave is just beginning to fall on the mirror, whose instantaneous position is MM. The same portion of the wave at a later instant, after it has been reflected at the angle θ', is shown by $A'B'$, the point A being now in contact at A' with the mirror, which is in the new position $M'M'$. While A traveled along the ray AA', B traversed BB'; hence $AA' = BB'$. The angles BAA' and $BB'A'$, being angles between ray and wave, are right angles. It follows, therefore, by similar triangles, that angle

$$B'A'B = ABA',$$

or

$$\theta' - \epsilon = \theta + \epsilon \tag{43}$$

where ϵ is the angle QBA'. Furthermore, while A went from A to A' at the speed c of light, the mirror moved from MM to $M'M'$ at the speed u. Hence, if $A'Q$ is a perpendicular dropped from A' onto MM,

$$\frac{u}{c} = \frac{A'Q}{AA'} = \frac{BA' \sin \epsilon}{BA' \sin (\theta + \epsilon)} = \frac{\sin \epsilon}{\sin (\theta + \epsilon)} \tag{44}$$

By eliminating ϵ between the last two equations, the equation

$$\tan \tfrac{1}{2}\theta' = \frac{c + u}{c - u} \tan \tfrac{1}{2}\theta \tag{45}$$

is obtained, expressing the law of reflection from a moving mirror.

Finally, from Eq. (42), for the change of wavelength $\Delta\lambda$ caused by reflection, we find

$$\frac{\Delta\lambda}{\lambda} = \frac{\lambda' - \lambda}{\lambda} = \frac{\sin \theta' - \sin \theta}{\sin \theta}.$$

We need the value of $\Delta\lambda$, however, only for an infinitesimal value of u and hence of $\theta' - \theta$. For such a value

$$\sin \theta' - \sin \theta = (\theta' - \theta) \frac{d}{d\theta} \sin \theta = (\theta' - \theta) \cos \theta$$

Also, from Eqs. (43) and (44), in which ϵ is an infinitesimal,

$$\theta' - \theta = 2\epsilon = 2 \sin \epsilon = 2 \frac{u}{c} \sin (\theta + \epsilon)$$

to the first order; and here $\sin (\theta + \epsilon)$ may be replaced by $\sin \theta$. We thus find, to the first order in u,

$$\Delta\lambda = 2 \frac{u}{c} \lambda \cos \theta \tag{46}$$

63. Effect of an Adiabatic Expansion upon Black-body Radiation.

Returning now to the sequence of operations described in Sec. 61, let us consider the effect of the adiabatic process (b) upon the spectral distribution of the radiation. In this process, black-body radiation initially at temperature T_1 imprisoned in a cylinder with perfectly reflecting walls is slowly expanded from an initial energy density ψ_1 to a new energy density ψ_2. Let the former restriction to a small expansion be dropped. The change in direction of the rays that is produced by the moving piston, according to Eq. (45) above, will tend to make the radiation no longer isotropic. We can obviate this inconvenient effect, however, by letting part of the walls of the cylinder reflect perfectly *but diffusely*. A surface of magnesium oxide does this very well. Then, if the expansion is made very slowly, because all rays (except a negligible few) strike the diffusing surface repeatedly, the radiation will be kept effectively isotropic; and the pressure on the piston, according to Eq. (35) above, will be at all times equal to $\frac{1}{3}\psi$.

Let the cylinder have a cross section A and a (variable) length l. Then, if ψ is the energy density at any moment, when the piston moves outward a distance dl, work $p \, dV = \frac{1}{3}\psi A \, dl$ is done on it by the force due to radiation pressure. This work is done at the expense of the enclosed energy, the total amount of which is $lA\psi$. Hence

$$\frac{1}{3}\psi A \, dl = -d(lA\psi) = -A\psi \, dl - Al \, d\psi$$

$$\frac{d\psi}{\psi} = -\frac{4}{3} \frac{dl}{l}$$

and, after integration,

$$\log \psi = -\log l^{4/3} + \text{const} \qquad \psi = Cl^{-4/3} \tag{47a,b}$$

C denoting a constant.

Now it can be shown by thermodynamic reasoning that an expansion of the type considered here cannot destroy the black-body property of the radiation. For, at a certain instant, suppose that the expansion has reduced the total energy density to ψ_2, and let T_2 be the temperature of an enclosure in which the density has this same value. Suppose that in the cylinder there were more radiation per unit volume of wavelengths near some value λ' than at the same wavelengths in the enclosure, and less radiation near some other wavelength λ''. It would then be possible to cause a little radiation to pass from the cylinder into a second enclosure at a temperature T_2' slightly above T_2, by covering the opening in the base of the cylinder with a plate transmitting wavelengths near λ' but reflecting all others and putting the cylinder into communication with the second enclosure through this opening. In a similar way, enough radiation near λ'' could be passed *into* the cylinder from an enclosure at a slightly *lower* temperature T_2'' to restore the total energy to ψ_2. Then the radiation could be compressed back to ψ_1, the changes in ψ and l and the amount of the work done being just the reverse of these quantities during the expansion. Finally, putting the cylinder again into communication with the enclosure at T_1, we could allow the spectral distribution to be restored to that proper to a black body at T_1, but without any net transfer of energy between cylinder and enclosure, since the total energy density has already been restored to that corresponding to T_1. Thus we should have performed a cyclic operation, the *only* effect of which is to transfer heat energy from an enclosure at T_2'' to one at a higher temperature T_1''. But this is inconsistent with the second law of thermodynamics.

Thus black radiation must remain black during any slow adiabatic expansion or compression. Its density and temperature, however, decrease. In the case under discussion, the last equation, in combination with Eq. (40), gives

$$T \propto \frac{1}{l^{1/3}} \tag{48}$$

To determine the effect on the spectral distribution, we must find the average rate at which wavelengths are increased. Suppose, first, that the walls of the cylinder and the piston reflect specularly. Then any ray

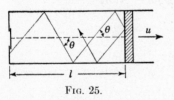

FIG. 25.

preserves its angle of inclination to the axis of the cylinder θ in spite of repeated reflections (cf. Fig. 25) and has, therefore, a constant component of velocity $c \cos \theta$ perpendicular to the piston. The ray strikes the piston $(c \cos \theta)/2l$ times a second, and its wavelength, according to (46), increases each time by $(2u\lambda \cos \theta)/c$, u being the speed of the piston. Thus its wavelength increases at a rate

$$\frac{d\lambda}{dt} = \frac{c \cos \theta}{2l} \frac{2c\lambda \cos \theta}{c} = \frac{u\lambda}{l} \cos^2 \theta \qquad \text{cm per sec}$$

If rays of wavelength λ are equally distributed in direction, the average value of $\cos^2 \theta$ for all of them is $\frac{1}{3}$, according to Eq. (34); hence the average value of $d\lambda/dt$ for these rays is

$$\frac{d\lambda}{dt} = \frac{u\lambda}{3l} = \frac{\lambda}{3l}\frac{dl}{dt}$$

since $u = dl/dt$.

To simplify the calculation, suppose now that there is a diffusely reflecting spot on the walls. Then all the rays will take turns moving in the various directions, and all rays of wavelength λ will undergo the average change of wavelength just calculated. This conclusion can be confirmed by a more complete analysis for which we have no space. The last equation can be integrated thus:

$$\frac{d\lambda}{\lambda} = \frac{1}{3}\frac{dl}{l}, \qquad \log \lambda = \log l^{\frac{1}{3}} + \text{const} \qquad \lambda \propto l^{\frac{1}{3}} \propto \frac{1}{T} \qquad (49a,b,c)$$

by (48). Thus we have the conclusion that each spectral component of black-body radiation must change in wavelength in such a way that $\lambda \propto 1/T$.

64. The Wien Displacement Law. Now let us fix our attention on a particular spectral range from λ_1 to $\lambda_1 + d\lambda_1$, containing energy $\psi_{\lambda 1} d\lambda_1$ per unit volume in an enclosure at temperature T_1. An adiabatic expansion which lowers the temperature to T_2 changes the limits of this range, according to the result just reached, to λ_2 and $\lambda_2 + d\lambda_2$, where

$$\frac{\lambda_2}{\lambda_1} = \frac{\lambda_2 + d\lambda_2}{\lambda_1 + d\lambda_1} = \frac{T_1}{T_2} \qquad \therefore \frac{d\lambda_2}{d\lambda_1} = \frac{T_1}{T_2} \qquad (50a,b)$$

The energy in $d\lambda_1$ is at the same time decreased, and in the same ratio as is the total energy; for, in the argument that led up to Eq. (47), we might have started with only the radiation in $d\lambda_1$ present in the cylinder. Hence, $\psi_{\lambda 2}$ being the new value of ψ_λ,

$$\frac{\psi_{\lambda 2}\, d\lambda_2}{\psi_{\lambda 1}\, d\lambda_1} = \frac{\psi_2}{\psi_1} = \frac{T_2{}^4}{T_1{}^4}$$

and using (50b),

$$\frac{\psi_{\lambda 2}}{\psi_{\lambda 1}} = \frac{e_{\lambda 2}}{e_{\lambda 1}} = \frac{T_2{}^5}{T_1{}^5} \qquad (51)$$

Here e_λ is the emissive power of a black body, given in terms of ψ_λ by Eq. (37).

Thus, if the values of ψ_λ or e_λ at two different temperatures are compared, not at the same wavelength but at wavelengths inversely proportional to T, then their values will be found to be proportional to the *fifth power* of the absolute temperature. This conclusion is known as the

Wien displacement law. It can also be expressed by saying that at a wavelength varied so that the product λT is held constant, ψ_λ/T^5 or e_λ/T^5 has the same value at all temperatures. Thus if either of these ratios is plotted against λT as abscissa, a single curve valid at all temperatures will be obtained.

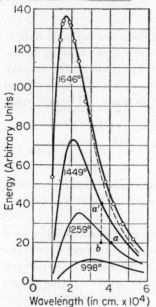

FIG. 26. Distribution of energy in the spectrum of a black body at various temperatures.

In Fig. 26 are shown the energy distribution curves obtained for the spectrum of a black body by Lummer and Pringsheim,[1] and in Fig. 27 is shown a composite curve for e_λ/T^5 as a function of λT, plotted from these data. The theoretical prediction is seen to be fulfilled.

An important conclusion from the displacement law is that the wavelength λ_m at which e_λ and ψ_λ have their maximum values is inversely proportional to the absolute temperature. The value of $\lambda_m T$ is 0.2898 cm deg, so that at 0°C λ_m = 0.0106 mm; at 2000°C, λ_m = 12,750 angstroms.

65. The Formula for Black-body Radiation.

From the results obtained, it is clear that the ratio e_λ/T^5 is a function of λT not depending otherwise on T. Writing $f(\lambda T)$ for this function, whose shape is shown by the curve in Fig. 27, we have then $e_\lambda/T^5 = f(\lambda T)$ or

$$e_\lambda = T^5 f(\lambda T) = \frac{1}{\lambda^5} F(\lambda T) \qquad (52)$$

where $F(\lambda T) = (\lambda T)^5 f(\lambda T)$. Thus, by reasoning based on thermodynamics, the problem of black-body radiation is reduced to the determination of a *single unknown function, $f(\lambda T)$ or $F(\lambda T)$. All attempts to obtain the correct form for this function from classical theory, however, failed.*

Two of the formulas that were proposed on a classical basis nevertheless deserve mention. Wien proposed a formula that was derived from special assumptions concerning the process of emission and absorption of radiation, namely,

$$\psi_\lambda = c_1 \lambda^{-5} e^{-c_2/\lambda T} = \frac{c_1}{\lambda^5} e^{-\frac{c_2}{\lambda T}} \qquad (53)$$

where c_1 and c_2 were certain constants that remained to be found. Rayleigh made a suggestion based on very general reasoning,[2] and on the

[1] *Verhandl. deut. physik. Ges.*, vol. 1, pp. 23, 215, 1899; vol. 2, p. 163.

[2] The arguments of Wien and of Rayleigh are described in Preston's "Theory of Heat."

basis of this suggestion Jeans arrived at a formula that was free from all unknown constants. The Rayleigh-Jeans formula was found to fit the experimental curve at very long wavelengths; whereas, by assigning proper values to c_1 and c_2 Wien's formula could be made to fit at wavelengths shorter than the wavelength of maximum emission (cf. Fig. 30 in Sec. 72). The reasoning employed by Rayleigh and Jeans is full of interest and also furnishes an excellent background for Planck's introduction of quanta; hence their reasoning will be described. It is based upon the classical law of the equipartition of energy, which will be stated first.

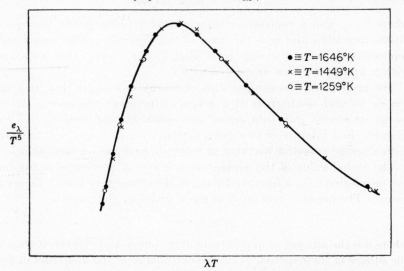

FIG. 27. Experimental verification of the black-body displacement law.

66. The Principle of the Equipartition of Energy.

Any mechanical system has a certain number of degrees of freedom, which may be defined as the minimum number of independent coordinates in terms of which the positions of all the masses composing the system may be specified. For example, a block sliding in a groove has 1 degree of freedom; if it is sliding on ice with no possibility of being set into rotation, it has 2 degrees of freedom, whereas if it can also rotate about a vertical axis, it has 3. A monatomic gas molecule behaving as if it had only energy of translation has 3 degrees of freedom, corresponding to the 3 coordinates x, y, z that might be used to specify its position in space. Diatomic molecules might behave like rigid dumbbells that never rotate about an axis drawn through the two atoms but can rotate independently about two perpendicular axes; such molecules would have 5 degrees of freedom. If the molecule is not rigid, but the atoms can vibrate with respect to each other, then there is an additional degree of freedom corresponding to this vibration, and the total number is 6. A triatomic molecule will have at least

6 degrees of freedom (unless all atoms lie on a line), 3 for translation and 3 for rotation about 3 mutually perpendicular axes; if vibration of the atoms within the molecule is also possible, there will be 9 degrees of freedom in all.

The energy associated with any degree of freedom varies rapidly as the molecules collide with each other, but the *average* value of this energy taken over a sufficient length of time may be steady. The energy of translation of a molecule can be written

$$\tfrac{1}{2}mv_x{}^2 + \tfrac{1}{2}mv_y{}^2 + \tfrac{1}{2}mv_z{}^2$$

where v_x, v_y, and v_z represent components of velocity in the three coordinate directions and m is the mass of the molecule. The term $\tfrac{1}{2}mv_x{}^2$ represents the kinetic energy associated with x, $\tfrac{1}{2}mv_y{}^2$ that associated with y, and $\tfrac{1}{2}mv_z{}^2$ that associated with z.

The principle of the equipartition of energy now states that, *in a system in thermal equilibrium* at a given temperature, *the average kinetic energy associated with each degree of freedom has the same value.* For example, in a mixture of two gases, a term such as $\tfrac{1}{2}mv_x{}^2$ will have the same average value for one kind of molecule as it has for any other.

The actual value of the average kinetic energy per degree of freedom can be inferred from a formula derived in the elementary kinetic theory of gases. The pressure p of an ideal gas is given by the formula

$$p = \tfrac{1}{3}nm\overline{v^2}$$

where n is the number of molecules in unit volume and $\overline{v^2}$ is the average of the square of their speeds.[1] The kinetic energy of the molecules in unit volume, therefore, is

$$\tfrac{1}{2}nm\overline{v^2} = \tfrac{3}{2}p$$

Now, by the gas law, $p = RT/V$, where R is the gas constant for a grammolecule of a gas and V is the volume occupied by a gram-molecule. The kinetic energy of the molecules in a gram-molecule will thus be

$$V(\tfrac{3}{2}p) = \tfrac{3}{2}RT \tag{54}$$

Dividing this quantity then by Avogadro's number N_0 and also by 3, representing the number of degrees of translational freedom of a molecule, we find as the mean kinetic energy per degree of freedom $\tfrac{1}{2}(R/N_0)T$. The ratio R/N_0, representing the gas constant for a single molecule, is an important universal constant called the Boltzmann constant, usually denoted by k. Its value is

$$k = \frac{8.314 \times 10^7}{6.023 \times 10^{23}} = 1.380 \times 10^{-16} \text{ erg per deg}$$

[Or, $k = (1.3804 \pm 0.0001) \times 10^{-16}$; see reference cited in Sec. 48.]

[1] See any book on kinetic theory.

The mean *kinetic* energy per degree of freedom is thus $\frac{1}{2}kT$. There may also, however, be *potential* energy in the system. In a motion of simple harmonic vibration, the average values of the potential and kinetic energies will be equal, and the entire mean energy associated with such a degree of freedom will be kT.

The principle of the equipartition of energy has been shown in a fairly convincing way to follow as a consequence of Newton's laws of motion as applied to complex systems. It has been strikingly confirmed by observations upon the Brownian movements of small particles suspended in a fluid, which we have not space here to describe; these particles move about in thermal agitation like gigantic molecules. It is abundantly clear today, however, that the principle has only limited validity in relation to the internal motions of molecules of ordinary size.

67. Degrees of Freedom in an Enclosure. The suggestion was made by Lord Rayleigh in 1900 and by Jeans in 1905 that the law of the equipartition of energy might be applied to the radiation problem by computing the number of modes of free vibration of the electromagnetic field in an enclosure and then assuming that there is associated with each mode average energy of magnitude kT, as for a simple oscillator. The modes of vibration are readily counted, in the following way.

Maxwell's equations for the electromagnetic field in free space may be written, in terms of the components E_x, E_y, E_z of the electric field in electrostatic units, the components of the magnetic field H_x, H_y, H_z in electromagnetic units and the speed of light c in centimeters per second, as follows:

$$\frac{\partial E_z}{\partial y} - \frac{\partial E_y}{\partial z} = -\frac{1}{c}\frac{\partial H_x}{\partial t} \qquad \frac{\partial H_z}{\partial y} - \frac{\partial H_y}{\partial z} = \frac{1}{c}\frac{\partial E_x}{\partial t}$$

$$\frac{\partial E_x}{\partial z} - \frac{\partial E_z}{\partial x} = -\frac{1}{c}\frac{\partial H_y}{\partial t} \qquad \frac{\partial H_x}{\partial z} - \frac{\partial H_z}{\partial x} = \frac{1}{c}\frac{\partial E_y}{\partial t}$$

$$\frac{\partial E_y}{\partial x} - \frac{\partial E_x}{\partial y} = -\frac{1}{c}\frac{\partial H_z}{\partial t} \qquad \frac{\partial H_y}{\partial x} - \frac{\partial H_x}{\partial y} = \frac{1}{c}\frac{\partial E_z}{\partial t}$$

$$\frac{\partial E_x}{\partial x} + \frac{\partial E_y}{\partial y} + \frac{\partial E_z}{\partial z} = 0 \qquad \frac{\partial H_x}{\partial x} + \frac{\partial H_y}{\partial y} + \frac{\partial H_z}{\partial z} = 0$$

To make steady vibrations possible, let the walls of the enclosure have infinite electrical conductivity, so that they reflect perfectly and no energy can escape. Then at the walls there is the boundary condition that the component of the electric vector **E** parallel to the walls must vanish, to avoid infinite current in the walls.

For convenience, let the enclosure have the form of a rectangular box with the x, y, z axes drawn along three edges. Then it is easy to verify by substitution that the following equations define a solution of Maxwell's equations satisfying the boundary conditions:

$$k_1 E_x = A \cos k_1 x \sin k_2 y \sin k_3 z \sin \omega t$$
$$k_2 E_y = B \sin k_1 x \cos k_2 y \sin k_3 z \sin \omega t$$
$$k_3 E_z = C \sin k_1 x \sin k_2 y \cos k_3 z \sin \omega t$$
$$\omega k_2 k_3 H_x = c(k_2{}^2 C - k_3{}^2 B) \sin k_1 x \cos k_2 y \cos k_3 z \cos \omega t$$
$$\omega k_1 k_3 H_y = c(k_3{}^2 A - k_1{}^2 C) \cos k_1 x \sin k_2 y \cos k_3 z \cos \omega t$$
$$\omega k_1 k_2 H_z = c(k_1{}^2 B - k_2{}^2 A) \cos k_1 x \cos k_2 y \sin k_3 z \cos \omega t$$

Here A, B, and C are arbitrary constants subject to the restriction that $A + B + C = 0$, and

$$k_1 = \pi \frac{i_1}{l_1} \qquad k_2 = \pi \frac{i_2}{l_2} \qquad k_3 = \pi \frac{i_3}{l_3} \qquad \omega^2 = c^2(k_1{}^2 + k_2{}^2 + k_3{}^2)$$

i_1, i_2, i_3 being any set of positive integers and l_1, l_2, and l_3 the edge lengths of the enclosure. The i's represent the number of segments occurring in the standing waves in the respective coordinate directions.

Since only two of the amplitudes A, B, and C can be chosen arbitrarily, this solution represents two independent modes of vibration superposed, both corresponding to running waves of frequency $\nu = \omega/2\pi$ or

$$\nu = \frac{c}{2}\left(\frac{i_1{}^2}{l_1{}^2} + \frac{i_2{}^2}{l_2{}^2} + \frac{i_3{}^2}{l_3{}^2}\right)^{\frac{1}{2}} \tag{55}$$

The two independent modes can be defined in many different ways, but there will always be two, and it can be shown, by means of expansions in three-dimensional Fourier series, that any mode of vibration at this frequency ν can be resolved into the chosen two modes with suitable amplitudes. The two modes correspond to the two independent planes of polarization of a beam of running waves.

Now for our purpose we need to find out how many modes have frequencies within any given small range of frequency. To do this, we may imagine each possible set of i's to be represented by a point in a three-dimensional plot, the coordinates of the point being

$$x = i_1/l_1 \qquad y = i_2/l_2 \qquad z = i_3/l_3$$

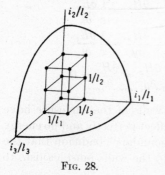

FIG. 28.

These points will lie at the corners of rectangular cells whose edges are $1/l_1$, $1/l_2$, $1/l_3$ long (two of them being shown in Fig. 28). There are just as many cells as there are points; for although each cell has eight points at its corners, each point serves as a corner to eight cells. Hence, the volume of a cell being $1/l_1 l_2 l_3$, there are $l_1 l_2 l_3$ cells and points in each unit volume of the plot.

Consider now the points representing frequencies less than a given value. These points will lie inside the positive octant of the sphere represented by the equation

$$\nu^2 = \frac{c^2}{4} (x^2 + y^2 + z^2)$$

the radius of the sphere being $2\nu/c$.   The number of included points will equal the volume of the octant multiplied by the point density, which is $l_1l_2l_3$.   Multiplying also by 2, since there are two modes of vibration at each frequency, and then dividing by the volume of the original enclosure, which is $l_1l_2l_3$, we thus find for the number n of modes of vibration of the field per unit volume of the enclosure with frequencies less than a given value of ν

$$n = 2 \frac{1}{8} \frac{4}{3} \pi \left(\frac{2\nu}{c}\right)^3 \frac{l_1l_2l_3}{l_1l_2l_3} = \frac{8\pi\nu^3}{3c^3} = \frac{8\pi}{3\lambda^3}$$

where $\lambda = c/\nu$.   The number dn of modes per unit volume with wavelengths in a range $d\lambda$ will thus be

$$dn = 8\pi \frac{d\lambda}{\lambda^4} \tag{56}$$

(The negative sign obtained in differentiation is dropped here since we wish both dn and $d\lambda$ to be positive.)

68. The Rayleigh-Jeans Formula.   Suppose now that the walls of the enclosure are not quite perfectly reflecting, so that thermal equilibrium at temperature T can be established between the walls and the enclosed electromagnetic field.   Then, according to the classical principle of the equipartition of energy, the average energy of each mode of vibration will be kT.   The radiant energy per unit volume in the wavelength range $d\lambda$, which we have denoted by $\psi_\lambda \, d\lambda$, will thus be $kT \, dn$ or $8\pi kT \, d\lambda/\lambda^4$, whence

$$\psi_\lambda = 8\pi kT\lambda^{-4} \tag{57}$$

Equation (57) is the Rayleigh-Jeans formula for black-body radiation. It will be noted that the formula contains *no new constants* at all.   At sufficiently *long wavelengths this formula is found to agree with observation*, but near the maximum in the spectrum, or at shorter wavelengths, it gives much too large values (cf. Fig. 30 in Sec. 72).   Furthermore, it assigns no maximum at all to ψ_λ.   In fact, according to (57), the energy density in the enclosure would be infinite; for there is no lower limit to the possible wavelengths of vibrations in the field, and $\int_0^\infty \lambda^{-4} \, d\lambda \to \infty$.

In reality, on the other hand, the radiation density in an isothermal enclosure is ordinarily much less than the energy density due to thermal agitation of the molecules of a solid body; for example, at 1000°K, ψ_2 is only about 7.5×10^{-3} erg per cm³, as compared with a total density on the order of 10^{10} ergs per cm³ in iron.   At temperatures above 1,000,000°, on the other hand, the comparison would be reversed.   Infinite energy in the electromagnetic field would make the specific heats of all material bodies infinite.

The failure of classical theory in this simple and striking manner showed clearly that there was a fundamental defect in the theory at some point.

69. Planck's Investigation of Black-body Radiation.   The correct black-body formula was finally discovered in 1901[1] by Max Planck.   By introducing a radical innovation quite at variance with previous concepts, he discovered a function of λT which gave a formula in complete agreement with experiment.   *This was the birth of the quantum theory.*

Planck arrived at his formula as the result of a long-continued effort to make theory fit the facts.   The experiments of Hertz on electromagnetic waves had seemed to give final confirmation to the electromagnetic theory of light, and this convinced Planck that the key to the black-body spectrum would be found in the laws governing the absorption and emission of radiation by electric oscillators.   We may imagine that the walls of an isothermal enclosure contain electric oscillators of all frequencies, essentially similar to the Hertzian oscillator, and that the emission and absorption of radiation by the walls are caused by these oscillators.

Investigation by means of electromagnetic theory, however, led Planck, before 1900, to the conclusion that an electric oscillator, in the long run, would affect only radiation of the *same frequency* as that of the oscillator itself.   Thus, in the state of equilibrium, there would be a definite ratio between the density of radiation of any frequency ν and the average energy of the oscillators of that frequency.   The problem of the black-body spectrum was thus reduced to the problem of the average energy of an oscillator at a given temperature.   If he then assumed the classical value kT for this average energy, as derived from the equipartition of energy, he was led, in a slightly different way, to the Rayleigh-Jeans formula, which he knew to be incorrect.

Planck, however, did not accept the principle of the equipartition of energy for oscillators.   On the basis of a different assumption he was led at first to Wien's formula for the radiation density as stated in Eq. (53); and he believed for a time that this formula must necessarily be correct. In 1900, however, new measurements of the black-body spectrum by Lummer and Pringsheim, and by Rubens and Kurlbaum, showed definitely that Wien's formula could not be correct.   So Planck set to work to find an improved formula.   First he discovered an *empirical* modification of Wien's formula that fitted the observations.   Then he sought to modify the statistical theory of the distribution of energy among a set of oscillators so that the theory would lead to his new formula.   He succeeded in doing so only after making a new assumption that broke drastically with classical principles.   To facilitate understanding his assumption, a brief description of the statistical theory will be given.

70. Distribution of Energy among Oscillators in Thermal Equilibrium.
Consider a linear oscillator consisting of a mass m that vibrates in simple harmonic motion; let its displacement be x and its momentum $p = m\, dx/dt$.   The potential energy of the oscillator can be written in the form $\frac{1}{2}\beta x^2$, β denoting a constant (the force constant); its kinetic energy is $\frac{1}{2}m(dx/dt)^2 = p^2/2m$.   Thus its total energy is

$$\epsilon = \frac{p^2}{2m} + \frac{1}{2}\beta x^2 \tag{58}$$

and by elementary theory its frequency of vibration ν has the value

$$\nu = \frac{1}{2\pi}\sqrt{\frac{\beta}{m}} \tag{59}$$

When a large number of such oscillators are in thermal equilibrium, the energy of an individual oscillator varies widely but the energies of the entire group are distributed in energy in a certain way that depends on the absolute temperature T.   In classical statistical mechanics[1] it is shown that the number dN of the oscillators that have their values of x and p lying in given ranges of value dx and dp is expressed by the formula

$$dN = NCe^{-\epsilon/kT}\, dx\, dp \tag{60}$$

Here k is Boltzmann's constant (Sec. 66) and C is a constant of proportionality such that $\int dN = N$.   This formula is similar to Maxwell's formula for the distribution of the molecular velocities in a gas, and both formulas are special cases of a more

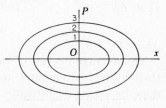

FIG. 29. The momentum-coordinate plane for a harmonic oscillator.

general formula that holds in classical mechanics for any dynamical system.

Since we are interested here only in the energies of the oscillators, it will be convenient to throw the formula into a different form.   Let us construct a plot on which x and p are taken as cartesian coordinates (Fig. 29).   Each oscillator is represented by a point on this plot which moves about as the oscillator vibrates.   So long as the oscillator is free from disturbing forces, x and p change in such a way that the energy remains constant; hence the representative point moves along a curve given by Eq. (58) with a fixed value of ϵ.   Such curves are obviously

[1] Cf. E. H. Kennard, "Kinetic Theory of Gases," chap. IX, 1938; J. E. Mayer and M. G. Mayer, "Statistical Mechanics," 1940; R. W. Gurney, "Introduction to Statistical Mechanics," 1949.

ellipses. Let two such ellipses be drawn for slightly different energies ϵ and $\epsilon + \Delta\epsilon$. Throughout the elliptical ring between these ellipses, if $\Delta\epsilon$ is very small, the quantity $e^{-\epsilon/kT}$ is sensibly constant; hence, in a state of thermal equilibrium, the number of oscillators represented by points in this ring will be, from (60),

$$\Delta N = NCe^{-\epsilon/kT} \iint dx\, dp \tag{61}$$

The integral $\iint dx\, dp$, however, is simply the area of the elliptical ring, and its value is easily found in terms of $\Delta\epsilon$. We first note that the entire area inside an ellipse whose semiaxes are x_m and p_m is

$$S = \pi p_m x_m \tag{62}$$

Here x_m and p_m also represent the maximum values of x and of p, respectively, during a vibration of an oscillator having an energy ϵ; substituting in (58) first $x = x_m$ and $p = 0$ and then $x = 0$ and $p = p_m$, we find

$$x_m = \sqrt{\frac{2\epsilon}{\beta}} \qquad p_m = \sqrt{2m\epsilon}$$

$$S = 2\pi\epsilon\sqrt{\frac{m}{\beta}} = \frac{\epsilon}{\nu} \tag{63}$$

by (59). The area of a ring corresponding to an increment $\Delta\epsilon$ is thus $\iint dx\, dp = \Delta S = \Delta\epsilon/\nu$. Hence (61) can also be written in the form

$$\Delta N = NC_1 e^{-\epsilon/kT}\, \Delta\epsilon \tag{64}$$

where $C_1 = C/\nu$.

The average energy of the oscillators can now be found by summing their individual energies and dividing by N. Ordinarily this would be done by means of integrals, but for our present purpose we shall prefer to employ discrete sums. Let ellipses centered at the origin be drawn so as to divide the xp plane into rings of equal area h; and let these rings, of which the innermost is actually an elliptical area, be numbered 0, 1, 2, . . . from the center outward, as in Fig. 29. Then the total area *inside* ring number τ is $S = \tau h$; and, by Eq. (63), the energy of an oscillator represented by a point on the inner boundary of ring number τ is

$$\epsilon = S\nu = \tau h\nu$$

The number of oscillators N_τ on ring τ can thus be written, from (64),

$$N_\tau = N_0 e^{-\tau h\nu/kT}$$

where N_0 replaces $NC_1\, \Delta\epsilon$. The total energy E of all oscillators is then, approximately,

$$E = \sum_0^\infty \tau h\nu N_\tau = N_0 h\nu e^{-h\nu/kT}(1 + 2e^{-h\nu/kT} + 3e^{-2h\nu/kT} + \cdots)$$

$$= N_0 h\nu e^{-h\nu/kT}(1 - e^{-h\nu/kT})^{-2}$$

since by the binomial theorem the last series is of the form

$$1 + 2x + 3x^2 + \cdots = (1 - x)^{-2}$$

In a similar way it is found that

$$N = \Sigma N_r = N_0(1 + e^{-h\nu/kT} + \cdots) = N_0(1 - e^{-h\nu/kT})^{-1}$$

For the *average energy* per oscillator we have then, finally,

$$\bar{\epsilon} = \frac{E}{N} = \frac{h\nu}{e^{h\nu/kT} - 1} \tag{65}$$

This expression represents also the energy of a particular oscillator averaged over any length of time that is not too short. For, being similar, the oscillators will all have the same average energy in the long run, and this average must be E/N.

In classical theory it is now necessary to let $h \to 0$. The approximations made then disappear. Using the series $e^x = 1 + x + x^2/2 + \cdots$, we find that, to the first order in h,

$$e^{h\nu/kT} - 1 = \frac{h\nu}{kT}$$

Hence, in the limit as $h \to 0$, $\bar{\epsilon} = kT$. This is the same value for the average energy of a harmonic oscillator that was deduced from the equipartition of energy in Sec. 66, and it leads, as we have seen, to the incorrect Rayleigh-Jeans formula.

71. Planck's Quantum Hypothesis. The new assumption introduced by Planck was equivalent to *keeping h finite* in the preceding formulas. In the first formulation of the new theory,[1] Planck assumed that the oscillators associated with a given ring all have the energy proper to the inner boundary of that ring. Then Eq. (65) for ϵ holds exactly. According to this assumption, the energy of an oscillator cannot vary continuously but must take on one of the discrete set of values 0, $h\nu$, $2h\nu$ . . . , $rh\nu$, ... The actual original form of Planck's assumption was that the energy of the oscillator must always be an integral multiple of a certain quantity, ϵ_0, but he then showed that, for oscillators of different frequencies, ϵ_0 must be proportional to ν if the radiation law is to harmonize with the Wien displacement law. Thus he assumed that $\epsilon_0 = h\nu$ where h is a constant of proportionality. The connection between h and areas on the xp plane for the oscillator, as described above, was recognized by Planck later.

It must be emphasized that the assumption of a discrete set of possible energy values, or energy levels, for an oscillator was completely at variance with classical ideas. According to this assumption, if the energies

[1] M. Planck, *Ann. Physik*, vol. 4, p. 553, 1901.

of a large number of oscillators were measured, some might be found to
have zero energy, some $h\nu$ ergs each, others $2h\nu$, and so on.   But not a
single oscillator would be found which had energy, say, $1.73h\nu$.   When
the energy of a given oscillator changes, therefore, it must change suddenly and discontinuously.   According to the older conceptions, on the
other hand, the interchange of energy between two "systems," as, for
example, between one gas molecule and another or between radiation and
oscillators, is a perfectly continuous process, and the energy of an oscillator would of necessity likewise vary continuously.   Such continuity of
energy values is imperatively demanded by classical physics.   For example, the electric and magnetic vectors in a light wave may have any values
whatsoever, *from zero up;* and, accordingly, the wave may have any
intensity, *from zero up.*   The emission and absorption of this energy by
the walls of an enclosure should, likewise, be a perfectly continuous
process.

The problem of the absorption and emission of radiation, in fact, presented serious difficulties for the new theory.   If the energy of an oscillator can vary only discontinuously, the *absorption and emission of radiation* must likewise be *discontinuous processes.*   As long as the oscillator
remains in one of its "quantum states," as we now call them, with its
energy equal to one of the allowed discrete values, it cannot be emitting
or absorbing radiation according to the laws of classical physics, for then
the conservation of energy would be violated.   This is entirely contrary
to classical electromagnetic theory; for classical theory absolutely requires
an isolated, accelerated electric charge to radiate energy.

According to Planck's new theory, *emission* of radiation occurs only
when the oscillator "jumps" from one energy level to another; if it jumps
down to the next-lower energy level, the energy $h\nu$ that it loses is emitted
in the form of a short pulse of radiation.   *Absorption* was also assumed at
first to be discontinuous.   An oscillator, Planck assumed, can absorb a
quantum $h\nu$ of radiant energy and jump instantaneously (or nearly so)
up to its next-higher energy level.   This assumption met with special
difficulties, however.   For the quantum of radiant energy emitted by an
oscillator, according to the classical wave theory, would spread out over
an ever expanding wave front, and it is hard to see how another oscillator
could ever gather this energy together again so as to absorb it all and
thereby acquire the energy for an upward quantum jump.   Absorption
ought, therefore, on Planck's theory, to be impossible.

To avoid this difficulty, Planck later modified his theory so as to allow
the oscillators to absorb in a continuous manner, only the process of
emission being discontinuous.   The energy of an oscillator could then
take on all values, as in classical theory; but, every time that the energy
passed one of the critical values, $\tau h\nu$, there was assumed to exist a certain

chance that the oscillator would jump down to a lower energy level, emitting its excess energy as a quantum of radiation. This came to be known as the "second form" of Planck's quantum theory. It can be shown that, in this form of the theory, the oscillators are evenly distributed over each ring on the px plane, instead of being all on the inner boundary, and the mean energy of all oscillators is, instead of the value given by (65),

$$\bar{\epsilon} = \frac{h\nu}{e^{h\nu/kT} - 1} + \frac{1}{2} h\nu \tag{66}$$

Having read thus far, the student may perhaps have reached a state of confusion as to *what were* the essential assumptions of Planck's quantum theory! This confusion can be no worse than that which existed in the minds of most physicists in the year, say, 1911. The situation was made still more puzzling by the success of Einstein's theory of the photoelectric effect, described above (Sec. 52); for Einstein assumed not only that radiation came in quantized spurts but that each spurt was closely concentrated in space, contrary to the wave theory. Confusion usually reigns while important physical advances are being made; it is only afterward that a clear-cut logical path can be laid down leading straight to the goal.

One of the aims of this book will be to show how the theory gradually became clarified. It will be found that the following two new ideas introduced by Planck have been retained permanently and form a part of modern "wave mechanics" (Chap. 6):

1. *An oscillator*, or *any similar physical system*, has a *discrete set of possible energy values or levels;* energies intermediate between these allowed values never occur.

2. *The emission and absorption of radiation are associated with transitions* or jumps *between two of these levels, the energy thereby lost or gained by the oscillator being emitted or absorbed, respectively, as a quantum of radiant energy, of magnitude* $h\nu$, ν being the frequency of the radiation. The difficulties with the theory of electromagnetic waves were overcome when the theory of wave mechanics was applied to the electromagnetic field itself (Sec. 162).

It should be emphasized that Planck's revolutionary assumptions were not based upon an extension of the ordinary lines of reasoning of classical physics. Quite the contrary; they represented an *empirical modification* of classifical ideas made in order to bring the theoretical deductions into harmony with experiment. Had the magnitude of the quantum of energy turned out to be not $h\nu$ but something *independent of the frequency*, the new theory might well have taken the form of a simple atomicity of energy, similar to the atomicity of electricity represented by the electronic charge. Such is not the case, however. Rather, it is the new universal constant h that represents the essentially new element introduced into physics by the quantum theory. We shall find h playing an important part in a wide variety of atomic phenomena.

72. Planck's Radiation Law. Planck actually derived his new radiation formula by considering the interaction between the radiation inside an isothermal enclosure and electric oscillators which he imagined to exist in the walls of the enclosure. A more direct and equally satisfactory procedure is to combine Planck's new expression for the mean energy of an oscillator with the analysis of the electromagnetic field by the method of Rayleigh and Jeans, in which the various modes of oscillation of the field inside an enclosure are treated as if they were oscillators. In Sec. 67, Eq. (56), we found that there would be $8\pi \, d\lambda/\lambda^4$ such modes of oscillation or degrees of freedom per unit volume in the wavelength range λ to $\lambda + d\lambda$. If we multiply this number by $\bar{\epsilon}$ as given by Eq. (65), we obtain

$$\psi_\lambda \, d\lambda = 8\pi \frac{d\lambda}{\lambda^4} \frac{h\nu}{e^{h\nu/kT} - 1}$$

Let us substitute here $\nu = c/\lambda$, c being the speed of light in vacuum. Thus we obtain, as Planck's new radiation law,

$$\psi_\lambda = \frac{8\pi ch}{\lambda^5} \frac{1}{e^{ch/\lambda kT} - 1} \tag{67}$$

[Strictly speaking, we should have used for $\bar{\epsilon}$ the value given by Eq. (66), which agrees with the value obtained from wave mechanics. The effect of this change would be to add in ψ_λ a term independent of temperature. Since only *changes* in ψ are perceptible, however, this term would be without physical effect.]

It is easily shown that Planck's formula reduces to a form of Wien's formula near one end of the spectrum, and to the Rayleigh-Jeans formula near the other end. Thus, if the value of the product λT is *small* enough, i.e., for sufficiently small wavelengths, or at sufficiently low temperatures for any given wavelength, the exponential term in the denominator in (66) is much larger than unity, so that in comparison with it the term -1 can be dropped. Then (67) becomes

$$\psi_\lambda = 8\pi ch\lambda^{-5}e^{-ch/\lambda kT}$$

which agrees with Eq. (53) or Wien's formula if in that equation we choose $c_1 = 8\pi ch$, $c_2 = ch/k$. For *large* values of λT, on the other hand, i.e., for sufficiently long waves or at sufficiently high temperatures, we may expand the denominator in (67) by means of the series

$$e^x = 1 + x + \frac{x^2}{2} + \cdots$$

obtaining

$$e^{ch/\lambda kT} - 1 = \frac{ch}{\lambda kT} + \frac{c^2h^2}{2\lambda^2k^2T^2} + \cdots$$

If λT is large enough, only the first term of this series need be kept; then we have, from (67),

$$\psi_\lambda = \frac{8\pi kT}{\lambda^4}$$

approximately. This is the Rayleigh-Jeans formula as stated in Eq. (57).

In Fig. 30 is shown a comparison between the several spectral-energy distribution formulas and the experimental data. The circles show

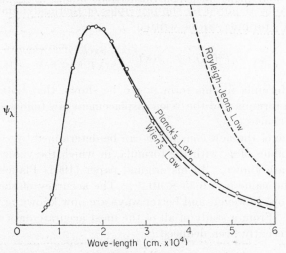

FIG. 30. Comparison of the three radiation laws with experiment at 1600°K. The ordinate represents ψ_λ or e_λ, on an arbitrary scale.

observations by Coblentz[1] on the energy distribution in the spectrum of a black body at 1600°K. The full line shows the distribution predicted by Planck's formula. The lower dotted line, which coincides with the full line from short wavelengths up to about $\lambda = 2.2$ μ, corresponds to Wien's formula as given in Eq. (53). The upper dotted line is from the Rayleigh-Jeans formula. The superiority of Planck's formula is at once evident. Thus, whatever one may think of the theoretical assumptions and reasoning by means of which Planck arrived at his formula, there seems to be no doubt that it correctly represents the observations on black-body radiation.

The reason that the curve for Planck's formula drops below the Rayleigh-Jeans formula is to be found in a failure of the classical principle of the equipartition of energy. This is easily seen from Eq. (66). At

[1] *Natl. Bur. Standards Bull.*, vol. 13, p. 476, 1916.

short wavelengths, the -1 can be dropped in the denominator in that equation and we can write, as the approximate average energy of an oscillator,

$$\bar{\epsilon} = h\nu \, e^{-h\nu/kT} + \tfrac{1}{2}h\nu$$

Thus, the part of $\bar{\epsilon}$ that varies with temperature decreases rapidly toward zero as $\nu \to \infty$. The high-frequency modes of oscillation of the electromagnetic field in the enclosure, which should all have mean energy kT according to classical theory, remain almost entirely in their lowest quantum states and so contribute little to the observable density of radiant energy.

It may be noted in conclusion that Planck's formula has the form that we found to be required by the principles of thermodynamics (Sec. 65). For Planck's formula can be written

$$\psi_\lambda = T^5 f(\lambda T) \qquad f(\lambda T) = \frac{8\pi ch}{(\lambda T)^5} \frac{1}{e^{ch/k(\lambda T)} - 1}$$

From the formula in this form it can be shown that both the Stefan-Boltzmann formula and the Wien displacement law follow as mathematical consequences.

The value of the new constant h can be determined by comparing the observed values of ψ_λ with the formula, in which the values of all other quantities are known. In his original paper (1901) Planck obtained in this way the value $h = 6.55 \times 10^{-27}$. The accuracy of thermal data is relatively low, however, and better ways are now known of inferring the value of h. From a study of all of the most accurate data the following value has recently been deduced:[1]

$$h = 6.625 \times 10^{-27} \text{ erg sec}$$

(or 6.625×10^{-34} joule sec; more precisely, 6.6252 ± 0.0005). The physical dimensions of h, as energy times time, are easily inferred from the equation $\epsilon = \tau h\nu$ or $h = \epsilon/\tau\nu$, in which τ is a mere numeric.

[1] DuMond and Cohen, *Revs. Mod. Phys.*, vol. 25, p. 691, 1953.

CHAPTER 5

THE NUCLEAR ATOM AND THE ORIGIN
OF SPECTRAL LINES

We have seen in the last chapter that attempts to explain the experimentally observed laws of the distribution of energy in the continuous spectrum emitted by a black body were unsuccessful until Planck introduced the revolutionary concept of radiation quanta. Planck's hypothesis became both *possible and necessary*, because the very careful experiments of Lummer and Pringsheim had proved that Wien's law of temperature radiation was untenable.

A somewhat similar sequence of events is to be found in the development of our present extensive knowledge of the *line* spectra of atoms and molecules. Corresponding to the empirical laws of temperature radiation, there was accumulated a vast array of very accurate measurements of the wavelengths of lines in the spectra of various substances, considerable impetus being given to this work because of the rigorous demands of spectroscopy as a method of chemical analysis. From these data, certain relations were discovered empirically between the frequencies of various lines in the spectra of certain elements. These relations pointed to some fundamental mechanism, common to all atoms, as the origin of characteristic line spectra. The gradual accumulation of evidence bearing on the problem of atomic structure, on the one hand, and the increasing importance of these spectral relations, on the other, culminated, about 1913, in the proposal, by Bohr, of the theory of atomic structure and the origin of spectra which bears his name. This theory constituted an extension in a new field of the quantum theory which had been introduced by Planck to explain the law of the distribution of energy in temperature radiation. Bohr's theory has been superseded by modern quantum mechanics (or wave mechanics), but certain features of his theory retain a permanent interest.

In the present chapter, we shall begin by considering briefly the development of the empirical laws of spectral series. Next we shall take up the lines of evidence that were accumulated bearing on the structure of the atom, culminating in the nuclear theory of atomic structure proposed by Rutherford.   Then we shall consider the way in which these two lines of development were combined by Bohr in his quantum theory of the atom.

73. Spectroscopic Units.   In stating the wavelengths of spectral lines, which are always very small, various submultiples of the meter are commonly employed as units of length in different parts of the spectrum, viz.,

The micron, symbol μ $= 10^{-4}$ cm (or 10^{-6} meter)
The millimicron, symbol $m\mu$ $= 10^{-7}$ cm
The angstrom,[1] symbol A $= 10^{-8}$ cm
The X-unit, symbol X.U. $= 10^{-11}$ cm (approximately; see Sec. 151)

In physical theory *frequency* ν is more fundamental than wavelength. We do not, however, measure frequencies *directly;* laboratory measurements yield *wavelengths,* and frequencies are *computed* from these and from the velocity of light c by the relation $c = \nu\lambda$.   Frequencies may be expressed in vibrations per second, but this involves very large numbers. Furthermore, the calculated frequency is affected by any error there may be in the assumed velocity of light.   For these reasons, it is customary in spectroscopy to use, instead of the frequency itself, the *wave number*, or number of waves per centimeter in vacuum, which we shall denote by $\tilde{\nu}$. The unit for $\tilde{\nu}$ is written cm^{-1}; it may be read "waves per centimeter." Thus

$$\tilde{\nu} = \frac{1}{\lambda} \text{ cm}^{-1} \qquad \nu = c\tilde{\nu}$$

λ being the wavelength in vacuum expressed in centimeters.   Or, if λ_μ is the wavelength in microns or λ_A the wavelength in angstroms,

$$\tilde{\nu} = 10^4 \times \frac{1}{\lambda_\mu} \text{ cm}^{-1} = 10^8 \times \frac{1}{\lambda_A} \text{ cm}^{-1}$$

[1] Strictly speaking, the angstrom is not defined from the meter as a *primary* standard of length.   Michelson and Benoist in 1895 and, later (1907), Fabry, Perot, and Benoist measured the wavelength of the red cadmium line in terms of the standard meter; this line is very narrow, so that its wavelength can be measured with great accuracy.   The two measurements were almost exactly in agreement, the wavelength according to the latter measurement being

6,438.4696 angstroms

The International Union for Solar Research, in 1907, adopted this value of the wavelength of the red cadmium line as the *primary* standard of wavelengths on the basis of which all other wavelengths were to be expressed.   It is specified that the medium is to be dry air at 15°C (hydrogen scale) and a pressure equal to 760 mm Hg at a place where the acceleration due to gravity is 980.67 cm per sec². Formally, this amounts to a new definition of the angstrom in terms of the wavelength of the cadmium line such that this wavelength is *exactly* 6,438.4696 angstroms.   The same standard was adopted in 1927 by the International Committee on Weights and Measures.

Very roughly, the visible region (4,000 to 7,000 A) extends from 14,000 to 25,000 cm^{-1}; from 14,000 down to 1,000 is the near infrared region (out to 10 μ); from 1,000 to 100, the far infrared. The ultraviolet region extends from 25,000 to 100,000 cm^{-1} (1,000 A). The principal x-ray region is from 10^7 to 10^8 cm^{-1}.

The wavelength of a line *in air* is slightly different from the wavelength *in vacuum*. Since ordinary spectroscopic work is done in air, wavelengths above (about) 2,000 A are commonly given *in air*.[1] Below 2,000 A, however, they are usually given in vacuum, since vacuum spectrographs are commonly employed for work in that region. The two wavelengths are related by the equation

$$\lambda_{vac} = \mu\lambda_{air}$$

where μ is the refractive index of air; thus the relation actually used ordinarily in obtaining wave numbers from optical wavelengths in air, or vice versa, is

$$\tilde{\nu} = \frac{1}{\mu\lambda_{air}}$$

The difference between λ_{vac} and λ_{air} is somewhat less than 1 part in 3,000. Tables have been published to facilitate the conversion from λ_{air} to $\tilde{\nu}$ or vice versa.[2] As an example, for the D_1 line of sodium,

$$\lambda_{air} = 5,895.92 \text{ A} = 0.589592 \ \mu = 5.89592 \times 10^{-5} \text{ cm}$$
$$\lambda_{vac} = 5,897.55 \text{ A} \qquad \tilde{\nu} = 16,956.19 \text{ cm}^{-1}$$
$$\nu = 5.0834 \times 10^{14} \text{ sec}^{-1}$$

74. Early Search for Regularities in Spectra. One of the first features of spectra to be noticed was that the spectrum of a given element depended a great deal upon its mode of excitation. When the spectrum was produced by a *spark*, many lines were observed which were absent, or at least much weaker, when a steady arc or a flame was employed. These lines are said to form the *spark spectrum* (formerly, the "enhanced" spectrum) of the element, those lines present in the arc forming its *arc spectrum*. It was later established that arc spectra are emitted by neutral atoms, spark spectra by ionized atoms.

As soon as dependable wavelength measurements became available, numerous investigators, reasoning from the analogy of overtones in acoustics, sought for harmonic relations in the lines found in the spectrum of a given element. This search proved fruitless; but certain relations of a different type were discovered. Liveing and Dewar,[3] about 1880, empha-

[1] Cf. the extensive table, "Massachusetts Institute of Technology Wavelength Tables," Wiley, New York, 1939.

[2] Cf. H. Kayser, "Tabelle der Schwingungszahlen," S. Hirzel, Leipzig, 1925.

[3] *Proc. Roy. Soc. (London)*, vol. 29, p. 398, 1879; vol. 30, p. 93, 1880.

sized the physical similarities occurring in the spectra of such elements as the alkali metals. They called attention to the successive *pairs* of lines in the arc spectrum of sodium and pointed out that these pairs were alternately "sharp" and "diffuse" and that they were more closely crowded together toward the short-wavelength end of the spectrum, suggesting some kind of series relation, which, however, they were unable to discover. A little later, Hartley[1] discovered an important numerical relationship between the components of doublets or triplets in the spectrum of a given element. If frequencies, instead of wavelengths, are used, Hartley found that *the difference in frequency between the components of a multiplet* (i.e., doublet or triplet) *in a particular spectrum is the same for all similar multiplets of lines in that spectrum.*

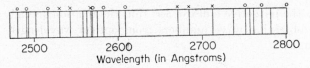

FIG. 31. Some lines in the spectrum of zinc in a limited wavelength range in the ultraviolet. The lines marked with a cross (X) belong to one series of triplets, lines marked (O) belong to another series.

Hartley's law made it possible to isolate from the large number of lines in any given spectrum those groups of lines which were undoubtedly related. Figure 31 shows the lines in the zinc spectrum from about 2,500 to 2,800 A. Two triplets having constant frequency differences are marked by crosses (X). This same spectral region, however, contains another overlapping series of triplets, which are designated by circles (O). The sorting out of these related lines required a great deal of diligent and patient study.

The beginning of our knowledge of spectral-series formulas dates from the discovery by Balmer,[2] in 1885, that the wavelengths of the nine then known lines in the spectrum of hydrogen could be expressed very closely by the simple formula

$$\lambda = b \, \frac{n^2}{n^2 - 4} \tag{68}$$

where b is a constant the numerical value of which, to give λ in angstroms, is 3,645.6 and n is a variable integer which takes on the successive values 3, 4, 5, . . . for, respectively, the first (beginning at the red), second, third, . . . line in the spectrum. Balmer compared the predictions of this formula with the best values then available for the wavelengths of the hydrogen lines. The four lines in the visible region had been measured by Ångström and others; five ultraviolet lines in the spec-

[1] *J. Chem. Soc.*, vol. 43, p. 390, 1883.
[2] *Ann. Physik*, vol. 25, p. 80, 1885.

trum of white stars had been measured by Huggins.   Table 5-1, taken from Balmer's paper, shows the comparison of the formula with the

TABLE 5-1. WAVELENGTHS OF THE FIRST NINE HYDROGEN LINES COMPUTED
BY BALMER FROM HIS FORMULA $\lambda = 3{,}645.6 \dfrac{n^2}{n^2 - a^2}$ $(a = 2)$

Line	n	λ (computed), A	λ (observed), A	
H_α	3	6,562.08	6,562.10	(Ångström)
H_β	4	4,860.80	4,860.74	(Ångström)
H_γ	5	4,340.0	4,340.10	(Ångström)
H_δ	6	4,101.3	4,101.2	(Ångström)
H_ϵ	7	3,969.7	3,968.1	(Huggins)
H_ζ	8	3,888.6	3,887.5	(Huggins)
H_η	9	3,835.0	3,834.0	(Huggins)
H_θ	10	3,797.5	3,795.0	(Huggins)
H_ι	11	3,770.2	3,767.5	(Huggins)

measured wavelengths.   The agreement is seen to be excellent in the visible spectrum, but the discrepancy increases to nearly 1 part in 1,000 for H_ι.   Balmer questioned whether this discrepancy indicated that the formula was only an approximation or whether the data were in error. Recent measurements have considerably revised Huggins' data but have also revealed the need for a slight correction to Balmer's formula.

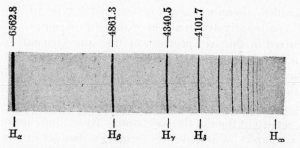

FIG. 32. The Balmer series of atomic hydrogen, in emission. H_∞ marks the theoretical position of the series limit. (*Photograph by G. Herzberg, Ann. d. Physik, vol. 84, p. 565, 1927; reprinted by courtesy of Prentice-Hall, Inc., New York, from G. Herzberg, "Atomic Spectra and Atomic Structure," 1927.*)

Balmer correctly predicted that in this series of lines in hydrogen no lines of longer wavelength than H_α would be found and that the series should "converge" at $\lambda = 3{,}645.6$ A, since the fraction $(n^2 - 4)/n^2$ approaches unity as n becomes large.   In Fig. 32 is reproduced a photograph of the first few lines of the Balmer Series; in Fig. 33 is shown another photograph of the same series starting from the seventh line, more strongly exposed so as to bring out more lines.

The impetus which Balmer's discovery gave to work in spectral series is another illustration of the highly convincing nature of relations which are expressible in *quantitative* form. Soon after the publication of his work, intensive investigations in spectral series were initiated by Kayser and Runge and by Rydberg.

FIG. 33. Higher members of the Balmer series, in emission, starting from the seventh line and showing the continuum. (*After G. Herzberg, see credit for Fig. 32.*)

75. Spectral Series and Their Interrelations.

In announcing his discovery, Balmer had raised the question as to whether or not his formula might be a special case of a more general formula applicable to other series of lines in other elements. Rydberg set out to find such a formula.[1] Using the comparatively large mass of wavelength data then available, Rydberg isolated other series of doublets and triplets of constant frequency difference, according to Hartley's law of constant wave-number separation. In all cases, these series showed a tendency to converge to some limit in the ultraviolet. He found that he could distinguish two types of such series: a type in which the lines were comparatively sharp, which he called, therefore, *sharp* series; and a type which, because the lines were comparatively broad, he called *diffuse* series. Both types of series occurred in the arc spectrum of the same element. In many arc spectra, he found also a third type of series in which the doublet or triplet spacing *decreased* as the frequency or ordinal number of the line increased, as if tending to vanish at the convergence limit of the series; these he called *principal* series, because they commonly contained the brightest and most persistent lines in the spectrum. By a "line" in this connection is meant a complex of actual lines forming a doublet or triplet, which is seen as a single line in a spectroscope of moderate resolving power. The chief lines of the principal, sharp, and diffuse series of sodium are plotted in Fig. 34, marked p, s, d, respectively.

Eventually Rydberg found that many observed series could be represented closely by an equation of the form

$$\tilde{\nu}_m = \tilde{\nu}_\infty - \frac{R}{(m + \mu)^2} \qquad (69)$$

μ and $\tilde{\nu}_\infty$ being constants which vary from one series to another. Obvi-

---

[1] A brief account of Rydberg's work is given by him in *Phil. Mag.*, vol. 29, p. 331, 1890. For a fuller account see E. C. C. Baly's "Spectroscopy."

ously, by properly choosing the ordinal number m of the lines, μ can always be made less than 1 in such a formula. The constant $\tilde{\nu}_\infty$ represents the high-frequency limit to which the lines in the series ultimately converge. The Balmer formula is a special case of this more general "Rydberg formula"; for Eq. (68) can be written

$$\tilde{\nu} = \frac{1}{\lambda} = \frac{1}{b} - \frac{4}{bm^2} = \tilde{\nu}_\infty - \frac{R}{m^2}$$

with $\tilde{\nu}_\infty = 1/b$, $R = 4/b$, $m = 3, 4, 5, \ldots$. This is of the type of (69) with $\mu = 0$.

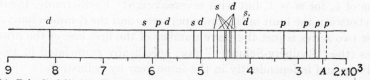

FIG. 34. Principal lines in the spectrum of the neutral sodium atom: p = principal, s = sharp, d = diffuse series. Dotted lines indicate series limits. The first line of the sharp series, in the infrared at 11,393 A, is not shown.

The constant R in Eq. (69), now called the Rydberg constant, was found to have the same value for a large group of series for each substance, and very nearly the same for all substances. Its slight variation from one atom to another is now known to be due to differences in the atomic weight, the effect of which can be calculated theoretically (Sec. 81). It is thus possible to calculate what R would be for an atom of infinite weight; this value is denoted by R_∞, the value for a particular kind of atom being denoted by another appropriate suffix. The values as found from spectroscopic observation are:

For hydrogen atoms, H^1 $R_H = 109,677.58$ cm^{-1}
For deuterium atoms, H^2 $R_D = 109,707.42$ cm^{-1}
For helium, He^4 $R_{He} = 109,722.27$ cm^{-1}
For atoms of infinite weight $R_\infty = 109,737.31$ cm^{-1}

76. Further Relations between Series. Spectral Terms. Rydberg noticed also several remarkable relationships between different spectral series belonging to the same element. He noted that the *sharp and the diffuse series appeared to have a common convergence limit.* Next, he observed that this common limit was equal to a *term* in the formula for the *principal* series, viz., to the term $R/(m + \mu)^2$ with m set equal to 1; and that a similar equality held between the *limit* of the *principal* series itself and the variable *term*, for $m = 1$, in the formula for the *sharp* series.

Because of these remarkable relations, the formulas for the three series in question could be rewritten in the following form:

$$\tilde{\nu}_p = \frac{R}{(1+S)^2} - \frac{R}{(m+P)^2} \qquad m = 1, 2, \ldots \qquad (70a)$$

$$\tilde{\nu}_s = \frac{R}{(1+P)^2} - \frac{R}{(m+S)^2} \qquad m = 2, 3, \ldots \qquad (70b)$$

$$\tilde{\nu}_d = \frac{R}{(1+P)^2} - \frac{R}{(m+D)^2} \qquad m = 2, 3, \ldots \qquad (70c)$$

Here we have indicated that, at least for the alkali metals, m starts from 1 in the principal series but from 2 in the others.

Two additional relations are at once apparent from the formulas. If we set $m = 1$ in the formula for $\tilde{\nu}_s$, we obtain the same number as the value of $\tilde{\nu}_p$ for $m = 1$, but with reversed sign! Furthermore, the difference between the limit of the principal series and the common limit of the other two series is just the wave number of the first line of the principal series (the "Rydberg-Schuster" law, specifically enunciated in 1896 by Rydberg and independently in the same year by Schuster).

The structure of these formulas suggested to Rydberg the possibility that the first term on the right might also vary, in the same manner as does the second, thus giving rise to additional series of lines; for example, we might expect to find a series represented by the formula

$$\tilde{\nu} = \frac{R}{(2+S)^2} - \frac{R}{(m+P)^2} \qquad m = 3, 4, \ldots$$

Lines or series of this sort were actually discovered later by Ritz. Such lines are called *intercombination lines* or *series*, and the possibility of their occurrence is known as the *Ritz combination principle*. Many examples of them are now known.

The most significant features about atomic spectra in general thus seem to be the following:

1. *The wave number of each line is conveniently represented as the difference between two numbers.* These numbers have come to be called *terms*.

2. *The terms group themselves naturally into ordered sequences, the terms of each sequence converging toward zero.*

3. *The terms can be combined in various ways to give the wave numbers of spectral lines.*

4. *A series of lines, all having similar character, results from the combination of all terms of one sequence in succession with a fixed term of another sequence. Series formed in this manner have wave numbers which, when arranged in order of increasing magnitude, converge to an upper limit.*

The simple picture presented here, however, requires considerable extension. In writing Rydberg formulas for spectral "lines," we have ignored the fine structure of the lines, by means of which series were first picked out; *singlet* series, in which each line is single, are known in many elements, but more commonly the lines form *doublets*, *triplets*, or groups of even more components.   In such cases, a separate Rydberg formula must be written for each component line.   In the spectra of the alkali metals, for example, doublets occur, so that six formulas instead of three are required for a complete representation of the chief series.   Furthermore, the Rydberg formula itself is only a first approximation.   Further discussion of details will be postponed to a later chapter.

The remarkable properties possessed by spectral series pointed clearly to the existence within atoms of a comparatively simple and universal mechanism by which spectra are emitted.   In terms of classical ideas, however, it was very difficult to imagine a mechanism which could emit spectra having the observed features.   It was natural to assume that the higher members of a series were of the nature of overtones.   Among acoustic vibrations, many cases are met with in which the frequencies of the overtones are not integral multiples of the fundamental frequency; examples are the vibrations of bells and of the common tuning fork. But no cases are known in which the frequencies of the overtones converge to an upper limit.   Furthermore, the Ritz combination principle is without analogy in the classical theory of vibrating systems.

The key to the origin of spectral lines was not discovered until certain other lines of evidence had led to the adoption of radically new conceptions concerning the structure of atoms.

77. Early Views on Atomic Structure.   Speculations as to the structure of the atom date from the early years of the nineteenth century.   In 1815 Prout proposed the hypothesis that the atoms of all elements are composed of atoms of hydrogen; but this view failed of acceptance when it was established that the atomic weights of some elements differ markedly from multiples of the atomic weight of hydrogen.

The discovery of the electron in 1897 led to renewed interest in the internal structure of atoms by indicating that they must contain both negative electrons and positive charges.   Two questions then arose: (1) How many electrons are there in an atom? and (2) How are the electrons and the positive charges arranged?   Evidence was soon obtained from the scattering of x-rays, to be described in Sec. 148, which indicated that the number of electrons in an atom of the lighter elements was equal to about half the atomic weight, except that the atom of hydrogen contains a single electron.   As to the arrangement of the electrons, it seemed on the basis of classical ideas that two conditions must be met.   (1) The ensemble of positive charges and electrons in an atom must be stable; the electrons, for example, must be held by forces of some sort in fixed positions of equilibrium about which they may vibrate, when disturbed, with the definite frequencies required to explain the characteristic line spectra of the elements.   (2) Except when so disturbed, the electrons must be at

rest, since otherwise they would emit radiation in accord with the requirements of electromagnetic theory.   The much larger mass of the atom as
a whole was assumed to belong to the positive charges, which for this
reason would vibrate very little.

A possibility considered by J. J. Thomson was that the positive electricity might be distributed continuously throughout a certain small
region, perhaps with uniform density throughout a sphere.   The electrons
might then be embedded in the positive electricity, occupying normally
certain positions of equilibrium, and executing harmonic vibrations about
these positions when slightly disturbed.   Frequencies in the visible spectrum might thereby be emitted if the sphere of positive electricity were
of the order of 10^{-8} cm in radius.   But Thomson was unable to show that
these frequencies could be such as to form a series converging to an upper
limit, and eventually his theory came into conflict with the experiments
of Rutherford and his collaborators on the scattering of α-particles, which
are now to be described.

78. The Scattering of Alpha-particles by Atoms.   The α-rays from
radioactive materials had been shown to be positively charged particles
which have a mass almost exactly equal to that of the helium atom and a
positive charge numerically equal to twice the charge on the electron.
Since helium was known to be produced by radioactive substances which
emit α-rays, the latter were identified with helium atoms which have lost
two electrons.   The α-particles, whose initial velocity is of the order of
2×10^9 cm per sec, could be studied by means of the flashes of light or
scintillations which they produce on striking a zinc sulfide screen, the
impact of a *single* particle producing a visible flash which is readily
observed under a low-power microscope.

If a stream of α-particles, limited by means of suitable diaphragms to
a narrow cylindrical pencil, be allowed to strike a zinc sulfide screen placed
at right angles to the path of the particles, the scintillations will occur
over a well-defined circular area equal to the cross section of the pencil.
If, now, a thin film of matter, such as gold or silver foil, is interposed in
the path of the rays, it is found that they pass quite readily through the
foil, but that the area over which the scintillations occur becomes larger
and loses its definite boundary, indicating that some of the particles have
been deflected from their original direction.   This spreading out of the
stream of particles on passing through thin layers of matter, solid or
gaseous, is called "scattering."

Qualitatively, it is easy to explain the origin of the forces which cause
the deflection of the α-particle.   The particle itself has a twofold positive
charge.   The atoms of the scattering material contain charges, both
positive and negative.   In its passage through the scattering material,
the particle experiences electrostatic forces the magnitude and direction

of which depend on how near the particle happens to approach to the centers of the atoms past which *or through which* it moves.

If we assume the Thomson model of the atom, the path of an α-particle in passing *through* an atom might be as indicated in Fig. 35(a). The major part of the deflection will arise from the electrostatic repulsion on the α-particle due to the charge on the positive sphere, which, for the heavier atoms at least, has a mass many times that of the α-particle. The electrons within the positive sphere, being capable of motion about their respective positions of equilibrium and possessing a mass which is very small compared with the mass of the α-particle, will produce no appreciable deflection of the latter but will themselves be pulled from their positions of equilibrium and set vibrating or even expelled from the atom. The total deflection of any given particle in passing through or past a number of such atoms in a thin layer of scattering material varies according to the laws of probability. Such a process is called *multiple*, or *compound*, scattering. According to Rutherford, the number of α-particles N_ϕ which, as a result of *multiple* scattering, should be scattered by such an atom through an angle ϕ *or greater* is given by

$$N_\phi = N_0 e^{-(\phi/\phi_m)^2}$$

where N_0 is the number of particles for $\phi = 0$, and ϕ_m is the average deflection after passing through the scattering material.

Now Geiger had shown[1] experimentally that the most probable angle of deflection of a pencil of α-particles in passing through gold foil $1/2,000$ mm thick is of the order of $1°$. It is evident, therefore, from the last equation, that the probability for scattering through large angles becomes vanishingly small; for $30°$, for example, it would be of the order of 10^{-13}. Geiger showed that the observed scattering obeyed this probability law for small angles of scattering but that *the number of particles scattered through large angles was much greater than the theory of multiple scattering predicted.* Indeed, Geiger and Marsden showed[2] that 1 in 8,000 α-particles was turned through an angle of *more than* $90°$ by a thin film of platinum, i.e., was, in effect diffusely *reflected*. This so-called "reflection," however, was shown to be not a surface phenomenon but rather a volume effect, since the number of particles turned through more than $90°$ increased, up to a certain point, with increasing thickness of the scattering foil. It was also found that the proportion of particles diffusely reflected increased approximately as the $\frac{3}{2}$ power of the atomic weight of the foil. It was impossible to explain this excess scattering of α-particles at large angles on the basis of multiple scattering by a Thomson atom and the laws of probability.

[1] *Proc. Roy. Soc. (London)*, vol. 83, p. 492, 1910.

[2] *Ibid.*, vol. 82, p. 495, 1909.

79. The Nuclear Atom.　*a. Rutherford's Hypothesis.*　In a classical article[1] published in 1911, Rutherford proposed a new type of atomic model capable of giving to an α-particle a large deflection as a result of a *single* encounter.　He assumed that in an atom *the positive charge and most of the atomic mass are concentrated in a very small central region*, later called the nucleus, about which the electrons are grouped in some sort of configuration.　Since normally atoms are electrically neutral, the positive charge on the nucleus must be Ze where e is the numerical electronic charge and Z is an integer, characteristic of the kind of atom.

The deflection of an α-particle by such a nucleus might be as illustrated in Fig. 35(*b*).　Rutherford calculated the distribution of α-particles to be

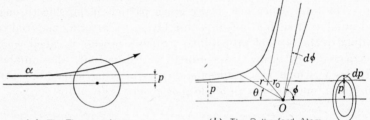

(*a*) The Thomson Atom　　　(*b*) The Rutherford Atom

Fig. 35. Comparison of deflections of an α-particle by (*a*) the Thomson atom and (*b*) the Rutherford nuclear atom.

expected as the result of *single-scattering* processes by atoms of this type. The deduction of his formula is easy and may be given here.

Let the charge on the α-particle be $2e$ and its mass m, and assume that the nucleus has a mass so much greater that, for a first approximation, it may be assumed to remain at rest.　Let the α-particle approach at speed v_0 along a line passing at a distance p from the nucleus; its energy is thus $mv_0^2/2$ and its angular momentum about the nucleus at O is mv_0p. Let r and θ be polar coordinates for the α-particle with origin at O, θ being measured from a line drawn from O in a direction toward the distantly approaching particle [Fig. 35(*b*)].

Then the particle has perpendicular components of velocity dr/dt and $r\,d\theta/dt$; and its angular momentum about O at any time is $mr^2\,d\theta/dt$. It also has potential energy due to repulsion by the nucleus of magnitude $2Ze^2/r$ and initially zero.　Thus, adding the kinetic energy, we have from the laws of conservation of energy and of angular momentum

$$\tfrac{1}{2}m\left[\left(\frac{dr}{dt}\right)^2 + r^2\left(\frac{d\theta}{dt}\right)^2\right] + \frac{2Ze^2}{r} = \tfrac{1}{2}mv_0^2 \tag{71a}$$

$$r^2\frac{d\theta}{dt} = v_0p \tag{71b}$$

[1] *Phil. Mag.*, vol. 21, p. 669, 1911.

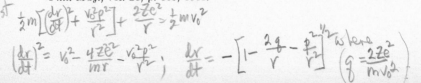

A factor m has been canceled in (71b). By eliminating $d\theta/dt$ it follows that

$$\frac{dr}{dt} = -v_0 \left(1 - \frac{2q}{r} - \frac{p^2}{r^2} \right)^{\frac{1}{2}} \qquad q = \frac{2Ze^2}{mv_0^2} \qquad (72a,b)$$

in which the negative sign is chosen because, during the approach, $dr/dt < 0$. Dividing this equation into (71b) and noting that

$$\frac{d\theta/dt}{dr/dt} = \frac{d\theta}{dr}$$

we have

$$\frac{d\theta}{dr} = -\frac{p}{r^2} \left(1 - \frac{2q}{r} - \frac{p^2}{r^2} \right)^{-\frac{1}{2}}$$

The integral of this equation that vanishes at $r = \infty$, as is easily verified by substitution in the last equation, is

$$\theta = \cos^{-1} \left[\frac{p}{\sqrt{p^2 + q^2}} \left(1 - \frac{2q}{r} - \frac{p^2}{r^2} \right)^{\frac{1}{2}} \right] - \cos^{-1} \frac{p}{\sqrt{p^2 + q^2}}$$

At the point of closest approach to the nucleus, $dr/dt = 0$. Hence, by (72a), the radical must vanish; then $\theta = \theta_0 = \pi/2 - \cos^{-1} (p/\sqrt{p^2 + q^2})$. The second half of the path, as the particle recedes again, is symmetrical with the first half. Hence, the total increase in θ is $2\theta_0$; and the final deflection ϕ, or the total change in the direction of motion of the particle, is

$$\phi = \pi - 2\theta_0 = 2 \cos^{-1} \frac{p}{\sqrt{p^2 + q^2}} \qquad \therefore\ p = q \cot \frac{\phi}{2} \qquad (73a,b)$$

Now to find the statistical distribution of the scattered α-particles, let them approach along parallel paths so that N_0 of their paths cross each unit area of any plane drawn perpendicular to the paths. Then the number approaching with the value of p in a given range dp will be $dN = 2\pi N_0 p\, dp$, since their paths cross the plane at points in a circular ring of radius p and width dp [Fig. 35(b)]. Their deflections will lie in a numerical range $d\phi$ such that, from (73b),

$$dp = \frac{q}{2} \frac{d\phi}{\sin^2 (\phi/2)}$$

After deflection, the paths of these particles lie in a conical element of solid angle of radius $\sin \phi$ and width $d\phi$ and hence of magnitude $d\omega = 2\pi \sin \phi\, d\phi = 4\pi \sin (\phi/2) \cos (\phi/2)\, d\phi$. The number N_1 of these particles falling per unit area on a screen distant R from the nucleus will be equal to $dN/R^2\, d\omega$, or, after inserting values of p, dp, $d\omega$, and then of q,

$$N_1 = \frac{2\pi N_0 p\, dp}{R^2\, d\omega} = \frac{e^4 N_0}{m^2 v_0^4} \frac{Z^2}{R^2} \frac{1}{\sin^4 (\phi/2)} \qquad (74)$$

If the charge on the impinging particle is $Z_1 e$ instead of $2e$, N_1 is multiplied by $Z_1^2/4$. This formula is subject to correction, however, for the motion induced in the scattering nucleus, which may be appreciable for light atoms.

According to Rutherford's formula (74), the number of particles per unit area striking a screen placed at a given distance from the scattering material and perpendicular to the direction of motion of the scattered particles should be proportional (1) to $1/\sin^4 (\phi/2)$; (2) to the thickness t of the material; (3) to Z^2; and (4) inversely to the square of the kinetic energy of the particles (i.e., to v_0^{-4}).

b. Experimental Confirmation. These predictions were completely verified by the experiments of Geiger and Marsden.[1] Their data are shown graphically in Fig. 36, in which the logarithm of the number of scintilla-

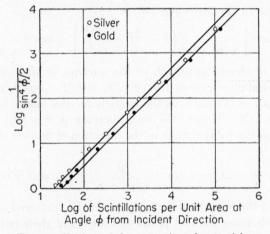

FIG. 36. The law of the scattering of α-particles.

tions on the screen per minute is plotted as abscissa against the logarithm of $1/\sin^4 (\phi/2)$ as ordinate. If these two quantities are proportional to each other, the points for each substance should lie on a straight line inclined at 45° with the axes. The two lines in the figure are drawn at *exactly* 45°, and the observed points are seen to agree well with the predictions. This is the more remarkable since the numbers of scintillations varied in the experiment over a very wide range of values, the left-hand points on the plots representing 22 particles per minute for silver and 33 for gold, whereas the right-hand points represent 105,400 and 132,000, respectively.

The prediction of Rutherford that the scattering should, for small thicknesses, be proportional to thickness was confirmed by the observa-

[1] Geiger and Marsden, *Phil. Mag.*, vol. 25, p. 605, 1913.

tions.   Geiger and Marsden also showed that "the amount of scattering by a given foil is approximately proportional to the inverse fourth power of the velocity (inverse square of the energy) of the incident α-particles," over a range of velocities such that the number of scattered particles varied as 1:10.

c. *Atomic Number.*   Geiger and Marsden further concluded, from a study of the variation of scattering with atomic weight and of the fraction of the total number of incident particles scattered through a given angle, (1) that the scattering is approximately proportional to the atomic weight of the scatterer over the range of elements from carbon to gold, and (2) that "*the number of elementary charges composing the center of the atoms is equal to half the atomic weight.*"   This second conclusion was in agreement with Barkla's experiments on the scattering of x-rays.   Thus, carbon, nitrogen, and oxygen should have, respectively, 6, 7, and 8 electrons, around a nucleus containing, in each case, an equal amount of positive charge.   These elements are, respectively, the sixth, seventh, and eighth elements in the periodic table.   The hypothesis was natural, therefore, that the number of electrons in the atom, *or the number of units of positive charge on its nucleus,* is numerically equal to the ordinal number which the atom occupies in the series of the elements, counting hydrogen as the first.   Thus originated the concept of the *atomic number* of an element, symbol Z, which we may think of variously as (1) the ordinal number of the element in the series of the elements starting with $Z = 1$ for hydrogen, or (2) the positive charge carried by the nucleus of the atom, in terms of the numerical electronic charge e as a unit, or (3) the number of electrons surrounding the nucleus in the neutral atom.

These experiments of Geiger and Marsden so completely confirmed the conclusions which Rutherford had reached by postulating the nuclear type of atom that, in spite of certain weighty objections, his atomic model was at once adopted.

d. *Some Difficulties.*   The objections to the nuclear type of atom were based on questions of stability.   No stable arrangement of positive and negative charges at rest can be invented; it can be proved, in fact, that such an arrangement is impossible (Earnshaw's theorem).   An electron might, however, be imagined to revolve around a nucleus as the earth revolves around the sun.   But then, according to the laws of classical electromagnetic theory, since the electron would be subject to a constant acceleration toward the nucleus, it would *radiate energy.*   This energy can come only from the energy of the system.   The system will, therefore, "run down"; the electron will approach the nucleus along a spiral path and, as can easily be shown, will *give out radiation of constantly increasing frequency.*   This, however, does not agree with the observed emission of spectral lines of fixed frequency.

It was at this point that Bohr introduced his epoch-making theory of the structure of the atom and of the origin of spectra. His theory constituted an extension of Planck's theory of quanta to Rutherford's nuclear atom, in an attempt both to remove the difficulties of the nuclear model and to explain the origin of the characteristic spectra of the elements.

80. The Bohr Theory of Atomic Hydrogen. The essential features of Planck's original quantum theory as described in Sec. 71 were two:

1. An oscillator can exist only in one of a number of discrete quantum states, and to each of these states there corresponds a definite allowed value of its energy.

2. No radiation is emitted while the oscillator remains in one of its quantum states, but it is capable of jumping from one quantum state into another one of lower energy, the energy lost in doing so being emitted in the form of a pulse or quantum of radiation.

Successful applications of the first of these assumptions had already been made in other fields, notably by Einstein and especially by Debye in the specific heat of solids, which will be discussed in Chap. 9. Nicholson had also attempted to apply the theory to spectra, and with some success, but he was unable to make it yield a series of lines converging to a limit. Bohr discovered how to apply similar ideas to a hydrogen atom of the Rutherford type and succeeded in arriving at a theoretical formula for its spectrum that agrees with observation.[1]

Bohr assumed that an electron in the field of a nucleus was not capable of moving along every one of the paths that were possible according to classical theory but was restricted to one of a certain set of allowed paths. While it was so moving, he assumed that it did not radiate, contrary to the conclusion from classical theory, so that its energy remained constant; but he assumed that the electron could jump from one allowed path to another one of lower energy and that, when it did so, radiation was emitted containing energy equal to the difference in the energies corresponding to the two paths.

As to the *frequency* of the emitted radiation, he considered several alternative hypotheses but finally adopted the same assumption that Planck had made for his oscillators. That is, if W_1 and W_2 are the energies of the atom when moving in its initial and final paths, respectively, the *frequency* ν of the radiation emitted is determined by the condition that

$$\nu = \frac{W_1 - W_2}{h} \tag{75}$$

where h is Planck's constant. This assumption had the additional advantage of agreeing with that made by Einstein in arriving at his

[1] N. Bohr, *Phil. Mag.*, vol. 26, p. 1, 1913.

highly successful photoelectric equation [Sec. 52, Eq. (29)]. For the latter reason, Eq. (75) came later to be known as the *Einstein frequency condition*.

Concerning the formulation of the condition that determines the allowed paths, Bohr was also in some doubt. While the electron remains in one of its "stationary states," as he called them, he supposed it to revolve in a circular or elliptical orbit about the nucleus in accordance with the classical laws of mechanics. But what fixes the size and shape of this orbit? Bohr showed that it would suffice to assume a certain relation between the frequency of the emitted radiation and the frequency of revolution of the electron in its orbit. In the end, however, he preferred to postulate that the orbit is a circle, with the nucleus at its center, and of such size that the *angular momentum of the electron about the nucleus is an integral multiple of the natural unit $h/2\pi$*.

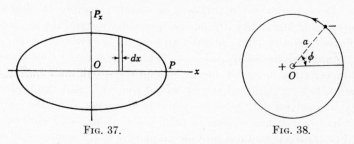

FIG. 37.   FIG. 38.

It was recognized later that the postulate in this form is in harmony with the final interpretation that Planck had found for h in the case of the harmonic oscillator. We saw in Sec. 70 that the state of the oscillator might be represented by a point on a plane, with the coordinate x and the momentum p of the oscillator taken as cartesian coordinates, and that, as long as the energy of the oscillator remained constant, this point would move along an ellipse (Fig. 37). The condition for a stationary state or quantum state of the oscillator was that the area enclosed by this ellipse should be an integral multiple of h. For the enclosed area, we can obviously write $\oint p_x\, dx$, $\oint$ meaning integration over a complete cycle. While x ranges from its minimum to its maximum value, p_x is positive (above Ox in Fig. 37); whereas during the other half-cycle, as x decreases again so that $dx < 0$, p_x is negative, and $p_x\, dx$ is again positive. Planck's condition for a quantum state of the oscillator can, therefore, be stated as follows:

$$\oint p\, dx = nh \tag{76}$$

This rule is easily modified so as to apply to a revolving electron. If we take, as its coordinate, its angular displacement ϕ from a fixed line (Fig. 38), the (generalized) momentum p_ϕ corresponding to ϕ is the ordinary angular momentum. Equation (76) thus takes the form, for the revolving electron,

$$\oint p_\phi \, d\phi = nh$$

But here p_ϕ is constant during a revolution, so that

$$\oint p_\phi \, d\phi = p_\phi \oint d\phi = 2\pi p_\phi$$

Thus, from the last equation, we have, as the condition for a quantum state, Bohr's quantum condition, $p_\phi = nh/2\pi$, n being any positive integer.

Bohr's theory represents a remarkable combination of principles taken over from classical theory with postulates radically at variance with that theory. He solved the old problem of stability merely by *postulating* that the cause of instability, the emission of radiation and the accompanying radiation reaction, did not exist so long as the electron remained in one of its allowed stationary orbits. The electron could thus remain in its stationary state of lowest energy indefinitely, without spiraling down into the nucleus, as classical theory would require. But the problem of stability was solved only at the expense of throwing away the only picture we had of the mechanism by which the atom could emit spectral lines. For Bohr's postulates provide no picture of the sequence of events *during transitions between orbits*.

A hybrid theory of this sort was widely felt to be unsatisfactory; but we shall see in the next section that it was astonishingly successful. In the next chapter we shall describe the wave-mechanical theory that ultimately replaced the Bohr theory. This theory leads very nearly to the same set of energy values for the quantum states of the hydrogen atom as does the theory of Bohr, but it suggests a quite different picture of the behavior of the electron while in a quantum state. In the new theory, it is only about half true that the electron is in motion in the atom, even when it is in one of its higher quantum states; at least, it cannot be said to follow a definite orbit. Because of the abstractness of the new theory, the original simple Bohr picture is commonly felt to retain something more than mere historical interest.

81. Quantum States of One Electron in an Atom. The allowed values of the energy as given by Bohr's theory for an atom containing a single electron are easily deduced from his basic assumptions. Let the nuclear charge be Ze, Z being the atomic number and, therefore, an integer, and e being the numerical electronic charge, in electrostatic units. The atom may be a neutral hydrogen atom, or a singly ionized atom of helium, or a doubly ionized lithium atom, and so on.

It was assumed that the electron revolves in a circle with angular momentum

$$p_\phi = ma^2\omega = n\frac{h}{2\pi} \tag{77}$$

where m is the electronic mass, a the radius of the orbit, and ω the angular velocity of revolution.   To satisfy the laws of mechanics, we must have the necessary centripetal force on the electron supplied by the force of attraction due to the nucleus, whence

$$ma\omega^2 = \frac{Ze^2}{a^2} \tag{78}$$

Eliminating ω, we find for the radius of the orbit

$$a = \frac{n^2h^2}{4\pi^2me^2Z} \tag{79}$$

The energy of the electron will be partly kinetic and partly potential. If we call the energy zero when the electron is at rest at infinity, its potential energy in the presence of the nucleus, according to the usual electrostatic formula (charge times potential), is

$$U = -\frac{Ze^2}{a}$$

Its kinetic energy is

$$K = \frac{1}{2}mv^2 = \frac{1}{2}ma^2\omega^2 = \frac{1}{2}\frac{Ze^2}{a}$$

by (78).   The total energy is $W = K + U$, or

$$W_n = -\frac{1}{2}\frac{Ze^2}{a} = -\frac{2\pi^2me^4Z^2}{h^2n^2} \tag{80}$$

by (79).   Here and in Eq. (79) n may have any integral value: $n = 1$, 2, 3, ...

From Eq. (80), we see that, the larger the value of n, the smaller numerically but the larger in algebraic value is the energy of the system. The lowest value of W_n is that corresponding to the first orbit.   This state is called the *normal* (quantum) state, or ground state, of the atom, since it should be the most stable state and the one ordinarily occupied by the electron.

It is interesting to note that according to Eq. (79) the radii of the successive allowed orbits are proportional to n^2, or to 1, 4, 9, 16, ...   If in (79) we substitute $Z = 1$ for hydrogen and $h = 6.625 \times 10^{-27}$, $e = 4.803 \times 10^{-10}$, $m = 0.9108 \times 10^{-27}$ gram, and $n = 1$, we find for the radius of the smallest Bohr circle for hydrogen, or the radius of its orbit in the normal atom,

$$a = a_0 = \frac{h^2}{4\pi^2 m e^2} = 5.292 \times 10^{-9} \text{ cm} \qquad (81)$$

The diameter of the orbit is thus close to 10^{-8} cm, which agrees very well with estimates of the atomic diameter obtained from kinetic theory.

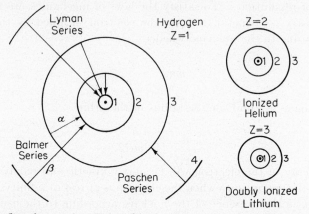

FIG. 39. The first three or four Bohr orbits for three atoms, drawn to a common scale.

This is a first indication that the new theory may be able to explain, among other things, the apparent sizes of molecules. In atoms containing only one electron but a larger nuclear charge, the orbits are all smaller in the ratio $1/Z$. In Fig. 39 are shown in correct relative proportions the first three Bohr orbits for hydrogen and for the ions He⁺ and Li⁺⁺.

Our calculation requires, however, a certain correction. What we have developed is a fixed-nucleus theory. In reality, if the electron revolves at a fixed distance from the nucleus, its path in space will be a circle about the *center of mass of the combined system*. At the same time the nucleus itself revolves in a smaller circle. If a is the distance of the electron from the nucleus and a', a'' the respective distances of electron and nucleus from the center of mass (Fig. 40), then

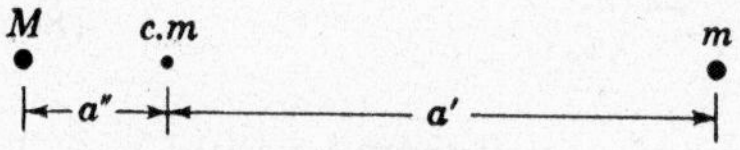

FIG. 40.

$$a' = \frac{M}{M + m} a, \qquad a'' = \frac{m}{M + m} a$$

where M is the mass of the nucleus.

The total angular momentum about the center of mass is then the sum of that due to the electron and that due to the nuclear motion, or

$$m a'^2 \omega + M a''^2 \omega = \left[m \frac{M^2}{(m + M)^2} + M \frac{m^2}{(m + M)^2} \right] a^2 \omega = \frac{mM}{m + M} a^2 \omega$$

Let us introduce the *reduced mass* of the electron, defined as

$$m' = \frac{mM}{m + M} \tag{82}$$

Then we can write for the total angular momentum $m'a^2\omega$, and, if we assume that Bohr's postulate has reference to the total angular momentum of the atom, we have, in place of (77),

$$m'a^2\omega = n\frac{h}{2\pi} \tag{83}$$

Furthermore, in the left-hand member of the dynamical equation (78), a, representing the radius of the electronic orbit in space, is now to be replaced by a'. The same result is obtained, however, if, retaining a, we replace m by m' as defined by Eq. (82). In the *right-hand* member of (78), however, a represents the distance between the electron and the nucleus and must be left unchanged. Thus in place of (78) we have

$$m'a\omega^2 = \frac{Ze^2}{a^2} \tag{84}$$

The expression for the potential energy U is unaltered. The kinetic energy of the electron, however, will now be $\frac{1}{2}ma'^2\omega^2$, to which is to be added that of the nucleus, or $\frac{1}{2}Ma''^2\omega^2$; the total kinetic energy of the atom is thus

$$\left(\frac{1}{2}ma'^2 + \frac{1}{2}Ma''^2\right)\omega^2 = \frac{1}{2}\frac{mM}{m + M}a^2\omega^2 = \frac{1}{2}m'a^2\omega^2 = \frac{1}{2}\frac{Ze^2}{a}$$

by (84). The total energy is thus

$$W_n = -\frac{1}{2}\frac{Ze^2}{a}$$

as before.

It is easily seen now that the effect of these changes is simply to replace m by m' as given by Eq. (82) in all the equations previously written, including Eqs. (79) and (80), so that these latter equations become

$$a = \frac{n^2h^2}{4\pi^2m'e^2Z} \qquad W_n = -\frac{2\pi^2m'e^4Z^2}{h^2n^2} \tag{85a,b}$$

We note that the nuclear motion causes the orbital radii and the allowed energies to vary slightly with M, or with the atomic weight.

In addition to the *discrete set* of allowed orbits just described, in any one of which the electron is capable of moving with negative total energy, Bohr assumed that it could also move with *any value whatever of positive energy*. In such a case the orbit would be a hyperbola, as some of the orbits of comets have been supposed to be. Thus we have, in all, a *discrete set* of allowed *negative* energies, or energy levels, converging to the value zero and, also, from zero up, a *continuum* of allowed *positive* energies. Since the zero value of the energy corresponds to the electron at rest at infinity, *the numerical value of the (negative) energy of the normal state also represents the least energy required to ionize the atom by complete removal of the electron.*

A final remark should be added to forestall misunderstanding. Wave-mechanical theory, also, assigns definite values of angular momentum to the various quantum states of atoms, but these values are not the same as those assigned by the Bohr theory. The *energy levels*, however, turn out to be the same [except for a minor correction (Sec. 120)].

82. Spectrum of a One-electron Atom. According to Bohr's postu-lates, a hydrogen atom radiates when the electron jumps from one quan-tum state into another state of lower energy. The difference in the two energies is emitted as a single quantum of radiant energy, the frequency of which is given by the Einstein relation, or

$$\nu = \frac{W_1 - W_2}{h} \tag{86}$$

Inserting here for W_1 and W_2 the values given by Eq. (80) for states with quantum numbers n_1 and n_2, we have, therefore, for the frequency of the line emitted when the atom jumps from state n_1 to state n_2,

$$\nu = \frac{2\pi^2 m e^4 Z^2}{h^3} \left(\frac{1}{n_2^2} - \frac{1}{n_1^2} \right) \tag{87a}$$

or, in terms of wave numbers,

$$\tilde{\nu} = R Z^2 \left(\frac{1}{n_2^2} - \frac{1}{n_1^2} \right) \qquad R = \frac{2\pi^2 m e^4}{c h^3} \tag{87b,c}$$

These expressions are positive, since necessarily $n_1 > n_2$.

For hydrogen ($Z = 1$), the latter formula becomes

$$\tilde{\nu} = R \left(\frac{1}{n_2^2} - \frac{1}{n_1^2} \right) \tag{88}$$

Bohr noted that a formula of Balmer's type is obtained if, in (88), we put $n_2 = 2$ and allow n_1 to take on all values from 3 up. This permitted at once a crucial *quantitative test* of the new theory. When Bohr inserted the best values of his day, $e = 4.7 \times 10^{-10}$, $e/m = 5.31 \times 10^{17}$ with e in electrostatic units, and $h = 6.5 \times 10^{-27}$ (as found from Planck's for-mula for black-body radiation), he found for the coefficient in (88)

$$\frac{2\pi^2 m e^4}{h^3} = 3.1 \times 10^{15}$$

This, then, should be the value (in terms of frequency) of the Rydberg constant R. As calculated from Balmer's spectroscopic formula, on the other hand, the value of R was

$$3.29 \times 10^{15}$$

Bohr considered that "the agreement between the theoretical and observed values is inside the uncertainty due to experimental errors in the constants entering in the expression for the theoretical value."

As the precision of experimental work has increased, the calculated value of R has approached the value inferred from spectroscopic observations until today the agreement is within the estimated experimental error. The theoretical formula appears to rest upon a very sound theoretical basis. For this reason, and because the precision of spectroscopic work greatly exceeds that of all independent methods of inferring the values of the constants m, e, and h, the spectroscopic value of R_∞, as stated in Sec. 75, was accepted as a primary constant subject to no adjustment in the calculations of DuMond and Cohen.[1] What this value furnishes directly is a value of the combination me^4/ch^3.

The theoretical series limit, for a spectral series defined by a fixed value of n_2, as obtained by setting $n_1 = \infty$ in Eq. (88), is

$$\tilde{\nu}_\infty = \frac{RZ^2}{n_2{}^2} \tag{89}$$

It can also be imagined, however, that an electron moving past a hydrogen nucleus along a hyperbolic orbit may drop into one of the allowed closed orbits, emitting all its excess energy in a single quantum. In this case, W_1 would have a *positive* value W and the frequency of the emitted photon would be

$$\tilde{\nu} = \frac{W - W_2}{ch} = \tilde{\nu}_\infty + \frac{W}{ch}$$

Since W can vary continuously from 0 upward, such jumps would give rise to a continuous spectrum extending from $\tilde{\nu}_\infty$ toward shorter wavelengths. Such a continuum is clearly visible in Fig. 33 (Sec. 74).[2]

It should be noted that the emitted spectral frequencies are quite distinct from the *frequency of orbital revolution* of the electron. This latter frequency can be found by solving (77) and (78) in the last section for ω; it is

$$\nu_{\text{orb}} = \frac{\omega}{2\pi} = \frac{4\pi^2 me^4 Z^2}{h^3} \frac{1}{n^3}$$

[1] *Revs. Mod. Phys.*, vol. 25, p. 691, 1953.

[2] The continuum actually overlaps the series slightly in this figure. This may be due to some interference of the atoms with each other; in its higher quantum states, according to Eq. (79), the hydrogen atom must be effectively very large, for example, $400a_0$ or 2×10^{-6} cm for $n = 20$.

For comparison, Eq. (87a) may be written thus:

$$\nu = \frac{4\pi^2 m e^4 Z^2}{h^3} \frac{n_1 + n_2}{2n_1{}^2 n_2{}^2} (n_1 - n_2)$$

It can easily be seen that, since $n_1 > n_2$,

$$\frac{1}{n_1{}^3} < \frac{n_1 + n_2}{2n_1{}^2 n_2{}^2} < \frac{1}{n_2{}^3}$$

Hence, if $n_1 - n_2 = 1$, the frequency ν of the emitted radiation is intermediate between the frequencies of orbital revolution in the initial and final states. Only for very large n, for which the orbital frequencies in successive orbits become indistinguishable, do the emitted and orbital frequencies tend to coincide. Furthermore, putting in succession $n_1 - n_2 = 2, 3, \ldots$, we have an approximation to various harmonic overtones of a fundamental frequency. Thus, quantum jumps in which $\Delta n > 1$ correspond to the overtones in the case of classical vibrations. This is an example of a principle elaborated later by Bohr and known as the "correspondence principle."

83. The Spectrum of Atomic Hydrogen. The energies of the lowest eight states of the hydrogen atom are shown in Table 5-2, expressed in three different units. They are calculated from Eq. (85b) with the observed value of the Rydberg constant R_H inserted in place of the coefficient $2\pi^2 m' e^4 Z^2 / h^2$. It is often convenient to express such energies in wave-number units; the difference of two energies then gives at once the wave number of the corresponding spectral line. If W_e is an energy in ergs, its value $W_{\tilde{\nu}}$ in wave-number units or cm^{-1} is

$$W_{\tilde{\nu}} = \frac{W_e}{ch} \tag{90}$$

TABLE 5-2. ENERGY VALUES OF SOME STATES OF THE HYDROGEN ATOM

State	Energy		
	Wave-number units	Ergs	Electron-volts
$n = 1$	$-109{,}678$	-217.3×10^{-13}	-13.58
2	$-\ 27{,}420$	$-\ 54.3$	$-\ 3.394$
3	$-\ 12{,}186$	$-\ 24.2$	$-\ 1.508$
4	$-\ \ 6{,}855$	$-\ 13.58$	$-\ 0.849$
5	$-\ \ 4{,}387$	$-\ 8.69$	$-\ 0.543$
6	$-\ \ 3{,}047$	$-\ 6.04$	$-\ 0.377$
7	$-\ \ 2{,}238$	$-\ 4.44$	$-\ 0.277$
8	$-\ \ 1{,}714$	$-\ 3.40$	$-\ 0.212$

Another convenient unit is the electron-volt, often called simply a volt. If V_v denotes the energy equivalent to $h\nu$ in electron-volts, or the equivalent volts, then $h\nu = hc/\lambda = ch\tilde{\nu} = eV_v/299.79$ ergs and, inserting $e = 4.803 \times 10^{-10}$, $h = 6.625 \times 10^{-27}$, $c = 2.9979 \times 10^{10}$, we obtain the useful conversion formulas

$$\tilde{\nu} = 8,066 V_v \qquad \lambda_{vac} = \frac{12,398}{V_v} \quad A \qquad\qquad (91a,b)$$

λ_{vac} denoting the corresponding wavelength in vacuum.

In spectroscopic work, however, it is more usual to employ, not the negative energies themselves, but their numerical magnitudes, called *term values* or simply *terms*. The wave number of a spectral line is then obtained by subtracting the term value for the *initial* state from that for the *final* state.

TABLE 5-3. SOME TERM VALUES AND LINES FOR THE HYDROGEN ATOM

λ, A	$\tilde{\nu}$, cm^{-1}	Terms, cm^{-1}	Quantum number n
Lyman series		109,678	1
1,215.7	82,258	27,420	2
1,025.8	97,491	12,186	3
972.5	102,823	6,855	4
949.5	105,291	4,387	5
Balmer series		27,420	2
6,562.8	15,233	12,186	3
4,861.3	20,565	6,855	4
4,340.5	23,032	4,387	5
4,101.7	24,373	3,047	6
Paschen series		12,186	3
18,756	5,331	6,855	4
12,821	7,799	4,387	5
10,939	9,139	3,047	6
10,052	9,948	2,238	7
Brackett series		6,855	4
4.05 μ	2,468	4,387	5
2.63	3,808	3,047	6
2.16	4,617	2,238	7
1.94	5,141	1,714	8

In Table 5-3 are shown the first four lines of each of the best-known series in the spectrum of atomic hydrogen, and the associated term values. Column 4 gives the quantum number for each term. The first term value given in column 3 is in each case the convergence wave number or limit for that series; the wave number $\bar{\nu}$ of each line is obtained by subtracting from the convergence limit the term as given opposite the wave number of the line. The wavelength λ is calculated as $\bar{\nu}^{-1} \times 10^8$ divided by the refractive index of air.

The relations between the energies and the series of lines are better seen from an *energy-level diagram*. In Fig. 41a in Sec. 85 is shown such a diagram, necessarily incomplete, for atomic hydrogen. Each horizontal line represents an energy level, higher energies being plotted above. The line at $n = 1$ represents the normal state of the atom; the line at $n = \infty$ represents the electron at rest at infinity, the atom being just ionized; and above this is the continuum of positive energies for the free electron. Wave numbers are shown on a scale reading downward. Energies measured from the normal state as zero are also shown, expressed in electron-volts. A few of the transitions which give rise to lines are shown in an obvious manner by arrows. The diagram brings out clearly the fact that each series ends on a particular energy level.

84. Ionized Helium. A helium atom which has lost both electrons is a bare nucleus and cannot radiate energy. One which has lost only a single electron, however, resembles a hydrogen atom, except that $Z = 2$ and the nucleus is nearly four times as heavy. The spectrum emitted by such atoms is known as the *spark spectrum* of helium, because it is emitted much more strongly when the helium is excited by a spark than when it is excited by an arc. The *arc spectrum* of helium, emitted by the neutral atom, will be considered later (Sec. 126).

Putting $Z = 2$ in Eq. (87b) we should have for the frequencies of the spectral lines emitted by ionized helium

$$\bar{\nu} = 4R \left(\frac{1}{n_2{}^2} - \frac{1}{n_1{}^2} \right) \tag{92}$$

Thus *ionized helium should emit the same spectrum as hydrogen except that all frequencies are four times as great*, or all wavelengths a quarter as great.

This conclusion from the theory agrees with observation except for a slight numerical discrepancy which becomes significant when measurements of precision are considered. As was explained in Sec. 81, m in Eq. (80), or in formula (87c) for the Rydberg constant, must, strictly speaking, stand for the reduced mass m' of the electron as given by Eq. (82). Hence, the Rydberg constant for a one-electron atom the nucleus of which has a mass M is

$$R = \frac{M}{m + M} R_\infty \qquad R_\infty = \frac{2\pi^2 m e^4}{ch^3} \qquad\qquad (93a,b)$$

Here m stands for the ordinary electronic mass, 0.911×10^{-27} gram.

One use that can be made of these relations is to deduce the ratio of the mass of the electron to the mass of a hydrogen or helium atom from values of R calculated from spectral data. For this purpose it will be convenient to write R_H and R_{He} for R referring to hydrogen and to ionized helium, respectively, and to introduce the masses M_H and M_{He} of the entire neutral atom, so that the two values of the nuclear mass M are, respectively, $M_H - m$ and $M_{He} - 2m$. Then

$$R_H = \frac{M_H - m}{M_H} R_\infty \qquad R_{He} = \frac{M_{He} - 2m}{M_{He} - m} R_\infty$$

Eliminating R_∞, it is readily found that

$$\left[1 - \frac{M_H}{M_{He}} \left(1 - 2\frac{R_{He} - R_H}{R_{He}} \right) \right] \frac{m}{M_H} - \frac{M_H}{M_{He}} \left(\frac{m}{M_H} \right)^2 = \frac{R_{He} - R_H}{R_{He}}$$

This equation is most easily solved by iteration: first drop the small term in $(m/M_H)^2$ and solve for m/M_H, then insert this provisional value in the previously dropped term and solve again for m/M_H. Inserting here, from Sec. 75, $R_H = 109{,}677.58$, $R_{He} = 109{,}722.27$, and the ratio of the ordinary atomic weights

$$\frac{M_H}{M_{He}} = \frac{1.0081}{4.004}$$

we find $M_H/m = 1{,}837.5$. A slightly more accurate value, obtained from a consideration of all relevant data and cited in Sec. 48, is $1{,}837.1$.

Using the value of m/M_H we can calculate R_∞ from the observed value of R_H by means of the formula

$$R_\infty = \left(1 + \frac{m}{M_H} \right) R_H$$

It is in this or an equivalent way that "experimental" values of R_∞ are obtained.

In a similar way, *doubly ionized lithium* is found to emit the hydrogen spectrum with all frequencies multiplied (almost exactly) by 9; *trebly ionized beryllium* emits them increased in the ratio 16; and so on. The first line of the Lyman series for quadruply ionized boron ($Z = 5$) has been found by Edlén at 48.585 A, with a frequency 25.04 times that of the first Lyman line of hydrogen.

85. Energy Levels and Series Relations for Sodium. Energy-level diagrams analogous to that for hydrogen can be constructed for all atoms.

Such a diagram makes very evident a simple explanation in terms of the energy levels for those striking properties of spectral series and of their interrelations which were described above.   As an illustration we may return here to a further brief discussion of the spectrum of neutral sodium.

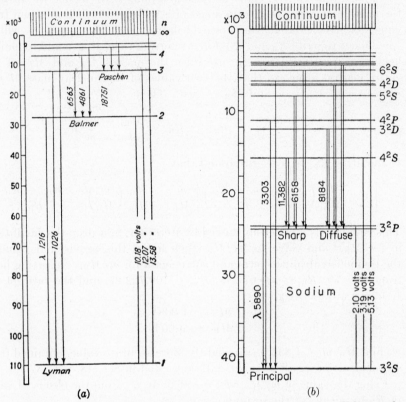

FIG. 41. The lower energy levels of (a) hydrogen and (b) sodium atoms.   Values at the left are in cm⁻¹; a few differences are shown at the right in electron-volts.   The 3^2P doublet separation is greatly exaggerated.   The transitions giving rise to the first three lines of the chief series are shown by arrows.

A partial energy-level diagram for sodium is shown in Fig. 41(b); it contains levels only for those quantum states that occur as the valence electron moves out toward infinity (for a more complete treatment of the sodium spectrum see Secs. 116, 117, and 119).   The levels are labeled on the diagram in spectroscopic notation, but this is immaterial for our present purpose.   Most of the levels are really double, two levels lying very close together, but only one such pair is shown as such on the diagram (and on a much exaggerated scale), the others being represented by a single line each.   (For the explanation of the doubling and of a similar but more minute fine structure of the hydrogen levels, see Secs. 119 and

120.)   The levels labeled S, however, including the normal state, are strictly single.

A brief inspection of the level diagrams in Fig. 41 reveals the following explanation for the properties of the spectral series.   That each series must converge to a finite limit arises from the simple fact that the largest energy difference possible between levels is limited to the energy required to ionize the atom, starting from the lowest state for the series in question. The *principal* series of lines for sodium, including as its first member the ordinary D lines, arises from transitions ending on the normal state, which, as just stated, is single.   The doublet character of the lines of this series is due, therefore, to the doublet nature of the upper level; and, since the spacing of these levels decreases rapidly with increasing energy, the spectral doublets close up as their ordinal number increases.   The *sharp* and the *diffuse* series both end on the doublet level next above the normal state; hence, they have a common convergence limit.   The lines of these series, as observed, usually appear to be doublets of constant frequency difference, this difference being that between the sublevels of the final state; hence, Hartley's law commonly appears to be obeyed by both series.   A further slight splitting of the *diffuse* lines will be discussed later in Sec. 119.   Finally, the basis for the Rydberg-Schuster law is simple and obvious: the difference between the common convergence limit of the sharp and the diffuse series and the limit of the principal series is just the difference between the lowest two energy levels; and this is also equal to the wave number of the first line of the principal series.

The convergence limit of the principal series, corresponding to a jump of the electron from a state of rest at infinity into the normal state, obviously corresponds to an energy that is (1) numerically equal to that of the normal state, when this is measured downward from zero at infinity, and (2) equal to the minimum energy that must be given to the atom to remove an electron from it, i.e., to the *ionization energy* of the neutral atom.   The ionization energy is usually expressed in electron-volts and called the *ionization potential*, representing the potential through which an electron must rise in order to acquire enough energy to ionize the atom by impact.   It is 5.14 volts for sodium, 13.60 volts for a hydrogen atom.

The discussion of spectra in terms of energy levels is thus much simpler than the direct discussion in terms of the lines themselves.   Whatever may happen in the future to our picture of the behavior of the electrons in an atom, energy levels are undoubtedly here to stay.

86. Excitation and Ionization of Atoms by Electrons.   A free atom is ordinarily in its normal state or state of lowest energy; in order to emit radiation, it must somehow be transferred into a state of higher energy. If it loses one or more electrons in the process, it is said to be ionized; if it loses no electrons and so remains electrically neutral, it is said to be merely *excited*.

A convenient way to excite atoms—and a process that accounts for much of the luminosity from vacuum tubes—is to bombard them with electrons; this bombardment is also effective in decomposing molecules into free atoms. In order to excite an atom, the bombarding electron must have kinetic energy at least equal to the energy that must be given to the atom to raise it into a quantum state of higher energy. (A small correction due to the much slower motion of the atom itself is ignored here.) The first experimental indication of this relation was reported by Franck and Hertz in 1914.[1] In the course of a long series of experiments

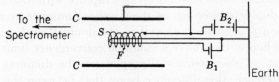

FIG. 42. The apparatus of Foote, Meggers, and Mohler for studying excitation potentials.

on the energy gained by a free electron in passing through a gas under the influence of an electric field, they concluded that electrons with an energy of 4.9 ev or more (but not less) could excite the spectral line at 2,536 A in mercury vapor. The energy lost by an atom in emitting a quantum of such radiation is

$$h\nu = 6.62 \times 10^{-27} \times \frac{3 \times 10^{10}}{2,536 \times 10^{-8}} = 7.83 \times 10^{-12} \text{ erg}$$

whereas 4.9 ev equals $4.9 \times 1.62 \times 10^{-12} = 7.94 \times 10^{-12}$ erg. The energy in electron-volts necessary to raise an atom from its normal state into a given excited state, expressed simply in volts, is called the *excitation potential* for that state.

A detailed study of such phenomena in sodium and potassium vapor was reported by Foote, Meggers, and Mohler[2] in 1922. Their apparatus is shown diagrammatically in Fig. 42. A filament F of tungsten or lime-coated platinum is heated by a battery B_1 to such temperature that it emits electrons. Around the filament is a spiral grid S, which, by means of a battery B_2 or potentiometric source of pd, is maintained at any desired *positive* potential with respect to the filament. Around S and electrically connected thereto is a metal cylinder CC; S and CC are thus at the same potential. Inside CC is the gas or vapor under study, maintained at a suitable pressure. Electrons, emitted by the filament, are

---

[1] J. Franck and G. Hertz, *Verhandl. deut. physik. Ges.*, vol. 16, p. 512, 1914.

[2] Foote, Meggers, and Mohler, *Astrophys. J.*, vol. 55, p. 145, 1922; cf. also Foote and Mohler, "The Origin of Spectra."

accelerated toward the grid S, which is so close to F that with proper regulation of the gas pressure comparatively few atoms of the gas are struck by the electrons in their passage from filament to grid. After leaving the grid, the electrons move in the field-free space between S and CC, in which space, because of the greater distance S to CC, the electrons collide with the gas molecules causing the excitation of the latter, provided the energy of the electrons is sufficiently great.

With sodium vapor inside the cylinder, no luminosity is observed in the vapor until the potential difference between the grid and the filament reaches 2.09 volts. For voltages slightly above this value, the spectrograph shows that the sodium vapor emits the well-known D lines, *and those only*. The mean wavelength of these lines is 5,893 A, corresponding, according to Eq. (91b), to 2.10 volts. Thus the observation can be explained by the assumption that, to cause emission of D-line radiation, the electrons, colliding with the atoms, excite some of them into levels lying 2.10 ev above the normal level, after which the atoms jump back into their normal levels with the emission of a D-line photon.

As the voltage was raised above 2.09 volts, the D lines continued to appear, but no other lines were seen until the voltage exceeded 5.12 volts; then the complete arc spectrum (principal, sharp, diffuse series, etc.) appeared. The reason for the appearance of the arc spectrum only above 5.12 volts becomes clear from an inspection of the energy-level diagram for sodium in Fig. 41(b). An electron with energy of 5.13 volts or more has sufficient energy to excite a neutral sodium atom into any other atomic level; or, it may remove an electron, after which the ionized atom will pick up an electron again and emit quanta of various frequencies as it undergoes transitions into states of lower energy and eventually into its normal state.

The reason for the absence of all lines at electron energies below 2.09 volts is also obvious. The line 11,382 A, for example, requires only $12,398/11,382 = 1.09$ volts; but the initial state for the emission of this line lies 3.19 volts above the normal state and an atom cannot possibly be raised into this level by a single collision with an electron having energy less than 3.19 volts. It is not clear, however, why in these observations *no* lines other than the D lines were seen at voltages a little below the ionization voltage of 5.13 volts. The line 3,303 A, for example, ends on the normal level and requires only 3.75 volts.

In the observations it was further found that the so-called *spark* spectrum of sodium appeared when the electron energy exceeded 35 volts. This spectrum is ascribed to *ionized* atoms in which a *second* electron has been raised to a higher level by another collision with an electron from the filament. The spark spectrum thus arises from transitions between levels belonging to ionized atoms.

87. Absorption and Reemission of Radiation.   *a. Absorption.*   On the classical theory, the characteristic frequencies emitted by an atom should be identical with the natural frequencies of the atom.   Conversely, if light of one of these frequencies falls upon the atom, it should set the atom into resonance, some of the energy being thereby abstracted or "absorbed" from the incident beam.   It follows that the *absorption spectrum* of a gas should be exactly the same as its emission spectrum.

For certain spectral lines this conclusion is substantiated by experiment in the well-known phenomenon of the *reversal* of spectral lines, of which phenomena the most conspicuous are the dark lines in the solar spectrum. The reversal of the *D* lines of sodium is a familiar laboratory or lecture demonstration.   But many of the lines emitted by a gas in a discharge tube are not ordinarily observable in its absorption spectrum.   For example, neon gas is highly transparent to visible light; it does not absorb the red wavelengths whose emission is responsible for the brilliance of neon signs.

The explanation of these facts on the Bohr theory is easily seen.   The process of absorption will be just the reverse of the process of emission; a quantum of radiant energy is absorbed while simultaneously the atom jumps from one quantum state into a state of *higher* energy.   The *possible* frequencies for the lines should, therefore, be the same in absorption as in emission.   But in order to absorb a given line, the atom must already be in the state which is the lower state for that line.   Since the atoms of a monatomic gas under ordinary conditions are in their normal states, they can absorb only those lines which start, in absorption, from the normal state.   For neon, all lines that involve the normal state lie in the ultraviolet.   Sodium vapor shows in absorption only the *principal series* [cf. diagram in Fig. 41(*b*) in Sec. 85].   From the head of this series a *continuous* absorption band extends toward higher frequencies.   This band is obviously caused by processes in which the energy of the incident photon $h\nu$ exceeds the ionization potential, so that the atom becomes ionized with the ejection of an electron at considerable speed.   That is, we have here photoelectric emission from the sodium atoms, the electron being ejected with kinetic energy

$$\tfrac{1}{2}mv^2 = h\nu - eV_0$$

where V_0 is the ionization potential of the atom and e the numerical electronic charge.   The equation is a special case of Einstein's photoelectric equation.

When atoms *in excited states* are present, as in a discharge tube, additional lines may appear in the absorption spectrum.

b. Resonance Radiation and Fluorescence.   The energy acquired by an atom through an absorption process may subsequently be lost in one of several different ways.   An important way is by a radiative transition into a state of lower energy.   The atom may drop back into its normal state, from which it was removed by the process of absorption; in this case the radiation emitted has the same frequency as the radiation originally absorbed.   The net effect of such absorptions and reemissions is a powerful scattering of the incident light in all directions.   To this phenomenon R. W. Wood gave the name *resonance radiation*.   He showed[1] many years ago that a bulb containing sodium vapor at very low pressure would, when irradiated by light from an intense sodium flame, emit the D lines, and those only.   The resonance was very sharp.   An examination of the reemitted D lines showed that they were very narrow, their width corresponding almost exactly to the width predicted from the Doppler effect at the temperature of the sodium vapor.   The width of the lines of the exciting source was much greater, since the temperature of the source was much higher than that of the vapor.   On analyzing the light which had *passed through* the vapor, it was found that there was a narrow absorption line at the centers of the broad D lines.

This experiment of Wood's was in beautiful agreement with the classical theory.   But (the fourth) Lord Rayleigh showed[2] that if sodium vapor is illuminated by the *second* line of the principal series, $\lambda = 3,303$ A, both that line and the D lines were emitted by the vapor.   The emission of the D lines under such circumstances is a case of *fluorescence*, and, like fluorescence in general, is difficult to explain on the classical theory; whereas the explanation by the quantum theory is easy.   The absorption of $\lambda = 3,303$ leaves the atom in the excited state known as $4\ ^2P$ [see Fig. 41(b)].   From this state it cannot pass at once, for a reason described later (Sec. 116), into the $3\ ^2P$ state, which is the initial state for the D lines, but it can jump into a $4\ ^2S$ state, in a transition not shown on the diagram, with the emission of an infrared quantum; and then from this state it can jump into the $3\ ^2P$ state, with the emission of a quantum of $\lambda = 11,404$ or $11,382$, which is the first (doublet) line of the sharp series; and then finally into the normal state.   Thus, the single quantum absorbed from the incident light is eventually reemitted as three fluorescent quanta.   A second but less likely possibility is a jump from $4\ ^2P$ to $3\ ^2D$, and then into $3\ ^2P$ with emission of the first line of the diffuse series.

Excitation by the absorption of quanta is analogous to excitation by electron impact, but with an important difference.   The atom may become excited when colliding with an electron the energy of which *equals or exceeds* that required for the increase in energy level; whereas excitation by absorption takes place only when the energy of the incident

[1] See R. W. Wood, "Physical Optics."

[2] R. J. Strutt, *Proc. Roy. Soc.* (*London*), vol. 98, p. 272, 1916.

quantum is almost *exactly equal* to that required to produce the change of state.

c. Effects of Collisions with Atoms. The atoms of a gas are continually colliding with each other owing to thermal agitation. The result of a collision may be that one of the molecules is raised into an excited quantum state, the necessary energy being derived from the kinetic energy of the colliding molecules. For monatomic molecules, however, a very high temperature is necessary if such excitation is to occur frequently. It may also happen that one of the colliding molecules is already excited and in the collision drops down into a state of lower energy, while the second molecule becomes excited; the combined kinetic energies of the molecules may simultaneously undergo a change. Collisions resulting in excitation of a previously unexcited molecule were called at one time "collisions of the first kind," while collisions in which an excited molecule is returned to its normal state, the energy of excitation appearing as increased kinetic energy of the two molecules, were called "collisions of the second kind."

Such phenomena were well illustrated in experiments[1] on mercury vapor excited to resonance radiation by the absorption of its own line $\lambda = 2,536$ A ($h\nu = 4.9$ volts). If with the mercury vapor is mixed the vapor of thallium, the characteristic lines of the *latter element appear in addition* to the mercury resonance radiation when the mixture is illuminated with the mercury line $\lambda = 2,536$. The mercury resonance radiation is then weaker than when no thallium is present. Pure thallium vapor is not excited to resonance by the mercury line. This is explained by assuming that mercury atoms are first raised to an excited state by absorption of the line $\lambda = 2,536$; some of these excited atoms by collision with thallium atoms then transfer their energy of excitation to the latter, which subsequently radiate their characteristic lines in returning to the normal state. The thallium lines so produced correspond to energy transfers in the thallium atom of *less* than 4.9 volts.

Again, Cario showed that the presence of argon in mercury vapor materially reduces the intensity of the resonance radiation when the mixture is illuminated by the 2,536 line, but in this case no argon radiation is emitted. Yet an examination of the light transmitted through the mixture shows that the presence of the argon caused no diminution in *absorption* of the incident light. This effect is explained by assuming that collisions of the second kind take place between the excited mercury atoms and the argon atoms, the energy of excitation of the former being transformed into kinetic energy of both atoms.

[1] Loria, *Phys. Rev.*, vol. 26, p. 573, 1925; Cario, *Z. Physik*, vol. 10, p. 185, 1922; and Cario and Franck, *Z. Physik*, vol. 17, p. 202, 1923.

d. Ionization Potentials.   As was remarked in Sec. 85, the ionization potential of an atom can also be calculated from the convergence limit of its "principal series," or the series for which the normal state is the final state in the emission of a line. The ionization potential is the equivalent of this convergence limit in volts. Ionization potentials calculated in this way from spectroscopic data agree well with those obtained by electrical methods. Higher ionization potentials can also be defined, the *second* ionization potential representing the energy necessary to remove a *second* electron from the atom, and so on. These higher ionization potentials can be calculated from the convergence limits of other series. Because of the greater precision obtainable, the spectroscopic method of determining ionizing potentials is usually employed.

For example, in the arc spectrum of helium there is a singlet series of lines due to transitions ending on the normal state, with a convergence frequency[1] $\tilde{\nu} = 198{,}298$ cm^{-1}. According to Eq. (91a), this corresponds to a first ionization potential of 24.58 volts. That is to say, it takes energy equal to 24.58 ev to remove one of the two electrons from a helium atom. When this has been done, the ion behaves as a one-electron atom. Equation (92) gives (with $n_1 = \infty$, $n_2 = 1$) as its ionization energy, $4R$,

TABLE 5-4. SOME IONIZATION POTENTIALS IN VOLTS

Element		I	II	III	IV	V	VI
H	1	13.5978					
He	2	24.58	54.41				
Li	3	5.39	75.6	122.4			
Be	4	9.32	18.21	153.8	217.7		
B	5	8.28	25.12	37.93	259.3	340.2	
C	6	11.27	24.38	47.88	64.49	391.7	
N	7	14.55	29.61	47.62	77.4	97.9	
O	8	13.62	35.09	55.12	77.3	114.	138.1
F	9	17.3	34.8	62.4	86.7	113.7	156.4
Ne	10	21.56	41.0	63.4			
Na	11	5.14	47.2	70.7			
Mg	12	7.65	15.03	80.	109.		
Al	13	5.99	18.83	28.45	119.4	153.4	
Si	14	8.15	16.34	33.49	45.14	165.6	
P	15	10.9	19.9	30.2	51.1	65.03	
S	16	10.4	23.4	35.0	47.30	63.	88.1
Cl	17	13.02	23.7	39.9	53.2	67.4	
Ar	18	15.75	27.85	40.75			
K	19	4.34	31.8	47.			

[1] Bacher and Goudsmit, "Atomic Energy States—as Derived from the Analyses of Optical Spectra," p. 220.

where R is the Rydberg constant for helium, or $R = 109,722.27$. Thus $\nu_\infty = 4R$, or $438,889$, and the *second* ionization potential of helium is $438,889/8,066 = 54.41$ volts.

Values of many of the ionization potentials for the lighter elements are given in Table 5-4. Most of them were calculated from data in Bacher and Goudsmit's "Atomic Energy States," the numbers there given for the "absolute value of the lowest state" being divided by 8,066 to obtain values of the ionization potential in volts. First ionization potentials (for the neutral atom) are given under I, second under II, and so on.

88. The Boltzmann Distribution Law. In the last section, one other easy method of exciting spectral emission has not been mentioned. Many elements in gaseous form, especially the vapors of metals, emit line spectra upon being heated; thus sodium vapor heated by a Bunsen flame emits the familiar D lines, whether the vapor is mingled with the flame itself or is enclosed in a tube. In such cases, it is evident that the atoms or molecules are excited by *thermal agitation*.

If the substance is in thermal equilibrium, a simple theoretical formula can be given for the relative numbers of the atoms or molecules that are in each quantum state. It is deduced from statistical mechanics that, in the case of thermal equilibrium, the average number N_i in a quantum state in which the atomic or molecular energy is ϵ_i is

$$N_i = Ce^{-\epsilon_i/kT} \tag{94}$$

where k is Boltzmann's constant (Sec. 66), T is the absolute temperature, and C is a constant of proportionality. If N is the total number of atoms or molecules, we must have

$$N = \sum_i N_i = C \sum_i e^{-\epsilon_i/kT}$$

the sum extending over all possible quantum states. By eliminating C between these two equations we can also write

$$N_i = \frac{Ne^{-\epsilon_i/kT}}{\sum_j e^{-\epsilon_j/kT}} \tag{95}$$

It often happens, however, that a number of quantum states have the same energy, and then it may be more convenient to group these states into a multiple state. Suppose we have formed in this manner all the multiple states that we can, no two multiple states having the same energy. Let these multiple states be numbered off in a single series, and let the energy of multiple state number τ be ϵ_τ and the number of fundamental states composing it w_τ; the number w_τ is called the *statistical weight* of the state. Then by Eq. (94), when thermal equilibrium exists, the number N_i is the same for each of the fundamental states composing a multiple state, so that the number of atoms or molecules in multiple state number τ is just $w_\tau N_i$. Calling this number N_τ, we can write for it, replacing ϵ_i by ϵ_τ,

$$N_\tau = C w_\tau e^{-\epsilon_\tau/kT} \tag{96}$$

These formulas constitute special cases of what is known as the *Boltzmann distribution formula* for quantized systems.

As an example, the sodium D lines result, as we have seen, from transitions between either of two excited levels lying close together and the normal level (cf. Sec. 85). For our purpose we may treat the upper two levels as a single composite level. Then it follows from the more modern theory of wave mechanics, to be described in the next two chapters, that this composite upper level is composed of six fundamental states, so that for it $w = 6$, whereas, for the normal level, $w = 2$. The two levels lie $h\nu = 3.36 \times 10^{-12}$ erg apart. Hence, indicating them by subscripts 1 and 0, respectively, we have for the numbers of atoms in them

$$N_1 = 6C e^{-\epsilon_1/kT} \qquad N_0 = 2C e^{-\epsilon_0/kT}$$

In the case of sodium in a Bunsen flame at 1800°C, this gives

$$\frac{N_1}{N_0} = 3e^{-(\epsilon_1-\epsilon_0)/kT} = 3e^{-3.36\times10^{-12}/2073\times1.38\times10^{-16}} = 2.3 \times 10^{-5}$$

Thus only a very small part of the sodium atoms are excited in this manner at any given time. They suffice, however, to cause a considerable emission of sodium light. With further increase of temperature the higher members of the principal series and members of other series are found to appear.

89. The Extension of Bohr's Theory. In his original paper, Bohr remarked that the orbit of the electron in a hydrogen atom might be an ellipse instead of a circle. A detailed theory of elliptical orbits was developed by Sommerfeld several years later. The geometrical ideas involved still possess a certain interest.[1]

According to the laws governing motion under an inverse-square force, an elliptical orbit will have one of its foci at the nucleus and the energy of the system will depend only on the length of the major axis of the ellipse. The orbit will lie in a fixed plane, so that the motion can be described by means of two coordinates, for which we may take polar coordinates r, θ,

---

[1] For a more complete account see A. Sommerfeld, "Atomic Structure and Spectral Lines," Methuen, London, 1929; also Ruark and Urey, "Atoms, Molecules and Quanta," p. 132.

with the origin at the nucleus. Then, as θ increases through 2π, r increases from its minimum value at one end of the ellipse to a maximum at the other end, after which it decreases again to a minimum. Thus r executes what is called a "libration" during each revolution of the electron. Sommerfeld assumed that the same generalized quantum condition which had been postulated for the harmonic oscillator and the circular orbit, as represented by Eq. (76) in Sec. 80, will hold for r; that is, he assumed that

$$\oint p_r \, dr = n'h$$

where p_r is the momentum in the radial direction, the integral is taken throughout a libration, and n' is a positive integer or 0. For θ, he assumed with Bohr that the angular momentum is an integer k times $h/2\pi$. (In his books Sommerfeld writes n_ϕ or just n for k and sometimes n_r for n'.) Sommerfeld showed then that the energy depends only on the "total" quantum number,

$$n = k + n'$$

and is, in fact, *the same function of n as in Bohr's theory.* Thus up to this point nothing is gained except a greater variety of orbital shapes. As an example, for $n = 3$, we can have the Bohr circle with $k = 3$ and $n' = 0$ or either one of two ellipses with major axis equal to the diameter of the circle, with $k = 2$, $n' = 1$ or $k = 1$, $n' = 2$, respectively.

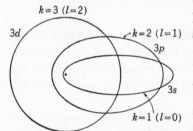

These orbits are shown to scale in Fig. 43, labeled also with wave-mechanical and spectroscopic symbols (Sec. 104).

Sommerfeld then showed, however, that, if allowance is made for the known *variation of electronic mass with speed,* the energy of the elliptical motion is slightly different from that of the circular motion, and in this way he arrived at a splitting, or fine structure, of the levels of one-electron atoms, which appeared

FIG. 43. The Bohr-Sommerfeld orbits for $n = 3$.

to be in quantitative agreement with observation. Sommerfeld's theory, however, included no consideration of the effects of electron spin.

In the meantime, Bohr and others were endeavoring to extend the theory to atoms containing more than one electron. Little quantitative success was achieved in this direction. In particular, no plausible arrangement of orbits could be devised for the two electrons of helium which would give the correct value for the first ionization potential (24.6 volts). In a broader way, Bohr endeavored to understand the known variation of chemical and physical properties from atom to atom through the periodic table, but without great success.   The truth is that two principles essential for the understanding of complex atoms were at that time unknown—the Pauli exclusion principle and the phenomenon of electron spin.   Accordingly, we shall follow the old quantum theory no further and shall devote the next chapter to a description of the modern theory of wave mechanics.

CHAPTER 6

WAVE MECHANICS

One must be prepared to approach the subject of this chapter philosophically, prepared to accept conclusions which are, at first thought, seemingly at variance with our senses and with a belief that has persisted almost unquestioned from the time of the Greeks, viz., that matter is made up of particles. We have seen in Chap. 3 that light possesses both undulatory and corpuscular characteristics. But even so, we might say, light differs from matter; whereas we can determine the nature of light only by indirect observation, matter we can *see*. We observe directly that a handful of sand *is* made up of real particles. In ordinary experience they certainly do *not* exhibit wavelike characteristics. The particles of sand which we see so clearly are, however, made up of molecules or atoms, and these of electrons and protons and neutrons, *none of which we can see directly any more than we can see light waves or photons*. It is with these *so-called* particles, evidence concerning which is almost as indirect as with photons, that the wave theory of matter is primarily concerned.

We shall attempt in this chapter to give merely a brief introduction to this most important subject. Our purpose will be to show how the concept of matter waves can be developed more or less naturally from the previous concepts of both classical and quantum physics and to summarize the pertinent experimental evidence. Certain features and results of the new mathematical theory known as *wave mechanics* will also be described, but no complete presentation of mathematical details will be attempted, as this would require mathematical tools and techniques much beyond the scope of this book.

90. Matter Waves. *a. Matter and Energy.* With the discovery of the law of the conservation of energy toward the middle of the nineteenth century, it became accepted by physicists that the physical universe is made up of two great entities, viz., matter and energy, each of which is "conserved." These two great conservation laws provided much of the foundation upon which classical physics was built. By 1900, the corpuscular nature of matter had become firmly established; likewise the undulatory nature of light. By 1910, furthermore, Planck's quantum theory and the Einstein photoelectric equation together with various lines of experimental evidence had made it clear that, impossible as it then seemed, physicists would have to accept the hypothesis that light itself possesses corpuscular characteristics.   By 1920 the dual nature of radiant energy was generally recognized, although not understood, and, with the gradual accumulation of experience, physicists had almost become accustomed (perhaps "resigned" would be more nearly correct!) to using either the corpuscular or the undulatory theory of light, according to the experimental phenomena in hand.

During all this time, there was no suggestion that *matter* was anything but corpuscular.   But, in 1924, Louis de Broglie[1] made the very bold suggestion that particles of matter, and in particular electrons, might possess certain undulatory characteristics, so that they, too, might exhibit a dual nature.   He suggested also a way in which the undulatory characteristics of electrons might perhaps furnish a new basis for the quantum theory.   He did not develop his ideas into an exact theory, however. His way of thinking was rather akin to that of the ancient Greeks.   The reasoning used might almost be paraphrased as follows: "(1) Nature loves symmetry.   (2) Therefore the two great entities, matter and energy, must be mutually symmetrical.   (3) If (radiant) energy is undulatory and/or corpuscular (?), therefore matter must be corpuscular and/or undulatory (?)."

Had nothing further happened, de Broglie's speculations would doubtless soon have been forgotten.   Reasoning of this sort, in the mind of a genius, may point the way to an advance, but, before definite scientific progress can be achieved, the new ideas must be precisely formulated and compared with experiment.   The importance of doing this was overlooked by the ancient Greeks.   De Broglie's speculation set a German, E. Schrödinger, to thinking; and he discovered how to develop a precise mathematical theory.[2]   With additions by Born, Heisenberg, Dirac, and others, this theory has become the highly successful quantum mechanics of the present day.   In what follows, we shall endeavor to arrive at the basic assumptions of Schrödinger's theory by developing de Broglie's ideas in a natural and logical manner.

b. *Matter Waves.*   In his first paper, de Broglie is concerned primarily with developing a theory of light in terms of "light quanta," or photons. If the energy of the light is concentrated in photons, how are the phenomena of interference to be understood?   There must be waves *of some sort* associated with the photons, in order to account for the observed interference effects.   We can no longer suppose that the energy is spread out

[1] De Broglie, *Phil. Mag.*, vol. 47, p. 446, 1924; *Ann. phys.*, vol. 3, p. 22, 1925.

[2] Schrödinger, *Ann. Physik*, vol. 79, pp. 361, 489, 734; vol. 80, p. 437; vol. 81, p. 109, 1926.

over these waves, as in classical theory; nevertheless, the waves must somehow determine where, in an interference pattern, the photons can produce effects by being absorbed. The details of interference patterns depend largely upon the phase relations of the waves; hence, de Broglie called the latter *phase waves*. He assumed their frequency ν to be such that the energy in a photon equals $h\nu$.

Now, a material particle carries energy; and "it would seem that the basic idea of the quantum theory is the impossibility of imagining an isolated quantity of energy without associating with it a certain frequency."[1] Material particles ought, therefore, like photons, to be accompanied by phase waves of some sort; and these waves ought, under suitable circumstances, to give rise to interference effects. Furthermore, the waves associated with a particle moving at speed v should have a frequency equal to the energy of the particle divided by h.

Regarding the energy, however, there is a divergence between the assumptions of de Broglie and of Schrödinger. De Broglie includes in the energy the rest energy, m_0c^2, the existence of which is suggested by the theory of relativity (Sec. 39). Schrödinger, on the other hand, prefers to construct first a nonrelativistic theory. He assumes the mass of the particle to be constant and equates just the ordinary energy, kinetic plus potential, to $h\nu$. In this respect we shall follow Schrödinger, reserving comment on the relativistic form of the theory, which must be used for high-speed particles, to a later section (Sec. 105). We shall assume, therefore, that any material particle of mass m moving at speed v has associated with it waves of frequency ν given by the relation

$$h\nu = \tfrac{1}{2}mv^2 + V \tag{97}$$

where h is Planck's constant, m is the mass of the particle, and V is its potential energy, due to electric fields or to other causes.

The physical nature of these waves was left indefinite by de Broglie. We cannot go to the extreme of supposing that a material particle *is* just a group of waves; for then its mass and energy, and also its charge if it has a charge, would of necessity be spread out over these waves and would, in consequence, soon become scattered widely in space, contrary to the observed facts. It is of the nature of waves to diverge toward all sides. We should not be disturbed, however, by the impossibility of visualizing the waves. We should remember our experience in optics. Using classical theory, it was easy to picture light as wave motion; but, if we retain this concept, it is very difficult to picture a beam of light as a moving stream of photons. Similarly, as long as we retain the particle concept of an electron or proton, we cannot hope to form a concrete

[1] Translated from *Ann. phys.*, vol. 3, p. 32, 1925.

picture of the accompanying waves.   Perhaps, even, they are only mathematical waves, so to speak, a device that we employ for the purpose of
making calculations and predicting the results of observation.   In adopt-
ing this standpoint, we are doing only what has been done, in various
ways, many times previously in physical science.   Strictly speaking, we
have no very exact knowledge of the fundamental nature of a magnetic
field, and yet we do not hesitate to use the symbol H with all due familiarity.

91. Mechanics as Geometrical Optics of the Waves.   If waves are
associated with all material particles and play a part in determining their
motion, then there should be a parallelism between the laws of mechanics
and the laws of wave motion.   For the particles certainly obey the laws
of mechanics, at least in some cases.   Now it was pointed out long ago
by Hamilton that there does exist a close parallelism between the laws of
mechanics and the laws of ordinary *geometrical optics*.   De Broglie suggests, accordingly, that the familiar laws of particle mechanics may
represent an approximation which is valid under such circumstances that
the laws of geometrical optics hold for the matter waves.

One of the fundamental laws of ordinary geometrical optics is that,
in a homogeneous medium, light travels in straight lines or rays.   This
assumption is very nearly correct as long as the lateral dimensions of the
beam are large compared with the wavelength of the light.   Under these
conditions one might say that the "particle" characteristics of light
appear to predominate, although we now know that the rectilinear propagation of light is entirely consistent with the wave theory.   When, however, the cross section of the beam is of the same order of magnitude as
the wavelength of the light, rectilinear propagation no longer holds,
diffraction phenomena are observed, and undulatory characteristics of
light predominate.   If we carry the similarity over to mechanics, might
we not expect that, for very small particles of matter, the ordinary laws
of mechanics—found by Newton to be applicable to the phenomena
of "macromechanics"—would fail, and, by analogy with light, we
should find that matter shows undulatory properties in the realm of
"micromechanics"?

If we assume that the phenomena of ordinary mechanics constitute
those of geometrical optics for matter waves, then, as de Broglie showed,
we can find out a great deal about the properties that these waves must
have in order that, under suitable conditions, the laws of mechanics may
hold.   Geometrical optics may be said to be based upon two laws, those
of reflection and of refraction.   The law of reflection as applied to matter
waves presents no difficulty, for it is essentially the same as the law
governing the rebound of an elastic body from a hard wall.   Refraction
of the waves, on the other hand, obviously corresponds to the deflection

of a particle by the action of forces.   Let us study this latter phenomenon further.

92. Refraction of Matter Waves.

To take a mechanical phenomenon which imitates a simple case of refraction in geometrical optics, let a pencil of electrons from a suitable gun G (Fig. 44) enter through orifice a an enclosed metal box A, the potential of which relative to the filament of the gun is V.   Let these electrons emerge from A through orifice b and enter through c another box B, which is maintained at a potential $V + \Delta V$.   The electric field between the two boxes will change the component of velocity of the electrons perpendicular to the adjacent surfaces, and the electrons will therefore enter B with a change in their direction of motion.   Let v_A and v_B (Fig. 44) be the velocities of the electrons in

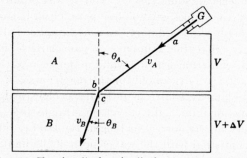

FIG. 44. Showing "refraction" of a pencil of electrons.

A and B, respectively, and θ_A, θ_B the angles between these directions and the normal to the box faces at b and c.   Since the electric field does not change the component of velocity in the lateral direction, we may write

$$v_A \sin \theta_A = v_B \sin \theta_B \qquad \frac{\sin \theta_A}{\sin \theta_B} = \frac{v_B}{v_A}$$

Now if we were dealing with light waves undergoing refraction, or any other kind of waves, the relation would be

$$\frac{\sin \theta_A}{\sin \theta_B} = \mu = \frac{u_A}{u_B}$$

where μ is the relative refractive index of the two media and u_A, u_B are the corresponding speeds of wave propagation.   Comparison of the last two equations gives the result $u_A/u_B = v_B/v_A$.   We may conclude that, if matter waves follow the electron along its path, *the wave speed u must be inversely proportional to the speed v of the electron*, or

$$u = \frac{b}{v} \qquad\qquad\qquad (98)$$

where b is a constant during the motion that remains to be discovered. Since, if E is the total energy of the electron and U its potential energy (here $-eV$), we have $\frac{1}{2}mv^2 = E - U$, and since for matter waves we assume that $E = h\nu$, we can also write (98) in the form

$$ u = b \left[\frac{m}{2(E - U)} \right]^{\frac{1}{2}} = b \left[\frac{m}{2(h\nu - U)} \right]^{\frac{1}{2}} \tag{99} $$

Here b may be different for different values of E or ν.

The same equation must hold for matter waves accompanying any kind of particle, although perhaps with a different value of b. It is evident that the wave speed u will vary along the path whenever U varies. Furthermore, u will vary with the frequency ν, so that the waves will exhibit the phenomenon of dispersion, even in free space where $U = 0$.

Parenthetically, it should be remarked, to avoid misunderstanding, that the well-known "electron microscope" does not depend for its operation upon such wave properties of the electrons. In this microscope the electrons move essentially according to classical mechanics, although their motion is sometimes treated in terms of the equivalent refractive index described above. The only connection that matter waves have with the electron microscope is that their wavelength will ultimately set a limit to the possible resolving power that can be attained, just as the resolving power of ordinary microscopes is limited by the finite wavelength of light. The wavelength of the electron waves, however, we shall presently find to be so small that the resolving power of existing electron microscopes is limited by other factors.

93. The de Broglie Wavelength. The *wavelength* to be expected for matter waves can be discovered by developing another suggestion—likewise due to de Broglie. It follows from Eq. (98) that, in general, an individual wave cannot stay with the particle permanently, since u and v will usually differ. It is well known, however, that whenever the wave velocity (or phase velocity) varies with frequency, as it does here, a *finite group* of waves moves with a velocity different from the phase velocity. This phenomenon is easily observed on water. Close inspection of a group of waves advancing over a water surface will show that the individual waves advance twice as fast as does the group as a whole; new waves continually arise at the rear of the group, pass through it, and die out at the front. Let us assume, therefore, with de Broglie, that the *group velocity* of matter waves is equal to the *particle velocity*, so that a group of them can accompany the particle in its motion.

It is readily shown[1] that a finite group of waves having almost the form

---

[1] See, for example, R. W. Wood, "Physical Optics"; or R. A. Houstoun, "Treatise on Light."

of sine waves with wavelength λ advances with a group velocity u' of magnitude

$$u' = u - \lambda \frac{\partial u}{\partial \lambda} = -\lambda^2 \frac{\partial}{\partial \lambda} \frac{u}{\lambda} = -\lambda^2 \frac{\partial \nu}{\partial \lambda}$$

where $\nu = u/\lambda$ and represents the wave frequency. Here a partial derivative is written to indicate that u and ν may vary with other factors than λ (e.g., the refractive index may not be uniform). Our assumption as regards matter waves requires, therefore, that for them

$$-\lambda^2 \frac{\partial \nu}{\partial \lambda} = v$$

But, differentiating Eq. (97) with V held constant,

$$h \frac{\partial \nu}{\partial \lambda} = mv \frac{\partial \nu}{\partial \lambda}$$

Eliminating $\partial \nu / \partial \lambda$,

$$\frac{\partial v}{\partial \lambda} = -\frac{h}{m} \frac{1}{\lambda^2}$$

and, integrating,

$$v = \frac{h}{m} \frac{1}{\lambda} + C$$

The value of C cannot be uniquely determined. Making the simplest assumption, that $C = 0$, we find

$$\lambda = \frac{h}{mv} = \frac{h}{p} \tag{100}$$

where $p = mv$, the momentum of the particle. Then

$$b = uv = \nu \lambda v = \frac{h\nu}{m}$$

Wavelengths given by Eq. (100) are known as *de Broglie wavelengths.* It may be remarked that the equation holds for photons as well as for material particles; for the momentum of a photon is $h\nu/c = h/\lambda$. Equation (100) combines corpuscular and undulatory concepts in a very intimate way; for λ has a clean-cut meaning only in connection with a *wave* theory, and p, the momentum, is most naturally associated with a moving *particle*.

We can now compute the wavelengths to be expected for electron waves, atom waves, or molecule waves. For an electron moving at a velocity much below that of light with kinetic energy equal to V ev, we have

$$\tfrac{1}{2}mv^2 = \frac{eV}{300} \qquad p = mv = \sqrt{\frac{2meV}{300}}$$

e being the numerical electronic charge in electrostatic units.   Hence by (100) its wavelength is[1]

$$\lambda_e = h \sqrt{\frac{150}{meV}} = \frac{12.27}{\sqrt{V}} \times 10^{-8} \text{ cm} = \frac{12.27}{\sqrt{V}} \text{ A} \qquad (101)$$

if we introduce $m = 0.9108 \times 10^{-27}$ gram, $e = 4.803 \times 10^{-10}$ esu, $h = 6.625 \times 10^{-27}$ erg sec.   For 100-volt electrons, $\lambda_e = 1.23$ A; for 10,000-volt electrons, $\lambda_e = 0.123$ A.   Wavelengths can be calculated in a similar way for molecules or, for that matter, even for large masses such as billiard balls.   The larger the mass, the shorter is the wavelength at given speed.

It would be logical now, following the historical order, to describe at once the complete mathematical theory of matter waves, as worked out by Schrödinger.   All that we need, however, for a discussion of experiments on the diffraction and interference of these waves is their wave-

---

[1] If V exceeds a few thousand volts, it is necessary to take account of the variation of mass with velocity.   Using the relativistic equation for kinetic energy, Eq. (10) in Sec. 38, we have

$$\frac{eV}{300} = m_0 c^2 \left[\left(1 - \frac{v^2}{c^2} \right)^{-\frac{1}{2}} - 1 \right]$$

c being the speed of light.   From this equation, if we write

$$\frac{eV}{300 m_0 c^2} = \rho$$

we find

$$\left(1 - \frac{v^2}{c^2} \right)^{-\frac{1}{2}} = 1 + \rho \qquad v = c \sqrt{1 - (1 + \rho)^{-2}}.$$

Substituting these values in the relativistic equation for momentum, Eq. (9) in Sec. 37, we have for the momentum

$$p = \frac{m_0 v}{(1 - v^2/c^2)^{\frac{1}{2}}} = m_0 c \sqrt{(1 + \rho)^2 - 1} = m_0 c \sqrt{\rho(2 + \rho)}$$

Hence, by (100), which is readily shown to hold in the relativistic case also, after replacing a factor ρ by its value in terms of eV,

$$\lambda_e = h \sqrt{\frac{150}{m_0 eV}} \left(1 + \frac{1}{2} \rho \right)^{-\frac{1}{2}}$$

Here ρ represents the ratio of the electron's kinetic energy to its relativistic rest energy $m_0 c^2$, and the parentheses represent the effect of the variation in mass.   For $\rho \ll 2$, that is, $V \ll 10^6$ volts, we can write

$$\lambda_e = h \sqrt{\frac{150}{m_0 eV}} \left(1 - \frac{\rho}{4} + \frac{3}{32} \rho^2 + \cdots \right)$$

The correction to formula (101) is about 2.5 per cent for 50,000-volt electrons and about 8.5 per cent for 200,000-volt electrons.   For $\rho \gg 2$, that is, $V \gg 10^6$, we can use the expansion in powers of $1/\rho$:

$$\lambda_e = \frac{300 ch}{eV} \left(1 - \frac{1}{\rho} + \frac{3}{2} \frac{1}{\rho^2} + \cdots \right)$$

length. It may relieve the tedium of so much abstract discussion if we describe next the experiments which have shown that electrons and even molecules actually do possess certain wave properties.

94. Experiments on Electron Waves. *a. Reflection from a Crystal.* The first experiments on electron diffraction were reported[1] by Davisson and Germer 3 years after de Broglie's first paper appeared. They were studying the reflection of electrons from a nickel target and accidentally subjected a target to such heat treatment that it was transformed into a group of large crystals. Anomalies then appeared in the reflection from it. Following up this lead, they prepared a target consisting of a single crystal of nickel and bombarded its surface at normal incidence by a narrow pencil of low-voltage electrons; by means of a suitable "collector"

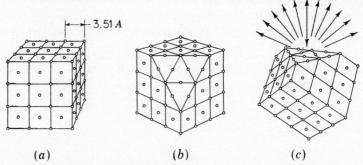

$$(a) \qquad\qquad (b) \qquad\qquad (c)$$

FIG. 45. (a) A nickel crystal, showing face-centered cubic structure. (b) Same, with a face cut at right angles to a diagonal. (c) An incident beam of electrons is scattered in all backward directions.

of small aperture, they studied the distribution in angle of the electrons reflected from the crystal. In this reflected beam, they found striking maxima and minima, which they were able to explain in terms of diffraction of the electron waves.

The diffraction of such waves by a crystal is very similar to the diffraction of x-rays, which has been studied extensively, and is described at length in a later chapter (cf. Sec. 150). Crystallographic studies by means of x-rays show that the nickel crystal is of the "face-centered cubic" type, as shown in Fig. 45,[2] i.e., the crystal can be imagined to be constructed of cubical unit cells each having an atom at each corner and one in the center of each face, with none inside the cube. The atoms are indicated by circles in the figure, certain ones being joined by lines in order to outline the unit cells. The length a_0 of the edge of the unit cube is 3.51 A. Figure 45(b) shows a face cut on the crystal at right angles to

---

[1] Davisson and Germer, *Phys. Rev.*, vol. 30, p. 705, 1927; *Proc. Natl. Acad. Sci.*, vol. 14, pp. 317, 619, 1928.

[2] This figure and Fig. 46 are used by permission of Dr. Davisson.

one of the diagonals of the cube. In Fig. 45(c) the direction of the incident electrons is shown by the heavy arrow. The lighter arrows show, schematically, that these electrons are reflected in all (backward) directions.

Considering only the surface layer of atoms in the triangular face of Fig. 45(c), it is readily seen that these atoms are arranged in rows parallel to one side of the triangle, and it is easily shown that the distance d between these rows has the value $d = 2.15$ A. Now it is fairly obvious that we may regard these rows of atoms as equivalent to the lines of a plane grating of grating space d. Radiation of wavelength λ incident normally on such a grating, the plane of incidence being taken normal to one side of the triangle, should be diffracted, as is light from a reflection grating, according to the well-known law

$$n\lambda = d \sin \theta \tag{102}$$

where θ is the angle between the normally incident beam and the diffracted beam and n is the order of diffraction (Sec. 150). It will be observed from Fig. 45 that the crystal is in reality equivalent to a series of such plane gratings, piled one above the other. Radiation penetrating to and diffracted backward from any one of these underlying layers will be combined with that diffracted from other layers, with the result that a diffracted beam will be observed at the angle θ unless the beams from the several layers happen completely to destroy each other.

In the apparatus used by Davisson and Germer, the "electron gun" consists of a heated filament emitting electrons, an accelerating field to give the electrons any desired velocity, and a series of collimating apertures to produce a (nearly) unidirectional beam. This monovelocity beam of electrons strikes the surface of the crystal at normal incidence, and the electrons are reflected, or scattered, in all directions. A collector for measuring the reflected electrons is so arranged that it can be adjusted to any angular position with respect to the crystal. The collector has two walls insulated from each other, between which a retarding potential is applied so that only the fastest electrons—those possessing nearly the incident velocity—may enter the inner chamber and be measured by the galvanometer. The crystal may be turned about an axis parallel to the axis of the incident beam, and thus any azimuth of the crystal may be presented to the plane defined by the incident beam and the beam entering the collector.

If a beam of low-voltage electrons is incident on the crystal, turned at any arbitrary azimuth, and the distribution of the scattered beam is measured as a function of the colatitude—the angle between the incident beam and the beam entering the collector—a curve similar to that in Fig. 46(a) is obtained, which refers to incident 36-volt electrons. If now the crystal is turned to the A azimuth, the distribution curve for 40-volt electrons [Fig. 46(b)] shows a slight "hump" at about colatitude 60°. With increasing voltage this hump moves upward and develops into a spur which becomes most prominent at 54 volts [Fig. 46(e)], at which voltage the colatitude of the spur is 50°. At higher voltages the spur gradually disappears.

The spur in its most prominent state of development offers convincing evidence for the existence of electron waves. From Eq. (101) the de Broglie

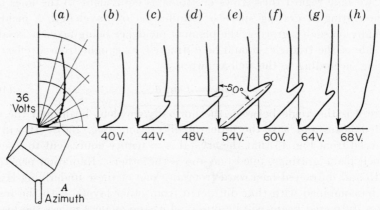

FIG. 46. The development of the diffraction beam in the A azimuth, showing maximum length of "spur" for 54-volt electrons, at colatitude 50°.

wavelength of 54-volt electrons should be $\lambda_e = 12.27/\sqrt{54} = 1.67$ A. From Eq. (102) we find as the observed wavelength

$$\lambda_e = d \sin \theta = 2.15 \sin 50° = 1.65 \text{ A}$$

The two values of λ_e are in excellent agreement.

A spur was also found at 55° colatitude with 181-volt electrons. This was interpreted as a second-order beam. For 181-volt electrons, $\lambda_e = 0.91$ A, whereas second-order diffraction gives

$$2\lambda_e = 2.15 \sin 55° \qquad \lambda_e = 0.88 \text{ A}$$

Over 20 such beams were reported, in three different azimuths. With improved apparatus, the agreement between observed and de Broglie values of wavelength was better than 1 per cent.

b. Transmission through a Crystal. Electrons, if given sufficient energy, are known to pass readily through thin films of matter such as metal foil or thin mica. If an electron beam has wave properties, then in its passage through matter we should observe some or all of the phenomena characteristic of the similar passage of x-rays.

Soon after the discovery of electron waves, Kikuchi[1] succeeded in obtaining electron diffraction patterns by passing a pencil of electrons through a thin mica crystal. Figure 47 shows the pattern obtained by passing 68,000-volt electrons through mica of the order of 10^{-5} cm thick. These observations are the exact analog of the first experiments on the diffraction of x-rays by Friedrich, Knipping, and Laue (Sec. 150).

Studies of metal foils with x-rays show that with appropriate treatment such foils are composed of polycrystalline material with a random orientation of crystal axes. Crystallographically, such foils are similar

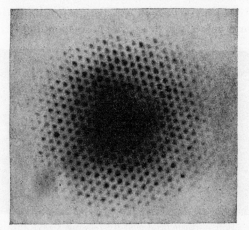

FIG. 47. Diffraction of 68,000-volt electrons by a thin sheet of mica. (*After Kikuchi, Japan. J. Phys., vol. 5, p. 83, 1928.*)

to crystalline powders. If in the Friedrich, Knipping, and Laue experiment with x-rays a powder or a foil is substituted for the single crystal, the observed diffraction pattern will consist of a series of concentric rings instead of spots. Such a pattern, produced by passing a pencil of x-rays through gold, is shown in Fig. 48(a). In Fig. 48(b) is shown the diffraction pattern obtained by passing 30,000-volt electrons through a film of gold; whereas Fig. 48(c) shows the pattern for 48,000-volt electrons passing through a film of silver. The similarity between the effects of x-rays and of electrons is striking.

Measurements of electron wavelengths have now attained such a degree of precision that they are regarded as a valuable source of information on the values of the fundamental constants.[2] If the speed v of the electrons is measured by a kinematical device, observations of λ or of h/mv furnish values of h/m, whereas, if the speed is calculated from an accel-

[1] *Japan. J. Phys.*, vol. 5, p. 83, 1928.

[2] DuMond and Cohen, *Revs. Mod. Phys.*, vol. 25, p. 691, 1953.

erating voltage V, so that $mv^2/2 = eV$, observations of λ are best regarded as furnishing values of $h/\sqrt{em}$.

95. Diffraction of Molecule Waves. Even *molecules* should exhibit wave properties under suitable conditions, according to the new theory. This, too, has been verified by experiment. A molecular beam is easily formed by allowing molecules of a gas to stream out of an enclosure through a small hole or slit into an evacuated chamber. Often the enclosure is heated, in order to vaporize the substance to be studied; it is then called an "oven." Two difficulties have to be overcome, however, which do not arise in working with electrons. The molecules issue with a maxwellian distribution of velocities, whereas for diffraction experiments a beam of uniform velocity is desirable, corresponding to monochromatic

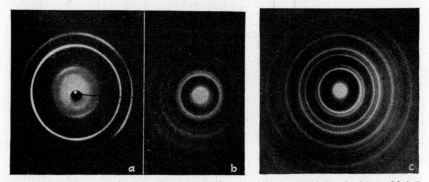

FIG. 48. (*a*) Diffraction pattern produced by passing x-rays through thin gold foil. (*Kindness of Dr. I. Fankuchen.*)   (*b*) Diffraction pattern produced by passing a pencil of 30,000-volt electrons through gold foil.   (*From Thomson, "Wave Mechanics of Free Electrons," Fig.* 19*b*.)   (*c*) Same for 48,000-volt electrons and a silver foil 500 A thick. (*Courtesy of Dr. L. H. Germer, Bell Telephone Laboratories, Inc.*)

waves. Then, too, neutral molecules are very much harder to detect than are charged particles.

Especially interesting is an experiment[1] performed by Estermann, Frisch, and Stern. They managed to select a beam of helium molecules or atoms having fairly uniform velocities by passing the beam through narrow slits in two parallel circular disks placed 3 cm apart, rigidly connected together and rotated about their common axis. The slits in the disks were adjusted so as to be opposite each other. An atom, after passing through a slit in the first disk, would arrive at the second disk too late to pass through the corresponding slit in that disk; but, if its velocity were just right, it would be in time to pass through the *next following slit*. Atoms moving faster or more slowly would arrive too soon or too late and would be stopped by the disk. After leaving the second disk, the

[1] Estermann, Frisch. and Stern. *Z. Physik*, vol. 73, p. 348, 1931.

beam fell upon the surface of a lithium fluoride crystal, by which it was reflected or diffracted.   To measure the intensity of the beam diffracted in a given direction, the helium atoms were allowed to pass through a small hole into a chamber where they accumulated until a certain pressure of helium was reached (of the order of 10^{-6} cm Hg).   This pressure was measured by the cooling effect of the helium on an electrically heated metal strip, owing to conduction of heat through the helium; the electric resistance of the strip was measured with a Wheatstone bridge as an indication of its temperature.

A strong diffracted beam of helium atoms was observed in addition to the regularly reflected beam.   In the most precise measurement, the maximum in the diffracted beam was found at 19.45°, corresponding to a wavelength of $\lambda = 0.600 \times 10^{-8}$ cm as calculated from the usual formula for diffraction by a crystal.   From the dimensions and rate of rotation of the disk, the velocity of the helium atoms was calculated to be 1.635×10^5 cm per sec; the corresponding de Broglie wavelength is, by Eq. (100),

$$\lambda = \frac{h}{mv} = \frac{hN_0}{Mv} = \frac{6.61 \times 10^{-27} \times 6.02 \times 10^{23}}{4.00 \times 1.635 \times 10^5} = 0.609 \times 10^{-8} \text{ cm}$$

(h = Planck's constant, N_0 = Avogadro's number, M = molecular weight.)   The agreement is within 1.5 per cent.   This result is particularly interesting, not only because it refers to an atom, but also because the velocity was measured in simple mechanical fashion instead of in some indirect manner.

96. The Schrödinger Wave Equation.   We shall return now to the discussion of the theory of matter waves.   In Secs. 90 and 91, we have described the line of thought which led de Broglie to the conception of such waves.   In his first paper, he managed to apply these ideas to the motion of an electron in the field of a nucleus and actually arrived at Bohr's formula for the energies of the quantum states.   In order to obtain discrete states, he replaced Bohr's quantum condition by the requirement that the orbit must contain an integral number of wavelengths of the waves, so that "resonance" may occur.   This is not a very satisfactory statement of the condition, however, because in such cases the wavelength is so large relative to the scale of the motion that diffraction effects would be enormous.   Schrödinger, refining de Broglie's idea, suggested that each quantum state represents a system of *standing waves*, or a *normal mode* of harmonic vibration, somewhat like the vibration of a violin string when sounding its fundamental or one of its overtones.

In order to find out what the normal modes of oscillation would be for the matter waves accompanying an electron, we require a more complete statement of the law governing their motion.   Now the usual basis of the mathematical theory of wave motion is furnished by a *differential equation*. Thus, for a violin string vibrating in a fixed plane, we have the equation, derived from the laws of mechanics,

$$\frac{\partial^2 \eta}{\partial t^2} = g^2 \frac{\partial^2 \eta}{\partial x^2}$$

in which η is the displacement of any point of the string at a time t, x is the coordinate of this point measured from one end of the string, and g is a constant depending on the tension in the string and its mass per unit length. In addition to this differential equation, we have also the *boundary condition* that $\eta = 0$ at all times at each end of the string.

We cannot follow an analogous method in arriving at the differential equation for the matter waves; for we know nothing of any medium to convey them. The best we can do is to try to guess a mathematical wave equation that will be in harmony with those properties which we have found the waves to have, and then to test our guess further by means of comparison between observations and other results deduced from this wave equation. Limitations of space and of the mathematical tools required for this book make it impossible for us to attempt here any extensive treatment of wave mechanics.[1] It may be worth while, however, to see how the properties that we have assigned to matter waves lead rather naturally to Schrödinger's differential equation for them; the application of the equation to a few important problems will then be considered.

For plane matter waves of frequency ν and wavelength λ moving toward $+x$, we might expect to be able to write

$$\Psi = A \sin 2\pi \left(\nu t - \frac{x}{\lambda} \right)$$

Ψ being the quantity, whatever it is, that oscillates in the waves. Since $\nu = W/h$ and, according to Eq. (101), $\lambda = h/p$ where W and p are, respectively, the total energy and the momentum of the associated particle, we can also write the last equation in the form

$$\Psi = A \sin \frac{2\pi}{h} (Wt - px) \tag{103}$$

in which the constants are connected by the relation

$$W = \frac{p^2}{2m} + V \tag{104}$$

[1] For a simple introduction, see S. Dushman, "Elements of Quantum Mechanics," 1938.

In this equation V is the potential energy of the particle, and $p^2/2m$ is its kinetic energy. Now, whatever the correct differential equation for Ψ may be, it should be such that any allowable function Ψ expressed in the form of Eq. (103) is a solution of it regardless of the value of W or p. Let us endeavor, therefore, to find by trial a differential equation such that, when the expression just given for Ψ is substituted in it, W and p cancel out in consequence of the known relationship expressed in Eq. (104).

A few derivatives of Ψ as obtained from Eq. (103) are

$$\frac{\partial \Psi}{\partial t} = \frac{2\pi}{h} WA \cos \frac{2\pi}{h} (Wt - px) \qquad \frac{\partial \Psi}{\partial x} = - \frac{2\pi}{h} pA \cos \frac{2\pi}{h} (Wt - px)$$

$$\frac{\partial^2 \Psi}{\partial t^2} = - \frac{4\pi^2}{h^2} W^2 A \sin \frac{2\pi}{h} (Wt - px) \qquad \frac{\partial^2 \Psi}{\partial x^2} = - \frac{4\pi^2}{h^2} p^2 A \sin \frac{2\pi}{h} (Wt - px)$$

The only combination of these derivatives that would enable us to use Eq. (104) seems to be one in which the *first* derivative with respect to t is combined with the *second* derivative with respect to x. We can get a term in V by using Ψ itself, undifferentiated, multiplied by V. We are thus led to try as a wave equation

$$\frac{\partial \Psi}{\partial t} = a \frac{\partial^2 \Psi}{\partial x^2} + bV\Psi \tag{105}$$

where the coefficients a and b remain to be determined.

If we substitute Ψ from (103) in this equation, however, we encounter a difficulty, since $\partial \Psi / \partial t$ contains a cosine, whereas $\partial^2 \Psi / \partial x^2$ and Ψ itself both contain a sine. However, we could equally well have started with a cosine instead of a sine; or we could use a *combination of cosine and sine*, such as

$$\Psi = A \sin \frac{2\pi}{h} (Wt - px) + B \cos \frac{2\pi}{h} (Wt - px)$$

where A and B are independent constants. The student is probably familiar with the use of such combinations as the general solution of a differential equation of the second order. If we substitute this latter expression for Ψ in (105) and then equate coefficients of the sine terms and the cosine terms separately on both sides of the equation, so as to have it satisfied for all values of x and t, we obtain results that can be written

$$W = a \frac{2\pi}{h} p^2 \frac{A}{B} - \frac{bh}{2\pi} V \frac{A}{B} = -a \frac{2\pi}{h} p^2 \frac{B}{A} + \frac{bh}{2\pi} V \frac{B}{A}$$

These equations will agree with (104), provided

$$a \frac{2\pi}{h} \frac{A}{B} = -a \frac{2\pi}{h} \frac{B}{A} = \frac{1}{2m} \qquad - \frac{bh}{2\pi} \frac{A}{B} = \frac{bh}{2\pi} \frac{B}{A} = 1$$

Eliminating either a or b from these equations, we obtain

$$\frac{A^2}{B^2} = -1 \qquad \therefore \frac{A}{B} = \pm i \qquad i = \sqrt{-1}$$

To agree with common practice, let us take $A/B = -i$. Then we obtain (since $1/i = -i$)

$$-ia\frac{2\pi}{h} = \frac{1}{2m} \qquad a = \frac{ih}{4\pi m} \qquad i\frac{bh}{2\pi} = 1 \qquad b = \frac{2\pi}{ih}$$

Thus (105) becomes

$$\frac{\partial \Psi}{\partial t} = \frac{ih}{4\pi m}\frac{\partial^2 \Psi}{\partial x^2} + \frac{2\pi}{ih}V\Psi$$

or, after multiplying through by $-h/2\pi i$,

$$-\frac{h}{2\pi i}\frac{\partial \Psi}{\partial t} = -\frac{h^2}{8\pi^2 m}\frac{\partial^2 \Psi}{\partial x^2} + V\Psi$$

For three-dimensional waves this will presumably read

$$-\frac{h}{2\pi i}\frac{\partial \Psi}{\partial t} = -\frac{h^2}{8\pi^2 m}\left(\frac{\partial^2 \Psi}{\partial x^2} + \frac{\partial^2 \Psi}{\partial y^2} + \frac{\partial^2 \Psi}{\partial z^2}\right) + V\Psi$$

or, in a condensed notation often used,

$$-\frac{h}{2\pi i}\frac{\partial \Psi}{\partial t} = -\frac{h^2}{8\pi^2 m}\nabla^2 \Psi + V\Psi \tag{106}$$

∇^2 (or Δ) standing for the "Laplacian operator" or the sum of the three space derivatives.

Equation (106) is Schrödinger's famous *wave equation containing the time*. The agreement of results deduced from this equation justifies the belief that the equation is valid for the matter waves associated with a particle of mass m as long as relativistic effects can be neglected. The equation is remarkable among the differential equations of mathematical physics in that it contains $i = \sqrt{-1}$. But for this factor it would resemble the equation for the flow of heat in a solid body, which likewise contains the first derivative with respect to the time. The motion of matter waves combines, in fact, some of the features of heat flow in a solid with other features resembling the propagation of mechanical disturbances, such as sound waves.

In case V is a constant, it is easily seen by direct substitution that a solution of (106) is

$$\Psi = C\,e^{-(2\pi i/h)(Wt - px)} \tag{107}$$

provided W and p are constants satisfying Eq. (104). Here C is an arbitrary constant, representing the wave amplitude. If $W > 0$ and $p > 0$, this solution of the wave equation represents plane waves of Ψ traveling toward $+x$; for, at a point moving with velocity W/p, the value of Ψ remains constant.[1] W and p represent energy and momentum of the associated particle, respectively; the frequency ν and the wavelength λ of the waves are easily seen to be $\nu = W/h$, $\lambda = h/p$, in accordance with conclusions reached previously. If $p < 0$ but $W > 0$, both the particle and the waves are moving toward $-x$.

If $W < 0$, as may happen if $V < 0$, the waves and the particle travel in opposite directions. We can always make this so, if we wish, by adjusting the arbitrary additive constant that occurs in V, as in any potential energy. The possibility of reversing the direction of motion of matter waves by a mere mathematical change of this sort is a clear indication that they cannot be ordinary real waves!

97. The Physical Significance of Ψ. The question at once arises: what is the physical significance of the mysterious Ψ that appears in the mathematical theory?

An answer sometimes given to this question is that Ψ is merely an auxiliary mathematical quantity that is introduced to facilitate computations relative to the results of experiment. For example, in the experiments described above on the diffraction of electrons by a crystal, the experimenter sets up an electron gun that fires electrons of a certain energy at a crystal. A detector placed at a certain angle gives indications which are taken to mean that electrons are being received. In order to develop a quantitative theory for such observations, we *assume* that a beam of electron waves of frequency $\nu = W/h$ falls on the crystal, and we *calculate* the intensity of the waves scattered in the direction of the detector. From this mathematical result we infer, following certain rules, what the indication of the detector should be. In order to make such calculations, it is not really necessary to attach any physical significance at all to the mathematical symbol Ψ.

There is much to be said for such a view. After all, observational results are the primary material of physics; the purpose of theories is to correlate these results, to group them into those regularities of experience that we call laws, and to predict the results of new experiments. Even the motion of the electron as a particle is only an auxiliary concept, introduced for convenience in describing and interpreting observational results; the evidence for the particle nature of the electron is in reality very indirect. If we carefully examine the history of the concept of the electron as a particle, we shall realize that this concept owes its origin to the well-established beliefs in the corpuscular nature of matter. The electron was regarded as one of the building blocks of matter and was,

---

[1] If a point moves with velocity W/p, in time dt it moves a distance $dx = W \, dt/p$; hence, $d(Wt - px) = W \, dt - p \, dx = 0$, and so $d\Psi = 0$.

therefore, visualized as a particle. Such auxiliary concepts as particles constitute very convenient aids to thinking and most physicists find it advantageous to make use of them. Whereas some experimental results are conveniently understood in terms of the electrons as particles, however, others can be understood only in terms of the interference of waves. It is worth while, therefore, to go as far as we can toward assigning some physical significance to these waves, or to the quantity Ψ in terms of which the mathematical theory of the waves is expressed. It turns out that this can be done, according to circumstances, in two rather different ways.

In dealing with an experiment on scattering such as that just described, a beam of waves of indefinite total length is commonly assumed, represented by a Ψ like that in Eq. (107). The *square of the absolute value of Ψ, $|\Psi|^2$, is then taken to be proportional* (for given particle energy) *to the number of particles in the beam that cross unit area per second*, the unit area being taken perpendicular to the direction of motion.[1] Thus, in an experiment on the diffraction of electrons, let n_0 electrons cross unit area per second in the incident beam and let Ψ_0 denote the mathematical expression assumed for Ψ in the waves representing this beam. Then, if calculation by means of the wave equation (106) gives Ψ_d as the value of Ψ in a certain direction of diffraction, the theoretical value for the intensity of the diffracted beam in that direction, defined as the number of diffracted electrons crossing unit area per second, is

$$n_d = \frac{|\Psi_d|^2}{|\Psi_0|^2}\, n_0$$

[provided the incident and the diffracted beams move in regions where V in (106) has the same value]. This procedure corresponds exactly to the method of handling similar problems in optics. The intensity of a beam of light, which might be defined as the number of photons crossing unit area per second, is proportional (in a given medium) to E^2, the square of the electric vector (Sec. 226). The principal difference here is that, Ψ being a complex number, we must use $|\Psi|^2$ instead of Ψ^2. Usually $\Psi^*\Psi$ is written instead of $|\Psi|^2$, Ψ^* denoting the complex conjugate of Ψ.

There are other cases, however, as in the photoelectric effect, in which one wishes to follow the flight of a single electron or other particle. Then Ψ is taken to refer to a single particle. Usually, in a given case, values of Ψ appreciably different from zero occur only within some finite region. A solution of the wave equation of this latter type is sometimes called a *wave packet*. In such a case it is natural to ask, where is the particle in relation to the wave packet? The accepted answer may be stated in terms

---

[1] Ψ is a complex number; by the absolute value of any complex number, $x + iy$ (where x and y are real), is meant $(x^2 + y^2)^{1/2}$, written $|x + iy|$.

of probabilities.   The *position of the particle* is usually considered *not to be defined any more closely than is indicated by the values of* Ψ.   At any given instant, if a suitable observation were made, the particle might be found at any point where Ψ is different from zero; the *probability* of finding it in the neighborhood of a given point is proportional to the value of $|\Psi|^2$ at that point.   More exactly, the *probability density* at any point is represented by $|\Psi|^2$; the *probability of finding the particle within any element of volume dx dy dz* is

$$|\Psi|^2 \, dx \, dy \, dz$$

The wave scalar Ψ itself is sometimes called a *probability amplitude* for position of the particle.

The interpretation just stated imposes upon Ψ a certain mathematical requirement.   For the *total probability* of finding the particle *somewhere* is, of course, unity.   Hence Ψ must satisfy the condition that

$$\iiint |\Psi|^2 \, dx \, dy \, dz = 1 \tag{108}$$

the triple integral extending over all possible values of x, y, and z.   A Ψ satisfying this requirement is said to be *normalized* (to unity).   Any solution of Eq. (106) that gives a finite value to the integral in Eq. (108) can be normalized; for, because the wave equation is linear and homogenous in Ψ, any solution can be multiplied by an arbitrary constant without ceasing to be a solution, and this arbitrary constant can be adjusted so as to satisfy Eq. (108).

There are also interesting relations between a wave packet and the *velocity* or *momentum* of the particle.   A detailed study, for which we have not space, brings out the following features.

Suppose the particle is in free space (that is, $V = 0$).   Then a possible solution of the wave equation is given by (107), in which C and p are constants and $W = p^2/2m$.   This solution, representing an infinite train of waves, is considered to correspond to a particle moving with energy W, momentum p, and velocity $v = p/m$.   It cannot be treated as a wave packet, however, for it makes

$$\iiint |\Psi|^2 \, dx \, dy \, dz = \infty$$

We may conclude that *it is not possible for a particle to have a perfectly definite momentum or velocity*.   We can, however, have as close an approach as we please to a definite momentum, for Ψ may be assumed to be indistinguishable from (107) over as large a region as desired, sinking to zero outside the boundary of this region; the constant C can then be chosen small enough so that $\iiint |\Psi|^2 \, dx \, dy \, dz = 1$.   A wave packet of this type will retain its form for a long time, traveling with a velocity roughly equal to the group velocity of waves of frequency $\nu = W/h$ or with a velocity roughly equal to p/m.

In general, any wave packet can be expanded in terms of wave trains like (107), just as any patch of light waves can be resolved into monochromatic trains. This amounts to representing Ψ by a Fourier integral. When this has been done in a suitable way, the coefficients of the various wave trains in the expansion constitute a probability amplitude for momentum; i.e., the square of the absolute value of any coefficient gives the probability that a suitable observation would reveal the particle as moving in the direction and with the momentum or velocity that is associated with the corresponding wave train. Thus, in general, according to wave mechanics, a particle does not have either a sharply defined position or a sharply defined momentum or velocity.

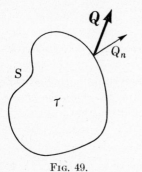

FIG. 49.

98. The Probability Stream Density. An analog of Poynting's theorem for the electromagnetic field can be found for matter waves. It can be shown from the wave equation that, if S denotes any surface enclosing a space τ (Fig. 49), then

$$\frac{d}{dt} \iiint_\tau |\Psi|^2 \, dx \, dy \, dz = - \iint_S \frac{h}{4\pi mi} (\Psi^* \, \nabla\Psi - \Psi \, \nabla\Psi^*)_n \, dS$$

where $\nabla\Psi$ is the gradient of Ψ, that is, a vector whose components in the x, y, z directions are $\partial\Psi/\partial x$, $\partial\Psi/\partial y$, $\partial\Psi/\partial z$, respectively, the subscript n denotes the component of this vector in the direction of the outward-drawn normal to the element dS of the surface S, and the integrals are taken, respectively, throughout the volume τ and over the surface S. The left-hand member of the equation represents the rate at which probability inside S is increasing. The right-hand member shows that this increase is accounted for if the probability is supposed to be streaming in space with a vector stream density $\mathbf{Q}$ defined as

$$\mathbf{Q} = \frac{h}{4\pi mi} (\Psi^* \, \nabla\Psi - \Psi \, \nabla\Psi^*) \tag{109}$$

The integral on the right then represents the rate at which probability is streaming outward across S.

If Ψ has the form shown in Eq. (107), then

$$\Psi^* = C^* e^{(2\pi i/h)(Wt - px)} \qquad \frac{\partial\Psi}{\partial x} = \frac{2\pi i}{h} p\Psi$$

$$Q = \frac{p}{m} |C|^2$$

since $C^*C = |C|^2$, Q denoting the magnitude of **Q**. Thus the significance of the beam represented by Eq. (107) as previously stated can be based upon the vector **Q** by assuming that the number of particles crossing unit area per second is $n_0 = Q = p|C|^2/m$.

99. The Indeterminacy Principle. The indefiniteness that we have just found to exist in the values of certain mechanical magnitudes associated with a particle, such as its position or momentum, is a fundamental feature of wave mechanics. The indefiniteness as to position can be minimized by making the wave packet very small (Ψ practically zero except within a very small region); but in that case it can be shown that the packet will spread rapidly. Consequently, if we were to observe the position of the particle a little later and then calculate its velocity by dividing the distance covered by the time that has elapsed, any one of a wide variety of results might be obtained. Thus, a small packet means a large indefiniteness in momentum and velocity. On the other hand, if we give to Ψ a form like that in Eq. (107) over a large region, in order to fix the velocity and momentum of the particle within narrow limits, there is a large indefiniteness in the position. In general, it can be shown that, if Δx denotes the effective range in the possible values that might be found by observation for the coordinate x of the particle, and if Δp indicates the similar range for momentum, then

$$\Delta p \, \Delta x \geqq \frac{h}{2\pi} \quad \hbar \tag{110}$$

where h is Planck's constant. This principle was first enunciated by Heisenberg in 1927,[1] who called it, in German, the principle of "Unbestimmtheit." This term has been variously translated as "indeterminacy," "indefiniteness," or "uncertainty." For an electron, if we define the indeterminateness in velocity as $\Delta v = \Delta p/m$, then $\Delta v \geqq 1.2(1/\Delta x)$ cm per sec, Δx being in centimeters. For a molecule of nitrogen,

$$\Delta v \geqq 2.3 \times 10^{-5} \frac{1}{\Delta x} \text{ cm per sec.}$$

The principle can be said to have its basis in the *wave properties* of matter. It even has an analog in the field of optics. A single sinusoidal wave of light of wavelength λ represents a certain amount of energy that is closely localized in space, but it does not constitute monochromatic light; for, upon passing through a spectroscope, it will spread widely in the spectrum (cf. Fig. 50). To have an approach to monochromatic light, we must have a train of many waves; and this means a corresponding dispersal of the energy in space.

[1] Heisenberg, **Z.** *Physik*, vol. 43, p. 172, 1927.

The conclusion that a wave packet cannot represent a particle as having at the same time a definite position and a definite momentum might seem to be in conflict with the fact that, in practice, both position and momentum are capable of measurement; e.g., from two snapshots of a rifle bullet, its position and velocity at a given instant can both be calculated. Heisenberg pointed out, however, that this is possible only because, on the scale of observation used in ordinary physical measurement, the indeterminacy required by Eq. (110) is so minute as to be lost in the experimental errors.

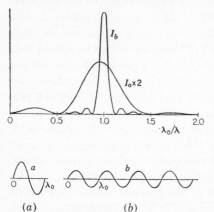

FIG. 50. Spectral-intensity curves (referred to frequency) for pulses of one and four waves.

It is quite otherwise for an electron, or a molecule. Consider, for example, how an electron might be located with *atomic* precision. We might use a microscope; but then we should have to use light of extremely short wavelength in order to secure sufficient resolving power. To distinguish positions 10^{-9} cm apart, for example, we should have to use γ-rays. Under these circumstances, however, the effect of the light on the electron cannot be neglected. If we are to "see" the electron, at least one photon must bounce off it and enter the microscope. In rebounding from the electron this photon will give it a strong Compton kick (see Sec. 160). Thus at the instant at which we locate the electron, its momentum undergoes a discontinuous change. Furthermore, there is an indefiniteness about the magnitude of this change, for it will vary according to the direction in which the scattered photon leaves the scene of action. We cannot limit closely the range of possible directions for the scattered photons that enter the microscope, by stopping down the aperture, without a serious loss of resolving power. A quantitative analysis of such observations leads again to Eq. (110).

It appears, then, that we cannot *at the same time* assign to an electron or other small particle, in terms of actual or possible observations, a definite position and a definite momentum (or energy). Thus, an assertion that both the position and the momentum of a particle have simultaneously certain precise values is a statement devoid of physical meaning; for, since 1900, it has become increasingly accepted as a principle of physics that only those magnitudes which can be observed, directly or indirectly, have physical significance. Our classical notion of a particle as something that can move along a sharply defined path, having at each instant a definite position and velocity, is therefore not fully applicable to electrons or protons or atoms or molecules. These small bits of matter may be said to have some particle properties, but they also possess certain wave properties, so that, in the classical sense of the words, they are neither true particles nor true waves. C. G. Darwin proposed to call them "wavicles."

After this discussion of the physical significance of Ψ, we shall now return to a further consideration of the mathematical theory. Whatever changes may occur in the future in the physical ideas that are considered to underlie wave mechanics, it seems probable that the mathematical theory is here to stay.

100. Stationary or Quantum States. So far we have discussed the motion of free particles only. Suppose now an electron or other particle is in a region where, because of a force field, it has a potential energy V depending on its position. To treat such cases, Schrödinger suggested seeking solutions of the wave equation which represent standing waves. In such waves the phase of the vibration is everywhere the same, whereas in running waves there exists, at any moment, a progression of phase along the wave train. In a mathematical expression for Ψ representing standing waves, therefore, the time must occur in a separate factor. The analogy of Eq. (107) suggests that we seek a solution of Eq. (106) of the form

$$\Psi(x,y,z,t) = e^{-(2\pi i/h)Wt}\psi(x,y,z) \tag{111}$$

Here Ψ, as indicated, is a function of the four variables x, y, z, t, whereas ψ is a function of only x, y, and z. The frequency of oscillation of such a Ψ is $\nu = W/h$. For, if t is increased by h/W, the exponent of e is thereby increased by $-2\pi i$, which multiplies Ψ by

$$e^{-2\pi i} = \cos 2\pi - i \sin 2\pi = 1$$

and so leaves Ψ unchanged. Since by assumption the frequency of harmonic matter waves always represents the energy divided by h, it follows that W represents the energy of the particle. It is easily shown that Eq. (111) defines the only possible form of Ψ in which t occurs as a separate factor.

When this expression for Ψ is substituted in Eq. (106), the factor $e^{-(2\pi i/h)Wt}$ occurs in each term and can be canceled out. The result is a differential equation for ψ:

$$-\frac{h^2}{8\pi^2 m} \nabla^2\psi + V\psi = W\psi \tag{112a}$$

or

$$\nabla^2\psi + \frac{8\pi^2 m}{h^2}(W - V)\psi = 0 \tag{112b}$$

This differential equation is known as Schrödinger's *amplitude equation*, or, more commonly, just as *Schrödinger's wave equation*.

Not every solution of Eq. (112a) can be used, however. As explained in Sec. 97, we must be able to make $\iiint |\Psi|^2\, dx\, dy\, dz$ finite. Now, if Ψ has the form shown in (111), its absolute value is

$$|\Psi| = \left|e^{-(2\pi i/h)Wt}\right| |\psi| = |\psi|$$

since $|e^{-ix}| = 1.$* Thus only those solutions of (112a) can be used to represent standing waves for which

$$\iiint |\psi|^2\, dx\, dy\, dz$$

is finite. In general, this condition can be met only for certain values of W; these are known as *characteristic values* (or *eigenvalues*). *These values of W are the allowed values of the energy corresponding to the stationary states, or quantum states, of the particle in the given force field.* Corresponding to each allowed value of W there are one or more different functions ψ, obtained as solutions of Eq. (112a); these are known as *characteristic functions* or *wave functions* (or *eigenfunctions*).

According to the physical significance that was assigned to Ψ in Sec. 97, the probability of finding the particle in a given element of space $d\tau$ is given either by $|\Psi|^2\, d\tau$ or by $|\psi|^2\, d\tau$, since, as we have seen, $|\Psi| = |\psi|$. When the particle is in a definite quantum state, $|\Psi|^2$ is constant and the distribution of probability does not change with time. Alternatively, however, the particle may be in a mixed state represented by a wave packet of the form

$$\Psi = c_1 e^{-(2\pi i/h)W_1 t}\psi_1 + c_2 e^{-(2\pi i/h)W_2 t}\psi_2 + \cdots \tag{113}$$

where c_1, c_2, . . . are constants (real or complex) and the W's and ψ's refer to different quantum states. In this case the probability density $|\Psi|^2$ varies with time and the particle can be regarded as moving around. The c's have the significance that $|c_n|^2$ is the probability of finding the particle in state number n, provided some experimental means exists of selecting particles in that quantum state. In certain problems, however, continuous ranges of allowed values of W also occur; in such cases, in Eq. (113), the sum over the states with discrete W's is supplemented by an integral analogous to a Fourier integral.

The problem of determining the allowed energy levels for a particle in a given force field thus reduces to the mathematical problem of finding the allowed solutions of a wave equation. Limitations of space prevent us, however, from pursuing the mathematical development of the theory in detail. We have space only for the discussion, mostly descriptive, of a few topics of fundamental importance.

---

* $|e^{-ix}| = |\cos x - i \sin x| = (\cos^2 x + \sin^2 x)^{1/2} = 1$, provided x is real.

101. Physical Magnitudes as Operators. It was early noticed that Schrödinger's equation can be derived from the classical expression for the energy of the moving particle by writing the kinetic part of this expression in terms of momentum and then substituting suitable differential operators for energy and momentum. This procedure lies close to Schrödinger's original line of thought. Let p_x, p_y, p_z denote the components of the momentum of a moving particle of mass m, so that $p_x = m\, dx/dt$, etc.; then the classical expression for its total energy W can be written

$$W = \frac{1}{2m}(p_x^2 + p_y^2 + p_z^2) + V$$

V denoting its potential energy. Now make the following replacements in terms of differential operators:

$$p_x \to \frac{h}{2\pi i}\frac{\partial}{\partial x}, \qquad p_y \to \frac{h}{2\pi i}\frac{\partial}{\partial y}, \qquad p_z \to \frac{h}{2\pi i}\frac{\partial}{\partial z}, \qquad W \to -\frac{h}{2\pi i}\frac{\partial}{\partial t}$$

$$(114a,b,c,d)$$

For example,

$$p_x^2 \to \left(\frac{h}{2\pi i}\frac{\partial}{\partial x}\right)\left(\frac{h}{2\pi i}\frac{\partial}{\partial x}\right) = -\frac{h^2}{4\pi^2}\frac{\partial^2}{\partial x^2}$$

The result is Schrödinger's equation containing the time, Eq. (106). The operator for the momentum as a vector is thus the vector differential operator

$$\mathbf{p} = \frac{h}{2\pi i}\nabla$$

$$(114e)$$

The operator for *angular momentum* is also of great interest in atomic theory. The classical expression for the angular momentum of a particle about the z axis is

$$xp_y - yp_x$$

Replacement of p_y and p_x gives as the corresponding operator in wave mechanics

$$\frac{h}{2\pi i}\left(x\frac{\partial}{\partial y} - y\frac{\partial}{\partial x}\right)$$

$$(115)$$

If polar coordinates are introduced with the z axis as axis, then

$$x = r\sin\theta\cos\phi \qquad y = r\sin\theta\sin\phi \qquad z = r\cos\theta$$

$$\frac{\partial}{\partial\phi} = \frac{\partial x}{\partial\phi}\frac{\partial}{\partial x} + \frac{\partial y}{\partial\phi}\frac{\partial}{\partial y} = x\frac{\partial}{\partial y} - y\frac{\partial}{\partial x}$$

Thus the operator for the z component of angular momentum can also be written

$$\frac{h}{2\pi i}\frac{\partial}{\partial\phi}$$

Analogous expressions are found for the x and y components. The operator for the square of the resultant angular momentum is, then,

$$-\frac{h^2}{4\pi^2}\left[\left(y\frac{\partial}{\partial z} - z\frac{\partial}{\partial y}\right)^2 + \left(z\frac{\partial}{\partial x} - x\frac{\partial}{\partial z}\right)^2 + \left(x\frac{\partial}{\partial y} - y\frac{\partial}{\partial x}\right)^2\right] \quad (116)$$

In wave mechanics physical magnitudes in general are represented by appropriate operators. The ultimate test of the validity of the operator assumed to represent a given magnitude will lie in a demonstration that the values of this magnitude as predicted by wave mechanics are in agreement with observation. The accepted condition that any physical magnitude P has a definite value or is quantized is that, if (P) denotes the corresponding wave-mechanical operator and Ψ the wave function for the system to which P belongs, then

$$(P)\Psi = P_n\Psi \quad (117)$$

where P_n is a real number, the value of P. Solutions of this equation satisfying appropriate boundary conditions represent stationary or quantum states for the magnitude P; and the set of allowed values of P_n includes the only correct values that can be obtained in an experimental measurement of P.

An important property of the allowed solutions Ψ_n of Eq. (117) is that they form a complete set of functions in terms of which any given wave function Ψ can be expanded in the analog of a Fourier series; thus

$$\Psi = \sum_n c_n\Psi_n$$

In some cases, however, a continuum of possible values of P occurs and then the sum must be supplemented or even replaced entirely by an integral analogous to a Fourier integral. If all functions are properly normalized, $|c_n|^2$ equals the probability of obtaining the value P_n as the result of a measurement of P performed upon a system initially in the condition represented by Ψ. It may also be remarked that, if the entire setup and measurement are repeated many times, the *average* of the observed values of P will be very close to the "expectation" of P defined as

$$\bar{P} = \int\Psi^*(P)\Psi \, dq \quad (118)$$

where dq includes all the coordinates involved in Ψ. This is easily verified by substituting the series for Ψ and recalling that $\int\Psi_n^*\Psi_n \, dq = 1$ but $\int\Psi_n^*\Psi_j \, dq = 0$ if $n \neq j$.

In the example first noted, if (W) is the operator for the energy W formed as described above, then the equation $(W)\psi = W\psi$ is equivalent to Eq. (112a). Similarly, if $\Psi = Ce^{-(2\pi i/h)(Wt-px)}$ as in Eq. (107), then

$$(p_x)\Psi = \frac{h}{2\pi i}\frac{\partial}{\partial x}\,\Psi = p\Psi$$

This shows that Ψ is a characteristic function for x momentum corresponding to the value p, which may be any number, positive or negative.

102. Particle in a Box; the Harmonic Oscillator. *a. Particle in a Box.*
Before discussing a few cases which find actual application in the theory of atoms or molecules, it may be instructive to consider first a very simple case that is easily worked out completely and which is useful in the treatment of gases. Consider first the one-dimensional case of a particle of mass m that can move freely in the x direction over the range $0 < x < L$ but rebounds when it strikes either end of this range. These conditions can be represented in Schrödinger's equation by assuming that $V = 0$ for $0 < x < L$ but rises with effectively infinite rapidity at the ends of the range. This latter feature can be shown to be equivalent to the *boundary condition* that $\psi = 0$ at $x = 0$ and at $x = L$. We must also set $\psi = 0$ at outside points. Schrödinger's equation (112a) then becomes

$$-\frac{h^2}{8\pi^2 m}\frac{\partial^2\psi}{\partial x^2} = W\psi \qquad -\frac{\hbar^2}{2m}\nabla_x^2\psi = E\psi \tag{119}$$

The general solution of this equation, as may be verified by substitution in the differential equation, is

$$\psi = C\sin bx + D\cos bx \qquad b = \frac{2\pi}{h}\sqrt{2mW} \qquad or\; b^2 = \frac{2mE}{\hbar^2}$$

This is the general solution because it contains two arbitrary constants, C and D, which is sufficient for a differential equation of the second order. To satisfy the boundary conditions, we substitute first $x = 0$, then $x = L$, and each time $\psi = 0$, obtaining

$$D = 0 \qquad C\sin bL + D\cos bL = 0$$

Thus either C or $\sin bL$ must vanish. To have any solution at all, we must have $C \neq 0$; hence b must have such a value that

$$\sin bL = 0$$

This restricts b to one of the values $b = \pi/L, 2\pi/L, 3\pi/L$, etc. Thus the only allowed wave functions are of the form $\psi = C\sin(n\pi x/L)$, where n is any positive integer. The arbitrary constant C may for simplicity be assumed to be a real number; since $\int_0^L \sin^2(n\pi x/L)\,dx = L/2$, the requirement that $\int_0^L |\psi|^2\,dx = 1$ then requires the value $C = \sqrt{2/L}$.

Thus the normalized wave functions for the particle are (see Fig. 51)

$$\psi_n = \sqrt{\frac{2}{L}} \sin n\pi \frac{x}{L} \qquad n = 1, 2, 3, \ldots \tag{120}$$

The corresponding characteristic or allowed values of the energy W, as found from the allowed values of b, are

$$W_n = \frac{n^2 h^2}{8mL^2} \tag{121}$$

These wave functions serve to illustrate an important general property of wave functions, that of *orthogonality*. For, if $W_n \neq W_k$, it is easily verified that

$$\int_0^L \psi_n \psi_k \, dx = 0 \tag{122}$$

If the particle is similarly confined within a *rectangular box* with edges parallel to the x, y, z axes of the lengths l_1, l_2, l_3, the normalized wave

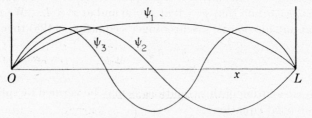

FIG. 51. The first three normalized wave functions for a particle in a box.

functions for the stationary states and the energy levels are easily seen to be

$$\psi = 2 \sqrt{\frac{2}{l_1 l_2 l_3}} \sin k_1\pi \frac{x}{l_1} \sin k_2\pi \frac{y}{l_2} \sin k_3\pi \frac{z}{l_3} \tag{123}$$

$$W = \frac{h^2}{8m} \left(\frac{k_1^2}{l_1^2} + \frac{k_2^2}{l_2^2} + \frac{k_3^2}{l_3^2} \right) \tag{124}$$

where k_1, k_2, k_3 denote any set of three positive integers.

b. The Harmonic Oscillator. The theory of an ideal harmonic oscillator finds many applications and deserves brief mention. Assume that $V = \frac{1}{2}\beta x^2$, β denoting a constant. Then the wave equation (112a) for a particle of mass m in one-dimensional motion becomes

$$-\frac{h^2}{8\pi^2 m} \frac{\partial^2 \psi}{\partial x^2} + \frac{1}{2}\beta x^2 \psi = W\psi \tag{125}$$

A mathematical study of this equation shows that the characteristic value of W can be written

$$W_n = (n + \frac{1}{2})h\nu_c \qquad n = 0, 1, 2, \ldots \qquad \nu_c = \frac{1}{2\pi} \sqrt{\frac{\beta}{m}} \tag{126a,b,c}$$

The constant ν_c happens to be equal to the frequency with which the mass m would vibrate according to classical theory, but it has no special physical significance here.

The normalized wave functions for the first three quantum states, corresponding to $n = 0$, 1, or 2, are found to be as follows, stated in terms of

$$\xi = 2\pi x \sqrt{\frac{m\nu_c}{h}} \qquad C_0 = \left(2 \sqrt{\frac{\pi m\nu_c}{h}}\right)^{\frac{1}{2}}$$

For $n = 0$: $\psi_0 = C_0 \, e^{-\xi^2/2}$ $n = 1$: $\psi_1 = \sqrt{2} \, C_0 \, \xi \, e^{-\xi^2/2}$

$$n = 2: \qquad \psi_2 = \frac{C_0}{\sqrt{2}} \, (2\xi^2 - 1) \, e^{-\xi^2/2}$$

103. Perturbation Theory.   In most cases the wave equation cannot be solved in terms of familiar mathematical functions. Resort must then be had either to numerical integration or to approximate methods. The best-known method of approximation, and one of very wide usefulness, is that known as perturbation theory. In this method certain minor terms are at first omitted from the wave equation, the simplified equation thus obtained is solved, and corrections to the energy and to the wave functions are then calculated to represent the effect of the terms that were omitted. The name arose from the analogous procedure of the astronomers, who first imagine each planet to move in an elliptical orbit about the sun and then calculate the perturbations of these motions caused by the attractions of the other planets.

This method is easily illustrated in the first case described in the last section. Suppose that the potential energy V is not exactly zero for $0 < x < L$ but has small values represented by $V = f(x)$. Equation (119) as thus modified can be written, for the nth quantum state with energy W'_n,

$$-\frac{h^2}{8\pi^2 m} \frac{\partial^2 \psi'_n}{\partial x^2} + f(x)\psi'_n = W'_n \psi'_n \tag{127}$$

We first simplify this equation by omitting $f(x)$, obtaining, with ψ'_n replaced by ψ_n for simplicity,

$$-\frac{h^2}{8\pi^2 m} \frac{\partial^2 \psi_n}{\partial x^2} = W_n \psi_n \tag{128}$$

The solutions of this equation are the *zero-order* wave functions ψ_n with zero-order energies W_n as stated in Eqs. (120) and (121).

As was indicated in Sec. 101, the functions ψ_n will represent a complete set of functions in terms of which any reasonably smooth function can be expanded. Hence we can write for the solution of (127)

$$\psi'_n = \psi_n + \sum_{j=1}^{\infty} b_j \psi_j \tag{129}$$

where the b_j's are small constants. In the present example this sum is simply a Fourier series. Substituting in Eq. (127) and using (128) repeatedly, with n changed to j, and omitting the limits on Σ to save space, we obtain

$$W_n\psi_n + \Sigma b_j W_j\psi_j + f(x)\psi_n + f(x)\Sigma b_j\psi_j = W'_n\psi_n + W'_n\Sigma b_j\psi_j \quad (130)$$

Here, however, the term $f(x)\Sigma b_j\psi_j$ is of the second order of small quantities, since $f(x)$ and b_j are both of the first order. For a first correction we drop this term.

Then, multiplying the equation through by $\psi_n\,dx$, integrating from 0 to L, and remembering that $\int\psi_n{}^2\,dx = 1$ and $\int\psi_n\psi_j\,dx = 0$ if $n \neq j$, we obtain

$$(1 + b_n)W_n + \int_0^L f(x)\psi_n{}^2\,dx = (1 + b_n)W'_n$$

$$W'_n - W_n = (1 + b_n)^{-1}\int_0^L f(x)\psi_n{}^2\,dx$$

Here the integral is a small quantity of the first order; hence b_n produces an effect of the second order and for consistency must be dropped. We thus find for the first-order correction to the energy

$$W'_n - W_n = \int_0^L f(x)\psi_n{}^2\,dx = \frac{2}{L}\int_0^L f(x)\sin^2\left(n\pi\,\frac{x}{L}\right)dx \quad (131)$$

To find the b_j's, we return to Eq. (130), with one second-order term omitted as before, multiply it through by $\psi_k\,dx$ with $k \neq n$, and integrate as before, obtaining

$$(W_k - W'_n)b_k + \int_0^L f(x)\psi_k\psi_n\,dx = 0 \quad (132a)$$

Here we may replace W'_n by W_n, since the error thereby introduced, $(W'_n - W_n)b_k$, is of the second order. Thus for a first-order correction

$$b_k = \frac{1}{W_n - W_k}\int_0^L f(x)\psi_k\psi_n\,dx \quad (132b)$$

The coefficient b_n remains arbitrary and may be adjusted so as to normalize ψ'_n.

The integral $\int_0^L f(x)\psi_k\psi_n\,dx$ is called a *matrix component* of $f(x)$ with respect to the functions ψ_k and ψ_n. Its possible values could be written in the form of a matrix with its rows numbered by k and its columns by n. Components for $n = k$ are called diagonal components (i.e., located on the leading diagonal of the matrix). Thus the first-order correction to W_n is given by the diagonal matrix component of $f(x)$ with respect to ψ_n. This is the most important result obtained from perturbation theory.

In other problems the wave functions may have complex values; or the perturbation term in the energy may be an operator (O) containing derivatives, of which $f(x)$ is merely a degenerate example. To allow for such possibilities in the present case, it would be necessary to write

$$\int_0^L \psi_n^*\psi_n\, dx = 1 \qquad \int_0^L \psi_n^*\psi_j\, dx = 0 \qquad \text{if } n \neq j$$

$$W_n' - W_n = \int_0^L \psi_n^*(0)\psi_n\, dx \qquad b_k = \frac{1}{W_n - W_k}\int_0^L \psi_k^*(0)\psi_k\, dx$$

The formulas are also easily generalized for three dimensions. For example, if the particle is in a three-dimensional box with edges l_1, l_2, l_3,

$$\int_0^{l_3} dz \int_0^{l_2} dy \int_0^{l_1} \psi_n^*\psi_n\, dx = 1 \qquad \int_0^{l_3} dz \int_0^{l_2} dy \int_0^{l_1} \psi_n^*\psi_j\, dx = 0$$

$$W_n' - W_n = \int_0^{l_3} dz \int_0^{l_2} dy \int_0^{l_1} \psi_n^*\, f(x,y,z)\psi_n\, dx$$

Further corrections of higher order can be computed by extending the procedure, but this is seldom attempted.

It is worth noting that in these results no special importance is attached to the *maximum value* of the perturbing potential $f(x)$. This feature is in strong contrast with classical mechanics. Suppose, for example, that nonzero values of $f(x)$ were confined to a small region, in which the maximum is f_0. Then, in classical theory, a particle with energy $W < f_0$ could not possibly cross the potential "hill" but would be confined definitely to one side of it. No such limitation exists in wave mechanics. A somewhat different case of the same feature is that traveling waves of Ψ corresponding to energy W, falling upon a potential hill of height exceeding W, can always penetrate and traverse it, although the penetration tends to be slight if the hill is either very high or very broad. The penetration is sometimes called "tunnel effect." Another example is described in Sec. 145.

104. The One-electron Atom. The theory for a single electron in the field of a nucleus, fortunately, can be worked out without much trouble. We have no space for actual mathematical developments but may notice some of the more interesting results.

a. Energy Levels and Wave Functions. An electron of numerical charge e, in the field of a nucleus of charge Ze, has a potential energy

$$V = -\frac{Ze^2}{r}$$

at a distance r from the nucleus. For the moment, assume that the nucleus is fixed. Then the wave equation (112a) reads

$$-\frac{h^2}{8\pi^2 m}\nabla^2\psi - \frac{Ze^2}{r}\psi = W\psi \tag{133}$$

m being the electronic mass.

Only a few details of the allowed solutions can be given here. The variables can be "separated" in the equation by using polar coordinates, r, θ, ϕ (Fig. 52). Solutions can then be found of the form

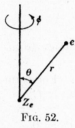

$$\psi_{nl\lambda} = C_{l\lambda}e^{i\lambda\phi}P_l^\lambda(\cos\theta)R_{nl}(r) \qquad (134)$$

Here $R_{nl}(r)$ is a certain function of r, P_l^λ denotes a certain function of $\cos\theta$, and $C_{l\lambda}$ is a normalizing factor. [Sometimes $R(r)/r$ is written in place of $R(r)$.] The symbols n, l, and λ denote three integers which occur in the customary expressions for the functions; these integers may have any values such that

Fig. 52.

$$|\lambda| \leqq l < n$$

Thus the possible values of n are $1, 2, \ldots$; for each n, $l = 0, 1, \ldots$, $n - 1$, and for each l, $\lambda = -l, -l + 1, -l + 2, \ldots, l - 1, l$. (Often the letter m, or m_l, is used in place of λ. The notation used here has certain advantages which will appear later in the study of many-electron spectra.) The numbers n, l, and λ serve as convenient labels for the wave functions and are commonly called quantum numbers. It is easily seen that λ must be an integer to keep the factor $e^{i\lambda\phi}$ single-valued. A few forms of P_l^λ are: $P_0^0 = 1$, $P_1^0 = \cos\theta$, $P_1^{\pm 1} = \sin\theta$;

$$P_2^0 = \tfrac{1}{2}(3\cos^2\theta - 1)$$

$P_2^{\pm 1} = 3\sin\theta\cos\theta$, $P_2^{\pm 2} = 3\sin^2\theta$.

The corresponding values of the energy turn out to be the same as those found by Bohr (Sec. 81):

$$W = -\frac{2\pi^2 me^4 Z^2}{h^2 n^2} \qquad (135)$$

In addition, any positive value of W may occur. The differential equation can be solved, also, for any *other negative* value of W, but in such cases ψ becomes infinite as $r \to \infty$ so that ψ cannot be normalized and cannot represent a possible state for the electron.

This problem illustrates an important feature that is frequently met with, called *degeneracy* of the wave functions or quantum states. For any value of n above 1, there are several independent wave functions for each allowed value of the energy. Corresponding to given l, the number λ ranges over $2l + 1$ different values from $-l$ to l, and, for given n, l ranges from 0 to $n - 1$. For each combination of a value of l with an allowed value of λ there exists a distinct wave function. All these functions, however, belong to the same value of W.

  b. Relations with Angular Momentum. When the atom is in a definite quantum state, the probability density, $|\Psi|^2$ or $|\psi|^2$, is everywhere con-

stant in time.   Thus it might be said in one sense that the electron is not
in motion.   Certain phenomena suggest, however, that, provided $l > 0$,
the atom should be regarded as possessing moment of momentum or
angular momentum about the nucleus; and this momentum is associated
with magnetic effects in the same way as is that of the classical motion in
an orbit.   Accordingly, for convenience, we shall speak of the electron
as "moving" in the field of the nucleus, and we may sometimes even
refer to this motion as "orbital."   The value of the angular momentum
furnishes a useful means of distinguishing between states that have the
same energy.

The student is doubtless familiar with the interpretation of ordinary
angular momentum as a vector quantity.   When a rigid body is rotating
about a fixed point, like a top about its point, there will be a certain axis
through the fixed point about which the angular momentum of the body
is a maximum.   About any other axis, inclined at an angle θ to the line
of maximum angular momentum, the angular momentum is equal to the
maximum value multiplied by $\cos \theta$.   The angular momentum can be
represented by a vector drawn in the direction of the axis about which
it is a maximum; the length of this vector can be made to represent the
magnitude of the maximum angular momentum, and its direction, indicated by an arrowhead, is commonly taken in the direction in which a
right-handed screw would advance along the axis while turning about it
in the same direction as the rotating body.   The angular momentum
about any other axis drawn through the fixed point is then represented by
the component of this vector in the direction of that axis.   The vector
may or may not coincide with the
instantaneous axis of rotation of the
body.

A similar treatment can be given
to the angular momentum of a moving particle.   In classical theory, the
electron can be regarded as moving
at every instant in a certain plane
drawn through the nucleus; the vector representing its angular momentum about the nucleus is commonly
drawn perpendicular to this plane
and in the direction specified in the

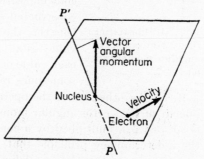

FIG. 53. Illustration of orbital vector
angular momentum.

last paragraph (see Fig. 53).   The angular momentum about any oblique
axis such as PP', being equal to the component in that direction of the
vector angular momentum, is represented by the projection on the given
oblique axis of the directed line that represents the vector angular
momentum.

If the operator for angular momentum about the z axis as written in Sec. 101 is applied to $\psi_{nl\lambda}$, the result is

$$\frac{h}{2\pi i}\frac{\partial}{\partial \phi}\,\psi_{nl\lambda} = \lambda\,\frac{h}{2\pi}\,\psi_{nl\lambda}$$

Thus the wave function $\psi_{nl\lambda}$ represents a state of the electron in the nuclear field in which its angular momentum about the axis of polar coordinates has the definite value

$$\lambda\,\frac{h}{2\pi}$$

Hence, in the set of $(2l+1)$ quantum states for given n and l, the

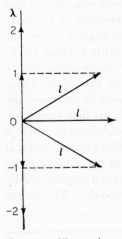

FIG. 54. Illustrating the quantization of angular momentum for $l = 2$.

angular momentum about the polar axis ranges by integral steps from a maximum of l units, each of magnitude $h/2\pi$, in one direction through zero to l units in the opposite direction. Such a variation of the angular momentum from one state to another is represented if we imagine that the angular momentum of the electron has a fixed value of l units but is inclined at any one of several fixed angles to the axis. This is illustrated in Fig. 54, in which the vector representing the angular momentum is assumed to have a length of 2 units and is shown in five alternative positions, corresponding to $\lambda = -2$, -1, 0, 1, 2. Only for $\lambda = \pm 2$ does the vector coincide with the polar axis. A *vector diagram* so constructed serves vividly to illustrate the relation between the quantum number l and the various values of λ. A separate diagram is to be drawn for each value of l. The relationships involved here are sometimes referred to as *space* quantization.

If, on the other hand, the operator representing a *perpendicular* component of the vector angular momentum $\mathbf{G}_l$ is applied to $\psi_{nl\lambda}$, the result is *not* just $\psi_{nl\lambda}$ multiplied by a constant. It is a general consequence of the indeterminacy principle that, whenever one component of a vector angular momentum has a definite value, other components do not. Measurement of a perpendicular component, for an atom in the state represented by $\psi_{nl\lambda}$, would yield one of several alternative multiples of $h/2\pi$ (provided $l > 0$), with an average expectation of zero. This is an important novel feature of wave mechanics; for, in classical mechanics the vector $\mathbf{G}_l$ would have a fixed direction and all its components would have definite values (so long as external forces did not act on the system). The classical vector $\mathbf{G}_l$ might, however, have any orientation about the axis while its axial component had a given value $\lambda h/2\pi$. Thus a quantum state is the analog, not of one classical motion, but of a class of motions.

An absence of fixed orientation and of fixed values for perpendicular components would occur if the vector $\mathbf{G}_l$ were revolving about the axis at a fixed angle. It sometimes assists the memory to imagine such a "precession" to be occurring. It should not be forgotten, however, that, in wave mechanics, the indefinitenesses in question hold even in the absence of all external forces.

If, now, the operator written in Eq. (116) for the *square* of the total angular momentum is applied to $\psi_{n l \lambda}$, it is found that this square is also definite, being quantized at the rather curious value $l(l + 1)h^2/(2\pi)^2$. For some purposes it is convenient to represent the vector $\mathbf{G}_l$ by a line drawn of a length representing, not $lh/2\pi$, but the magnitude $\sqrt{l(l + 1)}h/2\pi$. Obviously the vector will then not be parallel to the axis even when $\lambda = \pm l$, since the axial component of $\mathbf{G}_l$ cannot numerically exceed $lh/2\pi$. To visualize the relation between the quantum numbers, however, the simpler type of diagram described previously is more convenient.

No analogous physical significance can be attached to the quantum number n, sometimes called the *principal* quantum number. It should also be noted that in the theory as thus developed no allowance has been made for electron spin (Sec. 118).

c. Spatial Degeneracy of the Wave Functions. In the case under discussion the axis for the polar coordinates can be drawn in any desired direction. Thus the set of quantum states and of associated wave functions is in some degree a matter of arbitrary choice. This arbitrariness of the wave functions is another aspect of the general phenomenon of degeneracy, and its mathematical aspects deserve a short further discussion.

Whenever several wave functions are associated with the same value of the energy W, then any linear combination of them is another possible wave function for the same energy. Thus, let ψ_1, ψ_2, ψ_3, . . . , ψ_k be solutions of Eq. (133), for $W = W_1$. Then the linear combination ψ' where

$$\psi' = c_1\psi_1 + c_2\psi_2 + c_3\psi_3 + \cdots + c_k\psi_k \tag{136}$$

c_1, c_2, c_3, . . . , c_k being any constants, is also a solution of Eq. (133), as may be verified by substitution. Thus ψ' is as valid a wave function, and represents just as valid a quantum state for the energy W, as does any one of the functions ψ_1, ψ_2, . . . , ψ_k. The possible wave functions associated with W_1 are thus infinite in number. It is possible, however, to find a number k of them in terms of which all others can be written as linear combinations. These k functions can be chosen in infinitely many ways, but their number is always k.

Degeneracy of the quantum states has an exact analog in classical theory. For example, a drumhead can vibrate at a certain one of its higher frequencies with any diameter as a nodal line, such as A_1, B_1, B_2,

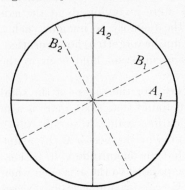

etc., in Fig. 55. The mode of vibration at this frequency is thus not unique. It is possible, however, to choose any two modes as fundamental modes, for example A_1 and A_2, or B_1 and B_2, and to write the displacement during any vibration at the frequency in question as resulting from the superposition of vibrations of suitable amplitudes in the two chosen fundamental modes. The type of vibration that actually occurs in a given case depends upon the manner in

FIG. 55. Possible nodal lines on a vibrating drumhead.

which the drumhead is set into vibration. Similarly, when an atom is in a degenerate state characterized by a definite energy, the exact quantum state or mixture of states that it occupies depends upon its past history.

In the case of the one-electron atom, if the axis of polar coordinates is taken in a different direction, the factor $R_{nl}(r)$ in the expression for $\psi_{nl\lambda}$ as given in (134) is the same as before, but the geometrical significance of the directional factor $e^{i\lambda\phi}P_l^\lambda(\cos\theta)$ is different. It can be shown, however, that the new directional factor can be written as a linear combination of the directional factors relative to the original axis, and, in fact, in terms of those factors, $2l + 1$ in number, which are labeled with the same value of l.

The infinite variety of the quantum states for given n and l corresponds to the infinity of different possible orientations of a Bohr orbit, and it is closely related to the isotropy of space.

d. Probability Density and Charge-cloud Density. The probability density corresponding to one of the wave functions $\psi_{nl\lambda}$ is easily seen from Eq. (134) to be

$$|\psi_{nl\lambda}|^2 = |C_{l\lambda}|^2[P_l^\lambda(\cos\theta)]^2[R_{nl}(r)]^2 \tag{137}$$

There is no suggestion here of *orbital motion*. The quantity $|\psi_{nl\lambda}|^2 \, d\tau$ represents the probability that, if the electron were located experimentally at any instant, it would be found in the element of volume $d\tau$ (Sec. 97). It would not be possible, however, to follow the electron in an orbital motion around the nucleus by means of a succession of such observations, as the astronomers follow the planets around the sun; for one observation with a γ-ray microscope of sufficient resolving power would suffice, because of the Compton effect, to knock the electron entirely out of the atom.

Often it is convenient to imagine the electronic charge e to be distributed in space as a sort of *charge cloud*, with a density η of magnitude

$$\eta = e|\psi|^2$$

Many effects of the atom on its surroundings are approximately the same as if the atom actually contained a distribution of charge of density η, acting according to the ordinary laws of electrostatics.

Owing to the absence of the coordinate ϕ in the right-hand member of Eq. (137), it is evident that, when the electron is in one of its quantum states, the probability density or charge-cloud density is symmetrical about the chosen axis of polars. The variation with θ, on the other hand, although symmetrical relative to the plane $\theta = \pi/2$, may be large. This variation is of minor interest, however, and for this reason it is more illuminating to consider the *average radial* variation in the density. Let $P_r \, dr$ denote the total amount of probability, or $\eta_r \, dr$ the numerical amount of charge, contained between two spheres of radii r and $r + dr$ drawn about the nucleus as a center. The volume between the two spheres is proportional to r^2. Hence it is easily seen that, if R_{nl} is separately normalized so that

$$\int_0^\infty r^2 \, R_{nl}{}^2 \, dr = 1$$

($C_{l\lambda}$ being such that $|C_{l\lambda}|^2 \iint [P_l{}^\lambda(\cos\theta)]^2 \sin\theta \, d\theta \, d\phi = 1$), then

$$P_r = r^2 R_{nl}{}^2 \qquad \eta_r = eP_r = er^2 R_{nl}{}^2$$

e. Further Details Concerning the Wave Functions. As examples, the following mathematical details may be given concerning the states of lowest energy, written in terms of the constant

$$a_0 = \frac{h^2}{4\pi^2 m e^2} = 5.29 \times 10^{-9} \text{ cm}$$

$n = 1, \qquad l = 0, \qquad \lambda = 0: \qquad \psi_{100} = \frac{1}{\sqrt{4\pi}} R_{10} \qquad R_{10} = 2\left(\frac{Z}{a_0}\right)^{3/2} e^{-Zr/a_0}$

$n = 2, \qquad l = 0, \qquad \lambda = 0: \qquad \psi_{200} = \frac{1}{\sqrt{4\pi}} R_{20}$

$$R_{20} = \frac{1}{\sqrt{2}}\left(\frac{Z}{a_0}\right)^{3/2}\left(1 - \frac{Zr}{2a_0}\right) e^{-Zr/2a_0}$$

$l = 1, \qquad \lambda = 0: \qquad \psi_{210} = \sqrt{\frac{3}{4\pi}} \cos\theta \cdot R_{21}$

$$R_{21} = \frac{1}{2\sqrt{6}}\left(\frac{Z}{a_0}\right)^{3/2} \frac{Zr}{a_0} e^{-Zr/2a_0}$$

$\lambda = \pm 1: \psi_{21,\pm 1} = \sqrt{\frac{3}{8\pi}} e^{\pm i\varphi} \sin\theta \cdot R_{21}$

for $n = 3$,

$$R_{30} = \frac{2}{3\sqrt{3}}\left(\frac{Z}{a_0}\right)^{3/2}\left[1 - \frac{2}{3}\frac{Zr}{a_0} + \frac{2}{27}\left(\frac{Zr}{a_0}\right)^2\right]e^{-Zr/3a_0}$$

$$R_{31} = \frac{4}{27}\sqrt{\frac{2}{3}}\left(\frac{Z}{a_0}\right)^{3/2}\left(1 - \frac{1}{6}\frac{Zr}{a_0}\right)\frac{Zr}{a_0}\,e^{-Zr/3a_0}$$

$$R_{32} = \frac{4}{81}\sqrt{\frac{1}{30}}\left(\frac{Zr}{a_0}\right)^2 e^{-Z/3a_0}$$

The constant a_0 is the same number that represented the radius of the smallest orbit for hydrogen [cf. Eq. (81)] in the Bohr theory.

For $Z = 1$, these formulas refer to hydrogen; for $Z = 2$, to ionized helium; and so on.

In Fig. 56 are plotted, for hydrogen, not R_{nl} but rR_{nl}; and in Fig. 57 are shown the corresponding curves for P_r or η_r, which is proportional to $r^2R_{nl}^2$. The areas under the latter curves would all be equal if they were

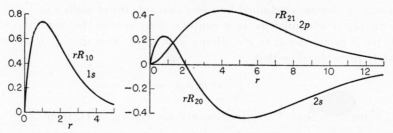

FIG. 56. The radial function rR_{nl} for several quantum states of the hydrogen atom.

plotted to the same vertical scale. The curves are labeled in the notation of the spectroscopists, the letters s, p, d, f, . . . being used to indicate $l = 0, 1, 2, 3, \ldots$, preceded by a number giving the value of n; thus:

$$
\begin{array}{cccccccc}
0 & 1 & 2 & 3 & 4 & 5 & 6 & 7 \ldots \\
s & p & d & f & g & h & i & k \ldots
\end{array}
$$

The reason for the choice of letters is stated in Sec. 116. All the radial factors R_{nl} show $(n - l)$ numerical maxima, with intervening points of zero value if $n - l > 1$.

Although nothing in the wave functions suggests the former Bohr orbits, a certain correspondence between them can be traced. The Bohr orbit has one more unit of angular momentum than has the corresponding quantum state, viz., k units of $h/2\pi$ where $k = l + 1$. In the normal or lowest-energy state there is no angular momentum, according to wave mechanics, as against 1 unit in the Bohr theory. States with $l = n - 1$ correspond to circular orbits, the other states to elliptical orbits of various eccentricities; the s state, $l = 0$, corresponds to the ellipse of maximum eccentricity for given n. The various values of λ correspond to various inclinations of the plane of the orbit to the axis.

A further connection with the Bohr orbits is found to be that, in states with $l = n - 1$, the maximum value of the radial probability density P_r or of the charge density η_r occurs at a value of r equal to the radius of the corresponding Bohr circle. In these states, as is evident from Fig. 57, the density forms a single broad hump; it is most widely distributed in the s states ($l = 0$). It is evident from the formulas that for s states ψ does not vanish at the nucleus ($r = 0$); this fact tends to give peculiar properties to these states.

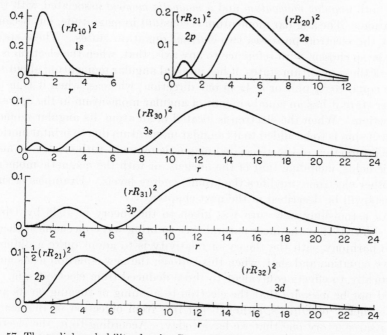

Fig. 57. The radial probability density $P_r = r^2 R_{nl}{}^2$ for several quantum states of the hydrogen atom (one curve being drawn twice for comparison).

As n increases, the curves for R_{nl}, or for P_r or η_r, spread out more and more, just as did the Bohr orbits; the atom swells, so to speak. If Z increases, on the other hand, it is evident from the formulas that the atom shrinks in inverse ratio to Z.

As a final remark, it may be stated that the mobility of the nucleus introduces exactly the same effect as we found it to do on the Bohr theory: the electronic mass m is replaced in all formulas by the reduced mass

$$m' = \frac{mM}{M + m}$$

(M = mass of nucleus).

105. Relativistic Effects and Electron Spin. The theory described so far has been a nonrelativistic one suited to cases of small energy only.

Like Newtonian mechanics, it requires modification to bring it into harmony with the principles of relativity. We cannot say much here about the relativistic form of wave mechanics; but it happens that its principal new feature can readily be described in terms of a physical picture. This feature was, in fact, discovered before the advent of wave mechanics.

In 1925, Uhlenbeck and Goudsmit pointed out[1] that certain features in atomic spectra could be explained if it was assumed that the electron "spins," or rotates about an axis through its center of mass, and that it has both *angular momentum* and a *magnetic moment* associated with this rotation. The angular momentum is constant in magnitude, but because of it the electron possesses two *internal* quantum states. These states can be so chosen, with reference to any axis, that, when the electron is in one of these quantum states, it has internal angular momentum about the axis equal to $\frac{1}{2}$ unit or $h/4\pi$ in one direction; whereas, when it is in the other state it has an equal amount of angular momentum in the opposite direction. When the electron is located in an atom, its angular momentum of spin is to be added to its angular momentum due to orbital motion. The interaction of the associated magnetic moment with electric or magnetic fields, including that of the nucleus, or with the magnetic moments of other electrons, modifies the atomic energy levels. Examples of such effects will be described in the next chapter.

An astonishing new turn was given to the theory in 1928 by Dirac. He showed[2] that the most natural way to bring wave-mechanical theory into harmony with the theory of relativity is to adopt quite a different wave equation and that, when this is done, the new equation leads automatically to effects equivalent to those deduced from electron spin. It need not be *assumed* that the electron is spinning or turning on its axis. This theory of Dirac's, although not free from objection, is the nearest to a satisfactory one that we have today. According to it, the electron does behave *as if* it had an internal angular momentum of the sort just described and an associated magnetic moment. Furthermore, if a wave packet is formed representing an electron, there is in it, in general, something like a closed current or eddy of probability that can be regarded as analogous to an actual spinning motion.

In the Dirac theory there are four wave functions for an electron instead of one. The complete Dirac theory is seldom used, however, in spectroscopic calculations. A simplified approximate form usually suffices in which only two functions, Ψ_1 and Ψ_2, are used, one for each direction of the spin moment. The spatial probability density is then

---

[1] Uhlenbeck and Goudsmit, *Naturwiss.*, vol. 13, p. 593, 1925; *Nature*, vol. 117, p. 264, 1926.

[2] Dirac, *Proc. Roy. Soc.* (*London*), vol. 117, p. 610; vol. 118, p. 351, 1928. Cf. also C. G. Darwin, *Proc. Roy. Soc.* (*London*), vol. 118, p. 654, 1928.

$|\Psi_1|^2 + |\Psi_2|^2$. The vector angular momentum of spin has a component in the direction of a chosen axis equal to $\mu h/2\pi$, where $\mu = \tfrac{1}{2}$ for one of the two functions and $\mu = -\tfrac{1}{2}$ for the other. The square of the total angular momentum is $s(s + 1)h^2/4\pi^2$ with $s = \tfrac{1}{2}$, or $3h^2/16\pi^2$. The quantum number s, however, never changes and hence is commonly ignored.

For a first approximation, the effect of the spin magnetic moment upon the energy may be ignored. When this is done, the separate wave functions for a one-electron atom may be simply the functions described in the last section, except that a fourth quantum number μ is now to be added; a time-free wave function including spin may be denoted by the symbol $\psi_{nl\lambda\mu}$. Since μ may have either one of two values, the effect of spin in this approximation is merely to double the number of quantum states. The modifications required when the effects of spin upon the atomic energy are considered will be described in Sec. 118.

106. Two Noninteracting Particles in a Box. In the next chapter an account will be given of the spectroscopy of atoms containing more than one electron. The wave-mechanical treatment of complex atoms, however, is too involved for detailed presentation in this book. For this reason, the most important new features that will be encountered will be illustrated here by extending somewhat further the simple example formerly treated.

Suppose that *two* similar particles are in the box described in Sec. 102 but that they do not interact with each other. Assume also for the present that no such phenomenon as electron spin need be considered. Let the coordinates of the particles be x_1 and x_2. Then, in classical mechanics, the combined (kinetic) energy W of the particles equals $(p_1^2 + p_2^2)/2m$, where p_1 and p_2 are their respective momenta. Replacing the momenta by operators as in Eq. (114a), we have as the time-free wave equation for the two particles

$$-\frac{h^2}{8\pi^2 m}\left(\frac{\partial^2 \psi}{\partial x_1^2} + \frac{\partial^2 \psi}{\partial x_2^2}\right) = W\psi \qquad (138)$$

Here ψ is a function of both x_1 and x_2; it has the significance that

$$|\psi|^2 \, dx_1 \, dx_2$$

is the probability of finding particle 1 in dx_1 and, simultaneously, particle 2 in dx_2. Our present problem is simple, however, in that solutions of (138) can be found which are products of functions of x_1 and x_2 separately. Such a solution, satisfying the boundary conditions and normalized so that $\int_0^L dx_1 \int_0^L dx_2 \, |\psi_{nk}|^2 = 1$, is

$$\psi_{nk} = \psi_n(x_1)\psi_k(x_2) = \frac{2}{L}\sin n\pi\frac{x_1}{L}\sin k\pi\frac{x_2}{L}$$

where ψ_n and ψ_k are one-particle functions defined as in Eq. (120), and n and k are any two positive integers. The associated energy of the system, as is easily discovered by substitution of ψ_{nk} in Eq. (138), is

$$W_{nk} = \frac{h^2}{8m} \frac{n^2 + k^2}{L^2} \tag{139}$$

This solution represents particle 1 as being in state n and particle 2 as in state k. *A new and very important form of degeneracy* now appears, however, which may be called *exchange degeneracy*. For, if x_1 and x_2 are interchanged in ψ_{nk}, provided $n \neq k$, another wave function corresponding to the same value of the energy is obtained, namely

$$\psi_{kn} = \frac{2}{L} \sin k\pi \frac{x_1}{L} \sin n\pi \frac{x_2}{L}$$

These functions as written, however, are not suitable for use in a perturbation calculation. For, if an attempt is made to correct for a small perturbing term $f(x_1,x_2)$ in the energy operator, a difficulty is encountered arising from the fact that ψ_{nk} and ψ_{kn} are associated with the same energy. Equations analogous to (132a) are obtained, and, among them, one in which n is replaced by nk and k by kn; after removing the prime from W'_{nk} in this equation, as was done in proceeding to (132b), the equation takes the form

$$(W_{kn} - W_{nk})b_{nk} + \int_0^L dx_1 \int_0^L f(x_1,x_2)\psi_{kn}\psi_{nk}\, dx_2 = 0$$

Here, however, $W_{kn} - W_{nk} = 0$; whereas the integral may not vanish.

The simplest and usual procedure in such cases is to substitute suitable *new combinations* of the degenerate wave functions. Instead of ψ_{nk} and ψ_{kn}, let us employ as zero-order functions two combinations of these functions so chosen that the matrix component of the given perturbation energy $f(x_1,x_2)$ between the new functions vanishes. The perturbation matrix is then said to be *diagonalized* with respect to these particular zero-order functions, a completely diagonal matrix being one that has zeros for all its elements except those on the leading diagonal (top left to bottom right). When such functions are used, the difficulty disappears.

The necessity of choosing suitable zero-order functions in cases of degeneracy has an exact classical analog. In the case of the vibrating drumhead described in Sec. 104c, if the symmetry is destroyed by the addition of a small eccentrically placed weight w, the effect on the frequency can be calculated by means of perturbation theory; but it is now necessary to start from a *particular choice* of the zero-order modes of vibration (see Fig. 58). One of the modified modes of vibration will closely resemble a zero-order mode in which the nodal line passes through the position of the added weight; the other new mode will have its nodal line in a perpendicular direction. One effect of the weight is thus to fix the nodal lines. Another effect is to replace the single zero-order frequency by two slightly unequal frequencies, each associated with one of the two alternative patterns of vibration. Thus the degeneracy is removed by the added weight.

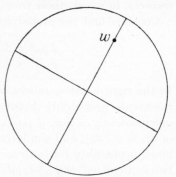

FIG. 58. Nodal lines on a loaded vibrating drumhead.

In the present case, the necessary combinations of ψ_{nk} and ψ_{kn} to serve as zero-order starting points for perturbation theory are found to be a *symmetric* one and an *antisymmetric* one defined as follows:

$$\psi_{nkS} = \frac{1}{\sqrt{2}} (\psi_{nk} + \psi_{kn}) \qquad \psi_{nkA} = \frac{1}{\sqrt{2}} (\psi_{nk} - \psi_{kn}) \qquad (140a,b)$$

If x_1 and x_2 are interchanged in these functions, it is obvious that ψ_{nkS} is unaltered, so that this function is symmetric for exchange of the two particles; whereas ψ_{nkA} just changes sign and is, therefore, antisymmetric for such exchange. The factor $1/\sqrt{2}$ is inserted to preserve the normalization. Symmetry for particle exchange, however, should not be confused with symmetry in the coordinates of one particle; an example of the first would be $\psi = (x_1 - x_2)^2$, of the second $\psi = x_1^2 x_2^4$.

The new functions are orthogonal to all independent wave functions, and also to each other; for a short calculation shows that

$$\int_0^L dx_1 \int_0^L \psi_{nkS} \psi_{nkA} \, dx_2 = 0$$

Furthermore, these functions have the property that the matrix component with respect to them of any operator that is *symmetric* in x_1 and x_2 vanishes. For example, suppose the complete wave equation contained a small potential term of the form $V = f[(x_1 - x_2)^2]$. Then $\int_0^L dx_1 \int_0^L f\psi_{nkS} \psi_{nkA} \, dx_2 = 0$. This is most quickly seen by noting that, if x_1 and x_2 are interchanged as variables of integration, which is always possible in a definite integral, the integral becomes

$$- \int_0^L dx_1 \int_0^L f\psi_{nkS} \psi_{nkA} \, dx_2$$

since ψ_{nkA} has changed sign; but the only number that is equal to its own negative is 0.

It will be noted that in both ψ_{nkS} and ψ_{nkA} the assignment of a particular particle to state n or to state k has disappeared. In two important respects, however, these functions have contrasting properties.

Consider first the probability densities

$$\psi_{nkS}^2 = \tfrac{1}{2}(\psi_{nk}^2 + \psi_{kn}^2) + \psi_{nk}\psi_{kn}$$
$$\psi_{nkA}^2 = \tfrac{1}{2}(\psi_{nk}^2 + \psi_{kn}^2) - \psi_{nk}\psi_{kn}$$

In the right-hand members of these two expressions, the *first* term represents the probability density on the assumption that the particles move independently. For, if particle 1 is in state n, the chance of finding x_1 in dx_1 is $\psi_n^2\,dx_1$, and similarly it is $\psi_k^2\,dx_2$ for x_2 in dx_2, so that the combined probability for both as independent events is the product of these two expressions, or $\psi_{nk}^2\,dx_1\,dx_2$; and similarly for the alternative arrangement represented by ψ_{kn}. The initial factor $\tfrac{1}{2}$ represents the probability of each arrangement.

The *second* term on the right, however, is a wave-mechanical novelty. Wherever x_1 and x_2 have nearly equal values, $\psi_{nk}\psi_{kn} = \psi_{nk}^2 = \psi_{kn}^2$, approximately, so that the effect of the last term is almost to double ψ_{nkS}^2 but to reduce ψ_{nkA}^2 almost to zero; when $x_1 = x_2$, $\psi_{nkA}^2 = 0$ exactly. Thus there exists an "exchange effect" that causes the particles to favor close proximity when the wave function describing their state is symmetric under exchange of their coordinates, but to avoid each other's company when the wave function is antisymmetric. It should be noted that this exchange effect is quite independent of any force-action between the particles. It has no analog in classical theory.

In the second place, consider again the first-order energy corrections due to a perturbation that is itself symmetric in the particles. For concreteness, suppose that the particles carry equal electric charges q and that their mutual electrostatic energy is f, where $f = q^2/r$, r being their distance apart. Then, in analogy with Eq. (131),

$$\Delta W_S = \iint \frac{q^2}{r}\,\psi_{nkS}^2\,dx_1\,dx_2 = \tfrac{1}{2}\iint \frac{q^2}{r}\,(\psi_{nk} + \psi_{kn})^2\,dx_1\,dx_2$$

$$\text{or}\quad \Delta W_S = \tfrac{1}{2}\iint \frac{q^2}{r}\,(\psi_{nk}^2 + \psi_{kn}^2)\,dx_1\,dx_2 + \iint \frac{q^2}{r}\,\psi_{nk}\psi_{kn}\,dx_1\,dx_2 \quad (141a)$$

$$\Delta W_A = \tfrac{1}{2}\iint \frac{q^2}{r}\,(\psi_{nk}^2 + \psi_{kn}^2)\,dx_1\,dx_2 - \iint \frac{q^2}{r}\,\psi_{nk}\psi_{kn}\,dx_1\,dx_2 \quad (141b)$$

Here it is possible to give to the first term in ΔW_S and ΔW_A a semi-classical interpretation. We can write

$$\iint \frac{q^2}{r}\,\psi_{nk}^2\,dx_1\,dx_2 = \int q[\psi_k(x_2)]^2\,dx_2 \int \frac{q}{r}\,[\psi_n(x_1)]^2\,dx_1$$

and the last integral, in dx_1, can be regarded as an expression for the potential at the point x_2 due to the cloud charge representing the first particle; whereas $q[\psi_k(x_2)]^2 \, dx_2$ is the density of the second charge cloud at this point. A similar interpretation can be put upon the contribution from ψ_{kn}^2. Thus the first term in ΔW_S and ΔW_A can be interpreted as the mutual potential energy of the two charge clouds due to classical Coulomb repulsion of the particles. The second term on the right in $(141a,b)$, on the other hand, positive in ΔW_S and negative in ΔW_A, contains an integral, known as the exchange integral, which has no direct analog in classical theory. Its opposite sign in the two cases arises from the wave-mechanical tendency already noted for the particles to cluster together in a symmetric state but to avoid each other in an antisymmetric state, thereby resulting in different mean values of the perturbing potential in the two cases. This effect occurs in addition to other possible effects caused by mutual attraction or repulsion of the particles, which may result in further corrections to the energies.

It may be remarked that the exchange effect gives rise here to a physical distinction that does not exist in classical theory. Even in the presence of the perturbing potential, there would be two possible classical motions differing only in that the two similar particles are interchanged, and, once started, these motions could not be distinguished from each other by observation. In wave mechanics, on the other hand, the two corresponding quantum states differ in energy.

Similar features occur in three-dimensional cases also. The exchange effect is limited, however, to *exactly similar* particles.

107. Electron Spin. The Exclusion Principle. In the example described in the last section, let the particles now be electrons, but let the box be large enough so that for a first approximation effects of electrostatic repulsion may be neglected. To be complete, the treatment must now be extended to include electron spin.

In dealing with many electrons, the handling of two separate wave functions for each electron, as described in Sec. 105, becomes very intricate. It is more convenient to introduce some sort of symbolism by which these separate functions can be combined symbolically into a single, composite wave function. The following concise notation, although not in general use, appears to be both convenient and adequate.

Let S_μ denote an electronic spin state characterized by the quantum number μ; to avoid writing fractions continually, however, it will be convenient to write S_α for $S_{1/2}$ and S_β for $S_{-1/2}$. A wave function for one electron may then be written $\psi = S_\alpha u_1 + S_\beta u_2$, where u_1 and u_2 are functions, real or complex, of the spatial coordinates (and, in general, also of the time). To make things come out right in products of wave functions, let us assume by definition that $S_\alpha^2 = S_\beta^2 = 1$ but

$$S_\alpha S_\beta = S_\beta S_\alpha = 0$$

Otherwise, S_μ is to behave like a real number. Then the probability density comes out correctly; thus

$$|\psi|^2 = \psi^*\psi = (S_\alpha u_1^* + S_\beta u_2^*)(S_\alpha u_1 + S_\beta u_2)$$
$$= u_1^* u_1 + u_2^* u_2 = |u_1|^2 + |u_2|^2$$

In dealing with more than one electron, we might now write a separate symbol S_μ for each. It is simpler, however, to write the sets of coordinates for the various electrons always in a standard order, and to attach subscripts to a single S in the same standard order to denote their spins. Then the general expression for ψ for two electrons will be

$$\psi = S_{\alpha\alpha}u_1(x_1,x_2,t) + S_{\alpha\beta}u_2(x_1,x_2,t) + S_{\beta\alpha}u_3(x_1,x_2,t) + S_{\beta\beta}u_4(x_1,x_2,t)$$

We will then postulate that $S_{\mu_1\mu_2}S_{\mu_1'\mu_2'}$ equals unity if $\mu_1' = \mu_1$ and $\mu_2' = \mu_2$ but otherwise equals zero.

We return now to the case of *two electrons in a box*. When their mutual repulsion is neglected, possible alternative wave functions corresponding to the same energy W_{nk} would seem to be the following four:

$$S_{\alpha\alpha}\psi_{nk} \qquad S_{\alpha\beta}\psi_{nk} \qquad S_{\beta\alpha}\psi_{nk} \qquad S_{\beta\beta}\psi_{nk}$$

Here, for example, $S_{\alpha\beta}$ indicates that the first electron has spin $\frac{1}{2}$ and the second $-\frac{1}{2}$, whereas $S_{\beta\alpha}$ indicates values $-\frac{1}{2}$ and $\frac{1}{2}$, respectively. If $n \neq k$, another set corresponding to the same energy W_{nk} would be obtained similarly from ψ_{kn}, making eight functions in all. At this point, however, account must be taken of a new fundamental principle.

The Exclusion Principle. *The wave function must be antisymmetric in the coordinates and spins of identical particles:* that is, if the coordinates and spins of one particle are interchanged as a group with those of another, the wave function must merely change sign. No reason can be given for this requirement; it is to be regarded as an independent fundamental postulate of wave mechanics. The requirement is believed to hold for electrons, protons, and neutrons, which have thus the same spin properties. It is probable that for some mesons ψ must be symmetric.

None of the wave functions so far written, however, has the required antisymmetry. It is necessary, therefore, again to substitute appropriate linear combinations of functions belonging to the same energy. Out of the eight product functions associated with energy W_{nk}, when $n \neq k$, the following four antisymmetric combinations can be made, and any other antisymmetric combination can be expressed in terms of these:

$$\psi_1 = \sqrt{\tfrac{1}{2}}S_{\alpha\alpha}(\psi_{nk} - \psi_{kn}) \qquad \psi_2 = \sqrt{\tfrac{1}{2}}S_{\beta\beta}(\psi_{nk} - \psi_{kn})$$
$$\psi' = \sqrt{\tfrac{1}{2}}(S_{\alpha\beta}\psi_{nk} - S_{\beta\alpha}\psi_{kn}) \qquad \psi'' = \sqrt{\tfrac{1}{2}}(S_{\beta\alpha}\psi_{nk} - S_{\alpha\beta}\psi_{kn})$$

Here, for example, simultaneous interchange of spatial coordinates and spins converts $S_{\alpha\beta}\psi_{nk}$ into $S_{\beta\alpha}\psi_{kn}$ and vice versa, so that the signs of both ψ' and ψ'' are reversed. The necessary reversals of ψ_1 and ψ_2 are produced by the spatial functions alone.

Our troubles are not yet over, however. The functions ψ' and ψ'' will probably not do as zero-order functions for use in perturbation theory! For, if f denotes a symmetric perturbation, we have

$$\int\int f\psi'\psi''\,dx_1\,dx_2 = -\int\int f\psi_{nk}\psi_{kn}\,dx_1\,dx_2$$

(Here $S_{\alpha\beta}S_{\beta\alpha} = S_{\beta\alpha}S_{\alpha\beta} = 0$ but $S_{\alpha\beta}S_{\alpha\beta} = S_{\beta\alpha}S_{\beta\alpha} = 1$.) The last integral is unlikely to vanish. For general use, therefore, it is preferable to substitute for ψ' and ψ'' the following new combinations proportional to their sum and difference:

$$\psi_3 = \tfrac{1}{2}(S_{\alpha\beta} + S_{\beta\alpha})(\psi_{nk} - \psi_{kn}) \qquad \psi_4 = \tfrac{1}{2}(S_{\alpha\beta} - S_{\beta\alpha})(\psi_{nk} + \psi_{kn})$$

It is now easy to show that, if f is symmetric for interchange of x_1 and x_2, then $\int\int f\psi_3\psi_4\,dx_1\,dx_2 = 0$.

It is an interesting fact that, from the properties of the spin momentum as an operator, it can be shown that ψ_1, ψ_2, and ψ_3 all give to the square of the resultant spin momentum a magnitude $S(S+1)h^2/(2\pi)^2$ with $S = 1$, and, furthermore, that the component of spin momentum in the direction of the axis that was used in defining S_α and S_β has the value $\Sigma h/2\pi$, where $\Sigma = 1, 0, -1$, for ψ_1, ψ_3, ψ_2, respectively. These values of Σ correspond to $\alpha + \alpha = 1$, $\alpha + \beta = 0$, $\beta + \beta = -1$. For ψ_4, on the other hand, $S = 0$ and $\Sigma = 0$.

The two alternative values of S can be regarded as resulting from the addition of electronic spin vectors of magnitude $\tfrac{1}{2}$ in either parallel or antiparallel positions, as in Fig. 59(a). The relation between S and the various possible values of Σ when $S = 1$ is illustrated in Fig. 59(b). Sometimes more information is put into such diagrams by drawing the vectors of lengths representing $[s(s+1)]^{1/2}$ or $[S(S+1)]^{1/2}$, but, as with the orbital momentum, this seems to be an unprofitable com-

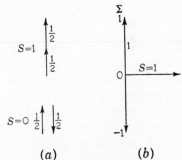

(a)   **(b)**

FIG. 59. Illustrating the addition of s vectors into an S vector, and the relation between Σ and S.

plication of the figures. Sometimes the states with $S = 1$ are described as states in which the electrons have "parallel spins," but this description seems questionable in the case of ψ_3.

To assist the memory, the four properly symmetrized wave functions thus obtained for the two electrons may be repeated in symbolic array; thus

$$
\begin{array}{ll}
S = 1 & S = 0
\end{array}
$$

$$
\left.
\begin{array}{ll}
\Sigma = & 1: \sqrt{\tfrac{1}{2}}\, S_{\alpha\alpha} \\
\Sigma = & 0: \tfrac{1}{2}(S_{\alpha\beta} + S_{\beta\alpha}) \\
\Sigma = & -1: \sqrt{\tfrac{1}{2}}\, S_{\beta\beta}
\end{array}
\right\}
(\psi_{nk} - \psi_{kn}) \qquad \tfrac{1}{2}(S_{\alpha\beta} - S_{\beta\alpha})(\psi_{nk} + \psi_{kn}) \quad (142)
$$

Thus, for $n \neq k$, the occurrence of spin with $s = \tfrac{1}{2}$, in combination with the exclusion principle, merely doubles the number of degenerate wave functions associated with the same energy W_{nk}.

It will be noted that all three functions for $S = 1$ are antisymmetric in the space coordinates alone, whereas the single function for $S = 0$ is symmetric. This feature gives to the functions *exactly the same contrasting exchange properties that were found to occur when spin was neglected.* Many quantitative results are the same, since the spin symbols disappear in all products of the wave functions. In particular, formula (141b) for ΔW_A due to a slight electrostatic interaction now holds without change for the three zero-order states with $S = 1$, whereas (141a) for ΔW_S holds for $S = 0$. It will be observed that ΔW_A is the same for all three values of Σ. Thus degeneracy of the energy levels due to spin is not completely removed by electrostatic interaction, or, in fact, by any perturbation that is symmetric in the coordinates of the two particles.

In conclusion, the important case $k = n$ remains to be noticed. In this case $\psi_{nk} - \psi_{kn} = 0$, so that only *one* antisymmetric wave function is obtained, with $S = \Sigma = 0$; it can be written

$$
\psi = \sqrt{\tfrac{1}{2}}\,(S_{\alpha\beta} - S_{\beta\alpha})\psi_{nn} \tag{143}
$$

If we try to start from $S_{\alpha\alpha}\psi_{nn}$ or $S_{\beta\beta}\psi_{nn}$, no usable wave function is obtained, after allowing for the exclusion principle. In these latter cases, n and μ both have the same value for the two electrons. This is an example of a general rule: *no two electrons can be in the same electronic quantum state.* In this form, the exclusion principle was enunciated by Pauli in 1925, before the discovery of wave mechanics.

Such statements about individual electronic quantum states have meaning, of course, only so long as the interaction between the electrons is sufficiently weak. Otherwise, the mathematical relation between the wave function ψ for the pair of electrons and wave functions for a single electron is less simple; ψ can, in fact, be written only in the form of an infinite series containing ψ_{nk}'s for all values of n and k.

The following final remark may be made concerning the physical significance of the exclusion principle. The requirement of antisymmetry in the coordinates and spins of similar particles holds, however far apart the particles may be.   Suppose, for example, a cathode ray is approaching collision with a hydrogen atom.   Then the correct wave function does not specify whether the electron that we label number 1 is the cathode ray or the atomic electron; there are equal probabilities for the two alternatives.   The labels that we attach to particular electrons seem to be a mathematical device devoid of physical meaning.   The mathematical solution does indicate that, if only one electron departs after the collision, it is probably the cathode-ray electron, but this conclusion, also, seems to have no physical significance.   In general the antisymmetric requirement has no appreciable consequences for physical observation when the electrons are very far apart.

108. Emission and Absorption of Radiation.   One of the most important properties of atoms and molecules is their ability to emit or absorb radiant energy.   In classical mechanics, emission of radiation results from the electromagnetic field emitted by accelerated electric charges (Sec. 227), whereas absorption results from work done on the charges by forces exerted on them by the electric vector of an incident field.   In wave mechanics, on the other hand, both emission and absorption are associated with transitions of atoms or molecules between quantum states of different energies.   No details of the mathematical arguments can be given, but the results obtained from theory are easily stated.

a. Transition Probabilities and Mean Life.   Let the quantum states for an atom all be numbered off in a single series.   Then, when an atom is in state n, there is a certain probability that during an interval of time dt it will jump spontaneously into another state j, with the emission of a photon of frequency $(W_n - W_j)/h$.   This probability is denoted by $A_{nj}\, dt$.   Out of a large number N of atoms in state n, NA_{nj} will jump per second into state j.

It is of interest to consider the history of N_0 atoms that start in state n.   If N of them are still in that state after a time t, then during time dt a number $-dN$ will leave by spontaneous radiative transitions, where

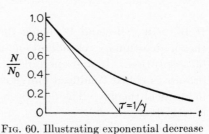

$$dN = -N\gamma\, dt \qquad \gamma = \Sigma(j) A_{nj}$$

Here $\Sigma(j)$ denotes a sum over all states into which a spontaneous jump can occur out of state n, that

FIG. 60. Illustrating exponential decrease by radiative transitions. $\tau = \tau_n$.

is, over all states having lower energy.   In a particular case, some A_{nj}'s may, of course, be zero.   Integrating (cf. Fig. 60),

$$N = N_0 e^{-\gamma t}$$

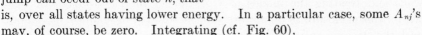

Obviously there is no absolute limit to the length of time that an individual atom may remain in a given quantum state. The *average* time τ_n spent by the atoms in state n is called the *mean life* of an atom in that state. To find it, consider N_0 atoms that have just entered this state. Then, during each dt, $N\gamma\, dt$ of them will leave the state after spending a time t in it; and, inserting the value of N from the last equation, we can write

$$\tau_n = \frac{1}{N_0} \int_0^\infty t(N_0 e^{-\gamma t}\gamma\, dt) = \gamma \int_0^\infty t e^{-\gamma t}\, dt$$

$$= -t e^{-\gamma t}\Big|_0^\infty + \int_0^\infty e^{-\gamma t}\, dt$$

after integrating by parts. But $t e^{-\gamma t} \to 0$ as $t \to \infty$; and

$$\int_0^\infty e^{-\gamma t}\, dt = 1/\gamma$$

Hence

$$\tau_n = \frac{1}{\gamma} = \left[\Sigma\,(j) A_{nj} \right]^{-1} \tag{144}$$

For atomic states involved in visible or ultraviolet emission, τ_n is commonly of the order of 10^{-8} sec; in the x-ray region it is much smaller.

Fortunately, absorption, also, can be treated in terms of the same coefficient A_{nj}. Let ν_{nj} be the frequency of a photon emitted during a spontaneous transition between states n and j; and let an atom in state n be bathed by isotropic radiation with a spectral density u_{nj} in the neighborhood of ν_{nj}, that is, let there be $u_{nj}\, d\nu$ ergs of radiant energy per cubic centimeter in a frequency range $d\nu$. Then it is found that during dt there is a chance $B_{nj}u_{nj}\, dt$ that the atom will jump into state j, where

$$B_{nj} = \frac{c^3}{8\pi h \nu_{nj}{}^3} A_{nj} \tag{145}$$

If $W_j > W_n$, W_n and W_j being the atomic energies for the two states, then a quantum $h\nu_{nj}$ of radiant energy disappears and the transition is one of absorption. If, however, $W_j < W_n$, energy $h\nu_{nj}$ is emitted and the process is called "induced emission." The latter possibility exists also in classical theory. The *total* probability of transition in the latter case is $(A_{nj} + B_{nj}u_{nj})\, dt$.

b. Calculation of Transition Probabilities. Values of A_{nj} can be calculated by considering an atom placed in an enclosure with reflecting walls and treating the modes of vibration of the electromagnetic field within this enclosure as oscillators subject to wave mechanics, in analogy with the classical treatment described in Sec. 67. There is an interaction between the field and the atom, and, if $W_j < W_n$, the result of this interaction is a transition of the atom into state j and an excitation of the field oscillators, with maximum amplitude of excitation for oscillators having a natural frequency near ν_{nj}. Oscillators with neighboring frequencies are also found to be excited to a lesser extent; this spread in the excitation of the field corresponds to the natural breadth of the emitted spectral line.

The result of the calculation is an expression for A_{nj} of which the most important part can be written

$$A_{nj} = \frac{64\pi^4 e^2 \nu_{nj}{}^3}{3hc^3} \left(|x_{nj}|^2 + |y_{nj}|^2 + |z_{nj}|^2\right) \tag{146}$$

Here e = electronic charge, h = Planck's constant, c = speed of light, x, y, z are the cartesian coordinates of the jumping electron, and x_{nj}, y_{nj}, z_{nj} denote matrix components between the two quantum states. If ψ_n, ψ_j denote the wave functions for the two states, then, for a one-electron atom

$$x_{nj} = \iiint x \psi_n^* \psi_j \, dx \, dy \, dz \tag{147}$$

with similar integrals for y_{nj} and z_{nj}.

The expression for A_{nj} has an interesting correspondence with classical results. As is noted in Eq. (311) of Appendix I, a charge e vibrating classically in linear motion with amplitude D and frequency ν_{nj} radiates energy at the average rate

$$\frac{16}{3} \frac{\pi^4 e^2 D^2 \nu_{nj}{}^4}{c^3} \quad \text{ergs per sec}$$

Dividing by $h\nu_{nj}$, the energy in a photon, we have

$$\frac{16\pi^4 e^2 D^2 \nu_{nj}{}^3}{3hc^3} \quad \text{photons per sec}$$

This agrees with the expression given for A_{nj} in Eq. (146), which represents the probability per second for photon emission, provided we drop y_{nj} and z_{nj}, in order to have one-dimensional motion, and substitute

$$D = 2|x_{nj}|$$

Because of such correspondences, the term in A_{nj} that is given in (146) is said to refer to *dipole* emission by the atom.

If the dipole terms in A_{nj} all vanish, this particular transition cannot occur by dipole emission and is said to be "forbidden" so far as dipole emission is concerned. A small probability of radiative transition may still exist, however, because of the omitted "quadrupole" or higher-order terms in A_{nj}.

CHAPTER 7

ATOMIC STRUCTURE AND OPTICAL SPECTRA

In the discussion of quantum theory in Chap. 5, we considered only atoms containing a single electron. We shall now attempt to explain the properties of the numerous kinds of atoms (and molecules) that contain two or more electrons.

The Rutherford-Bohr model of the atom was built out of raw material which grew in the field of physics. Originally, however, the atom was a child of chemistry. The ultimate theory of its structure must explain and agree with the facts of chemistry, which are just as cogent as are the facts of physics. In part of the present chapter, we shall deal with the explanation of the periodic table of the elements. In another part, we shall return to the study of spectra. The two topics are closely related; for wave mechanics furnishes the key to the theoretical understanding of both subjects. The mathematical theory encounters such great difficulties, however, that empirical evidence from the facts of spectroscopy has to be invoked in order to interpret some of the finer details of atomic structure which are important to the chemist.

A few features of the theory will first be described, in sufficient detail to furnish an adequate background for an understanding of the wave-mechanical basis for the periodic table.

COMPLEX ATOMS

109. The Central-field Approximation for a Many-electron Atom. If there were no repulsion between the electrons, the theory of complex atoms would be very simple. Each electron, being subject only to the field of the nucleus, might be in the same sort of electronic state as if it were alone in the atom. Actually, however, the effect of electronic repulsion must be large. The total negative charge on all electrons in a neutral atom is numerically equal to the positive charge on the nucleus, so that at points far outside the atom the electrons completely screen off the nuclear field and the net field is zero. Inside the atom, as the nucleus is approached, the screening becomes less and less, until near the nucleus the field of force becomes essentially that due to the nucleus alone. Even the innermost electrons, however, are affected by the presence of the others, for the work required to remove any electron to infinity is considerably diminished by the repulsion of the others.

Suppose, for example, that the total negative charge on the electrons were spread out continuously with spherical symmetry, its (negative) density ρ being a function only of the distance r from the nucleus. Then, by a familiar result in electrostatics, the charge in a shell of radius r_1 and thickness dr_1 (Fig. 61), of magnitude $4\pi\rho r_1{}^2\, dr_1$, would produce a potential of magnitude

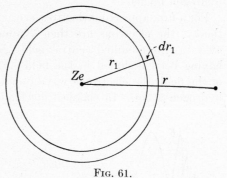

FIG. 61.

$4\pi\rho r_1{}^2\, dr_1/r$ at any external point r, and a corresponding electric field. Inside the shell it would produce no electric vector but only a uniform potential $4\pi\rho r_1{}^2\, dr_1/r_1$. The total electrostatic potential at a distance r from the nucleus would thus be

$$\phi(r) = \frac{Ze}{r} + \frac{1}{r}\int_0^r 4\pi\rho r_1{}^2\, dr_1 + \int_r^\infty 4\pi\rho r_1\, dr_1 \qquad (148)$$

Here all electrical quantities are in electrostatic units and e is the numerical electronic charge; Ze is the positive charge on the nucleus and is related to ρ by the equation $\int_0^\infty 4\pi\rho r_1{}^2\, dr_1 = -Ze$.

This classical picture suggested the following simplified wave-mechanical approach to the problem, which has been very useful. The total electronic charge is imagined to be spread out in a spherically symmetrical charge cloud analogous to that described for one electron in Sec. 104, and the combined field of potential $\phi(r)$ due to the nucleus and to this electronic charge is calculated by formula (148). The determination of such charge clouds is more precisely described in Sec. 122. As an example, the calculated radial density η_r of the cloud charge for a neutral argon atom is plotted in Fig. 62; ϕ is also plotted in a certain manner, as explained under the figure.

The field as thus obtained may be used as it stands in calculating the deflection of an external electron such as a cathode ray passing through the atom. An internal electron, however, will in reality be repelled only by the other electrons, not by itself. To correct for this fact, we should omit the part of the charge cloud that is due to the internal electron under consideration. For a first approximation this can be done simply by reducing the contribution of the charge cloud to $\phi(r)$ in the ratio

$(N - 1)/N$, N being the number of electrons in the atom and equal to Z if the atom is not ionized.   Outside a neutral atom the field will then reduce to that due to a single unit of nuclear charge, or to the field of a hydrogen nucleus.

For a first approximation to serve as the starting point for perturbation theory, the electrons are then assumed to move *without repelling each other* in this modified central field, the *average* effect of their repulsion having been included in the field.   Because of the spherical symmetry of the field, the electronic wave functions are almost as simple as in the hydrogen atom.   In classical mechanics, the vector angular momentum

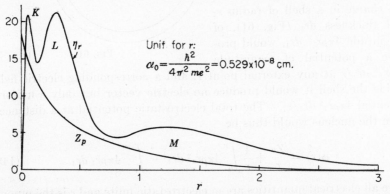

Fig. 62. The Hartree field and charge-cloud density for argon.   The potential energy of an additional electron inside the argon atom would be $-eZ_p/r$ (e = numerical electronic charge, r = distance from the nucleus); the amount of electronic charge between r and $r + dr$ in terms of e as a unit is $\eta_r\, dr$. K, L, M indicate the approximate locations of the K, L, and M shells.

would remain constant.   Analogously, it is found in wave mechanics that the electronic states are characterized by the same angular-momentum properties as in a one-electron atom; the wave functions contain, in fact, the same mathematical functions of θ and ϕ that are represented in Eq. (134) for a single electron, only the radial factor R_{nl} being different. The radial factor is still characterized, however, by a number n, and, as in a Coulomb field, it has $(n - l)$ numerical maxima, separated by zeros if $n - l > 1$.   (A Coulomb field of potential is one like that due to a positive point charge.)   The electronic states may thus be characterized by four quantum numbers $n\ l\ \lambda\ \mu$ which are subject only to the restrictions that n, l, and λ are integers or zero and

$$n > l \geqq |\lambda| \qquad \mu = \tfrac{1}{2} \text{ or } -\tfrac{1}{2}$$

The values of l may be represented by the letters s, p, d, . . . , as in Sec. 104e.

The *energy* of an electron in the modified central field depends, as in a Coulomb field, chiefly upon n, but in this more general case it varies also somewhat with l, increasing (algebraically) as l is increased. Thus the states of lowest electronic energy are the $1s$ states ($n = 1, l = 0, \lambda = 0, \mu = \pm \frac{1}{2}$); the next lowest are the $2s$ states ($n = 2, l = 0, \lambda = 0, \mu = \pm \frac{1}{2}$), with somewhat lower energy than the six $2p$ states ($n = 2, l = 1, \lambda = 1, 0,$ or $-1, \mu = \pm \frac{1}{2}$); and so on. Thus degeneracy exists; and for some purposes it is preferable to substitute other states than those characterized by λ and μ (Sec. 122).

The remark may be added that motion of the nucleus is of little interest in dealing with many-electron atoms.

110. Shells and Subshells. An assignment of all electrons to electronic quantum states will then define, in the zero order of perturbation theory, a quantum state for the atom as a whole. In assigning the electrons, however, account must be taken of the exclusion principle (Sec. 107); no two electrons may be assigned to the same electronic quantum state. Furthermore, it makes no difference which electron is assigned to a given state. Thus, to specify a zero-order quantum state for the atom, it suffices to specify a sufficient number of sets of the quantum numbers $n\, l\, \lambda\, \mu$, with no two sets alike in all four numbers, to accommodate all the electrons in the atom.

For the normal, or lowest-energy, state of the atom, the electrons must be assigned to states of the lowest energy possible. The first two electrons will go, therefore, into $1s$ states with $\mu = \frac{1}{2}$ or $-\frac{1}{2}$. Since no other states are possible with $n = 1$, the next two electrons must go into $2s$ states, with considerably higher energy, and the next six into $2p$ states, with slightly higher energy still. The next two will go into $3s$ states with much higher energy, and so on.

Thus the electrons in an atom normally fall into distinct groups differing in the value of the quantum number n. Electrons having the same n are said to belong to the same *shell*. Each shell is then regarded as divided into *subshells* according to the values of l. Any subshell may contain up to $2(2l + 1)$ electrons but no more. For λ can range from the value l down through zero to $-l$, making $2l + 1$ different values for λ, and in each case μ may be either $\frac{1}{2}$ or $-\frac{1}{2}$. The numbers of electrons in the various types of closed subshells are, therefore, as follows:

$$
\begin{array}{ccccc}
s & p & d & f & g \\
2 & 6 & 10 & 14 & 18
\end{array}
$$

The maximum possible number of electrons in a whole *shell*, on the other hand, is $2n^2$. For, if n is increased to $n + 1$, a new subshell is added with $l = n$ and containing, therefore, $2(2n + 1)$ electrons, and the number $2n^2$ likewise increases by $2[(n + 1)^2 - n^2]$ or $2(2n + 1)$, while

$2n^2$ is obviously correct for $n = 1$. A shell or subshell that contains as many electrons as it can hold is said to be completed or full or closed. It can only happen exceptionally that an atom contains only full subshells.

The shells are often referred to by the capital letters which became attached to them in the early days of x-ray study (Secs. 149b and 154). These designations are shown below, also, in part, in Table 7-1, in which the numbers and notation for the first three shells are summarized:

$$n = \qquad 1 \quad 2 \quad 3 \quad 4 \quad 5 \quad 6 \quad 7$$
$$\text{x-ray designation:} \quad K \quad L \quad M \quad N \quad O \quad P \quad Q$$

TABLE 7-1. ELECTRON SHELLS AND SUBSHELLS

Shell	K	L		M		
n	1	2		3		
Subshell, l	0	0	1	0	1	2
Letter designation	s	s	p	s	p	d
Number of electrons in subshell or shell..... $\left\{ \begin{array}{c} \\ \\ \end{array} \right.$	2	2	6	2	6	10
	2	8		18		

A more complete list is contained in Table 7-2 in Sec. 114.

The same kind of electronic structure occurs in ions as in neutral atoms. The modified central field is, however, somewhat different, reducing outside the atom to the Coulomb field due to a positive charge $N'e$ in the case of an N'-fold ionized atom.

THE PERIODIC TABLE OF THE ELEMENTS

111. General Features of the Periodic Table. Mention was made, in discussing the Rutherford atomic model, of the concept of atomic number. This concept was firmly established by the work of Moseley and others on x-rays, to be described later. An atomic number Z was thereby unambiguously assigned to each element, up to 92 for uranium. Thus the periodic table, drawn up by the chemists primarily on the basis of chemical facts, was established with the assurance that there were no *unknown gaps* in it. The atomic numbers of the elements are shown in Appendixes II and III.

The value of Z represents primarily the numerical ratio of the charge on the nucleus to the electronic charge, but it is also equal to the number of electrons surrounding the nucleus when the atom is in its normal, neutral condition. The chemical properties of an element are commonly associated with the neutral atom and may be regarded as depending upon either the nuclear charge or the number of the circumnuclear electrons in a neutral atom. The problem of the periodic table is to be solved, therefore, by determining the arrangement of the electrons in the atom and the physical and chemical properties that follow from this arrangement. Before the advent of wave mechanics, there were many speculations concerning the reasons for these properties.

A bird's-eye view of the chief features to be explained is best gained from an arrangement of the table given by Bohr and reproduced in Fig. 63. Perhaps the most striking feature is the recurrence of a noble or

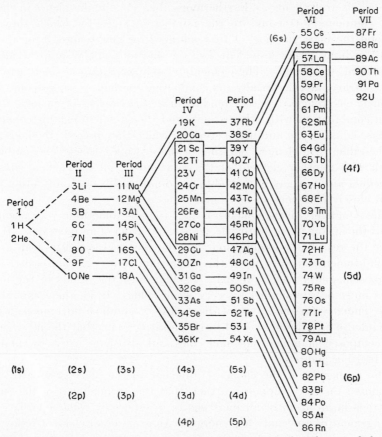

FIG. 63. Bohr's periodic table of the elements, in terms of modern symbols.

inert gas, forming a series of turning points in the progression of the elements. It was pointed out by Rydberg that the values of Z for the inert gases could be expressed by a simple numerical series:

$$Z = 2(1^2 + 2^2 + 2^2 + 3^2 + 3^2 + 4^2 + \cdots)$$

namely: helium, $2 \times 1^2 = 2$; neon, 10; argon, 18; krypton, 36; xenon, 54; radon, 86. The existence of this series suggested that the electrons might be arranged in layers containing, in succession, 2, 8, 8, 18, 18, 32 electrons.

The "inert" gases show comparatively little tendency for their atoms to join with other atoms in chemical combination. The elements standing in the table on either side of an inert gas, on the other hand, are strongly active chemically, and have contrasting properties. Those closely *following* an inert gas, like lithium, beryllium, potassium, calcium, and so on, are metallic and strongly electropositive; they readily form *positive* electrolytic ions. Furthermore, their maximum valence in chemical compounds is equal to the number of steps by which they lie beyond the inert gas (e.g., 1 for sodium, 2 for magnesium, 3 for aluminum; sodium forms univalent ions in solution; magnesium, bivalent; aluminum, trivalent). The elements closely *preceding* an inert gas, on the contrary, are electrically nonconducting, perhaps even gaseous, and strongly electronegative; they tend to form *negative* electrolytic ions, alone or in combination with other atoms, and they tend to exhibit chemical valence equal to the number of steps by which they precede the inert gas in the table. An element of either of these two kinds scarcely combines at all with another element of the same kind; but an element closely preceding an inert gas in the table combines readily with any other element closely following an inert gas.

These facts invite the conclusion that there is something very peculiar about the arrangement of the electrons in an atom of an inert gas. If we make the reasonable assumption that the chemical activity of an atom is conditioned somehow upon the magnitude of its external electric (or perhaps magnetic) field, we may conclude that the atoms of the inert gases must be surrounded by very weak fields. If so, there should be little tendency for the atoms of these gases to combine into molecules or to condense into liquid or solid form; and it is a fact that the inert gases are composed of monatomic molecules and also have very low boiling and freezing points.

The properties of the elements adjacent to the inert gases are then accounted for if we suppose, further, that the arrangement of the outer electrons in an atom of an inert gas is an especially *stable* one, i.e., an arrangement of especially low energy. An atom of an element following an inert gas in the table will then contain 1 or 2 extra electrons outside an inert-gas core (e.g., sodium has 1 and magnesium 2 electrons outside of a neon core); and these extra electrons may well be comparatively easy to detach. The tendency of such atoms to form positive ions would thus be explained. Furthermore, in the solid state these extra "valence" electrons may easily come loose under the attraction of neighboring atoms, functioning, therefore, as free electrons, so that the elements in question ought to be good conductors of electricity, which they are.

An element such as chlorine, on the other hand, could arrange its electrons as they are arranged in argon if it had 1 more electron. Elements closely preceding an inert gas in the periodic table might, therefore, be expected to exhibit a tendency to pick up an extra electron, thereby forming a negative ion. Some of these elements do, in fact, form negative ions that are more stable, i.e., have lower energy, than the neutral atom; this is true of the halogens and of oxygen and sulfur. In the solid state, such atoms would probably contain no electrons with a tendency to become free; thus, the absence of electrical conductivity in these elements would be accounted for.

These ideas furnish a ready explanation for the formation of a compound such as sodium chloride. In combining, the sodium atom loses 1 electron, its remaining 10 electrons then forming the stable configuration that is characteristic of neon (but, doubtless, somewhat more compressed because the nuclear charge of sodium is higher by 1 unit than that of neon). The chlorine atom adds the electron lost by the sodium to its own 17, making 18 electrons arranged in the stable argon configuration (but slightly expanded because of the weaker nuclear charge of chlorine). The electrostatic attraction of the 2 ions thus formed then binds them tightly together into a molecule. When the molecule of sodium chloride thus formed is put into water, the attraction of the ions is weakened and the molecules fall apart into the constituent ions, each with its outer group of electrons in the arrangement characteristic of an inert gas. In a crystal of sodium chloride, also, the grouping into molecules disappears; a crystal of this type is composed of ions but not of molecules. Thus many chemical and physical facts can be correlated if we make the assumption that the arrangement of the electrons occurring in an inert gas is a peculiarly stable one of low energy.

One of the principal problems of an explanatory theory of the atom is thus to account for the high stability of certain electronic configurations. Then an explanation must be found for the systematic sequences that occur in the periodic table between the inert gases. As the atomic weight increases, these sequences become longer and the elements of a sequence become more similar in chemical properties; many of the "rare earths" are even difficult to separate chemically. A successful theory should lead automatically to all these relations between chemical properties and atomic number on the basis of as few assumptions as possible.

112. The First Two Periods. The key to the periodic table was finally furnished by wave mechanics, with the help of two new principles that we have seen to be associated with it: the Pauli exclusion principle and the principle of electron spin. These two additions to the theory were not made until 1925. It will now be shown, taking the elements in the order of their atomic numbers, that the electronic groupings as inferred from wave mechanics enable us to understand the sequence of the elements. The *neutral atom* will be assumed to be under discussion.

a. Z = 1. Hydrogen. A single electron in an atom will normally be in a $1s$ electronic quantum state. Degeneracy exists because of the two possible values of μ.

b. Z = 2. Helium. Two electrons combined with a nucleus for which $Z = 2$ can both go into $1s$ states, with quantum numbers $(1\ 0\ 0\ \tfrac{1}{2})$, $(1\ 0\ 0\ -\tfrac{1}{2})$. It can be shown from wave mechanics that the electronic charge cloud in helium is spherically symmetrical about the nucleus. It follows easily, by Gauss's theorem, that there should be no electric field at all outside the atom. Atoms of helium ought, therefore, to exhibit comparatively little tendency to associate themselves into a liquid or solid phase, in agreement with observation. The *chemical* inertness of helium, on the other hand, results from other causes (see Sec. 113).

In helium the K shell is complete. The electronic formula of helium is $1s^2$. All heavier atoms will be expected to contain, next to the nucleus, a complete K shell of this sort.

c. Z = 3. Lithium. The third electron in lithium, outside the helium-like core, must occupy a state with $n = 2$. The electronic energy associated with a $2s$ wave function is somewhat less than that associated with a $2p$ function for an electron in the atomic central field (see Sec. 117); hence, we should expect the third electron to be in a $2s$ state when the atom as a whole is in its normal state. Spectroscopic evidence confirming this conclusion will be described later. The electronic constitution of normal lithium should be, therefore,

$$1s^2 2s$$

$1s^2$ denoting two electrons in $1s$ states. Since s means $l = 0$, we have $\lambda = 0$, but $\mu = \pm\tfrac{1}{2}$, so again there is a twofold degeneracy, or a "statistical weight" of 2, in the normal state of lithium.

The energy for a $2s$ wave function is found upon calculation to lie much higher than that for a $1s$ function. If the field were a Coulomb field, as for a one-electron atom, we could use Eq. (135) in Sec. 104, which shows that in such a field the $2s$ state ($n = 2$) lies only a quarter as far below the ionization level as does the $1s$ state ($n = 1$). Hence, the $2s$ electron should be comparatively easy to remove, certainly much easier than either electron in helium. Lithium ought, therefore, to form positive ions easily, and it ought to conduct electricity when in the solid state, the $2s$ electrons of the atoms easily coming loose and functioning as "free" electrons. Both conclusions are in agreement with fact. Since the ion formed by removal of the $2s$ electron is univalent, lithium should combine chemically with a valence of 1; such is the fact, as shown by such compounds as Li_2O, LiOH, LiCl.

To remove also a $1s$ electron from a lithium atom should require much more energy than to remove the $2s$ or "valence" electron. In harmony with this conclusion, the first ionization potential of lithium is observed to be only 5.39 volts, as against 75.6 volts for the second.   Furthermore, since there is little symmetry to be expected from a single electron in the second shell, the lithium atoms should be surrounded by stray electric fields and should readily group themselves into a condensed phase.   The melting point of lithium is 186°C.

The *arc* spectrum from lithium is predominantly that to be expected from a single electron, as described below (Secs. 116, 117, and 119). Evidently the emission of radiation is chiefly due to the outer or valence electron.   The so-called *spark* spectrum, on the other hand, which is ascribed to emission by singly ionized atoms of lithium, contains singlets and triplets of lines like the *arc* spectrum of *neutral helium*.   This is what we should expect on the basis of the theory, for a singly ionized lithium atom contains the same number of electrons as neutral helium.   The frequencies of corresponding lines are much higher than in helium, however, because the stronger nuclear charge causes all energy levels to lie much lower.

d. $Z = 4$.   *Beryllium.*   Two electrons outside the K shell can both be in $2s$ states but with opposite spins ($\mu = \pm \frac{1}{2}$).   The resulting element should be a metal rather like lithium but bivalent, since both $2s$ electrons should come off relatively easily.   Such is the case.   The oxide, hydroxide, and chloride have the formulas BeO, $Be(OH)_2$, $BeCl_2$.

The second electron is harder to remove than the first, however, since the second helps push the first off by repelling it; the first two ionization potentials of beryllium are 9.3 and 18.2 volts.   To remove a third electron, out of the $1s$ shell, requires 154 volts, and to remove the last one, 218 volts.

Again the spectral evidence confirms the theory.   The *arc* spectrum of beryllium is a two-electron spectrum of singlets and triplets like that of neutral helium.   In this case both valence electrons play a role in the emission.   In the *spark* spectrum, on the other hand, doublet lines like those from neutral lithium are found; these are emitted by singly ionized beryllium atoms.   A few singlet lines are also known in the spark spectrum; it is presumed that they are part of a two-electron spectrum emitted by doubly ionized beryllium atoms.   Two lines have even been found which are ascribed to triply ionized atoms.

So far it is obvious that the theory succeeds admirably.   But perhaps the student will have wondered why beryllium is not, like helium, a gas with a low boiling point.   For the $2s$ wave functions are just as symmetrical as the $1s$ functions.   As a matter of fact, even the single $2s$ function for the valence electron in lithium is symmetrical about the nucleus! Only a detailed study of the mathematics of the perturbation theory can really throw light on this question.   A satisfactory theoretical answer to such questions can be given, but it is hard to describe in concrete terms.

e. Z = 5. Boron. With five electrons in the atom, one of them must go into a $2p$ state. Boron is a trivalent element, as witness B_2O_3, $B(OH)_3$, BCl_3. It is not metallic, however; crystals of boron are good insulators. Evidently, with three electrons present in the L shell, conditions are not favorable to the formation of free electrons in the solid state. No simple reason for this is apparent, however.

To remove the $2p$ electron from a boron atom requires only 8.3 volts; to remove the two $2s$ electrons in succession requires 25 and 38 volts, whereas to remove one of the $1s$ electrons as well requires an additional 259 volts.

The next elements in order are most easily understood if we pass them by for the moment and consider neon next.

f. Z = 10. Neon. It is possible to put into an atom two $2s$ electrons and six $2p$ electrons, or eight in all, but no more electrons with $n = 2$. The L shell is then filled. With every possible value of λ and μ represented, it can be shown that the electronic charge cloud is symmetrical about the nucleus, as it is in helium; and now the symmetry is sufficiently complete so that a gas having a low boiling point results. Neutral neon in its normal state has the electronic constitution $1s^2 2s^2 2p^6$.

g. Z = 9. Fluorine: $1s^2 2s^2 2p^5$. If $Z = 9$, the neutral atom contains only seven electrons in the L shell or one less than enough to fill it. If one more electron were added, we should have a negative ion the exterior of which would be a closed shell, as in neutral neon. It cannot be expected that the same loss of energy would occur when an electron is added to a *neutral* atom as when it is added to a *positive ion;* but, on the other hand, the electron is added in the shell for $n = 2$ in an atom having a fairly strong nuclear field $(Z = 9)$. We can thus understand the fact that fluorine forms univalent negative ions which are stable, i.e., have lower energy than the neutral atom, and that it exhibits a negative valence of 1 in chemical combination. There should be little tendency for a *second* extra electron to be bound by the fluorine atom, for it would have to occupy a state with $n = 3$, the energy of which would lie considerably higher.

h. Z = 8, 7. Similarly, *oxygen* $(Z = 8, 1s^2 2s^2 2p^4)$ commonly exhibits a negative valence of 2 in chemical combination, as in lithium oxide, Li_2O; and *nitrogen* $(Z = 7, 1s^2 2s^2 2p^3)$ is commonly trivalent, as in lithium nitride, Li_3N. More often, however, nitrogen is united with oxygen into a compound radical, as in $LiNO_3$.

The examples of Li_2O and Li_3N illustrate the tendency of elements immediately following a rare gas in the order of atomic number to combine with those just preceding some rare gas. This can be interpreted as arising from a lowering of the energy when closed subshells are formed in both atoms. In forming the molecule Li_2O, for example, an electron passes over from each lithium atom to the oxygen atom, leaving the lithium atoms with closed $1s^2$ shells like helium, while the oxygen acquires a closed $2s^22p^6$ shell, as in neon.

i. $Z = 6$. *Carbon:* $1s^22s^22p^2$. With four electrons in the L shell, carbon would seem to have an equal chance either to lose electrons or to add more in an effort to form the closed group of eight. Actually, it probably never does either! The four equal valences of carbon are famous, but its compounds are not formed by a transfer of electrons. Carbon is a typical transition element. In some forms (amorphous carbon, graphite), it exhibits fair metallic conductivity; but in diamond it is an excellent insulator.

At this point, we may with advantage interrupt the discussion of the elements in order to describe more fully the wave-mechanical theory of valence. This forms part of the general theory of the force-actions between atoms.

113. Valence Bonds. Chemists have long regarded the binding of atoms into molecules as being of two distinct types. In some compounds, called "homopolar," the various atoms seem to play similar roles; examples are the compounds in which carbon atoms are joined to each other, and also the diatomic molecules of certain elements, such as N_2 or Cl_2. Other compounds, called "heteropolar" or simply "polar," are distinguished by the fact that the atoms easily fall apart as charged ions; examples are salts like NaCl. It was suspected even before the advent of wave mechanics that the nonpolar bonds might arise from some sort of cooperative action between a superficial electron in one atom and a similar electron in the other, whereas in a polar compound it was assumed that an electron became transferred from one atom to the other.

This interpretation of the two kinds of bonds was later derived, with characteristic modifications, from the wave-mechanical theory. In order to explain how the binding comes about, consider in a general way the interaction of two neutral atoms as they approach each other from a distance. To a first approximation, the electrons in each atom may be treated as being equivalent to a spherically symmetrical charge cloud surrounding the nucleus. In this approximation neither atom is surrounded by an electric field, since both are electrically neutral; hence there is no force-action between them. The picture of the electrons as revolving in orbits, on the other hand, suggests that, although on the average the field due to the electrons might just cancel the nuclear field, there should also be a rapidly fluctuating residual field. This field would polarize the other atom, by repelling its electrons, and would consequently exert a fluctuating attractive effect upon it. The analog of this classical effect is encountered when the wave-mechanical perturbation theory is developed further; an attraction of one atom for another, sometimes called a van der Waals attraction, is then found to exist. This attraction is responsible for the phenomenon of cohesion, but it has not much to do with the binding of atoms into chemical compounds.

Chemical forces come into play only when atoms approach so closely that their *electronic charge clouds begin to overlap*. New effects then occur. The most important of these is the *electron-exchange effect*, which was described in a simple case in Secs. 106 and 107. Its consequences are of opposite character according as the two electrons involved have the same or opposite spins.

Where charge clouds due to electrons of the *same spin* overlap, the result is a *repulsion* between the atoms. The exchange effect tends to thin out the charge density in the region of overlap. Now the region in which overlap first occurs will be the region lying between the approaching atoms, and this region is one of relatively low energy for an electron because of relatively close proximity to both nuclei. Hence, the exchange effect, by shifting some of the electronic charge clouds out of this region into regions of higher energy, raises the total atomic energy. The atoms tend therefore to fly apart, since they will tend to move so as to diminish their combined energy.

If, on the other hand, the overlapping charge clouds belong to electrons of *opposite spin*, the exchange effect draws charge density *into* the region of overlap and so lowers the mutual atomic energy. The atoms tend, therefore, to come closer together, as if they *attracted* each other.

When all the electrons in an atom are considered, the sign of the net exchange effect depends on the relative arrangement of the electrons in the two atoms. As between an electron and a closed subshell, which contains equal numbers of electrons of both spins, the net exchange effect turns out to result in repulsion. This is the cause of the observed general mutual *impenetrability* of atoms and molecules; it is due chiefly to repulsion between complete subshells as wholes. During a collision caused by thermal agitation, a very slight overlap of the charge clouds suffices to develop sufficient repulsion to cause the molecules to rebound from each other. Hence in such collisions the centers of the molecules remain relatively far apart. In the case of argon, for example, the "radius" of the atom as calculated by means of the kinetic theory of gases, which represents about half the distance between two atoms in an ordinary collision, is at the value 3.45 of the abscissa in Fig. 62, and is thus entirely off the plot. Only a minute part of the charge cloud lies as far as this from the nucleus.

If, on the other hand, each atom has an electron sticking out on its surface, so to speak, beyond any closed subshells that may also be present, these two valence electrons, one in each atom, are able to adjust their spins so that they are opposite. The exchange effect between these two electrons can then draw the atoms together into a molecule. Atoms thus combined by means of a pair of electrons acting by virtue of the exchange effect are said to be held together in the molecule by a *covalent bond;* and binding of this type is believed to account for the compounds called *homopolar* by the chemist. Exactly as many covalent bonds can be formed for a given atom as there are extra electrons in it outside of closed subshells, so long as these electrons do not more than half fill the next possible subshell. The atom will thus exhibit chemical valence equal to the number of these extra electrons.

If, however, the extra electrons more than half fill a new subshell, the number available to form covalent bonds tends not to exceed the number of electrons that stand alone in the subshell unmatched by other electrons having the same λ but opposite spin. This number is also equal to the number of electrons that would be required to complete the subshell, or to the number of "holes" in it. Thus, when a subshell is more than half full, we can imagine the covalent bonds to be formed by the *holes* in connection with superficial electrons, or perhaps with similar holes, in other atoms. Electrons in an incomplete outer subshell are called *valence* electrons. Perhaps this term might also be extended to the holes in those subshells that are more than half full.

The presence of holes leads also to the existence of a second distinct type of chemical bonding. If the charge cloud of an extra electron lying outside of a closed subshell on one atom comes opposite a hole in an incomplete subshell in another atom, the charge cloud may be drawn into the hole, so to speak, thereby getting closer to the nucleus of the second atom than it can to its own nucleus and therefore moving into a location of lower energy. In this way two ions are formed, one charged positively and the other negatively. The two ions may then be drawn together into a molecule by electrostatic attraction. In this way are explained the *heteropolar* compounds of the chemist, and particularly the *ionic compounds* between strongly electropositive and strongly electronegative elements, examples of which have been mentioned above.

Both modes of formation result in the same number of valence bonds per atom. Furthermore, in reality all grades of transition occur between the two types; or, rather, the mathematical treatment is best described by saying that all actual chemical bonds are partly of one type and partly of the other. Bonds between strongly electropositive and strongly electronegative elements (i.e., between those closely following or closely preceding an inert gas) are predominantly ionic (except in the case of hydrogen!). In general, however, most chemical bonds are predominantly covalent. Molecules such as O_2 and N_2 are also held together by predominantly covalent bonds.

A special case is presented by atoms whose electrons are all included within completed shells or subshells. Such atoms should exhibit no tendency whatever to enter into chemical combination, and when in the gaseous state they should have monatomic molecules. In this way is explained the occurrence of the noble gases such as helium and neon.

114. Remainder of the Periodic Table. The second octet of elements, from $Z = 11$ to $Z = 18$, parallels closely the first octet. *Sodium* ($Z = 11$, $1s^2 2s^2 2p^6 3s$) contains a single valence electron outside the neon core, but this electron has a $3s$ wave function, as against the $2s$ function for the valence electron of lithium. Sodium is univalent, as in NaOH and the familiar NaCl. Its arc spectrum is a typical one-electron spectrum. In general, it resembles lithium closely. *Magnesium* ($Z = 12$) is a bivalent element similar to beryllium. It burns with a brilliant white flame to form the oxide MgO. It has an arc spectrum of singlets and triplets resembling that of helium. *Aluminum* ($Z = 13$) is trivalent, like boron, but it is metallic and an excellent conductor of electricity. The "sesquioxide," Al_2O_3, occurs in crystalline form as sapphire and ruby. *Silicon* ($Z = 14$) is a good deal like carbon. The dioxide, SiO_2, however, which occurs in quartz, is a substance of extremely high melting point, whereas the analogous compound, CO_2, is a gas! Only an elaborately refined application of wave mechanics can explain contrasts such as these. *Phosphorus* ($Z = 15$), although chemically much more active, forms compounds analogous to those of nitrogen. In the poisonous gas phosphine, or PH_3, it is trivalent, just as nitrogen is in gaseous ammonia, NH_3. *Sulfur* ($Z = 16$) corresponds to oxygen. In H_2S, it is bivalent, just as oxygen is in H_2O. *Chlorine* ($Z = 17$) is univalent and easily forms negative ions in solution; in general, it resembles fluorine closely but is less active. Finally, in *argon* ($Z = 18$), we reach again an atom composed of complete subshells, with electronic formula $1s^2 2s^2 2p^6 3s^2 3p^6$. Thus, argon has completed K and L shells and, outside these, two more completed subshells. The M shell is not yet full, since there are no $3d$ electrons. Nevertheless, the symmetry of the $3p^6$ configuration is evidently enough to make the external field around argon very weak, so that it behaves as an inert gas with a very low boiling point ($-186°C$).

At $Z = 19$, we should naturally expect the addition of an electron in a $3d$ state (that is, $n = 3$, $l = 2$). For, in the one-electron atom, we found the energy to increase regularly with increasing values of n; hence, we might expect that even in our modified field any wave function with $n = 4$ would correspond to a higher electronic energy than a $3d$ function. But the next element, potassium, closely resembles sodium and lithium, not only in chemical properties but also in its spectra even to the finest details.   There is abundant reason to believe that atomic spectra in the visible and ultraviolet regions are emitted by electrons in the periphery of the atom.   These spectra, therefore, furnish valuable information concerning the state of the outermost electrons.   Can it be, then, that the valence electron of potassium is not a $3d$ but a $4s$ electron?   It has been remarked that in the modified central field a $4s$ level ($l = 0$) would lie lower than a $4d$ ($l = 2$); conceivably it could lie even below a $3d$. That this happens in potassium was eventually established by careful wave-mechanical calculation.   Thus the last electron to be added in potassium ($Z = 19$) is in a $4s$ state, resulting in the complete formula $1s^2 2s^2 2p^6 3s^2 3p^6 4s$.

The next element, calcium ($Z = 20$), corresponds rather well to magnesium in the preceding octet, but beyond this point the sequence becomes quite different and much less interesting.   Lack of space will not permit

TABLE 7-2. COMPLETED ELECTRON SHELLS AND SUBSHELLS

n, l	X-ray symbol	Electron symbol for sub-group	Electrons in subgroup $2[(2l + 1)]$	Element at which subgroup is completed	Electrons in completed n group, $2n^2$	Element at which n group is completed
1, 0	K	$1s$	2	He(2)	2	He(2)
2, 0	L_I	$2s$	2	Be(4)		
2, 1	$L_{II,III}$	$2p$	6	Ne(10)	8	Ne(10)
3, 0	M_I	$3s$	2	Mg(12)		
3, 1	$M_{II,III}$	$3p$	6	A(18)	18	Cu(29)
3, 2	$M_{IV,V}$	$3d$	10	Cu(29)		
4, 0	N_I	$4s$	2	Zn(30)		
4, 1	$N_{II,III}$	$4p$	6	Kr(36)		
4, 2	$N_{IV,V}$	$4d$	10	Pd(46)	32	Lu(71)
4, 3	$N_{VI,VII}$	$4f$	14	Lu(71)		
5, 0	O_I	$5s$	2	Cd(48)		
5, 1	$O_{II,III}$	$5p$	6	Xe(54)		
5, 2	$O_{IV,V}$	$5d$	10	Au(79)	50	
5, 3	$O_{VI,VII}$		14			
5, 4	$O_{VIII,IX}$		18			
6, 0	P_I	$6s$	2	Ba(56)		
6, 1	$P_{II,III}$	$6p$	6	Rn(86)		
6, 2	$P_{IV,V}$		10			
7, 0	Q_I	$7s$	2	Ra(88)		

further detailed discussion of the periodic table. It will only be noted that at cerium a novel feature begins. From cerium (58) to lutecium (71), the 14 possible $4f$ electrons are added in turn, inside already completed $5s$ and $5p$ subshells. The exteriors of all these atoms are closely similar, so that we have the group of chemically very similar rare earths.

The probable electronic constitution of the well-known elements, when in their normal state, is shown in Appendix III. For briefer reference, an outline showing the points of completion of successive subshells and shells is also given in Table 7-2, with inclusion of the designations of the subshells that are used in x-ray theory.

OPTICAL SPECTRA

In previous chapters we have become acquainted with a few features of atomic spectra. We saw in Chap. 5 that a general characteristic of such spectra is the occurrence of series of lines converging toward short-wavelength limits. In Chap. 6, we have seen how wave mechanics was able to supply a quantitative theory of the general features of spectra emitted by one electron in the field of a nucleus, yielding the same formulas as did the original quantum theory of Bohr. A brief account will now be given of some representative phenomena of the spectra emitted by atoms or molecules containing more than one electron and of their theoretical interpretation by means of wave mechanics. In connection with this discussion, we shall also return briefly to the one-electron atom itself in order to discuss the "fine structure" of its lines, which is due to spin and other relativistic effects. In the present chapter, however, the discussion will be limited to spectra whose emission is connected with the motion of the exterior electrons of atoms or molecules, these spectra occurring in the infrared, visible, or ultraviolet regions. The high-frequency radiation known as x-rays will be reserved for special treatment in a later chapter.

115. Angular Momentum and Its Selection Rules. Before discussing specific types of spectra, a general feature may first be described that is always present in the absence of electric or magnetic fields or other form of external disturbance. In classical mechanics, as was remarked in Sec. 104, the vector angular momentum of any isolated system remains constant in time. Analogously, *the quantum states of any atom not subject to external forces can be so defined that, when the atom is in one of them, both its component of angular momentum about any chosen axis drawn through its center of mass, and the square of its angular momentum, have fixed values, their respective magnitudes being*

$$M \frac{h}{2\pi} \qquad J(J + 1) \frac{h^2}{(2\pi)^2}$$

*where J and M are two quantum numbers characteristic of the quantum
state. The number J is a positive integer or half-integer or zero, and M has
one of the $(2J + 1)$ integrally spaced values between $M = -J$ and $M = J$,
inclusively. Thus, M is integral or half-integral according as J is.* For
example, if $J = 0$, $M = 0$; if $J = \frac{1}{2}$, $M = \frac{1}{2}$ or $-\frac{1}{2}$; if $J = 1$, $M = 1$
or 0 or -1; etc.   Often M_J is written for M.

The rule for determining whether J and M are integral or half-integral
can be discovered by considering the electronic quantum states described
in Sec. 109.   In those states there is, for each electron, an integral value
of the quantum number λ, and also a value of μ which is either $\frac{1}{2}$ or
$-\frac{1}{2}$; and the total angular momentum of the electrons about the chosen
axis is $[\Sigma(\lambda + \mu)]h/2\pi$, where the sum Σ is to be taken for all electrons in
the atom.   Thus,

$$M = \Sigma(\lambda + \mu) \qquad M = \Sigma(m + \mu) \qquad (149)$$

From this equality and the character of the values of λ and μ it is at once
obvious that *M and hence also J must be integral when the atom contains an
even number of electrons, and half-integral when it contains an odd number.*
It can also be seen that the maximum possible value of M, and hence
also of J, is $(\Sigma l) + N/2$ where N is the total number of electrons in the
atom; for the maximum value of any
individual λ is l, and for each electron
μ cannot exceed $\frac{1}{2}$.

The relationship of the quantum
numbers J and M can be visualized
with the help of a vector diagram, in
the same way in which the relation
of l and λ was visualized for a single
electron (Sec. 104b).   Let a vector of
length J be drawn at such an angle
that its projection on the chosen axis
is of length M.   If $M = \pm J$, the
vector will lie along the axis.   Two
cases are illustrated in Fig. 64.   If

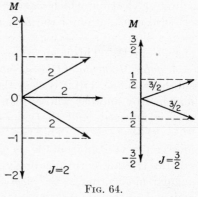

FIG. 64.

$J = 2$, five positions of the J vector are possible, corresponding to
$M = -2, -1, 0, 1, 2$; if $J = \frac{3}{2}$, four positions can occur, corresponding
to $M = -\frac{3}{2}, -\frac{1}{2}, \frac{1}{2}, \frac{3}{2}$.

As in the case of the one-electron atom (Sec. 104c), the vector angular
momentum has no definite azimuth around the axis and its components
perpendicular to the axis have no definite values.   Thus each JM quantum state corresponds to a class of possible classical motions having different fixed directions of the momentum vector.

Selection Rules.   Wave mechanics leads to the following selection rules
for J and M, which are of great importance in spectroscopy.   In any

atomic jump associated with the dipole emission or absorption of a photon, *J may remain unchanged or it may increase or decrease by unity, but not by any larger amount.* That is, if J_1 and J_2 are the values of J for the two states between which the jump occurs, then either $J_1 = J_2$ or $J_1 - J_2 = 1$ or $J_1 - J_2 = -1$. The same rule holds also for M. *No jump can occur, moreover, from a state with $J = 0$, to another state with $J = 0$.* In symbols,

$$\Delta J = 0 \text{ or } \pm 1 \text{ (and not } 0 \rightarrow 0) \qquad \Delta M = 0 \text{ or } \pm 1 \qquad (150a,b)$$

These selection rules are not always strictly obeyed, however; sometimes jumps occur by quadrupole emission for which $\Delta J = \pm 2$ or $\Delta M = \pm 2$. Spectral lines due to such jumps are mostly very weak.

These selection rules have analogies in classical theory (and were first proposed on this basis). Orbital angular momentum, in classical mechanics, is associated with rotation. Suppose that a body capable of rotation contains an electrical vibrator of some sort; and let this vibrator emit electromagnetic radiation of frequency ν when the body is at rest. Then, if the body is set rotating with angular velocity ω, the radiation emitted will contain just the three frequencies ν, $\nu + \omega$, $\nu - \omega$. The reason is similar to that for the analogous effect of a magnetic field upon a classical vibrating electron, which was described in Sec. 46 in connection with the classical explanation of the Zeeman effect. The three classical frequencies $\nu + \omega$, ν, $\nu - \omega$ correspond (in emission) to the three possible changes in M. This is an example of Bohr's correspondence principle.

Angular Momenta of Closed Subshells. From the description of atomic subshells in Sec. 110 it is clear that in a closed subshell every electron is matched by another whose quantum state differs only in that the sign of λ is reversed; and the values of μ are similarly paired off. Thus $M = \Sigma\lambda^m + \Sigma\mu = 0$. This fact suggests that $J = 0$ also, and this surmise can be verified from the theory. Furthermore, $\Sigma\lambda = 0$ and $\Sigma\mu = 0$, separately, and, correspondingly, it can be shown that the total orbital angular momentum of the electrons in a full subshell likewise vanishes, and so does the resultant angular momentum of spin.

Thus, in considering the total angular momentum of an atom, all closed subshells can be ignored. An atom of a noble gas, in its normal state, in which the electrons are all grouped into closed subshells, is thus necessarily in a state with $J = 0$. An atom containing one or more peripheral electrons outside the inner closed subshells will have angular momenta, orbital, spin, or total, that are determined entirely by the peripheral electrons, with no contributions from the closed subshells. The consideration of atomic angular momenta is thereby greatly simplified.

116. Alkali-type Spectra. At this point we may to advantage describe the gross features of the simplest type of spectra, that emitted by atoms containing a single valence electron outside one or more closed subshells. Among neutral atoms of this sort may be mentioned those of the alkali metals, lithium, sodium, potassium, rubidium, and cesium. Other examples are singly ionized atoms of beryllium, magnesium, calcium, strontium, or barium; doubly ionized atoms of boron or aluminum; and so on.

In an atom of this type only the valence electron should be optically active, and only its quantum numbers should vary. For the moment, let us disregard electron spin. The energy of an atom containing a single electron in a Coulomb field then depends only on the quantum number n; in more general fields, however, wave-mechanical calculations indicate that it should also vary with the quantum number l. This latter number has the same relation to the orbital angular momentum of the electron as in a Coulomb field; and in the present case it represents also the total orbital momentum of all electrons in the atom, the contributions from the inner closed subshells vanishing. To fit our notation into that generally employed for complex atoms, therefore, we shall employ in place of l the capital letter L, which is commonly used for the *total orbital* momentum. In any atom the possible values of L are zero or any positive integer; and levels are commonly labeled with a capital letter according to the following scheme, analogous to that employed for one electron:

$$L = 0, \quad 1, \quad 2, \quad 3, \quad 4, \quad 5, \quad 6, \quad 7$$
$$\quad\;\; S \quad\; P \quad\; D \quad\; F \quad\; G \quad\; H \quad\; I \quad\; K$$

The letter indicating the value of L may then be preceded, in the case of a single active electron, by a number giving the value of n.

The array of possible levels thus inferred from theory is qualitatively as shown (in part) in Fig. 65. The S terms ($L = l = 0$) begin with $n = 1$, the P terms ($L = l = 1$) with $n = 2$, and so on; for always $n > l$. The allowed transitions between these levels are indicated in the figure by oblique lines. The quantum number L is usually subject to the selection rule that ΔL cannot exceed unity; hence, no jumps can occur, for example, between S and D levels. In the case of a single active electron, furthermore, the restriction is actually a little more stringent; for, it is a special rule that the l of the jumping electron *must* change by unity. Hence, when $L = l$, we must have

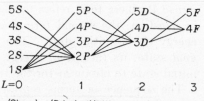

L=0   1   2   3

(Sharp) (Principal)(Diffuse) (Fund)

Fig. 65. Partial LS term system of a typical alkali metal (some of the lowest terms shown are sometimes missing). Lines indicate allowed transitions.

$$\Delta L = \pm 1$$

Thus, jumps cannot ordinarily occur in such spectra between two S levels or between two P levels, and so on.

The theoretical array of energy levels is reminiscent of the spectral terms employed by Rydberg to represent the chief series in the spectra of the alkalies (the fine structure mentioned in Sec. 85 being disregarded). According to Eqs. (70a,b,c) in Sec. 76, the wave numbers of the lines of these series are given by the following formulas:

Sharp: $$\tilde{\nu} = \frac{R}{(1 + P)^2} - \frac{R}{(m + S)^2} \qquad m \geqq 2$$

Principal: $$\tilde{\nu} = \frac{R}{(1 + S)^2} - \frac{R}{(m + P)^2} \qquad m \geqq 1$$

Diffuse: $$\tilde{\nu} = \frac{R}{(1 + P)^2} - \frac{R}{(m + D)^2} \qquad m \geqq 2$$

Thus the wave numbers are the differences between expressions or "spectral terms" of three different types:

$$\frac{R}{(m + S)^2} \qquad \frac{R}{(m + P)^2} \qquad \frac{R}{(m + D)^2}$$

where R is the Rydberg constant (Sec. 75). By varying m in these expressions we obtain three sets of terms similar to the first three sets of energy values as derived from wave mechanics. It is reasonable to assume that Rydberg's terms correspond to these latter sets. The Rydberg terms converge to 0 as $m \to \infty$, just as the theoretical energy levels converge to zero as $n \to \infty$, provided we agree to call the energy 0 at the ionization limit. The terms, however, are positive, whereas the energies are all negative. Hence, the terms must represent the *numerical values* of the energy without the negative sign. In the formulas for $\tilde{\nu}$, then, the *second* Rydberg term refers to the *initial* atomic state for the transition in question; the second term together with its minus sign equals the energy of the initial state. The *first* term in the formula refers to the *final* state; its (negative) energy is subtracted from the energy of the initial state to obtain $h\nu$ for the transition.

The sequence of terms represented by the first of the three expressions shown above, $R/(m + S)^2$, represents, therefore, the sequence of initial states for the various lines of the sharp series. These terms are observed to combine only with terms in the second sequence, $R/(m + P)^2$. Hence, the first sequence of terms must be those derived theoretically with $L = 0$, or the "S" terms; for the latter is the only theoretical sequence that combines with only one other sequence. The second of the Rydberg sequences must then be the P terms, with $L = 1$; for S terms combine only with P terms, by the selection rule for L. The *sharp* series of lines thus arises from transitions between an S level (exclusive of the lowest) and the lowest of the P levels. *The principal* series, on the other hand, arises from transitions between various P levels and the lowest S level. The lowest S level is the lowest possible value for the energy and represents the normal state of the atom.

The third set of levels, represented by $R/(m + D)^2$, which combines with P but not with S levels, must, then, be the D levels ($L = 2$). The *diffuse* series of lines thus arises from transitions between the various D levels and the lowest P level. A fourth observed series of lines, named long ago the "fundamental" series, has a convergence limit equal to the difference between the convergence limit of the diffuse series and the frequency of the first line of this latter series, i.e., to the difference in energy between the state of ionization and the lowest D level. The final state for the transitions that give rise to this fourth series must, therefore, be the lowest D level. But the initial energies for the fundamental series are not those of the P terms. They must be, then, the F levels, with $L = 3$. The fundamental series is thus due to transitions from an F level to the lowest D level.

In this way, we arrive at the following interpretation of the chief series of the alkali metals:

Sharp: $nS \rightarrow n_0P$ $n > n_0$
Principal: $nP \rightarrow n_0S$
Diffuse: $nD \rightarrow n_0P$
Fundamental: $nF \rightarrow n_0D$

The identification thus made of the terms in the alkali spectra constitutes the historical reason for the use by spectroscopists of the mysterious letters S, P, D, F (from the words, "sharp, principal, diffuse, fundamental") to represent various values of L (or the corresponding small letters for one electron). For higher values of L it was agreed later to continue down the alphabet, skipping J.

As an example, a diagram of the energy levels for neutral sodium is shown in Fig. 66. Each level is represented in this diagram by a short horizontal line, the levels being grouped into sequences according to the value of L, in contrast to the arrangement in Fig. 41(b). The diagram shows also the splitting of the P levels, which will be discussed in Sec. 124; the subscripts on S, P, etc., denote J values distinguishing fine-structure sublevels, which are not shown separately for D and F. As usual, the energies are measured downward from zero for the state of ionization (with no kinetic energy in the removed electron), and are expressed in wave-number units. The numbers written opposite the lines representing levels are the accepted values of n, differing somewhat from Rydberg's original number m. At the right are shown for comparison some of the levels of hydrogen, the lowest one being far below the lowest sodium level and hence not shown. The numerical values of some of the terms are also listed in Table 7-4 in Sec. 119. The levels for all five alkali metals, represented by dots, are compared in Fig. 67. It will be noted that the normal state for all alkali metals is an S state.

The most important spectral lines are indicated in Fig. 66 by oblique lines, with wavelengths in angstroms appended; the widths of these lines

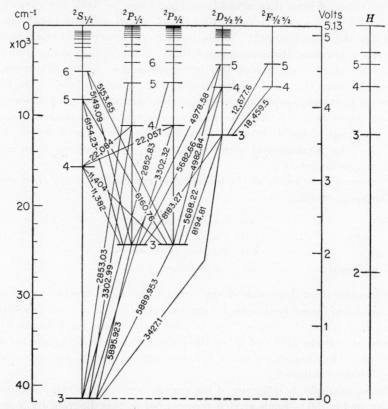

FIG. 66. Energy-level diagram for neutral sodium, showing also the origin of the principal spectral lines. Some of the levels of hydrogen are shown for comparison. (Wavelengths are in angstroms. The numbers opposite the levels are values of n.)

as drawn give a rough idea of the relative intensities of the lines as usually observed. One weak line is shown that violates the ordinary selection rule for L ($3D \rightarrow 3S$, $\Delta L = 2$).

117. Term Energies of the Alkali Metals. If the mathematical difficulties could be overcome, it should be possible to calculate the energy levels from the wave equation. Unfortunately, however (or fortunately), this cannot be done with any degree of precision, so that experiment is still necessary. Considerable interest attaches nevertheless to approximate theoretical values of the term energies, which can be obtained by solving the wave equation for an electron in the modified central field described in Sec. 109. We can mention only a few qualitative conclusions thus obtained from the theory.

Since the modified field, representing the combined effect of the nucleus and the core electrons, reduces to a hydrogenlike field at points well outside the core, it would be expected that the alkali levels would approach corresponding hydrogen levels as n increases. Bohr orbits for large n would lie entirely in this outer field; and, analogously, the wave function

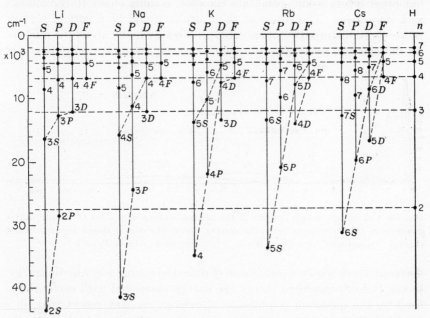

Fig. 67. The energy levels below 2,000 cm^{-1} of the five alkali metals and of hydrogen (except that for $n = 1$). All doublet structure is ignored.

is found to have appreciable values only in the same region. Such an approach to the hydrogen levels is very evident in Figs. 66 and 67. This correspondence serves to fix the value of n unambiguously for the D and F levels. The value of n for the lowest S and P terms is taken to be 2 for lithium, 3 for sodium, and so on, partly on the basis of the way in which the periodic table is built up and partly on the basis of wave-mechanical calculations.

All alkali levels, however, lie *below* the corresponding hydrogen levels; and levels for a given n lie progressively lower as L decreases. Perhaps such a variation with L, or with l of the valence electron, is plausible; for, the electronic wave function with smaller l has relatively larger values within the atomic core, where the atomic field is stronger than a hydrogen field. This is illustrated for sodium in Fig. 68; the quantity actually plotted for the valence electron, in curve $3s$ or $3p$ or $3d$, is its contribution to the radial charge density, η_r or $4\pi r^2 \psi \psi^*$, but the curves give also some idea of the penetration of ψ itself. If the electronic ψ lay almost entirely within such a stronger field, its associated energy would surely be lower. Such an argument is not conclusive, however; for in the mathematical theory the energies are determined by the boundary condition at infinity.

Difficulties are encountered also if we attempt to reason from the classical analogy. The classical orbit for $L = n - 1$ would be a circle, but other orbits would penetrate the core, coming closer to the nucleus as L decreases. The shape of those orbits would be a sort of scallop, rather like a distorted elliptical orbit precessing rapidly about the nucleus. As the electron penetrates the core, however, its total energy does not

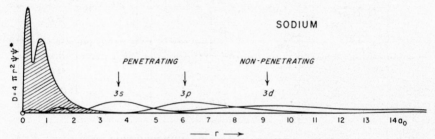

FIG. 68. Calculated charge density in the neutral sodium atom, for three alternative positions of the valence electron; the density due to the core is shown separately and shaded. (*Reprinted from H. E. White, "Introduction to Atomic Spectra."*)

decrease; there is only a conversion of potential energy into kinetic energy. In the Bohr-Sommerfeld theory the energy associated with each orbit is fixed by the quantum conditions. However, we may reflect that, in a Coulomb field similar in strength to the atomic field inside the core, the energies of corresponding orbital motions would all be lower than they would be in a field similar to that outside the core. It is thus at least not unreasonable that the energy level should sink as the degree of penetration into the core increases.

The relation with the hydrogen levels just noted suggests a certain mode of writing the alkali energies that is of interest. Expressed in wave-number units, the energy of the nth level for a hydrogen atom is $W_n^{(H)} = -R/n^2$, where R is the Rydberg constant [cf. Eqs. (80) and (87c) in Secs. 81 and 82]. For an atomic level in any other atom with energy W, an *effective principal quantum number* n_e can be defined by the similar equation

$$W = -\frac{R}{n_e^2} \qquad (151)$$

The difference $n - n_e$ for corresponding levels, sometimes denoted by μ, has been called the *quantum defect*. In the alkalies, it can be regarded as a measure of the effect of the departure of the central field from a Coulomb field. In terms of μ we have

$$W = -\frac{R}{(n - \mu)^2} \tag{152}$$

A formula similar in form is obtained from Rydberg's expression for the spectral terms

$$W = -\frac{R}{(m + \mu)^2}$$

The values of μ are not the same in the two formulas, however, nor did Rydberg's choice of m for a given term agree with the modern value of n; but, after choosing the lowest values of the integers n and of m in any convenient manner, the two values of μ can obviously be chosen for each n so as to bring the two formulas into agreement. Since Rydberg's formula is found to fit the observed terms fairly well when his μ is treated as a constant for given L, it follows that the quantum defect must likewise be almost a constant for the sequence of terms belonging to a given value of L.

The values of the quantum defect, $n - n_e$, or μ in Eq. (152), for some of the levels of sodium (disregarding the fine-structure splitting) are shown in Table 7-3. Their approximate independence of n is evident. The corresponding value of the effective quantum number n_e may be obtained in each case by subtracting the number shown here from n; thus for a $4P$ term, $n_e = 4 - 0.867 = 3.133$. A small value of the quantum defect means close approximation of the energy to the corresponding level for hydrogen.

TABLE 7-3. SOME VALUES OF THE QUANTUM DEFECT FOR NEUTRAL SODIUM

Term	$n = 3$	$n = 4$	$n = 5$	$n = 6$	$n = 7$	$n = 8$
S	1.373	1.357	1.352	1.349	1.348	1.351
P	0.883	0.867	0.862	0.859	0.858	0.857
D	0.010	0.011	0.013	0.011	0.009	0.013
F	.....	0.000	−0.001	−0.008	−0.012	−0.015

Formulas of the Rydberg type, as in Eq. (152), represent only a first approximation to the actual term values. For greater accuracy more complicated functions of n are sometimes employed in the denominator.[1] Such formulas are indispensable in determining series limits, and a knowledge of these limits is essential in order to fix the energies of the lowest

[1] Cf. H. E. White, "Introduction to Atomic Spectra," 1934; A. Fowler, "Report on Series in Line Spectra," 1922.

levels.   Once the energy or term value for a single level has been determined, others can be calculated from the observed frequencies of lines
arising from transitions involving known levels.

The term value or negative of the energy for the *lowest state* represents
also the *ionization energy* of the neutral atom.   In Fig. 69 are plotted
values of the ionization energy calculated in this way from spectroscopic
data and expressed in electron-volts.   The electronic subshell that contains the most easily removed electron is shown below the curve.   A systematic relation is evident between the quantum numbers of this electron
and the ionization potentials.

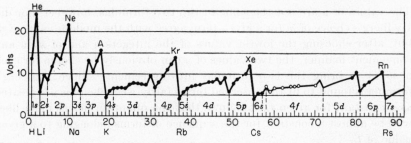

FIG. 69. Ionization potentials as a function of atomic number.   (*Reprinted from H. E.
White, "Introduction to Atomic Spectra."*)

118. The Spin-orbit Effect in a Central Field.

Consideration must
now be given to the fine structure that is observed in the lines of the alkali
spectra, as is illustrated by the familiar *D* lines of sodium.   A satisfactory
explanation of this fine structure was accomplished only when allowance
was made for the effects due to the magnetic moment that is associated
with electron spin.

For a system of two or more electrons, the complete relativistic theory
is not known, but the wave equation proposed by Dirac for a single electron (Sec. 105) suggests a formula that is believed to be satisfactory for
most spectroscopic purposes.   This formula will be written down and
then discussed in terms of a classical analogy.

Let $\mathbf{G}_s$ denote the vector angular momentum of spin of an electron and
$\mathbf{G}_l$ its vector angular momentum about the center of a spherically symmetrical electrostatic field in which it has potential energy $V(r)$, r denoting distance from the center.   Then the change in its energy, $\Delta_{ls}W$, due
to interaction between the spin magnetic moment and the field is the
wave-mechanical analog of the average value of H_{ls} where

$$H_{ls} = \frac{1}{2m^2c^2} \frac{1}{r} \frac{dV}{dr} \, \mathbf{G}_l \cdot \mathbf{G}_s \tag{153}$$

Here m is the electronic mass and c the speed of light, and $\mathbf{G}_l \cdot \mathbf{G}_s$ denotes
the scalar product of these vectors.

In the mathematics of Dirac the classical pictures that had previously been formed of the spinning electron disappear completely. It seems as if theoretical physics were coming to be based upon mere mathematical postulates rather than upon concrete pictures. On the other hand, it may be questioned whether human minds can think at all except in terms of imagery of some sort derived from sensory experience. Be that as it may, most physicists will probably wish to assist their thinking by the use of concrete pictures whenever this can be done to advantage. Classical analogs of the spinning electron seem likely, therefore, to retain a permanent interest.

Suppose the electron really were, as Lorentz thought it might be, a little hollow sphere of electricity held together in some unknown manner, and suppose the sphere were rotating. Then, the moving charges on its surface would constitute circular currents and the sphere would be surrounded by a magnetic field; it would behave as if it possessed a certain magnetic moment. The combination of electric and magnetic fields around it would also give rise to electromagnetic momentum, and calculation shows that the total moment of this momentum about the center of the sphere is just *half as great* in proportion to the magnetic moment as it is in the case of the revolution of an electron in an orbit.

Suppose, now, that such a rotating charged sphere is set into motion across a spherically symmetrical electric field. Then elementary theory would not lead us to expect any interaction between the electric field and the magnetic moment. But suppose we view the situation from a moving frame of reference in which the electron is momentarily at rest. If this frame has a component of velocity u perpendicular to the radius r and if the electrostatic potential due to the field is ϕ, then it follows from the relativistic equations of transformation (16) that, relatively to this moving frame, there will also be a magnetic field of magnitude $B = (u/c)(-d\phi/dr)$. Here we can replace u by G_l/mr, since u is also the velocity of the electron in the original frame. Interacting with the electron's magnetic moment, this magnetic field changes its energy by the amount eBG_{sa}/mc, where G_{sa} is the component of $\mathbf{G}_s$ in the direction of B, as is easily seen from Eqs. (174) and (171b) in Sec. 129. Substitution of the value of B expressed in terms of G_l, however, and of $\phi = -V/e$, gives for $\Delta_{ls}W$ *twice* the expression (153) written above! (Note that here $\mathbf{G}_l \cdot \mathbf{G}_s = G_l G_s$.) Actually, however, the calculation as just made is incomplete because the electron is being accelerated and hence the frame of reference in which it is momentarily at rest has to be changed continually. It was shown by Thomas[1] that this circumstance introduces a factor $\frac{1}{2}$ into the expression for $\Delta_{ls}W$.

---

[1] Thomas, *Nature*, vol. 107, p. 514, 1926.

A derivation of the energy change must also be possible, as an alternative, in terms of the usual frame of reference in which the nucleus is at rest. In this frame there is no magnetic field except that due to the moving electron itself. The effect now arises from a distortion of the electron. From Eqs. (5a,b,c) for the relativistic transformation of velocities, it can be shown that a rotating body which is symmetrical as viewed in a frame in which its center is at rest appears distorted in other frames. As a consequence, in the rotating electron the electric charge is piled up on the side of higher resultant velocity and reduced in density on the other side (Fig. 70). The center of charge is thereby displaced relatively to the center of mass, so that the electron has, effectively, an electric moment relative to its center of mass; it is subject, therefore, to a torque tending to make its axis of rotation perpendicular both to the field and to its linear velocity. The corresponding change in its energy in the field is found to be just that stated in (153).

Rarer

Denser

FIG. 70. A classical (Lorentz) spinning electron viewed along its axis of rotation.

The torque just mentioned would have no tendency to change the *magnitude* of the spin momentum $\mathbf{G}_s$ but would tend in general to alter its *direction*. There is also a compensating change in the direction of $\mathbf{G}_l$ arising from the fact that the displacement of the center of charge also introduces a component of force on the electron perpendicular to the plane of its orbit. Consequently, the resultant angular momentum, $\mathbf{G}_j = \mathbf{G}_l + \mathbf{G}_s$, remains fixed both in magnitude and in direction, while the vectors $\mathbf{G}_l$ and $\mathbf{G}_s$ precess around it together (unless $\mathbf{G}_l$ and $\mathbf{G}_s$ happen to be either parallel or antiparallel).

Quantum States with Spin-orbit Interaction. The classical picture just described is partially paralleled by certain features of the wave-mechanical theory. Because of the spin-orbit interaction, the quantum states for the electron cannot be just the $n\ l\ \lambda\ \mu$ states described in Sec. 109; for in these states fixed values are assigned to the axial components of $\mathbf{G}_l$ and of $\mathbf{G}_s$ separately. The true quantum states are, however, characterized by a fixed value of the axial component of $\mathbf{G}_j$, which can be written $mh/2\pi$; and the magnitude of $G_j{}^2$ is also fixed at a value $j(j + 1)h^2/(2\pi)^2$. (Often m_j is written for m.) The quantum number j represents, in units of $h/2\pi$, the maximum numerical value that the axial component of $\mathbf{G}_j$ can have in states characterized by a given value of j. The possible values of m are integrally spaced from a maximum equal to j down to $-j$, being thus $2j + 1$ in number. If $l = 0$, $j = \frac{1}{2}$, since then $\mathbf{G}_j = \mathbf{G}_s$; if $l > 0$, two values are possible, $j = l + s = l + \frac{1}{2}$ or $j = l - s = l - \frac{1}{2}$. Thus j and m always have half-integral values.

These relations may be represented by vector diagrams, of which two cases are shown in Fig. 71.   The s vector is drawn here in either the same or the opposite direction to the l vector, to form a resultant j vector, which is then itself drawn either parallel or at such an angle to the chosen axis that its projection on the axis is of length m.

The indefiniteness of all *components* of $\mathbf{G}_l$ and $\mathbf{G}_s$ when $\mathbf{G}_j$ is quantized is an example of a general principle.   When the vector sum of two or more angular momenta is quantized, the individual momenta cease to have any definite components, although their squares retain definite magnitudes [for example, $l(l + 1)h^2/(2\pi)^2$].   This corresponds to the fact that in classical mechanics the individual vectors may assume various directions without disturbing their vector sum.

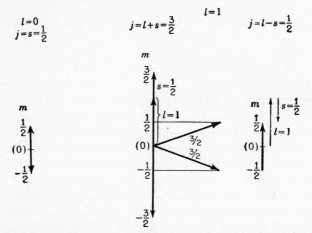

FIG. 71. Diagrams illustrating addition of l and s vectors into a j vector.

So long as spin-orbit interaction is absent, the electron may be either in an $n\, l\, \lambda\, \mu$ state with $\mathbf{G}_j$ unquantized, or in an $n\, l\, j\, m$ state with $\mathbf{G}_j$ quantized.   The slightest degree of spin-orbit interaction, however, limits the choice to an $n\, l\, j\, m$ state.

The $n\, l\, j\, m$ Wave Functions.   Linear combinations of the degenerate $n\, l\, \lambda\, \mu$ wave functions for given nl can easily be made to form zero-order $n\, l\, j\, m$ functions, which would be valid electronic wave functions without further change if there were no spin-orbit interaction.   It is necessary that $\Sigma\lambda + \Sigma\mu = m$.   To obtain thus a wave function with

$$m = j = l + \tfrac{1}{2}$$

the only possibility is that $\lambda = l$ and $\mu = \tfrac{1}{2}$; similarly, for $m = -j$, we take $\lambda = -l$, $\mu = -\tfrac{1}{2}$.   Thus these two particular zero-order jm functions are the same as two of the $\lambda\mu$ functions; and in these two states, as an exception, $\mathbf{G}_l$, $\mathbf{G}_s$, and $\mathbf{G}_j$ do simultaneously have definite axial components.   Otherwise, two $\lambda\mu$ functions with $\lambda = m - \tfrac{1}{2}$, $\mu = \tfrac{1}{2}$ and

$\lambda = m + \frac{1}{2}$, $\mu = -\frac{1}{2}$, respectively, are multiplied by the proper coefficients and added to form each jm function. The number of jm functions thus obtained is the same as that of the original $\lambda\mu$ functions; for there are $(2j + 1)$ functions for each j, and hence $2l + 2$ for $j = l + \frac{1}{2}$ and $2l$ for $j = l - \frac{1}{2}$, making $2(2l + 1)$ in all, which is just the number of the original $\lambda\mu$ functions for given l.

When the spin-orbit interaction is introduced, it is found that valid wave functions can be formed by changing only the radial factors in the zero-order $n\, l\, j\, m$ functions just described. The necessary change is different for the two values of j.

The *energy also* depends now on j, as well as on n and l. Thus each nl level with $l > 0$ is split by the spin-orbit effect into two sublevels. The selection rules stated in Sec. 115 for J and M become here selection rules for j and m:

$$\Delta j = 0 \text{ or } \pm 1 \text{ (and not } j = 0 \text{ to } j = 0) \tag{154a}$$

$$\Delta m = 0 \text{ or } \pm 1 \tag{154b}$$

119. Fine Structure in Alkali-type Spectra.

The theory developed in the last section is immediately applicable to the energy levels of a single valence electron outside one or more closed subshells, as described in Sec. 116. Since the closed subshells do not contribute to the angular momenta, the quantum numbers $l\, j\, m$ may be replaced by the numbers $L\, J\, M$, having reference to the whole atom.

The effect of spin-orbit interaction is then in general to split each of the energy levels or terms as previously described into two, one with $J = L + \frac{1}{2}$ and the other with $J = L - \frac{1}{2}$. Only the S terms ($L = 0$) are single, with $J = \frac{1}{2}$. Almost always the level with the larger J is found experimentally to have the higher energy and, therefore, the smaller term value, in agreement with a conclusion derived from wave mechanics. A J level is commonly indicated by adding the value of J as a subscript to the letter that is employed to denote the value of L; and a superscript 2 may be written in front of the letter to indicate that the level belongs to a doublet system.

Transitions between two given terms will then give rise to several spectral lines, forming a spectral multiplet. In accord with the selection rules for J, jumps are possible between the single level of any S term, $^2S_{\frac{1}{2}}$, and either of the two levels in a P term, $^2P_{\frac{1}{2}}$ and $^2P_{\frac{3}{2}}$. Between a P and a D, with levels $^2D_{\frac{3}{2}}$, $^2D_{\frac{5}{2}}$, three jumps are possible, viz.,

$$^2D_{\frac{3}{2}}\text{-}^2P_{\frac{1}{2}} \qquad ^2D_{\frac{3}{2}}\text{-}^2P_{\frac{3}{2}} \qquad ^2D_{\frac{5}{2}}\text{-}^2P_{\frac{3}{2}}$$

The jump $^2D_{\frac{5}{2}}\text{-}^2P_{\frac{1}{2}}$ is forbidden, since for it $\Delta J = 2$. A triplet of lines results in a similar way from the allowed transitions between any other pair of terms. Thus *the chief spectrum of the alkali metals should consist of spectral doublets and triplets.*   The origin of the lines just mentioned is illustrated qualitatively in Fig. 72.   Numbers are also added in the figure showing the relative intensities that the lines of each multiplet should have according to wave mechanics, under certain simple conditions.

For comparison with the theory, the wave numbers and separations of the first four lines of each of the chief series in the spectrum of neutral sodium are listed in Table 7-4.[1]   The theoretical conclusions are seen to be confirmed by the observations.   The *sharp* series, $nS \to 3P$, consists of spectral doublets, and, as shown in column 5 of Table 7-4, the frequency difference is constant within the experimental errors, representing the difference between the $3^2P_{1/2}$ and $3^2P_{3/2}$ levels.   This fact helps also to confirm the identification of the S levels as made above.

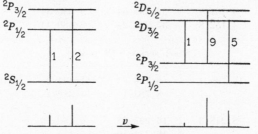

FIG. 72. Transitions between doublet levels. If S lies above P, the order of the spectral lines is reversed, similarly if P lies above D.

The *principal* series of lines, $nP \to 3S$, also consists of doublets but with frequency differences that represent the spacings between the two levels in various P terms and hence decrease rapidly with increasing n. This decrease is in accord with theoretical expectations.   For an electron in a Coulomb field, due to a nucleus of charge Ze, the separation of the two levels in a term with quantum numbers n and l, due to the spin-orbit effect, is calculated to be

$$\Delta \bar{\nu} = \frac{\alpha^2 R Z^4}{n^3 l(l+1)} = 5.84 \frac{Z^4}{n^3 l(l+1)} \qquad cm^{-1} \qquad (155)$$

where α is the "fine-structure constant," or $\alpha = 2\pi e^2/ch = 1/137.04$, and R is the Rydberg constant (in cm^{-1}).   This expression is the algebraic difference of the two values of $\Delta_s W$ given in Eqs. (158a,b).   Thus in a one-electron atom the spin-orbit separation decreases as $1/n^3$.   The observed decrease in the spectrum of sodium is even more rapid.

[1] Except for λ 11,404 and λ 11,382, the wavelengths of the lines were taken from the "Massachusetts Institute of Technology Wavelength Tables" and converted into wave numbers with the help of Kayser's "Tabelle der Schwingungszahlen"; the term values were then calculated from the wave numbers, the value of the $3S$ term (41,499.0) being taken from Bacher and Goudsmit's "Atomic Energy States."

TABLE 7-4. SOME LINES IN THE SPECTRUM OF NEUTRAL SODIUM

Initial term, cm⁻¹		$\bar{\nu}$, cm⁻¹	λ, A	Doublet $\Delta\bar{\nu}$
Principal series, $n\ ^2P \to 3\ ^2S$. $3S = 41,449.0$ cm⁻¹				
$3P_{1/2}$	24,492.8	16,956.19	5,895.92	17.19
$3P_{3/2}$	24,475.6	16,973.38	5,889.95	
$4P_{1/2}$	11,182.1	30,266.91	3,302.99	6.15
$4P_{3/2}$	11,175.9	30,273.06	3,303.32	
$5P_{1/2}$	6,406.4	35,042.64	2,852.83	2.46
$5P_{3/2}$	6,408.8	35,040.18	2,853.03	
$6P_{1/2}$	4,151.4	37,297.64	2,680.34	1.40
$6P_{3/2}$	4,152.8	37,296.24	2,680.44	
Sharp series, $n\ ^2S \to 3\ ^2P$				
$4S$	15,709.4	8,766.5	11,404.2	16.6
		8,783.1	11,382.4	
$5S$	8,248.3	16,227.28	6,160.76	17.22
		16,244.50	6,154.23	
$6S$	5,077.3	19,398.38	5,153.64	17.13
		19,415.51	5,149.09	
$7S$	3,437.2	21,038.40	4,751.89	17.14
		21,055.54	4,748.02	
Diffuse series,* $n\ ^2D \to 3\ ^2P$				
$3D$	12,276.12	12,199.50	8,194.81	17.20
		12,216.70	8,183.27	
$4D$	6,900.29	17,575.33	5,688.22	17.19
		17,592.52	5,682.66	
$5D$	4,412.3	20,063.30	4,982.84	17.16
		20,080.46	4,978.58	
$6D$	3,061.9	21,413.72	4,668.60	17.18
		21,430.90	4,664.86	

* Only the mean value of the $D_{5/2}$ and $D_{3/2}$ levels is shown and only the two strong lines,

$$nD_{5/2} \to 3P_{3/2} \qquad nD_{3/2} \to 3P_{1/2}$$

The lines of the *diffuse* series, $nD \rightarrow 3P$, should be *triplets*, according to the theory.   One line should be very weak, however.   The two brightest lines result from the jumps

$$n^2D_{5/2} \rightarrow 3^2P_{3/2} \qquad n^2D_{3/2} \rightarrow 3^2P_{1/2}$$

If Eq. (155) holds roughly for sodium, then, because of the factor $l(l+1)$ in the denominator, the separation $nD_{5/2} - nD_{3/2}$ should stand to the separation $nP_{3/2} - nP_{1/2}$ in the ratio $1/(2 \times 3):1/(1 \times 2)$ or as only $1:3$; and, as n increases, the D separation should rapidly diminish further.   Thus with ordinary resolving power the lines of the diffuse series can easily be observed as apparent doublets with a frequency difference that is nearly constant and equal to the difference $3P_{3/2} - 3P_{1/2}$.   Doublets of *exactly* this separation are formed by the faint line $D_{3/2} \rightarrow 3P_{3/2}$ and the brighter line $D_{3/2} \rightarrow 3P_{1/2}$.   The faint line is not usually seen; when it was discovered, it was called a "satellite" line.

Thus, the theory accounts very well for the principal features of the spectrum emitted by neutral sodium atoms.   It is equally successful with

TABLE 7-5. FIRST LINES OF THE PRINCIPAL SERIES FOR THE ALKALI METALS
AND ONE LINE OF HYDROGEN
λ is in angstroms, $\bar{\nu}$ in cm^{-1}

	H	Li	Na	K	Rb	Cs
Z	1	3	11	19	37	55
n	$3 \rightarrow 2$	2	3	4	5	6
$\lambda_{1/2}$	6,562.8	6,707.8	5,895.9	7,699.0	7,947.6	8,943.5
$\lambda_{3/2}$			5,890.0	7,664.9	7,800.2	8,521.1
$\bar{\nu}_{1/2}$	15,233	14,904	16,956	12,985	12,579	11,178
$\bar{\nu}_{3/2}$			16,973	13,043	12,817	11,732
$\Delta\bar{\nu}$	0.365	0.34	17	58	238	554

the other alkali metals, the spectra of which are qualitatively very similar to that of sodium.

The separation of the doublet levels, however, *increases rapidly with increasing Z*.   In Table 7-5 are shown the wavelengths and the wave numbers of the D lines or their analogs (i.e., the first lines of the principal series) for all of the alkali metals, and also the doublet differences for these lines.   The theoretical value of $\Delta\bar{\nu}$ for the first Balmer line of hydrogen, obtained by setting $Z = 1$, $n = 2$, $l = 1$ in Eq. (155), is also given for comparison.   The data in the table show that the D lines, which are 6 A apart in the sodium spectrum, become 422 A apart in the spectrum of cesium.

The enormous departure of $\Delta\bar{\nu}$ from the hydrogen value for all alkali metals except lithium, in spite of the progressive increase in n, is in strong contrast with the more moderate departure of the energy levels themselves, as shown by Fig. 67. This may be regarded as resulting from great sensitiveness of the spin-orbit effect to the character of the central field near the nucleus, which is clearly evident from the expression for the spin-orbit energy as given in Eq. (153). Near the nucleus the field of the nucleus itself must predominate, so that, approximately, $V = -Ze^2/r$, and

$$\frac{1}{r}\frac{dV}{dr} = \frac{Ze^2}{r^3}$$

which increases much more rapidly than does the numerical value of V itself as the nucleus is approached. The variation of the spin-orbit effect among the alkalies furnishes an excellent illustration of a general tendency of this effect to be small in atoms of low atomic number but to increase to an enormous magnitude as the atomic number becomes large.

120. Multiplet Levels for One-electron Atoms. The theory of the splitting of lines due to the spin-orbit effect as described in the last section should be valid also for atoms containing only a single electron. In the latter case, however, a curious accident occurs. In the nonrelativistic theory, as we have seen in Sec. 104, all states for a given n have the same energy, regardless of the value of l. In the relativistic theory this is not quite true. The wave equation contains certain other small relativistic terms besides those giving rise to the spin-orbit effect, and these

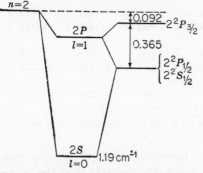

other terms cause the energy to vary somewhat with l. Now, in a one-electron atom this relativistic variation happens to be of the same order of magnitude as the spin-orbit effect itself; in fact, the net result of both effects would be that levels differing in l but not in j would *coincide*. (Actually the coincidence is not exact, at least in the case of S levels, but this was not discovered until about 1947.) The array of energy levels for one-electron atoms is thus very peculiar. Similar relativistic effects occur also in other atoms, but there the various L

FIG. 73. The fine structure for $n = 2$ for ordinary hydrogen: at left, nonrelativistic theory; center, as modified by the ordinary relativistic correction; right, as further modified by spin-orbit effects.

terms are so greatly displaced by the effects of the mutual electronic repulsion that the relativistic effects are relatively small.

The theoretical situation in the one-electron atoms as it was understood before 1945 is illustrated in Fig. 73, which represents hydrogen levels for

$n = 2$. The single line at the left represents the energy as given by Bohr's theory, Eq. (80) in Sec. 81. The two solid lines in the center of the diagram show this level as split into two, a P and an S term, in consequence of what is called the "ordinary" relativistic correction. The addition of the spin-orbit effect then splits the $2P$ term into the usual doublet with $j = \frac{1}{2}$ or $\frac{3}{2}$; but an additional "special" spin correction raises the $2S$ level so that it coincides with the $2P_{\frac{1}{2}}$ level. The net result, as shown at the right in the figure, is just *two separate levels*, a single one with $j = \frac{3}{2}$ and a composite level with $j = \frac{1}{2}$. In a similar way, the $3S_{\frac{1}{2}}$ level comes to coincide with the $3P_{\frac{1}{2}}$ level, and $3P_{\frac{3}{2}}$ also coincides with $3D_{\frac{3}{2}}$, whereas $3D_{\frac{5}{2}}$ stands alone; and so on. Thus for each value of n there are only n *different* energy levels, with $j = \frac{1}{2}, \frac{3}{2}, \frac{5}{2}, \ldots, n - \frac{1}{2}$; but all levels except that for the largest j, $j = n - \frac{1}{2}$, are double. The lowest level of all, with $n = 1$, is still single.

Approximate theoretical formulas for the various shifts are easily obtained by perturbation theory and are as follows. The *ordinary relativistic correction* to the energy, in cm^{-1}, is

$$\Delta_l W = \frac{3}{4} \frac{\alpha^2 R Z^4}{n^4} - \frac{\alpha^2 R Z^4}{n^3(l + \frac{1}{2})} \tag{156}$$

where R is Rydberg's constant in cm^{-1} and α is the "fine-structure constant":

$$\alpha = \frac{2\pi e^2}{ch} = 0.007297 = \frac{1}{137.04} \tag{157}$$

This correction splits each level for given n into n sublevels and accounts for the central part of Fig. 73. Before the advent of wave mechanics, a similar correction was obtained by Sommerfeld but with k or $l + 1$ instead of $l + \frac{1}{2}$.

The *spin-orbit correction* is then found to be, at least for $l > 0$,

$$j = l + \frac{1}{2}: \quad \Delta_s W = \frac{1}{l + 1} \frac{\alpha^2 R Z^4}{n^3(2l + 1)} \tag{158a}$$

$$j = l - \frac{1}{2}: \quad \Delta_s W = -\frac{1}{l} \frac{\alpha^2 R Z^4}{n^3(2l + 1)} \tag{158b}$$

For $l = 0$, the spin-orbit effect vanishes. The *special spin* correction is likewise found to vanish for $l > 0$, but for $l = 0$ it is

$$\frac{\alpha^2 R Z^4}{n^3}$$

This latter expression happens to be exactly what we get for $\Delta_s W$ if we put $l = 0$ in Eq. (158a). Hence, we can forget the special spin correction entirely provided we drop the restriction that $l > 0$ in using Eq. (158a). The spin corrections had no analog in the older quantum theory.

Upon adding $\Delta_l W$ to the proper value of $\Delta_s W$ and substituting for l in terms of j, the total shift in level is found to be, in cm^{-1},

$$\Delta W_{nj} = \frac{\alpha^2 R Z^4}{n^3} \left(\frac{3}{4n} - \frac{1}{j + \frac{1}{2}} \right) \tag{159}$$

It will be noted that ΔW_{nj} depends only on j and not independently on l. This formula provides the final net shifts shown in Fig. 73.

It happens, however, that the Dirac relativistic wave equation can also be solved exactly.[1]   The energy level for given n and j is found to be, in cgs units,

$$W_{nj} = mc^2 \left(\left\{ 1 + \frac{\alpha^2 Z^2}{[n - j - \frac{1}{2} + \sqrt{(j + \frac{1}{2})^2 - \alpha^2 Z^2}]^2} \right\}^{-\frac{1}{2}} - 1 \right) \tag{160}$$

If this expression is expanded in powers of α and then converted to cm^{-1}, it is found that, as far as terms of order α^2, W_{nj} is the sum of Bohr's value, $-RZ^2/n^2$, and ΔW_{nj} as given by (159).   Even the Dirac wave equation is not entirely accurate, however, for reasons described in the next section.   By accident, Sommerfeld's relativistic correction gave the same set of distinct energies as Eq. (159).

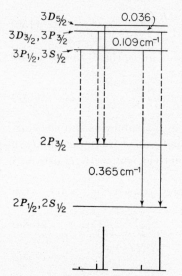

FIG. 74. Original theoretical fine structure of the Hα line ($n = 3 \rightarrow n = 2$) for atomic hydrogen.

121. Fine Structure of Spectral Lines from One-electron Atoms. *a. The Original Theoretical Patterns.* If the pair of levels having given values of n and j is treated as a single multiple level, no attention need be paid to the selection rule for l in determining the allowed jumps between such levels; it is sufficient to observe the rule for j (Sec. 118):

$$\Delta j = 0 \text{ or } \pm 1$$

If a jump is allowed by this rule, component quantum states satisfying the condition that $\Delta l = \pm 1$ can always be selected.

As an example, the levels and allowed jumps for $n = 3$ and $n = 2$ are shown in Fig. 74.   (The spacings between the j levels are shown to scale, but on the same scale the distance between the two groups would be some 24,000 times larger than as shown.)   The selection rule for j allows five transitions, as shown by the arrows.   If changes in l are considered as well, as a basis for the introduction of standard spectroscopic notation, we

[1] Cf. C. G. Darwin, *Proc. Roy. Soc. (London)*, vol. 118, p. 654, 1928.

find seven transitions, two pairs of them producing identical frequencies, according to the theory so far developed; denoting $l = 0, 1, 2$ by S, P, D as usual, we have as transitions: $3D_{5/2} \rightarrow 2P_{3/2}$, $3D_{3/2} \rightarrow 2P_{3/2}$, $3D_{3/2} \rightarrow 2P_{1/2}$, $3P_{3/2} \rightarrow 2S_{1/2}$, $3P_{1/2} \rightarrow 2S_{1/2}$, $3S_{1/2} \rightarrow 2P_{1/2}$, and $3S_{1/2} \rightarrow 2P_{3/2}$. The relative spacing of the five distinct lines is shown in the lower part of Fig. 74, the heights of the lines as drawn representing the theoretical relative intensities of the spectral lines on the assumption that all five quantum states for $n = 3$ are equally excited (i.e., that as many atoms are excited into one state as into another).

b. *First Comparison with Experiment for Hydrogen.* The "lines" of the Balmer series of hydrogen were early observed as close doublets. In 1887, Michelson and Morley measured the doublet separation for the line of longest wavelength, Hα or $n = 3 \rightarrow n = 2$, and found for it 0.253 cm^{-1}.

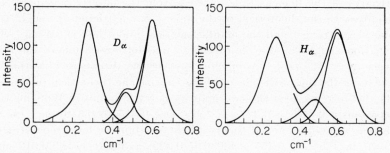

FIG. 75. Typical intensity curves obtained for the Hα line from hydrogen (Hα) and deuterium (Dα). Intensity is on an arbitrary scale, and the abscissa is numbered from an arbitrary point. (*After Williams.*)

Subsequent measurements by other investigators gave values ranging from 0.293 to 0.357. The modern interpretation of the doublet appearance is that the five component lines are smeared together because of the Doppler broadening of all lines due to the thermal motion of the molecules, but two of them are much more intense than the others. The only means of comparing the observations with the theoretical predictions is, therefore, to calculate the contour of the total line from the theory, using the theoretical separations of the fine structure and the theoretical estimates of the relative intensities of the component lines, and then making an approximate allowance for the Doppler effect.

The line Hα has been studied very carefully in this manner. In Fig. 75 are shown typical curves obtained by R. C. Williams[1] for the spectral distribution of intensity in the Hα line from ordinary hydrogen and from deuterium, or heavy hydrogen, the atoms of which are about twice as heavy as those of ordinary hydrogen and ought, therefore, to be influenced less by the Doppler effect. The discharge tube was cooled by liquid air

[1] R. C. Williams, *Phys. Rev.*, vol. 54, p. 558, 1938.

to minimize the broadening. The light from the tube was dispersed by a triple-prism spectrograph containing a quartz Fabry-Perot etalon placed in the parallel beam of the collimator, and photographs were taken of the spectral region containing the Hα line. The blackening on the film was measured with a Moll microphotometer using a thermocouple and galvanometer, and from these measurements the relative distribution of intensity in the line could be determined.

At most three of the theoretical component lines are evident in Fig. 75; one of the others is too close to the left-hand main line to be resolved, and the remaining one is evidently too weak to be seen. Theoretical line shapes, as influenced by the Doppler effect, are drawn in the figure for the three lines, the assumed strengths of the lines being so adjusted as best to reproduce the observed curve of resultant intensity. The strengths of the lines as thus inferred from the observations agree only oughly with the theoretical predictions. The left-hand line ought to be somewhat stronger and the middle one only about half as strong. Such deviations might be due, however, to unequal excitation of the initial levels ($S_{1/2}$, $P_{3/2}$, $D_{5/2}$). A much more serious discrepancy is that the *spacing* of the lines does not quite agree with the theoretical predictions. The distance between the two main peaks was found by Williams to be consistently 0.319 to 0.321 cm^{-1} for Dα, 0.315 to 0.319 cm^{-1} for Hα, whereas wave-mechanical theory predicts, from the level separations as shown in Fig. 74, $0.365 - 0.036 = 0.329$, a difference of 0.010 cm^{-1}. The small central peak seems also to occur at about 0.134 cm^{-1} from the right-hand one, whereas the theory gives for this separation 0.109 cm^{-1}.

c. Later Experimental Work. The cause of these discrepancies[1] between existing theory and observation remained a mystery for many years. It was suggested, however, by Pasternak in 1938 that the $2S_{1/2}$ level might for some unknown reason lie a little higher than the $2P_{1/2}$ level instead of coinciding with it. The composite bright line of highest frequency, $3P_{1/2} \rightarrow 2S_{1/2}$ and $3D_{3/2} \rightarrow 2P_{1/2}$, would thus appear to be shifted a little closer to the remaining lines.

In 1947 Lamb and Retherford reported observations in support of this explanation.[2] They succeeded in determining the difference between the $2P_{3/2}$ and the $2S_{1/2}$ levels, and then even the difference between $2P_{1/2}$ and $2S_{1/2}$, by measuring *the frequency of the corresponding spectral line* in absorption. The calculated frequency for $2P_{3/2} \rightarrow 2S_{1/2}$ is 0.365 cm^{-1}, equivalent to a wavelength of 2.74 cm, but methods of generating "micro-

[1] Cf. J. W. Drinkwater, O. Richardson, and W. E. Williams, *Proc. Roy. Soc. (London),* vol. 174, p. 164, 1940.

[2] W. E. Lamb, Jr., and R. C. Retherford, *Phys. Rev.,* vol. 72, p. 241, 1947; Retherford and Lamb, *Phys. Rev.,* vol. 75, p. 1325, 1949; Lamb, *Repts. Progr. in Phys.,* vol. 14, p. 19, 1951.

waves" of this order of magnitude are now available.[1] A number of difficulties had to be overcome, and elaborate planning was necessary. The investigation is an excellent example of the involved character of much modern experimentation. The apparatus is shown diagrammatically in Fig. 76.

The first problem was to produce excited hydrogen atoms in $2S_{\frac{1}{2}}$ states. To avoid the complications associated with electrical discharge tubes, use was made of a beam of hydrogen or deuterium issuing from a tungsten oven at about 2500°C. At this temperature the hydrogen was about 64 per cent dissociated into atoms. An electron beam was allowed to cross the beam of atoms and to excite some of them into higher states, including the $2S_{\frac{1}{2}}$ state. The latter state is metastable, since no jump can occur by dipole radiation into the normal $1S$ state ($\Delta l = 0$); thus the excited

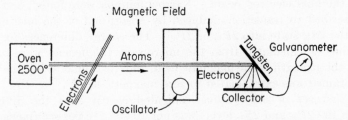

FIG. 76. Diagram of Lamb's apparatus for study of the hydrogen energy levels.

atoms were able to move an appreciable distance while remaining in the $2S_{\frac{1}{2}}$ state. It was necessary, however, to avoid the presence of electric fields, which, by a form of Stark effect, would modify the quantum states in such a way that, instead of pure $2S_{\frac{1}{2}}$ and $2P_{\frac{1}{2}}$ states, there would be two states each having as a wave function a combination of $2S_{\frac{1}{2}}$ and $2P_{\frac{1}{2}}$ wave functions; dipole jumps would then be possible out of both states by the process $2P_{\frac{1}{2}} \rightarrow 1S_{\frac{1}{2}}$, resulting in a quick loss of the excited atoms. This effect of an electric field is appreciable even when the $2P_{\frac{1}{2}}$ and $2S_{\frac{1}{2}}$ levels are slightly separated. Since entire freedom from electric fields is difficult to secure, a magnetic field was applied at right angles to the beam; each level was thus broken up into Zeeman components liberally separated from each other in proportion to the field strength, thereby minimizing any effects due to stray electric fields.

In the apparatus, the excited atoms next traversed a small metal tube, entering and leaving through openings in its walls. The tube, together with a metal strip down its center (not shown in Fig. 76), served as a wave guide for microwaves generated in a small oscillator at one end of the tube. The atoms then fell upon a tungsten plate, in which, by a collision process, those arriving in the $2S_{\frac{1}{2}}$ state were returned to their normal

[1] Cf. J. C. Slater, "Microwave Electronics," 1950; H. J. Reich, P. F. Ordung, and H. L. Skalnik, "Microwave Theory and Techniques," 1953.

states with the simultaneous emission of an electron. The stream of electrons thus generated was collected and measured. Typically, this stream amounted to about 10^{-14} ampere, and it was observed to be decreased by $13\!/\!_{20}$ when a strong steady electric field was applied between the conductors of the wave-guide tube; this fraction $13\!/\!_{20}$ was assumed to represent the atoms arriving in $2S_{1/2}$ states, which were caused by the electric field to undergo transitions into other states. The remaining $7\!/\!_{20}$ of the electron beam was ascribed to stray ultraviolet light generated somehow in the tungsten plate by the *exciting* electron beam located on the opposite side of the wave guide.

The method of observation was to set the frequency of the microwaves at a suitable fixed value, this frequency being hard to adjust continuously, and then to vary the strength of the magnetic field and observe the intensity of the final electron beam. Narrow minima were found, and these were ascribed to transitions induced by absorption of the microwaves, out of the $2S_{1/2}$ state into $2P_{1/2}$ or $2P_{3/2}$. The energy differences for these transitions as calculated from the microwave frequencies were plotted against the strength of the magnetic field, and, for a final result, the curve thus obtained was extrapolated to zero magnetic field.

The first set of observations indicated clearly that the difference between the $2P_{3/2}$ and $2S_{1/2}$ levels was not 10,095 Mc per sec (megacycles per second) or 0.365 cm^{-1}, as was predicted by existing theory, but about 1,000 Mc per sec or 0.0332 cm^{-1} less. The $2S_{1/2}$ level would thus lie roughly 0.033 cm^{-1} above $2P_{1/2}$, provided the latter level is not shifted. With new apparatus, using microwaves of about 30 cm wavelength, it was found possible also to induce transitions from $2S_{1/2}$ to $2P_{1/2}$ (by forced emission) and so to measure this energy difference directly. Later work gave as the observed difference 1,057.8 Mc per sec or 0.0353 cm^{-1} for hydrogen, and 1,059.0 Mc per sec for deuterium.[1]

The line $3P_{3/2} \rightarrow 2S_{1/2}$ thus no longer coincides exactly with $3D_{3/2} \rightarrow 2P_{1/2}$. If the $3P_{3/2}$ and $3D_{3/2}$ levels were equally excited, it can be calculated that the intensity ratio of these lines would be 2.08:5.0, so that the two would actually be observed as a single line shifted

$$\frac{2.08}{7.08} \, 0.0353 = 0.010 \text{ cm}^{-1}$$

in good agreement with Williams's observations.

d. Refinement of the Theory. A theoretical explanation of the shift of the $2S_{1/2}$ level was put forward almost simultaneously with the observations by Bethe.[2] It had long been suspected that a more thoroughgoing

---

[1] S. Triebwasser, E. S. Dayhoff, and W. E. Lamb, Jr., *Phys. Rev.*, vol. 89, p. 98, 1953.

[2] H. A. Bethe, *Phys. Rev.*, vol. 72, p. 339, 1947.

application of the wave-mechanical theory of the electromagnetic field, described briefly in Sec. 108, might lead to a slight revision of the theoretical values of atomic energy levels. In the usual theory of the hydrogen atom, the interaction between the nucleus and the electron is represented by a simple potential-energy term. This term, however, really represents the effect of an electromagnetic field of very simple type, and for consistency this field should be treated by the same general method that is used in dealing with the emission of radiation. When such a treatment is attempted, however, a divergent integral is obtained for the energy of an electron in the presence of a nucleus. The integral diverges, in fact, even for the energy of a free electron!

In classical electromagnetic theory, a similar difficulty had been encountered when the electron was treated as a point charge, but it had been possible to overcome this difficulty by assigning to it a finite size. If the electron were a sphere with all its charge on the surface, its electromagnetic mass would be equal to the observed mass m provided the radius of the sphere were $2e^2/3mc^2$ or 1.9×10^{-13} cm. Thus the hypothesis became possible that all mass is of electromagnetic origin. The inertia of charged particles would then arise from essentially the same electromagnetic action as that which is responsible for the inductive inertia of ordinary electric circuits.

An analogous wave-mechanical theory of electronic mass has never been achieved. Bethe pointed out, however, that the divergent integral that is obtained for the energy of a stationary free electron should represent its rest energy m_0c^2 and that allowance for this part of the energy has really already been made by introducing the constant $m = m_0$ into the wave equation. He proposed, therefore, to take as the binding energy of an electron in an atom the difference between the divergent integral obtained for the energy of the electron in the atom and the divergent integral for its energy when free, and he gave reasons for believing that the difference would be a convergent integral that could be evaluated.

This surmise was confirmed by more exact calculations. The result in the case under discussion is a slight correction to the accepted formulas for the binding energy, which is very much larger on the S states of a one-electron atom than on other states because for S states ψ does not vanish at the nucleus. The final theoretical values obtained are 1,057.2 Mc per sec for hydrogen and 1,058.5 for deuterium.[1] These values are only 0.5 Mc per sec below the experimental values, an extraordinary agreement (unless in some way fortuitous!).

It appears, therefore, that in Figs. 73 and 74 the $2S_{1/2}$ level should be drawn to lie above the $2P_{1/2}$ level by 0.035 cm^{-1} or about $\frac{1}{10}$ of the space between $2P_{1/2}$ and $2P_{3/2}$. In ionized helium the same shift was measured

[1] E. E. Salpeter, *Phys. Rev.*, vol. 89, p. 92, 1953.

experimentally as 14,000 Mc per sec, being 1.4 per cent greater than the calculated value.[1]

122. Many-electron Wave Theory. When an atom contains two or more electrons outside closed subshells, it is still true, as a rule, that in a radiative transition only one electron is active, but the atomic energy levels between which the jump occurs are themselves influenced by the presence of the other electrons. As a basis for the discussion of such cases, it may be worth while to describe briefly the wave equation for complex atoms, although no actual mathematical developments can be attempted.

The complete relativistic wave equation for two or more electrons is not known, but an approximate equation can be written down that is adequate for most purposes. The terms that occur in this equation may be classified as follows:

1. Terms representing kinetic energy and containing derivatives of ψ
2. Terms due to the nuclear field
3. Terms representing the mutual energy of the electrons due to their electrostatic repulsion
4. Spin-orbit terms representing interaction between the magnetic moment of each electron and its own orbital motion
5. Mixed spin-orbit terms representing interaction between each spin magnetic moment and the orbital motions of other electrons
6. Spin-spin interactions between the spin magnetic moments of the electrons
7. Other relativistic corrections, only partly known
8. Terms allowing for nuclear motion

Of these many terms, however, those in class 8 scarcely ever have appreciable effects, and classes 6 and 7 are important only for a few levels of light atoms, such as the 2^3P levels of neutral helium and ionized lithium. With inclusion of only the remaining five classes, the wave equation may be written down as follows:

$$-\frac{h^2}{8\pi^2 m} \sum_{j=1}^{N} \nabla_j^2 \psi - e^2 Z \sum_{j=1}^{N} \frac{1}{r_j} \psi + e^2 \sum_{j=2}^{N} \sum_{k=1}^{j-1} \frac{1}{r_{jk}} \psi + P\psi = W\psi \quad (161)$$

Here h, e, m, Z, and W are as in Eq. (133) and c is the speed of light; ∇_j^2 denotes ∇^2 (Sec. 96) expressed in terms of the coordinates of the jth electron, whose distance from the nucleus is r_j; and N is the number of electrons in the atom, equal to the atomic number Z for a neutral atom but less than Z for an ion. The units are cgs with e in electrostatic units. The terms in r_{jk} represent the mutual potential energy of the electrons; the term $P\psi$ represents the spin-orbit energies (Sec. 118).

[1] W. E. Lamb and M. Skinner, *Phys. Rev.*, vol. 78, p. 539, 1950.

Unfortunately, this equation cannot be solved in terms of ordinary functions; hence the perturbation approach is usually employed. Let us omit the spin-orbit term and replace the electrostatic-interaction terms by the central field described in Sec. 109, which includes a rough average of the electrostatic effects of the electrons on each other. If ϕ is the electrostatic potential due to the entire electronic charge cloud, the potential energy of an additional electron in this field is $V = -e\phi$; for an electron belonging to the atom itself, however, we substitute $(N - 1)V/N$. The zero-order approximate wave equation thus derived reads as follows:

$$H_0\psi = -\frac{h^2}{8\pi^2 m}\sum \nabla_j{}^2\psi - e^2 Z \sum \frac{1}{r_j}\psi + \frac{N-1}{N}\sum V_j\psi = W^0\psi \quad (162)$$

V_j denoting V expressed in terms of the coordinates of the jth electron.

In this equation the electronic variables occur separated, that is, each term contains the coordinates of only one electron. For this reason the solutions can be written as products of solutions of the simpler one-electron wave equation

$$-\frac{h^2}{8\pi^2 m}\nabla^2\psi - \frac{e^2 Z}{r}\psi + \frac{N-1}{N}V\psi = W\psi \quad (163)$$

If $\psi_1, \psi_2, \ldots, \psi_N$ are solutions of this equation with associated electronic energies $W_1, W_2, \ldots, W_N$, then it is easily verified by substitution that a solution of (162) is the product $\psi = \psi_1\psi_2 \cdots \psi_N$ with $W^0 = W_1 + W_2 + \cdots + W_N$. Here ψ_j is written in terms of the coordinates of the jth electron. Each of the W_j's represents the negative of the work required to remove one electron out of state ψ_j in the atom to rest at infinity, thereby ionizing the atom.

The potential field V is required to be such that the cloud charge arising from electrons with respective wave functions $\psi_1, \psi_2, \ldots, \psi_N$ just suffices, together with the nucleus, to reproduce the field itself. It is called for this reason a "self-consistent" field. Since the electronic wave functions cannot be found until the field is known, the problem might seem to be circular, but methods of handling it have been developed.[1] An example was shown in Fig. 62, and the calculated charge-cloud density for sodium was shown in Fig. 68.

Proceeding with perturbation theory, the correct wave equation (161) is then written in this form:

$$H_0\psi + \left(e^2\sum_{j=2}^{N}\sum_{k=1}^{j-1}\frac{1}{r_{jk}} - \frac{N-1}{N}\sum_{j=1}^{N}V_j\right)\psi + P\psi = W\psi \quad (164)$$

[1] Cf. D. R. Hartree, Proc. Cambridge Phil. Soc., vol. 24, p. 189, 1928; and E. U. Condon and G. H. Shortley, "Theory of Atomic Spectra," 1935, reprinted with corrections in 1951.

Here the terms in parentheses represent the difference between the true electrostatic interaction energy and its average value as represented by the modified field; this difference will be called the "residual electrostatic interaction." Corrections for this term and for the spin-orbit terms may then be made by means of the formulas of perturbation theory (Sec. 103), with use of the zero-order ψ's or product functions $\psi_1\psi_2 \cdots \psi_N$.

In refined work, allowance is also made for the fact that, with each electron moving in a modified field due only to the nucleus and to the remaining electrons, the individual electrons actually move in somewhat different self-consistent fields, whereas we have assumed them all to move in the same field. Furthermore, the zero-order energy of the atom is not just the value of W^0 in Eq. (162), or $W_1 + W_2 + \cdots + W_N$, because in the term $[(N - 1)/N]\Sigma V_j$ the mutual energies e^2/r_{jk} are counted twice; a special calculation is necessary to find the zero-order energy of the atom. For our purposes, however, neither of these complications is worth consideration.

Electronic Configurations and Coupling Schemes. The possible states of a single electron in the modified central field are characterized, as was explained in Sec. 109, by quantum numbers n and l. An assignment of n's and l's for all N electrons in the atom defines an *electronic configuration.* Such an assignment may be indicated either by a symbol such as $(n_1l_1, n_2l_2, \ldots, n_Nl_N)$ or in spectroscopic notation. As examples, $2s3d$ may denote a configuration of two electrons in which one electron has $n = 2$ and $l = 0$ while the other has $n = 3$ and $l = 2$. Again, $1p^2 2p$ means that there are 2 electrons with $n = 1$ and $l = 1$ and another with $n = 2$ and $l = 1$. In the entire absence of all perturbations, there is a single energy level for each configuration.

An important *selection rule* holds for configurations. In general, radiative transitions occur only between configurations that differ in just one of the (n,l) electronic states; and, furthermore, the values of l in the initial and final states must differ exactly by unity. Thus transitions may occur between a level belonging to a $2s3p$ configuration and a $2s3d$ level, but not between $2s3p$ and $2p3d$ because here both electronic states are different, and not between $2s3p$ and $2s4f$ because here $\Delta l = 2$ for the second electronic state. This selection rule diminishes enormously the number of transitions that have to be considered in spectroscopy. The rule holds strictly so long as the wave function corresponds exactly to a single configuration. In many cases, however, ψ contains components of appreciable magnitude belonging to other configurations, for which the sum $l_1 + l_2 + \cdots + l_N$ differs by an even integer. In such cases transitions, called two-electron jumps, may occur in which two electronic l's change, with $\Delta l = 2$ for the second.

Allowance must then be made by perturbation theory for the effects of the residual electrostatic energy and the spin-orbit interactions. The result is usually that the single energy level belonging in zero order to each configuration is split into two or more levels. Appropriate zero-order wave functions can be constructed out of either the $n \, l \, \lambda \, \mu$ wave functions or the $n \, l \, j \, m$ functions (Sec. 118). Any wave function for the atom can be expressed as a series in terms of either of these two families of functions. As a starting point for perturbation theory, linear combinations of the chosen functions are first made so as to diagonalize the perturbation matrix (cf. Sec. 103). It happens, however, in many atoms that one of the two perturbations just mentioned greatly predominates in its effects over the other, and in such cases it is convenient to allow first for the predominant perturbation and then to add a correction for the second as a supplementary smaller effect. According as one or the other of the two types of perturbation is treated first, two alternative procedures are obtained, known, respectively, as the LS and the jj coupling schemes. The LS scheme will be described and illustrated first.

123. LS or Russell-Saunders Coupling. In atoms that are not too heavy, the residual electrostatic interaction has a relatively large effect. For simplicity of discussion, let it be assumed for the present that spin-orbit interactions are entirely absent.

In classical mechanics, the electronic repulsions would have no effect upon the vector sum $\mathbf{G}_L$ of the orbital angular momenta of the electrons, so that in the absence of external forces this vector would remain constant. Analogously, according to wave mechanics, in the absence both of external forces and of spin-orbit effects, the quantum states of the atom are characterized by a fixed magnitude of $G_L{}^2$ denoted by $L(L+1)h^2/(2\pi)^2$, where L is a positive integer or zero. As was noted in Sec. 116, the letters S, P, D, F, G, H, I, K, etc., are often written to denote $L = 0, 1, 2, 3, \ldots$. The (degenerate) quantum states can also be chosen so that the component of $\mathbf{G}_L$ in the direction of any chosen axis is $\Lambda h/2\pi$ (or $M_L h/2\pi$), where the $(2L+1)$ alternative values of Λ (or M_L) are integrally spaced from $-L$ to L. Thus $Lh/2\pi$ is the maximum possible value of the component of $\mathbf{G}_L$ in any direction.

The resultant spin momentum $\mathbf{G}_S$ is also quantized, $G_S{}^2$ having a value $S(S+1)h^2/(2\pi)^2$; the possible values of S are integrally spaced downward from $N/2$ to $\frac{1}{2}$ or 0. The quantization of $\mathbf{G}_S$ is not a consequence of interaction between the spin magnetic moments, whose influence on spectroscopic phenomena is slight. The cause lies in the exclusion principle, because of which, as in the example described in Sec. 107, different types of spatial symmetry in the wave function must accompany different values of S. The component of $\mathbf{G}_S$ in the direction of the axis may have a value $\Sigma h/2\pi$ (or $M_S h/2\pi$), where Σ is any one of the integrally spaced numbers from S to $-S$. Since each electronic spin can contribute at most $h/4\pi$ to the axial component, the maximum possible value of Σ, and hence also the value of S, is $N/2$ for an atom containing N electrons. Both S and Σ are thus integers or zero, or half-integral, according as N is even or odd.

The statements so far made are valid regardless of the strength of the *residual electrostatic* interaction. When, as usually happens, this interaction itself can be treated as a *rather small perturbation*, zero-order approximate wave functions can be constructed out of products of electronic wave functions. For these we may advantageously choose the $n \, l \, \lambda \, \mu$ functions.

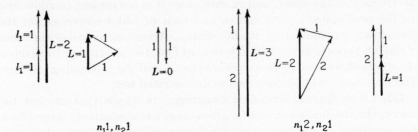

Fig. 77. Diagrams illustrating addition of two l vectors into an L vector.

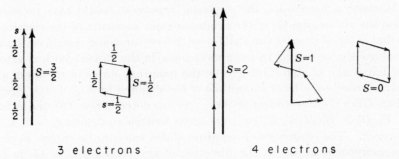

3 electrons   4 electrons

Fig. 78. Diagrams illustrating addition of s vectors into an S vector.

Consider a particular electronic configuration $(n_1l_1, n_2l_2, \ldots, n_Nl_N)$. The individual l vectors can be thought of as coupled vectorially into a properly quantized resultant L vector. If no two sets of the pairs (n, l) are the same, all integral values of L may occur from the sum of the l vectors down to the smallest that can be formed by vector addition of these vectors. Several cases are illustrated in Fig. 77; as another example, if $N = 3$ and $l_1 = l_2 = l_3 = 1$, then $L = 3$ or 2 or 1 or 0. If any $l = 0$, it may be disregarded; if all l's are zero, then $L = 0$. Similarly, the possible values of S can be regarded as arising from a coupling of the s vectors (Fig. 78). In constructing such diagrams for L or S, all closed subshells may be ignored since they would contribute nothing to the L or S vector sums.

In some configurations, however, two or more independent sets of LS quantum states occur having the same values of L and S. This fact is not revealed by the vector diagram.

Zero-order $L\,S\,\Lambda\,\Sigma$ *wave functions* are easily formed as linear combinations of the $n\,l\,\lambda\,\mu$ functions. The $L\,S\,\Lambda\,\Sigma$ quantum states are not usually characterized by definite values of the individual λ's and μ's; the individual axial components of electronic angular momentum are not definite (except in a few cases). This illustrates again the general rule concerning vector sums of angular momenta that was stated in Sec. 118, and corresponds to the fact in classical mechanics that fixing the vector sums $\mathbf{G}_L$ and $\mathbf{G}_S$ does not fix the individual vector momenta $\mathbf{G}_l$ and $\mathbf{G}_s$. It is readily seen that repulsion between electrons would usually have little average effect on the *magnitude* of any individual $\mathbf{G}_l$; it would merely speed the electron up and then slow it down again during its orbital motion. A component of this repulsion normal to the orbital plane, on the other hand, would cause a more or less steady precession of the individual $\mathbf{G}_l$ vectors about the fixed direction of their resultant, $\mathbf{G}_l$, in analogy with the effect of a torque applied to a gyrostat. Such precessional motions symbolize vividly the necessity of abandoning the λ's and μ's and quantizing only the resultant momentum when full account is taken of electronic repulsion. The motions themselves, however, have no analog in the wave-mechanical description of the quantum states.

Simple *selection rules* hold for L and S; this is the most important property of such quantum numbers. The rules are

$$\Delta L = 0 \text{ or } \pm 1 \text{ (and not } 0 \rightarrow 0) \qquad \Delta S = 0$$

The restriction that $\Delta S = 0$ corresponds to the fact that in classical mechanics the existence of spin and of its associated magnetic moment has no appreciable (direct) effect upon the emission of radiation. Because of this selection rule, in the absence of all spin-orbit interaction, the atomic energy levels fall into broad, noncombining classes, each distinguished by a different value of S; levels belonging to one class combine in the emission or absorption of spectral lines only with other levels belonging to the same class.

Under the selection rule for L, the so-called S levels ($L = 0$) can combine with P levels ($L = 1$); P levels can combine either with S or with D levels ($L = 2$); D levels can combine either with P or with F levels ($L = 3$); and so on. A special case of this selection rule has already been encountered in dealing with atoms containing a single valence electron (Sec. 116). The selection rule for L refers, however, only to dipole emission of radiation. Weak lines violating this rule are frequently seen.

The occurrence of atomic states characterized by quantum numbers

L and S obeying the selection rules just stated is called LS, or Russell-Saunders, coupling (of the electronic momenta).[1]

The LS Terms.   In zero order, only a single energy level belongs to a given configuration. The residual electrostatic interaction then splits this single level into several levels belonging to different pairs of values of L and S. That this interaction should separate levels differing in L is reasonable. In classical theory, different values of L would imply different relative orientations of the electronic orbits, and the average values of the repulsive potential energy of the electrons should therefore also be different. It may seem strange, however, that states differing only in S should likewise be separated in energy by electronic repulsions. The reason for such an effect lies in the different spatial symmetries of the wave functions associated with different values of S. The separation has little to do with the mutual energy of the spin magnets, although this would cause a slight separation if other causes were not active. In the mathematics, the separation of levels having different S results from "exchange integrals" of the electronic mutual energies, analogous to the example encountered in Sec. 106. These integrals have no classical analog. Wave mechanics thus introduces a distinction that is absent in classical theory; for, two classical motions differing only in that two electrons exchange roles would be physically indistinguishable.

124. LS Multiplets of Levels. To account for the observed fine structure of the spectral lines, account must then be taken of the *spin-orbit interactions* as a second perturbing energy much smaller (in light atoms) than the residual electrostatic energy. The spin-orbit interactions tend to disturb both the orbital and the spin momenta but not the grand vector sum of all angular momenta. In the classical analog, the vectors $\mathbf{G}_L$ and $\mathbf{G}_S$, unless actually parallel, would precess steadily about their resultant, $\mathbf{G}_J$. Suitable combinations must, therefore, next be made of the $L\ S\ \Lambda\ \Sigma$ functions themselves, thereby obtaining new functions characterized by quantum numbers J and M, with the significance and associated selection rules described in Sec. 115. Thus the $\Lambda\ \Sigma$ quantum numbers disappear in turn (with a few exceptions). Even in the absence of spin-orbit effects, the $L\ S\ J\ M$ quantum states *may* be used instead of the $L\ S\ \Lambda\ \Sigma$ states; in the presence of spin-orbit interaction, they *must* be used. The $L\ S\ \Lambda\ \Sigma$ and $L\ S\ J\ M$ functions constitute two more alternative families of functions in terms of which any wave function for the atom can be expressed in series form.

The possible values of J that can occur in a given LS term are all those integrally spaced values that satisfy the inequality

$$|L - S| \leqq J \leqq L + S$$

[1] Russell and Saunders, *Astrophys. J.*, vol. 61, p. 38, 1925.

Thus, if $L = 0$, it follows that $J = S$; whereas if $S = 0$, $J = L$, and in either case the multiplet of levels reduces to a singlet. Otherwise, it is easily seen that, whether S is integral or half-integral, if $L \geqq S$, J takes on all the $2S + 1$ integrally spaced values from $L + S$ down to $L - S$, inclusive; whereas, if $L < S$, J takes on the $2L + 1$ integrally spaced values from $S + L$ to $S - L$. Two cases are illustrated by vector diagrams in Fig. 79.

The number of J levels composing an LS term is called the *multiplicity* of the term and is commonly written as a superscript at the upper left-hand corner of the letter denoting the term. Thus ^2D denotes a doublet D term, with $L = 2$, $S = \frac{1}{2}$ and with two possible J values: $L + S = \frac{5}{2}$, $L - S = \frac{3}{2}$. To denote an individual level, the J value is added as a subscript. Thus a ^2D term contains the levels $^2D_{3/2}$, $^2D_{5/2}$. If $L = 2$, but $S = 1$, we have a *triplet* D term, with component levels $^3D_3$, $^3D_2$, $^3D_1$.

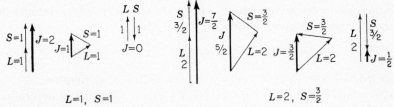

L=1, S=1   L=2, S=3/2

FIG. 79. Diagrams illustrating addition of an L and an S vector into a J vector.

Even when $L < S$, the same multiplicity, $2S + 1$, is indicated in the notation, although the number of levels now equals $2L + 1$ and therefore is less than $2S + 1$. The reason for this practice is that, because of the selection rule for S, $\Delta S = 0$ (Sec. 123), the value of $2S + 1$ tends to remain the same in a radiative transition. The terms can thus be classified into more or less noncombining groups according to the values of $2S + 1$, and the superscript serves to indicate at once to which class a particular term belongs.

Because of these relations, the *observed* number of levels composing a given multiplet obviously furnishes important information in regard to the values of L or of S that should be assigned to the term. If the observed number of levels is r, this number must equal either $2L + 1$ or (more commonly) $2S + 1$, hence, either $L = (r - 1)/2$ or, more likely, $S = (r - 1)/2$. A further test may then be made by noting whether or not the value of L or S so inferred is consistent with the selection rules as applied to transitions between the given multiplet of levels and other multiplets for which L or S may be assumed to be known.

The single energy level belonging originally to a given LS term is thus split by the spin-orbit interactions into two or more sublevels characterized by different values of J. The various L S J levels arising in this way from the $6s6p$ configuration in mercury are shown in Fig. 81. This configuration, with $l = 0$ and $l = 1$, gives rise by electrostatic interaction to singlet and triplet P terms, which are then split by the spin-orbit effect into $^1P_1$ and $^3P_0$, $^3P_1$ and $^3P_2$ levels. A $7p6p$ configuration would produce 10 final levels: $^1S_0$, $^1P_1$, $^1D_2$; $^3S_1$, $^3P_0$, $^3P_1$, $^3P_2$; $^3D_1$, $^3D_2$, $^3D_3$.

All allowed transitions between two multiplets of levels, taken together, give rise to a group of spectral lines which may be called a *spectral multiplet*. The student should distinguish carefully between multiplets of levels and multiplets of lines. Often one can tell only from the context whether the word "triplet," for example, refers to three energy levels or to three lines.

125. Spacing of the LS Multiplet Levels. For the spacing of the levels in an LS multiplet, wave mechanics furnishes a simple and useful formula, which holds quite accurately so long as the entire width of the multiplet is small relative to its difference in energy from all other energy levels. The increase in the atomic energy due to the spin-orbit effect, for any one of the J levels of a given multiplet, is ΔW where

$$\Delta W = \tfrac{1}{2}B[J(J + 1) - L(L + 1) - S(S + 1)] \tag{165}$$

Here B is a constant that varies from one multiplet to another.

The relative spacing of the levels in a given multiplet is determined by the term $\tfrac{1}{2}BJ(J + 1)$. The difference between the energies of a level for J and that for $J + 1$ is the difference in the corresponding values of ΔW, or

$$W_{J+1} - W_J = \tfrac{1}{2}B[(J + 1)(J + 2) - J(J + 1)] = B(J + 1) \tag{166}$$

This equation expresses Landé's interval rule: *The energy differences between two successive J levels are proportional, in a given LS term, to the larger of the two values of J*. The rule is of great help in determining the values of J that are to be assigned to various observed levels.

According to Eq. (165), ΔW is positive for some values of J and negative for others. The weighted average of ΔW vanishes, provided each level is weighted in proportion to the number, equal to $2J + 1$, of the M states composing it. The total energy of the weighted-average level is given by the formula

$$\bar{W}_{LS} = \frac{\sum_J (2J + 1)W_J}{\sum_J (2J + 1)} \tag{167}$$

It is to such a weighted-average level that a Rydberg formula really refers when it is written without regard to the fine structure of the terms.

As an alternative, a separate Rydberg formula is sometimes written for each component of the multiplets forming a series.

Equation (165) can be arrived at by the following semiclassical argument. Draw a vector diagram representing addition of the electronic vector orbital angular momenta G_{l1}, G_{l2}, . . . into a resultant G_L, similarly of the spin momenta G_{s1}, G_{s2}, . . . into G_S, and, finally, of G_L and G_S into G_J. A case is illustrated in Fig. 80. By Eq. (153) the total spin-orbit energy is proportional to $\Sigma(k = 1$ to $N)G_{lk} \cdot G_{sk}$, where N is the number of electrons involved. Now resolve each G_{lk} into components G'_{lk} and G''_{lk} respectively parallel and perpendicular to G_L, and similarly G_{sk} into G'_{sk} and G''_{sk} parallel and perpendicular to G_S.   Then

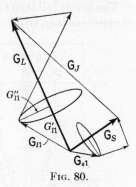

Fig. 80.

$$G_{lk} \cdot G_{sk} = G'_{lk} \cdot G'_{sk} + G'_{lk} \cdot G''_{sk} + G''_{lk} \cdot G'_{sk} + G''_{lk} \cdot G''_{sk}$$

But, according to wave-mechanical theory, the components G''_{lk} and G''_{sk} are indeterminate with equal probability for all directions.   It is as if the whole G_l figure were rigid and precessing at a uniform rate about G_L, and the G_s figure precessing similarly but at a different rate about G_S. In such a motion the last three terms of the last equation would average zero; let them therefore be dropped.   We can then write

$$G_{lk} \cdot G_{sk} = G'_{lk} \cdot G'_{sk} = G'_{lk}G'_{sk} \cos (G_L, G_S)$$

where $\cos (G_L, G_S)$ is the angle between the directions of G_L and G_S. Thus the spin-orbit energy is proportional to $(\Sigma G'_{lk}G'_{sk}) \cos (G_L, G_S)$ and so, for given L and S but different values of J, to $\cos (G_L, G_S)$ itself. But by geometry,

$$\cos (G_L, G_S) = \frac{1}{G_L G_S} (G_L{}^2 + G_S{}^2 - G_J{}^2)$$

$$= \frac{1}{G_L G_S} \frac{h^2}{4\pi^2} [L(L + 1) + S(S + 1) - J(J + 1)]$$

Here G_L, G_S, G_J stand for the magnitudes of the vectors, and the wave-mechanical values of $G_L{}^2$, $G_S{}^2$, and $G_J{}^2$ have been inserted.   Since $G_L G_S$ is independent of J, Eq. (165) follows.

Many examples of LS coupling could be described.   We have space in this book for only one or two.

126. The Arc Spectrum of Mercury.   The familiar arc spectrum of mercury presents spectroscopic features of great interest.   The principal levels and many of the lines are shown in the usual way in Fig. 81, wavelengths being given in angstroms.   The levels that are considered to form a sequence are placed under each other, with an appropriate spectroscopic designation at the top.

The levels fall into two classes: singlets, and levels that naturally group themselves into triplets, although in the case of the higher levels the sep-

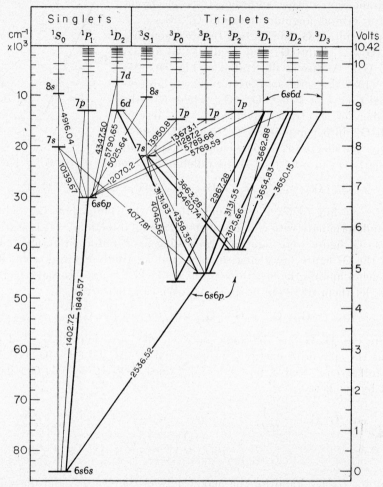

FIG. 81. The most important energy levels and spectral lines for the neutral mercury atom.

aration is too small to be shown in the diagram. Thus the spectrum evidently presents a fair example of LS coupling for two electrons. A number of intercombination lines, between singlet and triplet terms, are found, however, so that the LS coupling is not perfect in mercury.

Evidence from the theory of the periodic table indicates that mercury should have two electrons outside five completed shells. It is assumed that these electrons normally form the closed subshell $6s^2$ but that in those excited atomic states which are represented in the diagram one of these electrons is displaced into an electronic state of higher energy. Since one electronic l is thus always 0, the value of L is always equal to that of the other l. Thus each electronic configuration furnishes at most two LS terms, with $S = 0$ or 1. The configuration in the normal state of the atom, $6s6s$, gives only one term, and, in fact, only one level, with $L = S = J = 0$; thus the normal state of the mercury atom is a $^1S_0$ state. In four of the most important terms, viz., $6s6p$ ^1P, $6s6p$ ^3P, $6s6d$ ^1D, and $6s6d$ ^3D, the mere change of an electronic l with no change in n results in a comparatively large increment of atomic energy.

The intercombination line, $6s6p$ $^3P_1 \rightarrow 6s^2$ $^1S_0$, $\lambda = 2,536.52$, is one of the principal ultraviolet lines in the mercury spectrum. Its strength, however, is not necessarily an indication of a high transition probability between these levels. It is more likely that the strength of this line is due to a piling up of atoms in the $6s6p$ $^3P_1$ level. As the atoms are thrown into this state following collisions with electrons in the arc, or drop into it from higher levels, they have nowhere else to go, therefore they accumulate until through sheer numbers they are able to leave as fast as they enter. It is somewhat like water piling up in a pool until its depth becomes great enough to force a sufficiently rapid discharge through a small drain.

Atoms must accumulate also, of course, in the $^3P_2$ and $^3P_0$ levels of the $6s6p$ configuration. From these levels they cannot pass by a radiative jump to the normal state, for $^3P_2 \rightarrow {}^1S_0$ would mean $\Delta J = 2$, and $^3P_0 \rightarrow {}^1S_0$ would mean a jump from $J = 0$ to $J = 0$, both of which are forbidden by the selection rules for J. Levels lying above the normal state out of which radiative transitions are impossible are called "metastable" levels. An atom can stay in such a level for a long time if it is not disturbed by outside influences. It may eventually be brought back into the normal state, however, by a "collision of the second kind" (cf. Sec. 87c), and it is presumably in this manner that the atoms in the $^3P_2$ and $^3P_0$ levels are eventually returned to their normal state.

Contrary to the selection rule for S, that for L is pretty well obeyed. With values of L assigned as in the diagram, S terms combine only with P terms, P with S and D, and so on. However, a few weak lines, not shown on the diagram, have been observed corresponding to $\Delta L = 2$. All the transitions shown in Fig. 81 are in harmony with the selection rule for configurations. Only one electron changes its n and l, and always $\Delta l = \pm 1$.

The spectral lines can be grouped into *series*, if desired. Thus, within the singlet system, all lines ending on the lowest $^1S_0$ level form the singlet principal series. Only these and the line $\lambda = 2,536$ A can be observed in absorption in mercury vapor. Of the lines ending on the lowest ^1P level, those originating from ^1S terms form a sharp series, those originating from ^1D terms, a diffuse series, just as in sodium; and so on. Similar series can be picked out within the triplet system. It is really not very interesting to group the lines of such a complex spectrum into series, however, especially when the "fine structure" is as coarse as it is in the mercury spectrum. Thus the great spectral sextet of ultraviolet lines, $\lambda = 2,967$ to $\lambda = 3,663$, from the lowest ^3D to the lowest ^3P term, would constitute together the first "line" of the triplet diffuse series. The student will recognize the lines $^1D_2 \rightarrow {}^1P_1$ (λ 5,791), $^3S_1 \rightarrow {}^3P_2$ (λ 5,461), and $^3S_1 \rightarrow {}^3P_1$ (λ 4,358) as the familiar yellow, green, and blue lines emitted from the mercury arc.

It may also happen that, when the atom is excited, *both* valence electrons are displaced into higher electronic states. A few levels ascribed to the $6p^2$ configuration have been discovered.

Among other neutral atoms which have spectra similar to that of mercury may be mentioned helium; then the alkaline earths, beryllium, magnesium, calcium, strontium, and barium; and the close relatives of mercury, zinc and cadmium. Ions with similar electronic exteriors are C^{++}, Al^+, Si^{++}, Pb^{++} (the number of plus signs indicating the number of positive charges on the ion). Such atoms are called isoelectronic.

A second subclass of atoms with two optically active electrons is formed by those which, in their normal states, contain two s and two p valence electrons. In such cases the two s electrons usually (but not always) stay put, only the two p electrons being active. Examples of such atoms are neutral carbon, silicon, germanium, tin, and lead. Furthermore, certain observed spectra of the same type have been ascribed to singly (positively) ionized atoms of nitrogen, phosphorus, and bismuth.

127. Equivalent Electrons. Hitherto, it has been assumed that all the electrons in a configuration have either different n's or different l's. When two electrons have the same n and also the same l, they are called *equivalent electrons*. In configurations containing equivalent electrons, such as $5s^2$ or $5s7p^3$, certain LS terms that might otherwise occur are excluded through the operation of the exclusion principle.

Consider, for example, the simple configuration $1s^2$ in helium, or $6s^2$ in mercury. Four different combinations of the $n\ l\ \lambda\ \mu$ electronic states can be made for the two electrons; these may be indicated, in an obvious notation, as follows:

$$(n00\tfrac{1}{2},\ n00\tfrac{1}{2}) \qquad (n00\tfrac{1}{2},\ n00 - \tfrac{1}{2})$$
$$(n00 - \tfrac{1}{2},\ n00\tfrac{1}{2}) \qquad (n00 - \tfrac{1}{2},\ n00 - \tfrac{1}{2})$$

where $n = 1$ for helium or $n = 6$ for mercury. All these states have $l = 0$. Since the total angular momentum is the sum of the orbital and spin momenta, the first and last of the four combinations suggest atomic states with $M = 1$ or -1, and hence, with $J = 1$; but these particular combinations, in which both electrons are in the same electronic state, are ruled out by the exclusion principle.   Furthermore, the other two combinations differ only in that the two electrons exchange quantum states, and according to another aspect of the exclusion principle, as stated in Sec. 107, it makes no difference which electron is in which state; thus *each combination* of $n\ l\ \lambda\ \mu$'s, regardless of the order of these numbers, furnishes just one quantum state for the atom as a whole.   Hence we obtain out of the configuration under discussion a single atomic state, represented in wave mechanics by a single wave function ψ.   This must be a $^1S_0$ state, with $L = S = M = J = 0$.   The $^3S_1$ set of three states, with $M = 1, 0,$ or -1, is missing.

The same kind of reduction occurs, in particular, for any closed subshell.   When so many electrons are present with given values of n and of l that, in assigning them to different electronic states, every allowed value of λ and μ must be used, only a single combination of electronic states is possible, and it can lead to only a single atomic state.   This is necessarily a state with $J = 0$, since any other value of J requires the existence of several atomic states with different values of M.   Thus atoms whose electronic exterior is formed of closed subshells are necessarily in a $^1S_0$ state.

In the simple example just discussed, the reduction in the number of states happens to be in accord with the predictions of the vector diagram for LS coupling.   In more complicated cases, some of the LS terms that are predicted by the diagram are themselves missing.   General rules can be given for determining which states are allowed for any given configuration containing equivalent electrons.[1]   All the J levels belonging to a given LS term always appear or drop out together.

128. Coupling of the jj Type.   The validity of LS coupling is limited to atoms that are not too heavy.   As the nuclear charge increases, the spin-orbit effects become rapidly larger; as a consequence, the J levels tend less and less to group themselves into recognizable LS multiplets and the selection rules for L and S fail more and more.   Finally, in very heavy atoms the spin-orbit effects may predominate over the residual electrostatic interaction to such an extent that an approximation occurs to the other type of coupling mentioned in Sec. 122, known as "jj coupling."

In the zero-order stage of perturbation theory, let the electrostatic interaction of the electrons be ignored, except in so far as allowance is made for its average effect as represented in the central field.   Each electron can be assumed to occupy one of the $n\ l\ j\ m$ states described in Sec. 118.   A quantum state for the atom is then specified by assigning

[1] H. E. White, "Introduction to Atomic Spectra," 1934.

a set of such quantum numbers for each of the N electrons in the atom:

$$n_1\, l_1\, j_1\, m_1,\ n_2\, l_2\, j_2\, m_2,\ \ldots,\ n_N\, l_N\, j_N\, m_N$$

Electrons occupying closed shells may, however, be ignored provided these shells remain closed in all the radiative transitions that are considered. Since the electronic energy is independent of m, an energy level can be specified by writing down merely the values of

$$n_1\, l_1\, j_1,\ n_2\, l_2\, j_2,\ \ldots,\ n_N\, l_N\, j_N$$

In considering only those energy levels belonging to a particular configuration

$$n_1\, l_1,\ n_2\, l_2,\ \ldots,\ n_N\, l_N$$

it suffices to write down only a set of j's: $j_1, j_2, \ldots, j_N$, with the understanding that j_1 goes with $n_1\, l_1$, and so on. An energy level so specified

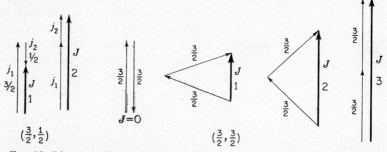

FIG. 82. Diagrams illustrating jj coupling for two nonequivalent electrons.

may be called a jj level or term. The number of jj levels belonging to a given configuration cannot exceed 2^N; for each j can assume at most two values, $l + \frac{1}{2}$ and $l - \frac{1}{2}$.

In addition to the selection rule for configurations, there is now a selection rule for j: $\Delta j = 0$ or ± 1. The special rules for jj coupling can thus be summarized in the following form:

1. Only one nlj set of quantum numbers can change in a radiative transition—"only one electron jumps at a time."

2. For the jumping electron,

$$\Delta l = \pm 1 \qquad \Delta j = 0 \text{ or } \pm 1$$

Allowance may then be made for the residual electrostatic interaction as a second smaller perturbation. To prepare for this, we make combinations of functions containing different electronic m's so as to quantize the resultant angular momentum $\mathbf{G}_J$, with the introduction of the usual quantum numbers J and M. This may be visualized as the addition of the electronic j vectors in various ways into a J vector. Two cases, for a group of two electrons, are illustrated in Fig. 82. In classical mechanics, the electrostatic forces would cause precessions of the electronic resultant angular momenta $\mathbf{G}_j$ about their vector sum $\mathbf{G}_J$.

The residual electrostatic interaction then has the effect of separating slightly the J levels belonging to each jj term, forming a jj multiplet of levels. A notation for these levels is easily invented. Thus, analogous

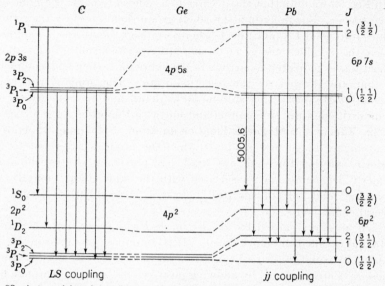

Fig. 83. A transition from LS to jj coupling. Within each multiplet of levels the spacing is drawn to scale, except that each group of ^3P levels should be drawn closer together. The ranges covered by the levels, in cm^{-1}, are: carbon, $2p^2$, 69,231.1 to 90,878.3; $2p3s$, 28,898 to 30,547; germanium, total range (term values uncertain), $4p^2$, 16,367; $4p5s$, 2,568; lead, $6p^2$, 30,365 to 59,821; $6p7s$, 10,383 to 24,863. One wavelength is given, in angstroms; the other lines lie in the ultraviolet.

designations of a J level with $J = 3$ might be, in jj or LS coupling, respectively,

$$
\begin{array}{cc}
jj & LS \\
(n_1 l_1, \ldots, n_N l_N)(j_1 \cdots j_N)_3 & n_1 l_1 \cdots n_N l_N \, {}^5D_3
\end{array}
$$

As the residual electrostatic interaction grows stronger, however, it tends to mix the various electronic zero-order functions together in the wave function; then it becomes less useful to attach the numbers $(n_1 l_1 j_1, \ldots)$ to the energy levels, and the associated selection rules tend to fail. All degrees of coupling intermediate between the ideal LS and jj types occur. The quantum numbers J and M, however, and their selection rules persist so long as the atom is free from external force.

An example showing the transition from LS to jj coupling is shown in Fig. 83. The relative positions of certain levels are shown for carbon $(Z = 6)$, germanium (32), and lead (82), corresponding levels being connected by dotted lines. In silicon (14), the corresponding set of levels is observed to be arranged much as in carbon, whereas tin (50) resembles lead in this respect. The number of closed subshells underlying the active electrons is different in the two cases, but this difference is immaterial to the relative arrangement of the levels.

In Fig. 83 we note that the J value of any level remains the same in all three spectra; but in carbon the levels group themselves by their energy values into good LS multiplets, whereas in lead they form jj groups, for which the j values are given in parentheses. The observed radiative transitions as indicated by arrows in the figure for carbon and lead include all that are allowed by the selection rules. The student will find it instructive to verify this statement in detail and to note which lines occur with one form of coupling and not with the other.

129. Effects of a Magnetic Field on an Atom. The quantum states of an atom are in general modified when the atom is subjected to non-uniform external forces of any kind. In particular, states which were formerly degenerate, i.e., associated with the same energy, may become separated, and certain spectral lines may consequently be split into several components.

Such an effect caused by an *electric field* was discovered by Stark in 1913 and is called the Stark effect. It is commonly observed in the light emitted by canal rays in a field of several thousand volts per centimeter. These rays are produced by allowing positive ions to escape through holes in the cathode of a discharge tube into the space behind the cathode. A good account of the Stark effect was given by Epstein with the use of Bohr's quantum theory, and it is completely explained by wave mechanics. The effect is of such minor interest in spectroscopy, however, that we shall say no more about it.[1]

A much more interesting and important case is the Zeeman effect, already discussed in Sec. 46 in terms of classical theory. It was there remarked that in some cases the predictions of classical theory are in agreement with experiment; such cases are called the *normal* Zeeman effect. More commonly, however, the observed pattern of lines is quite different, being then called *anomalous*. A few Zeeman patterns are illustrated in Fig. 84.

No explanation of the anomalous effect was found until electron spin was introduced. Furthermore, in the modern wave-mechanical treatment, there is, naturally, nothing closely resembling the electronic motion as described in the classical theory. Nevertheless, certain features of the classical picture still retain an interest, either because they are actually preserved in the new theory, or because they furnish a useful picture in terms of which the phenomenon can readily be visualized.

[1] See E. U. Condon and G. H. Shortley, *op. cit.*

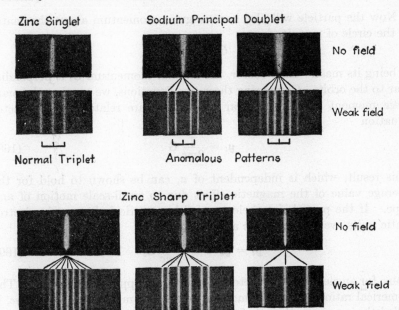

Zinc Singlet · Sodium Principal Doublet

No field

Weak field

Normal Triplet · Anomalous Patterns

Zinc Sharp Triplet

No field

Weak field

Anomalous Patterns

FIG. 84. Photographs of some Zeeman patterns in a weak magnetic field, viewed perpendicularly to the field. The brackets show in each case the position of a normal triplet in the same field. (*From H. E. White, "Introduction to Atomic Spectra."*)

The changes produced in the energy levels by a magnetic field can be regarded as resulting from the possession by the atom of a *magnetic moment*. In classical theory such a moment may arise from orbital motion of a charged particle. To take the simplest case, suppose the (algebraic) charge on the particle is q esu and that the particle revolves in a fixed circle of radius a at speed v (Fig. 85). Then it makes $v/2\pi a$ revolutions per second and so is equivalent to a current of $I = qv/2\pi a$ esu. It is well known that a current flowing in a plane loop enclosing area A is equivalent magnetically, at points not too close to the loop, to a magnet having a certain magnetic moment μ; if the current is I esu, then $\mu = IA/c$. In the present case $A = \pi a^2$; hence

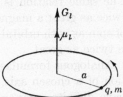

FIG. 85. Diagram illustrating the angular momentum G_l and magnetic moment μ_l due to a charge revolving in a circle.

$$\mu = \frac{qva}{2c}$$

The moment can be treated as a vector μ_l perpendicular to the plane of the orbit. Relative directions are shown in Fig. 85 for positive q.

Now the particle will also have angular momentum about the center of the circle of magnitude

$$G_l = mva$$

m being its mass.   As a vector, the angular momentum $\mathbf{G}_l$ is perpendicular to the orbit.   Comparing these two equations, we see that the magnetic moment and the angular momentum are related by the vector equation

$$\mathbf{\mu}_l = \frac{q}{2mc} \mathbf{G} \tag{168}$$

This result, which is independent of a, can be shown to hold for the average value of the magnetic effect due to small-scale motion of any type.   If the particle is an electron with numerical charge e in electrostatic units, we have $q = -e$ and

$$\mathbf{\mu}_l = \mathbf{\mu}_e = -\frac{e}{2mc} \mathbf{G}_l \tag{169}$$

Thus, for an electron, the vectors $\mathbf{\mu}_l$ and $\mathbf{G}_l$ are oppositely directed.   The numerical ratio of magnetic moment to angular momentum, or $e/2mc$, is called the *gyromagnetic ratio* for orbital motion of an electron.

A similar expression must then be added for the effect of *electron spin*.   For the classical electron described in Sec. 118, the relation between its vector magnetic moment $\mathbf{\mu}_s$ and angular momentum $\mathbf{G}_s$ due to spin is

$$\mathbf{\mu}_s = -\frac{e}{mc} \mathbf{G}_s \tag{170}$$

The same relation is furnished by the Dirac theory.   Thus, relatively twice as great a magnetic moment is associated with angular momentum of spin as with orbital angular momentum; the gyromagnetic ratio, e/mc, is twice as great.

Analogous formulas are obtained from wave mechanics.   In the direction of a chosen axis, the orbital and spin momenta of an electron may have definite components G_{la} and G_{sa}, respectively.   Then the electron will also have an effective magnetic moment μ_a in that direction of magnitude.

$$\mu_a = -\frac{e}{2mc}(G_{la} + 2G_{sa}) \tag{171a}$$

For a complex atom this becomes

$$\mu_a = -\frac{e}{2mc}\left(\sum G_{la} + 2\sum G_{sa}\right) \tag{171b}$$

where ΣG_{la} and ΣG_{sa} denote the effective or average total components of orbital and spin momenta due to all electrons.

Effect of a Magnetic Field on Angular Momentum. In classical theory, the vector moment of force due to a uniform magnetic field **B** is perpendicular to **B**, hence it has no tendency to alter the component of the vector angular momentum in the direction of **B**. Analogously, in wave mechanics it is found that in the presence of a steady, uniform magnetic field each quantum state of an otherwise isolated atom is characterized by a fixed value of the angular momentum about an axis parallel to the field; or, in cases of degeneracy, the quantum states can be so defined that this is true. The principal term in the expression for this angular momentum is $Mh/2\pi$; the quantum number M is integral or half-integral according to the rule stated in Sec. 115 and is subject to the selection rule there stated. There is also a much smaller component of momentum proportional to the magnetic field itself, but this is negligible in spectroscopy. The *total* angular momentum, however, may not be fixed, so that in a magnetic field there may be no quantum number J.

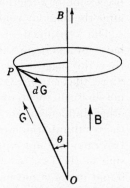

FIG. 86. Precession of a magnetic gyro in a magnetic field.

The following feature of classical electromagnetics is also of interest. Suppose that the magnetic moment $\mathbf{M}_0$ of a body is proportional to its vector angular momentum **G** about its center of mass. Draw OP to represent **G**, making an angle θ with an axis OB drawn in the direction of **B**. Then, during time dt, the torque on the magnet will add to **G** a vector increment $d\mathbf{G}$ of magnitude $M_0 B \sin \theta \, dt$, in a direction perpendicular to the plane POB (Fig. 86). This increment will change the direction of **G** but not its magnitude. It is clear, therefore, that the end of the vector OP will revolve in a circle about OB of radius $G \sin \theta$; since during dt it revolves through an angle $dG/G \sin \theta = M_0 B \sin \theta \, dt/G \sin \theta$ or $M_0 B \, dt/G$, it will revolve at an angular rate

$$\omega = \frac{M_0 B}{G} \qquad \text{radians per sec} \tag{172}$$

The vector **G** can thus be supposed to revolve or precess about OB at the rate ω. For an electron in orbital motion, its orbital angular momentum $\mathbf{G}_l$, of magnitude $G = -2mcM_0/e$ by (169), will thus precess at the numerical rate

$$\omega_l = \frac{eB}{2mc} \tag{173}$$

Its spin momentum $\mathbf{G}_s$, however, will precess at the double rate, $2\omega_l$.

The frequency ω_l is that of the "Larmor precession." According to a theorem due to Larmor, the introduction of a magnetic field modifies the classical motion of a set of electrons in the field of a nucleus chiefly as if a uniform rotation at angular velocity ω_l were superposed upon their original motion. The angular momentum of the electrons about an axis parallel to **B** is thereby slightly altered, as a result of inductive action during the production of the field, but this change is so small compared to the values of **G** due to orbital motion that it may be ignored in the present connection. Similar statements hold for electron spin.

It is worth noting that the Larmor precession is a broader phenomenon than the mere precession of the direction of G_l and occurs even when G_l is parallel to **B**. In this respect the Larmor precession differs from the precession of a frictionless gyro caused by external torques, which do not alter the angular velocity of the gyro about its axis.

The continued precessional changes in the directions of G_l and G_s have no analog in the wave-mechanical theory of a quantum state, but they do suggest certain valid conclusions and so assist the memory. Since all electronic G_l's precess at the same rate, the magnetic field should not disturb the *resultant* orbital momentum, which in the absence of other influences would merely itself precess at velocity ω_l. Similarly, the resultant spin momentum would precess at velocity $2\omega_l$. Since these two rates are not equal, however, it is clear that, in general, the vector sum of the two momenta will not be constant. Correspondingly, it is found in wave mechanics that a magnetic field has no disturbing effect upon LS coupling, but it does prevent the quantizing of the resultant G_J. In a weak field, J may continue to be a fairly good quantum number, but, as the field becomes strong, J disappears and its selection rules cease to hold.

Finally, it may be remarked that the change in the magnetic moment itself which accompanies the small change in the component of **G** parallel to **B** is the cause of *diamagnetism*. The *paramagnetism* exhibited by many substances, on the other hand, is ascribed to a statistical tendency of atoms possessing natural magnetic moments to favor orientations in which their moments are more or less lined up with the field. *Ferromagnetism* is believed to be due to a lining up of electronic spins in *different atoms* under special conditions. Microscopic domains of material thus become strongly magnetized, and when a field is applied these domains tend to change their direction of magnetization so as to favor the direction of the field. In certain other cases there is believed to be a converse tendency for the spins to assume *opposite* directions in neighboring atoms; this phenomenon, called antiferromagnetism, manifests itself by modifying the rate of variation of paramagnetism with temperature.

Effect of B on the Atomic Energy. A classical magnet of fixed vector moment **M** behaves in a uniform field **B** as if it had potential energy $-M_B B$, where M_B is the component of **M** in the direction of **B**. Similarly, provided the field is not too strong, an atom effectively has potential energy $-\mu_a B$, where μ_a is its component of magnetic moment, assumed definite, in the direction of an axis drawn in the direction of **B**. The energy of the atom in a weak field can thus be written

$$W = W_0 - \mu_a B \tag{174}$$

W_0 being its energy when $B = 0$.

It will be convenient to relate μ_a and $-\mu_a B$ to the total component of angular momentum in the field direction, which has been denoted by $Mh/2\pi$ but also equals $\Sigma G_{la} + \Sigma G_{sa}$. Thus we can write, from (171b),

$$\mu_a = -gM \frac{eh}{4\pi mc} \qquad g = \frac{\Sigma G_{la} + 2\Sigma G_{sa}}{\Sigma G_{la} + \Sigma G_{sa}} \tag{175a,b}$$

The factor g introduced here, called the Landé g factor, cannot exceed 2. The coefficient,

$$\mu_e = \frac{eh}{4\pi mc} = 0.9273 \times 10^{-20} \text{ emu} \tag{176}$$

represents a natural unit of magnetic moment called the Bohr magneton. In terms of μ_e we can write

$$\mu_a = -gM\mu_e \qquad W = W_0 + gM\mu_e B \tag{177a,b}$$

Because of its occurrence in such equations, M is often called the magnetic quantum number.

The modification required in these formulas when the field is strong enough to change the effective moment of the atom will be described in Sec. 133 (Paschen-Back effect).

According to the theory as described up to this point, the magnetic moment of an electron due to spin (or at least the component of this moment in a given direction) is 1 Bohr magneton, as is also the moment due to orbital motion in the smallest of the Bohr orbits in a hydrogen atom. These moments are, however, subject to minute corrections when calculations are made with extreme precision by means of the quantum theory of the electromagnetic field. A value of 1.00115 Bohr magneton has thus been found for the natural moment of the electron, in agreement with certain precise experimental results.[1]

130. Zeeman Effect in a Huge Field. The simplest type of Zeeman effect should be produced by a field so strong that complications due to all other sources can be ignored. Such a field we shall call "huge."

[1] E. Segrè et al., "Experimental Nuclear Physics," vol. 1, p. 408, 1953.

Consider first a single electron in a central field, placed in a uniform magnetic field B (measured in gauss, or a field of $B \times 10^{-4}$ webers per square meter). Since we are assuming that the spin-orbit effect is swamped by the huge field, we can use the $n\ l\ \lambda\ \mu$ quantum states (Sec. 109) with the axis drawn parallel to $\mathbf{B}$. When the atom is in one of these states, G_{la} and G_{sa} have the magnitudes

$$G_{la} = \frac{\lambda h}{2\pi} \qquad G_{sa} = \frac{\mu h}{2\pi}$$

Thus Eq. (171a) gives

$$\mu_a = -\frac{eh}{4\pi mc}(\lambda + 2\mu) = -(M + \mu)\mu_e$$

where $M = \lambda + \mu$. Since μ_a does not change (appreciably) with further increase in B, Eq. (174) gives for the energy

$$W = W_0 + (M + \mu)\mu_e B \tag{178}$$

Here $M + \mu$ is always an integer or zero.

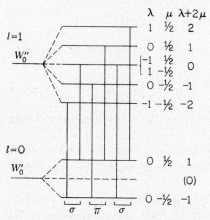

FIG. 87. Energy levels for one electron in a huge magnetic field. (The levels for $l = 0$ are atypical in that the middle one is missing.) Transitions giving rise to the same ν are bracketed.

From Eq. (178) we see that the magnetic field splits the single original level with energy W_0 into several magnetic levels, each characterized by a value of $M + \mu$. An example is illustrated in Fig. 87. Since $M + \mu$ may have any integral value from $l + 1$, when $\lambda = l$ and $\mu = \frac{1}{2}$, down to $-(l + 1)$, when $\lambda = -l$ and $\mu = -\frac{1}{2}$, there are in general $(2l + 3)$ magnetic levels in all; if, however, $l = 0$, there are only two levels, with $M + \mu = \pm 1$. All the levels except the upper two and the lower two are double. The levels are equally spaced, the difference in energy being $\mu_e B$.

Consider now transitions between two such sets of energy levels. We may write Eq. (178) for the two sets thus

$$W' = W_0' + (M' + \mu')\mu_e B$$
$$W'' = W_0'' + (M'' + \mu'')\mu_e B$$

As selection rules we have, besides $\Delta l = \pm 1$,

$$\Delta M = 0 \text{ or } \pm 1 \qquad \Delta\mu = 0$$

These rules are consistent with the rule that $\Delta\lambda = 0$ or ± 1.

Calculating frequencies as $(W' - W'')/h$ and writing

$$\frac{W_0' - W_0''}{h} = \nu_0$$

for the frequency of the line emitted in zero field, we find just three possible lines when the field is present:

$$M'' - M' = \Delta M = 0: \qquad \nu = \nu_0 \qquad\qquad (\pi)$$

$$\Delta M = -1: \qquad \nu = \nu_0 + \frac{\mu_e B}{h} \quad (\sigma)$$

$$\Delta M = +1: \qquad \nu = \nu_0 - \frac{\mu_e B}{h} \quad (\sigma)$$

Each of these lines results, in general, from several different jumps, so that it might be described as consisting of several lines superposed. The allowed transitions are shown in Fig. 87.

Comparing these results with those obtained from classical theory in Sec. 46, we see that we have here exactly the *classical triplet*. According to further conclusions from wave mechanics, even the polarization features should be the same as those deduced from classical theory. The undisplaced line, corresponding to $\Delta M = 0$, should be polarized with the electric vector in a plane parallel to the magnetic field, and it should be invisible when the radiation is viewed longitudinally (i.e., in a direction parallel to the field); such lines are called π lines (i.e., "parallel" as to polarization) or, sometimes, p lines. The other two lines, when the radiation is viewed transversely, should be plane polarized with the electric vector perpendicular to the magnetic field, whereas, when viewed longitudinally, they should be circularly polarized with opposite directions of rotation, as in the classical case; such lines are called σ lines (from the German "senkrecht" = perpendicular) or, sometimes, s lines. A Zeeman triplet agreeing thus in all respects, even in spacing, with the classical theory is called a *normal triplet*. An example originating in a different manner is shown in Fig. 84.

Concerning the *relative intensity* of the lines, wave mechanics makes the following predictions, among others. Suppose all the initial quantum states are excited equally. Under these conditions, the two σ lines will each be half as bright as the central π line, as seen transversely to the magnetic field; whereas, the σ lines will be twice as bright when viewed along the field as they are when viewed transversely. This latter result is easily seen to be in agreement with the classical theory of the Zeeman effect; each circular motion is equivalent to two linear vibrations at right angles to each other, but, in the transverse direction, radiation is received from only one of these, the one that lies in the line of sight being invisible. Furthermore, as much light is polarized in one way as in the opposite way, so that on the whole the emitted radiation is unpolarized; and the total intensity is equal in all directions.

The quantity $\mu_e B/h$, representing the separation in frequency of each outer line from the central line in a normal triplet, is sometimes called a Lorentz unit for the field B. Its value, measured in cm^{-1}, is

$$\tilde{L} = \frac{\mu_e B}{hc} = 4.669 \times 10^{-5} B \qquad cm^{-1} \qquad (179)$$

Thus the normal separation is 4.67×10^{-5} cm^{-1} per gauss. We note that $\tilde{L}$ does not contain Planck's constant h. It is because of this circumstance that classical theory gave correct results for certain cases of the Zeeman effect.

If allowance is now made for the spin-orbit effect as a perturbation, it is found that, in general, the energy levels become further split into doublets. In classical mechanics, the spin-orbit interaction has no tendency to alter the resultant angular momentum, whose component in the direction of the field is $Mh/2\pi$. Correspondingly, the matrix component of the spin-orbit energy between two states with different M's vanishes. Thus the two states with different M's that belong to the same value of $M + \mu$ constitute valid zero-order states for a perturbation calculation, and the energy levels of these two states may be found to be separated somewhat by the spin-orbit interaction. For example, states with $\lambda = 1$, $\mu = -\frac{1}{2}$ and $\lambda = -1$, $\mu = \frac{1}{2}$ fall together in the absence of spin-orbit interaction, with $M + \mu = \lambda + 2\mu = 0$; but M is $\frac{1}{2}$ for the first, $-\frac{1}{2}$ for the second. The number of actual lines in the Zeeman pattern is thereby increased, but, so long as the field is sufficiently intense, they fall into three groups resembling a normal triplet.

Experimental confirmation of these theoretical conclusions is not extensive even for one-electron atoms because very intense fields are required. However, the first three Balmer lines of hydrogen were observed as approximate normal triplets by Paschen and Back in a field of 26,900 gauss.[1] The fine structure due to the spin-orbit effect was not resolved but was presumably responsible for the broadness of the observed lines.

On an atom containing more than one electron, the effect of a *huge* magnetic field should be to split each energy level W_0 for zero field according to the more general equation

$$W = W_0 + (M + \Sigma\mu)\mu_e B \qquad (180)$$

the summation extending over all electrons in the atom. The normal triplet would then occur as with one electron. To obtain a good approx-

[1] F. Paschen and E. Back, *Ann. Physik*, vol. 39, p. 897, 1912.

imation to this type of pattern, however, would require a field of millions or even hundreds of millions of gauss.

131. Zeeman Effect in a Weak Field. It will be convenient to take up next the case of a "weak" field, i.e., a field weak enough so that the Zeeman splitting is small as compared even with the separations in the ordinary fine structure. In such a field, J is a good quantum number and the effect of the field is merely to separate slightly the states of different M that compose each J level.

For all levels of a given J state, the g factor occurring in (175b) and (177a,b) has a constant value. Thus *in a weak magnetic field the states composing a given J level and corresponding to different values of M become separated and equally spaced.* The value of g may vary, however, from one J level to another. The splitting can be visualized by

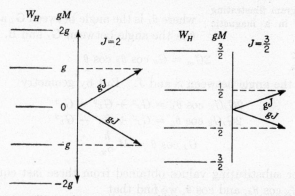

FIG. 88. Diagram illustrating (*a*) vector addition in a magnetic field and (*b*) the separation of the magnetic levels in a weak field.

means of an obvious modification of the vector diagram, as in Fig. 88 where vectors are drawn of length gJ instead of J.

Theoretical values of g can readily be calculated, since in a weak field the magnetic energy can be considered as a small perturbation. The calculation is especially easy when either LS or jj coupling holds. Only the LS case will be discussed here. It happens that the formula furnished by wave mechanics for this case also can be inferred from a semiclassical argument, as follows.

Let a vector diagram be drawn showing (1) the electronic orbital momenta $\mathbf{G}_l$ and spin momenta $\mathbf{G}_s$ added into resultants $\mathbf{G}_L$ and $\mathbf{G}_S$, respectively; (2) the addition of $\mathbf{G}_L$ and $\mathbf{G}_S$ into a resultant $\mathbf{G}_J$; and (3) the projection of $\mathbf{G}_J$ giving a vector component $\mathbf{G}_M$ in the direction of the magnetic field $\mathbf{B}$. See Fig. 89, which is drawn for three electrons but with $l_3 = 0$; for simplicity, only the subscripts of the $\mathbf{G}$'s are shown. Then, by an extension of the argument used in connection with Fig. 80, the component of any G_l perpendicular to G_L averages zero, and hence only the component of G_l parallel to G_L contributes to ΣG_{la}. The sum of these parallel components is G_L itself. But G_L, in turn, has a vector component perpendicular to G_J which averages zero and may be ignored in the same way; and then, similarly, of the vector component of G_L parallel to G_J, only its further component parallel to the field $\mathbf{B}$ averages to anything different from zero. Thus we see that, for average components G_{la} in the direction of $\mathbf{B}$,

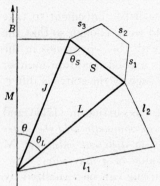

FIG. 89. Diagram illustrating LS coupling in a magnetic field.

$$\Sigma G_{la} = G_L \cos \theta_L \cos \theta$$

where θ_L is the angle between G_L and G_J, and θ is the angle between G_J and $\mathbf{B}$. Similarly

$$\Sigma G_{sa} = G_S \cos \theta_S \cos \theta$$

where θ_S is the angle between S and J. But by geometry

$$2G_J G_L \cos \theta_L = G_J{}^2 + G_L{}^2 - G_S{}^2$$
$$2G_J G_S \cos \theta_S = G_J{}^2 + G_S{}^2 - G_L{}^2$$

Also
$$G_J \cos \theta = M \frac{h}{2\pi}$$

Hence, after substituting values obtained from these last equations for $G_L \cos \theta_L$, $G_S \cos \theta_S$, and $\cos \theta$, we find that

$$\sum (G_{la} + 2G_{sa}) = \frac{Mh}{4\pi G_J{}^2} (3G_J{}^2 + G_S{}^2 - G_L{}^2)$$
$$= \frac{Mh}{2\pi} \left[\frac{3}{2} + \frac{S(S + 1) - L(L + 1)}{2J(J + 1)} \right]$$

since $G_J{}^2 = J(J + 1)h^2/4\pi^2$, $G_L{}^2 = L(L + 1)h^2/4\pi^2$, $G_S{}^2 = S(S + 1)h^2/4\pi^2$. Inserting this value and also $\Sigma(G_{la} + G_{sa}) = Mh/2\pi$ into Eq. (175b), we find, for LS coupling,

$$g = 1 + \frac{J(J + 1) + S(S + 1) - L(L + 1)}{2J(J + 1)} \tag{181}$$

For $J = 0$, any value of g may be assumed, since necessarily $M = 0$.

132. Zeeman Patterns of LS Multiplets in a Weak Field. For spectroscopic purposes it is convenient to divide all energies by hc so as to express them in equivalent wave numbers. In terms of the Lorentz energy unit defined in (179), Eq. (177b) may then be written

$$\tilde{W}_{JM} = \tilde{W}_{0J} + gM\tilde{L} \tag{182}$$

and the values of $\tilde{W}_{JM}$ corresponding to two different J levels may be written

$$\tilde{W}_{0J'} + g'M'\tilde{L} \qquad \tilde{W}_{0J''} + g''M''\tilde{L}$$

Substracting these two expressions, we have for the frequencies of the Zeeman lines between the two J levels, all of which would coalesce into one line if the magnetic field were absent,

$$\tilde{\nu} = \tilde{\nu}_0 + (g'M' - g''M'')\tilde{L} \qquad (183)$$

where $\tilde{\nu}_0 = \tilde{W}_{0J'} - \tilde{W}_{0J''}$ and represents the frequency when $B = 0$. If J', J'' are the corresponding values of J for the two levels, in Eq. (183) M' takes on integrally spaced values from $-J'$ to J', and M'' from $-J''$ to J'', subject only to the selection rule

$$\Delta M = M'' - M' = 0 \text{ or } \pm 1$$

As in Sec. 130, transitions in which $\Delta M = 0$ give rise to π lines; those in which $\Delta M = \pm 1$, to σ lines.

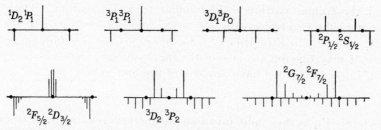

Fig. 90. Some Zeeman patterns for LS coupling in a weak field. Heights of lines indicate roughly the relative intensities of the lines. π lines are drawn above, σ lines below. The three dots indicate the position of the normal triplet in the same field.

All observed Zeeman patterns in weak fields are found to agree with Eq. (183) if suitable values of g' and g'' are inserted in it. If $g' \neq g''$, the observed pattern leads to a knowledge not only of g' and of g'' but also of the values of J for both levels, since the number of magnetic states for given J is $2J + 1$. (The student may be interested to invent a method for inferring values of J and g from such observations.) Thus, the Zeeman effect is of great utility in the analysis of spectra. A mathematical description of the anomalous Zeeman effect, in terms of an equation equivalent to (183), was worked out empirically by Landé before the discovery of wave mechanics.

It will be evident that a wide variety of patterns is possible. A few are diagramed in Fig. 90. *Corresponding lines* in the spectral multiplets of a given *series* should exhibit the *same* type of pattern; for such lines have a common final level, and their initial levels have the same J, S, and L and hence the same value of g. This conclusion is in agreement with observation; it is known as "Preston's rule," having been discovered empirically by Preston in 1898. Preston's rule is sometimes of use in deciding what lines belong together in a series.

A few special cases may be noted. It can happen that a spectral line is not split at all in a magnetic field. An example is the $5F_1 \rightarrow 5D_0$ transition, in which $g = 0$ for one level ($L = 3$, $S = 2$, $J = 1$) while necessarily $M = 0$ for the other; this case is illustrated by the line λ 5,713 A in the arc spectrum of titanium. Again, if $g' = g''$, the pattern may be a simple triplet; and if also $g = 1$ for both levels the triplet is a normal one, spaced as in classical theory. The normal triplet occurs also in all lines of any *singlet* spectrum. When $S = 0$, the electronic spins produce no net effect, and the orbital moments by themselves give rise to the classical pattern. Examples are the singlet spectrum of mercury (Sec. 126) or the singlet zinc line shown in Fig. 84. Zeeman had the good fortune to succeed first in resolving singlet lines in the spectra of zinc, cadmium, and tin.

The use of the general formulas will be illustrated by describing in detail the Zeeman pattern of the familiar D lines of sodium. These lines arise from the two transitions $^2P_{3/2} \rightarrow {}^2S_{1/2}$ and $^2P_{1/2} \rightarrow {}^2S_{1/2}$. For the $^2P_{3/2}$ state, we insert in Eq. (181) $J = \frac{3}{2}$, $S = \frac{1}{2}$, $L = 1$, obtaining $g = \frac{4}{3}$. Since M may take on any one of the four values $\frac{3}{2}$, $\frac{1}{2}$, $-\frac{1}{2}$, $-\frac{3}{2}$, gM in (177b) or (182) may have any one of the four values

$$\tfrac{6}{3}, \qquad \tfrac{2}{3}, \qquad -\tfrac{2}{3}, \qquad -\tfrac{6}{3}$$

The level $^2P_{3/2}$ is thus split into four magnetic levels removed from the position of the $^2P_{3/2}$ level in zero field by gM Lorentz units or $gM\tilde{L}$ cm^{-1}. Similarly, the state $^2P_{1/2}$ is split into two levels for which $g = \frac{2}{3}$ and $gM = \pm\frac{1}{3}$; and the $^2S_{1/2}$ level is split into two with $g = 2$, $gM = \pm1$. Figure 91 shows these levels, and also the transitions between them that are allowed by the selection rule $\Delta M = 0$ or ±1. The resulting line patterns are shown at the bottom of the figure. The expected displacement of each component line from the position for zero field is calculated, in Lorentz units, by subtracting the two gM values; e.g., for the left-hand σ component of D_2, we have $-\frac{2}{3} - 1 = -\frac{5}{3}$ Lorentz units, which is shown below the line in an obvious notation.

We note that D_1 or $^2P_{1/2} \rightarrow {}^2S_{1/2}$ should be resolved into four components, two π lines ($\Delta M = 0$) polarized parallel to the field and two σ lines ($\Delta M = \pm1$) polarized perpendicularly. D_2 or $^2P_{3/2} \rightarrow {}^2S_{1/2}$ should be resolved into six components of which the outer four are σ lines. A glance at the photograph in Fig. 84 shows that the theoretical predictions are confirmed by experiment, as to the patterns themselves, and at least roughly also as to intensities. Examination of the lines through a nicol prism shows that the polarizations also are correctly predicted.

133. The Paschen-Back Effect.   The formulas of the last section are limited to weak magnetic fields.   The term "weak" is, of course, relative, since fields in excess of 1,000 gauss are usually required to produce good Zeeman patterns.   A field is weak when the total spread of the Zeeman

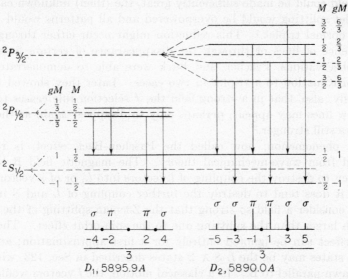

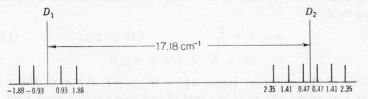

FIG. 91. Weak-field Zeeman effect for the D lines of sodium.   The same scale is used for all Zeeman separations, also for the theoretical relative intensities of the component lines as shown by the relative heights of the lines as drawn.   The position of the normal triplet in the same field is shown by three dots.   Dashed lines show the levels in zero field.

pattern of each line is small relative to the spacing of the lines themselves. Figure 92, for example, shows diagrammatically to scale the D lines of sodium with their respective Zeeman patterns in a field of 30,000 gauss. The Zeeman separations are seen to be small compared with the separa-

FIG. 92. Relative separations of the D lines of Na(11) and their Zeeman components in a field of 30,000 oersteds.

tion between D_1 and D_2.   For these lines, therefore, a field of 30,000 gauss is a "weak" field.   Consider, however, the Zeeman effect in lithium. The separation in zero field of the the two components of the first line of the principal series is of the order of 0.3 cm^{-1}.   A field of 30,000 gauss would be expected to produce Zeeman separations several times larger than this; according to (179), if $B = 30,000$, $\tilde{L} = 1.4$ cm^{-1}. For lithium, therefore, 30,000 gauss is a "strong" field.

The view was expressed by Paschen and Back in 1912 that, if the magnetic field could be made sufficiently great, the (then) unknown cause of multiplet splitting would be overpowered and all patterns would revert to the normal triplet.[1] This reduction might occur either through the coalescence of lines or through the disappearance of certain lines. In their observations, Paschen and Back were able to demonstrate such an approximation to a triplet in two cases. Later they showed experimentally, also, that in a strong field the J selection rule ceases to hold and new lines may appear, perhaps only to disappear again as the field becomes still stronger.[2]

This phenomenon, now called the Paschen-Back effect, is readily inferred from wave-mechanical theory. The magnetic field **B** has no tendency to destroy the coupling of l vectors into L, or of s vectors into S, but it does tend to destroy the further coupling of L and S into J. Let us consider a field so strong that the Zeeman splitting of the levels is much larger than the splitting due to the spin-orbit effect. Then the latter effect can be ignored entirely for a first approximation; and the atomic states may be the $L\ S\ \Lambda\ \Sigma$ states described in Sec. 123, with the axis drawn parallel to **B**. In a classical motion, the l vectors would now all precess about **B** at the same angular velocity ω_l and their resultant would precess with them. Similarly, the s vectors and their resultant would precess at the rate $2\omega_l$. Since, however, these rates are unequal, the *resultant* angular momentum would vary in magnitude, although its component in the direction of **B** would remain constant.

In wave mechanics, the total component in the **B** direction is $Mh/2\pi$, and here $M = \Lambda + \Sigma$; furthermore, $\Sigma G_{la} = \Lambda h/2\pi$ and $\Sigma G_{sa} = \Sigma h/2\pi$. Thus, as in a weak field, ΣG_{la} and ΣG_{sa} are independent of B, and from (175b) and (177a,b) we have, as an approximation valid in a sufficiently strong field,

$$g = 1 + \frac{\Sigma}{M} \qquad \mu_a = -(M + \Sigma)\mu_e \qquad (184a,b)$$

$$W = W_0 + (M + \Sigma)\mu_e B \qquad (185)$$

Because of the selection rules, $\Delta M = 0$ or ± 1, $\Delta \Sigma = 0$, the normal triplet now arises just as in the case of one electron in a huge field.

When account is taken of the spin-orbit interactions, however, it is found that the spacing of the levels is not quite constant, and levels

[1] F. Paschen and E. Back, *Ann. Physik*, vol. 39, p. 897, 1912, and vol. 40, p. 959, 1913.

[2] F. Paschen and E. Back, *Physica*, vol. 1, p. 261, 1921. See also W. C. van Geel, *Z. Physik*, vol. 51, p. 51, 1928.

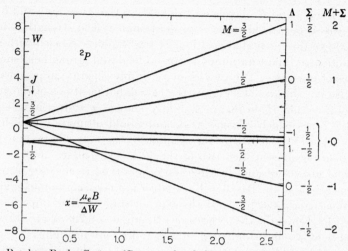

FIG. 93. Paschen-Back effect on ^2P energy levels in a magnetic field. W is energy in arbitrary units, ΔW the $\frac{3}{2}$-$\frac{1}{2}$ separation in zero field.   On the scale, $\Delta W = 1.5$; in x, ΔW is in ergs and B in gauss.

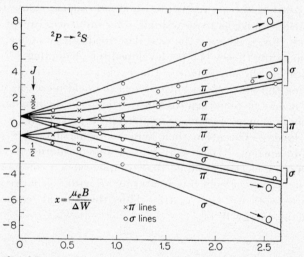

FIG. 94. Calculated Paschen-Back effect on a ^2P-^2S Zeeman pattern, with a few observations by Kent on lithium.

having the same value of $M + \Sigma$ but different M may be slightly separated.   A fine structure is thereby introduced into the strong-field pattern, of the same absolute order of magnitude as the original fine structure in the zero field.

The transition from a weak to a strong field is illustrated in Figs. 93 and 94 for a $^2P \rightarrow {}^2S$ transition such as that which gives rise to the D lines of sodium.   The plots are constructed relative to the spacing between the $P_{3/2}$ and $P_{1/2}$ levels in zero field, so that they are valid for any case of this type; the abscissa is proportional to field strength. In Fig. 93 are shown the calculated positions of the ^2P levels, labeled with values of M, and with quantum numbers for no field and strong field shown at the sides of the plot. The two ^2S levels simply separate in proportion to B and are not shown. In Fig. 94 the calculated positions of the 10 lines for the transition $^2P \rightarrow {}^2S$ are similarly shown, π and σ lines being so labeled. Lines which become weak and would ultimately vanish in an infinite field are indicated by the symbol "$\rightarrow 0$." It will be noted that, as the field becomes strong, two of the ^2P levels coalesce, and, of the 10 weak-field lines, 4 disappear while the others tend to coalesce in pairs.

Observations of the Paschen-Back effect are not easy to make, and few transitions have been followed through all stages. The imperfect data reported by Kent[1] for the D lines of lithium at λ 6,708 A are shown, for selected field strengths only, by crosses and circles in Fig. 94.

It should be added that in the discussion so far the magnetic field has been tacitly assumed not to be so extremely strong as to bring together levels belonging to different *terms*, such as a P and a D. If this limit could be exceeded, the normal triplet should disappear again, to reappear only in a field so huge as to swamp all other influences except that of the central field, thus producing the case described briefly in Sec. 130.

A corresponding theory can be developed for jj coupling. In any case, a help in tracing the movement of the levels is provided by the rule that levels having the same M do not cross as the field increases in strength.

Finally, it may be remarked that in a strong field the magnetic moment of the atom, in general, becomes variable and Eq. (174), $W = W_0 - \mu_a B$, no longer holds. The atom then behaves rather like a set of magnets connected by springs. It is easily proved, by considering forces on magnetic poles or on electric circuits, that to move such a compound magnet to a position where the field B is greater by dB with no change in its direction requires work $dW = -\mu_a\, dB$. Thus the general relation between μ_a, B, and the energy W is

$$\mu_a = -\frac{dW}{dB} \tag{186}$$

Continuing to write, as in (177a), $\mu_a = -gM\mu_e$, we may replace (177b) by a modified equation, thus: $W = W_0 + g_W M \mu_e B$; but, in general, $g_W \neq g$, and both g and g_W vary with B.

134. The Stern-Gerlach Experiment. The space quantization of atomic angular momenta, upon which we have based the discussion of the Zeeman effect, constitutes a characteristic feature both of the older quantum theory and of wave mechanics, in contrast with classical theory.

---

[1] N. A. Kent, *Astrophys. J.*, vol. 40, p. 337, 1914.

Its occurrence is not definitely confirmed by the existence of the Zeeman effect, however, in view of the partial success of classical theory in accounting for these phenomena.   An experiment which directly reveals the space quantization itself was proposed by O. Stern in 1921 and was carried out by him in collaboration with Gerlach.[1]

In elementary magnetic theory, it is shown that a magnet tends to move so as to increase the magnetic flux through it in the direction of its magnetic axis.   In a uniform field, the only result is that the magnet experiences a torque tending to line it up with the field.   In a *nonuniform* field, however, the magnet experiences a *translatory force* as well.

Suppose now that a slender beam of atoms having magnetic moments travels in the direction of the x axis across a magnetic field whose lines are approximately parallel to the y axis but whose magnitude increases rapidly in the direction of $+y$.   After passing through the field, let these atoms be collected on a suitable target.   Then atoms which have a component of their magnetic moment in the direction of the field will be deflected; if the component of the moment has the same direction as the field, they will be deflected toward $+y$; if it has the opposite direction, toward $-y$.

So far, the predictions of classical and quantum theory coincide. According to *classical* theory, however, each atom will enter the field with its magnetic axis inclined at some angle θ to the field, and the axis will then execute a Larmor precession about the field at the fixed angle θ. Since all values of θ occur among the atoms, their deflections will be distributed in continuous fashion, and the atoms, instead of forming a small spot on the target, will be drawn out into a continuous band.

According to *quantum* theory, on the other hand, each atom will enter the field in a certain quantum state, defined with the direction of the field as an axis.   Its magnetic moment in the direction of the field will be gM Bohr magnetons (if the field is not too strong), where g is the Landé splitting factor and M has one of several integral values [cf. Eq. (177a)]. The beam will be broken up, therefore, into separate beams and will form on the target a series of distinct spots, one for each possible value of M.

The arrangement used in the experiment of Stern and Gerlach is shown diagrammatically in Fig. 95.   The nonhomogeneous field was produced between pole pieces of which one had a sharp edge, so that near it the field was much stronger than elsewhere.   A strap-shaped beam of silver atoms was formed by evaporating silver in a heated oven O and allowing atoms from the vapor to stream out through collimating slits; the beam [shown by the small rectangle in Fig. 95(a)] traveled closely past the sharp edge of pole piece P_2 and was condensed on a plate at T.   With

[1] Stern, *Z. Physik*, vol. 7, p. 249, 1921; Gerlach and Stern, *Z. Physik*, vol. 8, p. 110; vol. 9, p. 349, 1922; *Ann. Physik*, vol. 74, p. 673, 1924.

no field, the beam formed a narrow line on the plate [Fig. 95(c), lower line]. When the magnetizing current was turned on, the line was not widened continuously but was divided into two lines, as shown in the upper part of Fig. 95(c), except at the ends, which were produced by atoms passing at some distance from the sharp edge. Space quantization of the silver atoms was thus clearly revealed. From careful measurements of the separation of the two lines and of the gradient of the magnetic field strength, it was calculated that each silver atom had a magnetic moment in the direction of the field of 1 Bohr magneton, with an error of 10 per cent at most.

These results, and others obtained subsequently, are in agreement with the predictions of wave mechanics. The silver atom is normally in a $^2S_{1/2}$ state, for which $g = 2$; thus, half the atoms should have $M = \frac{1}{2}$ and a moment in the direction of the field of $2 \times \frac{1}{2} = 1$ Bohr magneton,

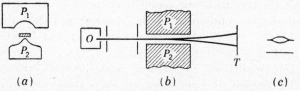

(a) (b) (c)

FIG. 95. Illustrative of the Stern-Gerlach experiment. (a) and (c) represent views seen in the direction of the beam; (c) shows the trace on the target (exaggerated) with and without the magnetic field.

whereas, for the other half, $M = -\frac{1}{2}$ and the moment is -1. Similar results were obtained subsequently, with greater precision, by Taylor[1] and by Leu[2] for sodium and potassium, which are likewise in $^2S_{1/2}$ states. Atoms of zinc and cadmium, in Leu's experiments, were unaffected by the magnetic field. Atoms of thallium gave a double line corresponding to a moment of $\frac{1}{3}$ magneton. Zinc and cadmium are normally in $^1S_0$ states, which have $M = 0$ and no magnetic moment. For thallium the normal state is inferred from spectroscopic evidence to be $^2P_{1/2}$; thus $M = \frac{1}{2}$ or $-\frac{1}{2}$ again, but $g = \frac{2}{3}$ instead of 1 [by Eq. (181), in which $J = \frac{1}{2}, S = \frac{1}{2}, L = 1$].

135. Isotope Structure and Hyperfine Structure. The ordinary fine structure due to spin-orbit interaction does not exhaust the possibilities of fine details in spectral lines. Even before 1900, Michelson and others had shown, by means of the interferometer, that many spectral lines possess a further structure much finer still; this came to be known as hyperfine structure.

[1] Taylor, *Phys. Rev.*, vol. 28, p. 276, 1926.
[2] Leu, *Z. Physik*, vol. 41, p. 551, 1927.

After the discovery that many chemical elements consist of several isotopes (Sec. 181), it was believed for a time that each component of a hyperfine pattern of lines was emitted by a different isotope. Later, however, hyperfine structure was discovered in the spectra of some elements which, as shown by the mass spectrograph, consist of only one isotope. An example is bismuth; the line λ 3,596 A contains six hyperfine components spread over a range of 0.3 A or 2.3 cm^{-1}. It was suggested by Pauli in 1924 that this effect might be due to an occurrence in the nucleus of angular momentum and an associated magnetic moment. It appears that both causes are operative. There is a tendency, therefore, to limit the expression hyperfine structure to the spectrum from a given isotope and to refer to the other type of effect as isotope structure. In the spectrum from a mixture of isotopes, both types of structure may occur superposed.

In light atoms such as H, B, Li, Ne, Cl, K, the *isotope shift* appears to arise from simple differences in the effects of nuclear motion. The simplest case is that of hydrogen, in which the isotope shift was used as a guide by Urey and his collaborators in the discovery of heavy hydrogen or deuterium.[1] The Rydberg constants for the two kinds of hydrogen atoms can be found by substituting $M = M_1$ and $M = 2M_1$ successively in Eq. (93a) in Sec. 84, which gives

$$R_1 = \frac{M_1 R_\infty}{M_1 + m} \qquad R_2 = \frac{2M_1 R_\infty}{2M_1 + m}$$

M_1 being the mass of a proton and m the mass of an electron. The difference in wavelength for a given line of wavelength λ will then be, nearly enough,

$$\Delta\lambda = -\frac{\lambda(R_2 - R_1)}{R_\infty} = -\frac{\lambda m}{2M_1}$$

Since $M_1/m = 1{,}836$, it follows that the Hβ line for deuterium should lie $4{,}861/3.674 = 1.32$ A on the violet side of that for ordinary hydrogen. This line was observed to be faintly visible, in the expected position, in the spectrum from a sample of common hydrogen, and it increased in strength as the hydrogen was subjected to operations which should increase the relative concentration of deuterium.

In the spectrum of a *heavy* atom, isotope shifts are found, in general, to be proportional to the differences in atomic mass. A photograph illustrating such structure in the spectrum of tungsten is shown in Fig. 96. The spectrum was formed with a Fabry-Perot etalon;[2] hence the same

[1] Urey, Brickwedde, and Murphy, *Phys. Rev.,* vol. 40, p. 1, 1932.

[2] Cf. G. R. Harrison, R. C. Lord, and J. R. Loofbourow, "Practical Spectroscopy," 1948.

pattern appears repeated many times in different orders. Tungsten consists chiefly of four isotopes, three about equally abundant and having mass numbers 182, 184, and 186, and 183 about half as abundant as the others. The three observed lines were ascribed to the more abundant isotopes, any effect of 183 being assumed to be masked by the others.

In such heavy atoms, however, the isotope shift cannot be explained as a simple difference in the effects of nuclear motion, which are far too small. The cause is believed to lie in some minor departure from simple Coulomb interaction between nucleus and electrons, associated with the finite size and shape of the nucleus, the effect varying from isotope to isotope. The nucleus might also be polarized electrostatically by the electron's field.

The theoretical treatment of *true hyperfine structure due to a nuclear magnetic moment* resembles closely the treatment of *LS* fine structure

Hyperfine – Structure   Tantalum   λ 5997

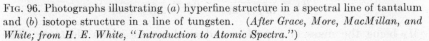

(a)

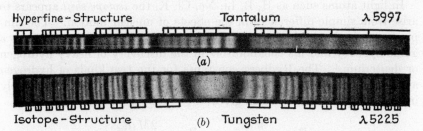

Isotope – Structure   (b)   Tungsten   λ 5225

FIG. 96. Photographs illustrating (a) hyperfine structure in a spectral line of tantalum and (b) isotope structure in a line of tungsten. (*After Grace, More, MacMillan, and White; from H. E. White, "Introduction to Atomic Spectra."*)

caused by the spin-orbit effect. The angular momentum of the nucleus is presumably associated with spin momenta of the protons and neutrons of which the nucleus is composed; hence it is commonly said to be due to nuclear "spin." The maximum possible value of the component of the nuclear angular momentum in any direction is denoted by $Ih/2\pi$; the square of the total would then be $I(I + 1)h^2/(2\pi)^2$. So far as is known, the spin number I is an integer or 0 whenever the mass number, or number of protons and neutrons in the nucleus, is even, and half-integral when the mass number is odd. Moreover, it appears that $I = 0$ whenever both the mass number and the atomic number Z are even. If $I > 0$, there exists in the usual way a second quantum number M_I restricted to integrally spaced values such that $|M_I| \leqq I$; thus the nuclear state is $(2I + 1)$-fold degenerate. Protons and neutrons have $I = \frac{1}{2}$; some other values of I are listed in Table 7-6.

If the Dirac relativistic theory for charged particles held for protons of mass M_p as well as for electrons, the effective magnetic moment of the proton would be, in analogy with Eq. (176) for electrons,

$$\frac{eh}{4\pi M_p c} = \frac{\mu_e}{1,836.0} \tag{187}$$

with a sign corresponding to rotation of a positive charge.   This is called a *nuclear magneton*.   It appears, however, that the proton moment is $+2.79$ nuclear magnetons; and even the neutron has a moment of magnitude -1.91.   In general, the moment μ_I (or μ) represents the maximum possible value for the component of the nuclear moment in any given direction, measured in nuclear magnetons.   In a nuclear orientation state in which the nuclear angular momentum about a given axis is $M_I h/2\pi$, its component of magnetic moment in the direction of this axis is $(M_I/I)\,\mu_I$. Values of μ_I are also listed in Table 7-6.

TABLE 7-6. NUCLEAR SPIN I AND MAGNETIC MOMENT μ_I*

Z		A	I	μ_I
0	n	1	½	-1.9128
1	H	1	½	$+2.79255$
		2	1	$+0.85735$
2	He	3	½	$(-)2.12741$
		4	0	
3	Li	6	1	$+0.8219$
		7	3/2	$+3.2559$
4	Be	9	3/2	-1.177
5	B	10	3	$+1.800$
		11	3/2	$+2.689$
6	C	12	0	
7	N	14	1	$+0.4036$
		15	½	-0.2830
8	O	16	0	
9	F	19	½	$+2.628$
11	Na	23	3/2	$+2.2171$
81	Tl	203	½	$+1.611$
		205	½	$+1.627$

* Z denotes atomic number and A atomic mass; μ_I is in nuclear magnetons.

The nuclear angular momentum may then be added vectorially to the resultant angular momentum of the atomic electrons by a process of IJ coupling exactly similar to the LS coupling of orbital and spin momenta. Such coupling is necessary whenever weak non-Coulomb interaction between the nucleus and the atomic electrons occurs.   For the grand resultant momentum there are then two new quantum numbers F and M_F, with $|J - I| \leqq F \leqq J + I$ and $|M_F| \leqq F$.

Interactions between the nucleus and the electronic motions and spins may then slightly separate levels having different F, forming a hyperfine multiplet of levels.   The number of these levels is $2I + 1$ if $J \geqq I$ but

$2J + 1$ if $J < I$.   If the interaction is magnetic in nature, equations are obtained of the same form as (165) and (166) for LS multiplets except that here L, S, and J are replaced, respectively, by J, I, and F.   As selection rules, in addition to others, we have

$$\Delta F = 0 \text{ or } \pm 1 \qquad \Delta M_F = 0 \text{ or } \pm 1$$

As an alternative, however, the interaction may arise from an asymmetry in the electrostatic field around the nucleus, usually of the quadrupole type, and in this case the formulas are more complicated.

TABLE 7-7. HYPERFINE STRUCTURE OF THE COMPONENTS OF THE DOUBLET
OF THALLIUM: $6s^2\, 6p\; ^2P_{\frac{1}{2},\frac{3}{2}} \to 6s^2\, 7s\; ^2S_{\frac{1}{2}}$

λ, A	$\Delta \bar{\nu}$, cm^{-1}	Intensity	λ, A	$\Delta \bar{\nu}$, cm^{-1}	Intensity
3,776.888		3	5,352.184		8
	0.40			0.60	
3,776.830		10	5,352.014		3
	0.71			0.14	
3,776.729		8	5,351.974		10

A *hyperfine spectral multiplet* results from transitions between the hyperfine levels composing two ordinary J levels.   Usually it happens that the spacing of the hyperfine sublevels in one of the two J levels is much larger than that in the other, so that the former spacing stands out in the multiplet as observed, the finer structure due to the other J level being frequently not resolved at all.   The result is then an easily recognizable "flag" type of pattern, a good example of which is shown in Fig. 96.

As an illustration of the theory, consider the following doublet in the spectrum of thallium (Tl 81):

$$6s^2\, 6p\; ^2P_{\frac{1}{2}} \to 6s^2\, 7s\; ^2S_{\frac{1}{2}} (\lambda = 3{,}777 \text{ A}; \bar{\nu} = 26{,}478 \text{ cm}^{-1}) \qquad (a)$$
$$6s^2\, 6p\; ^2P_{\frac{3}{2}} \to 6s^2\, 7s\; ^2S_{\frac{1}{2}} (\lambda = 5{,}352 \text{ A}; \bar{\nu} = 18{,}684 \text{ cm}^{-1}) \qquad (b)$$

Under high resolution[1] each line of this doublet is seen to be made up of three components.   Their wavelengths and estimated intensities are given in Table 7-7; their relative positions on a frequency scale are shown in Fig. 97.

To produce three component lines, as observed, there must be two hyperfine sublevels in each J level, just as in the production of the $D \to P$ triplets in the alkali spectra there are two J levels in each LS term (Sec. 124).   Hence here $2 = 2I + 1$, and so $I = \frac{1}{2}$ for the thallium nucleus.   Then for $J = \frac{1}{2}$, $F = I \pm \frac{1}{2}$ or $F = 1$ or 0; for $J = \frac{3}{2}$,

---

[1] Back, *Ann. Physik*, vol. 70, p. 367, 1923.

$F = 2$ or 1. The spacing of the hyperfine levels is easily determined from the observed separations in the spectrum. The level diagram and spectral fine structure for one line of the doublet are shown in Fig. 98. The

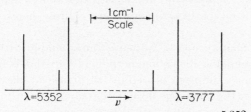

FIG. 97. Hyperfine structure of the thallium doublet $\lambda = \dfrac{5{,}352}{3{,}777}$ angstroms.

same pattern would result if the doublet separations were interchanged, but the Zeeman pattern for the hyperfine components unambiguously assigns the energy differences.[1]

Hyperfine spectra are an important source of information concerning the values of I and μ_I. To find μ_I, however, requires a wave-mechanical calculation, which is easiest for light atoms. The sign of μ_I affects the order of the F levels; very commonly, when $\mu_I > 0$, levels with larger F lie above those with smaller F, and vice versa for $\mu_I < 0$.[2]

Furthermore, complications frequently arise which have been ascribed to slight departures from spherical symmetry in the electrostatic field of the nucleus, especially such a departure as can be described by assuming an electric quadrupole moment in the nucleus. If $I > \frac{1}{2}$, such a moment may cause perturbations, large or

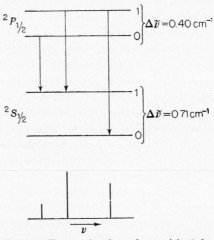

FIG. 98. Energy levels and transitions for the hyperfine structure of the thallium line $\lambda = 3{,}777$ angstroms.

small, in the hyperfine pattern; it may even be the sole cause of a hyperfine splitting.

136. Magnetic Beam Measurement of Nuclear Spins and Moments.
The method of magnetic beams has been refined until it constitutes a

[1] Back and Wulff, Z. Physik, vol. 66, p. 31, 1930.
[2] Cf. E. Segrè et al., "Experimental Nuclear Physics," 1953; S. Tolansky, "Hyperfine Structure in Line Spectra and Nuclear Spin," 2d ed., 1948.

powerful instrument for the determination of *nuclear* spins and magnetic moments. The final form of the method, that of *magnetic resonance*, is so superior that it has now superseded all other forms. The earlier work is instructive, however, and constitutes an excellent example of the gradual evolution of experimental procedures; hence it merits brief description.

Nuclear moments could be measured most simply with a beam of bare nuclei in a nonhomogeneous magnetic field, but this is usually impracticable. The next-simplest procedure is to use atoms or molecules in states in which the electrons do not contribute directly to the magnetic moment, as in atomic states with $J = 0$ or molecules in $^1\Sigma$ states. The magnetic moment of the proton was first measured by Stern and his collaborators,[1] using a beam of hydrogen molecules. In orthohydrogen (Sec. 144) the proton spins are effectively parallel and the resulting molecular moment is twice that of a proton. There is also, however, a small magnetic effect due to molecular rotation; this was corrected for by means of comparative observations on pure parahydrogen, in which the nuclear spins are effectively opposed and the proton moments cancel. The value thus found for the magnitude of the proton moment, then surprising, was 2.5 nuclear magnetons.

Somewhat earlier, Breit and Rabi had pointed out[2] that, as a basis for calculating nuclear moments from the spectral hyperfine structure to which they give rise, beam observations can be substituted for the difficult spectroscopic observation of the hyperfine structure. With atoms having $J > 0$, the method rests upon the fact that a strong hyperfine Paschen-Back effect can often be produced with magnetic fields of only a few hundred gauss. Precise formulas for this effect are easily derived from theory, in terms of the hyperfine separations as unknown constants.

The case $J = \frac{1}{2}$ and $I = \frac{1}{2}$ is illustrated in Fig. 99. W_m is the calculated displacement of an energy level due both to the magnetic coupling between the nucleus and the electrons and to the external field, if any; and ΔW is the difference between the levels with $F = 0$ and $F = 1$ when $B = 0$. In Fig. 99(*b*), μ_{eff} denotes the effective magnetic moment of the atom in the direction of a magnetic field **B** of external origin. This moment determines the deflection of the atom in a nonhomogeneous field, and it is almost entirely due to the electrons, because of the relatively minute size of the nuclear moments; for this reason, also, the constant μ_0 is indistinguishable from a Bohr magneton. As explained in Sec. 133, $\mu_{eff} = -dW/dB$, so that the ordinates in Fig. 99(*b*) are proportional to the slopes of the curves in Fig. 99(*a*). The abscissa is x, where

[1] R. Frisch and O. Stern, *Z. Physik*, vol. 85, p. 4, 1933; I. Estermann and O. Stern, *Z. Physik*, vol. 85, p. 17, 1933.

[2] G. Breit and I. Rabi, *Phys. Rev.*, vol. 38, p. 2082, 1931.

$$x = \frac{B}{\Delta W}\left(-\frac{\mu_J}{J} + \frac{\mu_I}{I}\right)$$

μ_I being the nuclear moment and μ_J the maximum moment due to the electrons in zero field, or $\mu_J = -gJ\mu_e$ by Eq. (177a); I is the nuclear spin, here assumed to be $\frac{1}{2}$. The atomic angular momentum in the direction of **B** is $mh/2\pi$; if B is zero, m becomes M_F. The figures are drawn for $\mu_I > 0$; if $\mu_I < 0$, they are reversed from top to bottom without change in the scales at the left, the level $F = 1$ then lying below $F = 0$.

When $B = 0$ and $x = 0$, only the two distinct hyperfine levels belonging to $F = I \pm J$ occur. As B and x increase, however, the various m levels for $F = 1$ become separated. This separation is due almost entirely to the electronic magnetic moment; it may be imagined that the

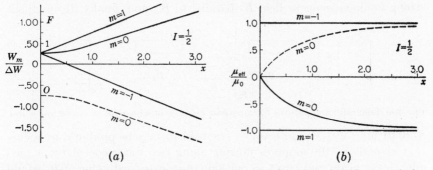

Fig. 99. Plot of energy and effective moment as a function of field strength for $J = I = \frac{1}{2}$.

nuclear and electronic spins are at first coupled together by the nuclear-electronic interaction and the electronic magnetic moment is thereby forced to assume various orientations. The total number of m states in the present case is four; in general, it is $(2I + 1)(2J + 1)$. Thus, if atomic beams in these various states can be separated in a magnetic field, their mere number at once furnishes the value of I, provided J is known for the electronic state. As B increases, however, the nucleus-electron coupling is weakened, and the quantum number F loses its significance; when $x \gg 1$, the levels form two groups corresponding to $M = M_J = \pm\frac{1}{2}$, representing a complete hyperfine Paschen-Back effect. Only a minute separation due to the nuclear moment μ_I persists.

In a first attempt to make use of these relationships,[1] a beam of H atoms was allowed to pass through a nonhomogeneous field of known characteristics, and the separation of the two beams containing atoms in the two inner states shown in Fig. 99(b) was measured. From the common value of $|\mu_{\text{eff}}|$ for these beams, the corresponding value of x, of the

[1] I. I. Rabi, J. M. B. Kellogg, J. R. Zacharias, *Phys. Rev.*, vol. 46, p. 157, 1934.

order of $\frac{1}{2}$, was calculated, thence ΔW, and thence, by means of wave-mechanical formulas, the value of $|\mu_I|$ for the proton.

A major difficulty in such work, however, arises from the spread of velocity among the atoms, which makes all beams very broad. To overcome this difficulty a refocusing arrangement was later introduced.[1] Another limitation is that the deflections do not depend upon the *sign* of μ_I. In order to determine this sign, Rabi also introduced a special device to cause transitions between the magnetic states.[2]

The setup thus developed[3] is illustrated in Fig. 100, which will serve also to illustrate the later method of magnetic resonance. The initial beam of atoms passes through a collimator slit S_c (perhaps 0.02 mm wide) into a weak, nonuniform magnetic field B_1, in which it is separated into components, then through a weak "transition field" B_t, followed by a strong nonhomogeneous field B_2 parallel to B_1, and, finally, through slit

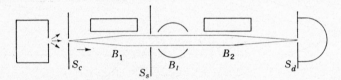

FIG. 100. Diagram of apparatus for magnetic analysis of a beam of atoms or molecules.

S_d (0.01 mm) into the detector. The field B_2 may be produced by a current of perhaps 100 amperes flowing along two water-cooled tubes parallel to the beam and offset to one side of it; a typical value of B_2 would be 12,000 gauss, with a gradient of 100,000 gauss per cm. By properly adjusting B_1 and B_2, atoms that have been deflected with a certain μ_{eff} in the first field can be refocused onto the slit S_d, those with different μ_{eff} being stopped by the slit. Variation in the velocity of the atoms does not interfere with this refocusing action. Because of the differing strengths of B_1 and B_2, μ_{eff} has for certain of the beams different values in these two fields. Hence, from the known characteristics of B_1 and B_2 when refocusing occurred for one of these beams, as revealed by a maximum response of the detector, it was possible to calculate the value of x for both B_1 and B_2 and then ΔW.

The purpose of the transition field B_t, as used by Kellogg, Rabi, and Zacharias, was to ascertain the sign of μ_I. This field was simply a weak, nonhomogeneous field differing in direction from B_1 and B_2. Its function will be illustrated with reference to Fig. 99(b). Let the selector slit S_s be set to transmit only the two beams with $\mu_{\text{eff}} > 0$, which can be focused

[1] I. I. Rabi and V. W. Cohen, *Phys. Rev.*, vol. 46, p. 707, 1934.

[2] I. I. Rabi, *Phys. Rev.*, vol. 49, p. 324, 1935—a clear exposition of the whole method up to this point.

[3] J. M. B. Kellogg, I. I. Rabi, J. R. Zacharias, *Phys. Rev.*, vol. 50, p. 472, 1936.

in turn on the detector by varying B_2. If $\mu_I > 0$, these beams have $m = -1$ or $m = 0$. When $B_t = 0$, both beams pass unaltered through the field B_2, which is parallel to B_1. The nonhomogeneous field B_t, however, tends to change the magnetic state of those atoms which leave B_1 with $m = -1$ in such a way that they enter B_2 with $m = 0$ or -1 and so are deflected differently in B_2; thus this beam is weakened by the presence of B_2. Atoms leaving B_1 with $m = 0$, on the other hand, will be unaffected by B_t; for there is no other state with $F = 0$ into which they can go, and, by a selection rule, a weak field B_t cannot change F. If, on the other hand, $\mu_I < 0$, the curves in Fig. 99(b) are inverted, both beams with $\mu_{\text{eff}} > 0$ belong to $F = 1$, and both are weakened by B_t. Thus, if *both* of the two peaks that are found in the intensity curve as B_2 is varied are observed to be weakened by turning on B_t, then it is concluded that $\mu_I < 0$; if *only one* is weakened, $\mu_I > 0$. In this way the sign of μ_I can be identified. Values of $+2.85 \pm 0.15$ for the proton and $+0.85 \pm .03$ for the deuteron (H^2) were thus obtained.

Magnetic-resonance Method. The final great improvement lay in replacing the weak, steady transition field by the combination of a *strong, homogeneous* field $\mathbf{B}_0$ parallel to the two deflection fields and a superposed *perpendicular oscillating* field $\mathbf{B}'$. In the strong field B_0 (several thousand gauss), the nucleus and the electrons are effectively decoupled, so that $m = M + m_I$, M referring to the electronic state, and

$$W = \left(gM\mu_e - \frac{M_I}{I}\mu_I \right) B_0 \tag{188}$$

(The field B_0 is still weak as far as the electrons alone are concerned.) The beams with various m values remain distinct through all three of the parallel fields B_1, B_0, B_2. Now let the frequency ν of the oscillating field B' be adjusted so as to be near the resonance value, $\nu = |W - W'|/h$, where W is the energy in B_0 of the atoms that are being focused onto the detector and W' is the energy of another magnetic state in that field into which transitions can be induced magnetically. Then some of the atoms will undergo such transitions and the beam reaching the detector will be weakened. The selection rules for such transitions are: $\Delta M = \pm 1$ or $\Delta M_I = \pm 1$; and it is immaterial whether $W \gtrless W'$. Thus, if ν has the value required for maximum weakening of the beam due to transitions in which $\Delta M_I = \pm 1$, then $|W - W'| = |\mu_I|B_0/I$ and $|\mu_I|$ is given by the simple formula $|\mu_I| = h\nu I/B_0$.

The wave-mechanical basis for this effect is so simple that it may be indicated briefly. The wave function including time for an atom in the field B_0 can be written, in analogy with Eq. (113),

$$\Psi = e^{-(2\pi i/h)W't}(C_1\psi_1 e^{-(2\pi i/h)(W-W')t} + C_2\psi_2 + \cdots)$$

ψ_1, ψ_2, etc., being wave-amplitude functions for the magnetic states of energies W, W', etc. When the oscillating field is applied, the C's are no longer constants. For example, increments may be added to C_2 at the expense of C_1. These increments will come with the time factor $e^{-(2\pi i/h)(W-W')t}$ attached, and, since this factor equals $\cos 2\pi\nu t + i \sin 2\pi\nu t$ with $\nu = (W - W')/h$, increments produced during successive half cycles will be alternately positive and negative and so will tend to cancel each other. If, however, the perturbing field itself alternates at the same frequency ν, this alternation will cause compensating changes of sign, and consequently the increments will all add up. Large changes in C_2 may then occur.

The classical analogy is also very useful in this case. According to Eq. (172) a classical moment $-gJ\mu_e$ associated with angular momentum $Jh/2\pi$, and a classical nuclear moment μ_I with associated angular momentum $Ih/2\pi$, would precess in the steady field B_0 at respective (numerical) frequencies ν_J and ν_I, where

$$\nu_J = \frac{g\mu_e}{h} B_0 \qquad \nu_I = \frac{\mu_I}{hI} B_0$$

These frequencies are just the resonance frequencies for transitions between magnetic states with $\Delta M = \pm 1$ or $\Delta m_I = \pm 1$, respectively. Now a perturbing magnetic field $\mathbf{B}'$ perpendicular to $\mathbf{B}_0$ would exert a torque tending to rotate both momentum vectors in a plane passing through $\mathbf{B}_0$ and so to alter their components taken in the direction of $\mathbf{B}_0$ (Fig. 101, where $\mathbf{B}'$ is perpendicular to μ_I). In general, because of the precessional motion, the resulting changes in the μ_I vector during successive elements of time will tend to cancel each other; but if $\mathbf{B}'$ *precesses at the same rate* and in the *same direction* as the μ_I vector, these changes will add up and a large change in the $\mathbf{B}_0$ component of μ_I will be produced. An alternating field, being equivalent to two equal steady fields rotating in opposite directions, would have half as great an effect.

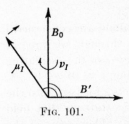

FIG. 101.

These conclusions are confirmed by calculation from wave mechanics.[1] Since the direction of precession reverses with the sign of μ_I, this sign can be inferred from the direction in which $\mathbf{B}'$ must rotate about the direction of $\mathbf{B}_0$ in order to induce transitions. When the more convenient oscillating field is used, this advantage is lost; but it was pointed out by Millman that the current in the leads to the loop of wire by which B_0 was produced introduces a spatial inhomogeneity into the B' field, and this

[1] I. I. Rabi, *Phys. Rev.*, vol. 51, p. 652, 1937.

feature gives rise to an easily observable *sign-dependent asymmetry* in the resonance curves as observed.[1] Thus the sign of μ_I can also be inferred.

The most convenient mode of observation is first to adjust the deflecting fields until the beam received by the detector is a maximum, indicating that a beam of atoms in one of the magnetic states is coming through the focusing system.   The oscillator is then set going at a suitable fixed frequency ν and the magnitude of B_0 is varied until a minimum in the beam intensity is obtained.   Then $|\mu_I| = hI\nu/B_0$. The number of beams requiring the same value of $h\nu/B_0$ for a minimum is one less than the number of the magnetic states corresponding to different values of M_I, or $2I$, and thus at once furnishes the value of I.

In the first paper describing this new method[2] the following results were reported: for Li^7, $I = \frac{3}{2}$, $\mu_I = +3.25$ nuclear magnetons; for F^{19}, $I = \frac{1}{2}$, $\mu_I = +2.622$.   Molecules of LiCl, LiF, and Li_2 were used, and the minima belonging to Li were identified by their occurring at the same ν/B_0 in all three molecules.   To identify the minima belonging to F, NaF was also used.   A resonance curve obtained for Li^7 is shown in Fig. 102.   Subsequently, H and D (or H^2) were studied in the molecules HD and DD, which are largely in states of zero rotation.[3]

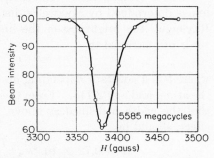

Fig. 102. Magnetic-resonance curve for a Li^7 nucleus.

The values of μ_I found for the proton $(I = \frac{1}{2})$ and the deuteron $(I = 1)$ were, respectively, $+2.785 \pm 0.02$ and $+0.855 \pm 0.006$ nuclear magnetons.

137. The Breadth of Spectral Lines.   No spectral line as observed is perfectly sharp, no matter how great the resolving power of the spectrometer. A line devoid of structure appears densest in the center and fades out on the edges.   For convenience, the *width* Δ of a line is defined to be the distance between two points, one on each side of the center, at which the intensity is half as great as it is in the center of the line (Fig. 103).   This is sometimes called the half-intensity width.   The principal causes of line broadening are the following:

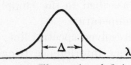

Fig. 103. Illustrating definition of line width Δ.

[1] S. Millman, *Phys. Rev.*, vol. 55, p. 628, 1939.

[2] I. I. Rabi, S. Millman, P. Kusch, J. R. Zacharias, *Phys. Rev.*, vol. 55, p. 526, 1939.

[3] J. M. B. Kellogg, I. I. Rabi, N. F. Ramsey, J. R. Zacharias, *Phys. Rev.*, vol. 56, p. 728, 1939.

a. Doppler Effect. The *observed* frequency of a spectral line may be slightly changed by motion of the radiating atom in the line of sight, owing to Doppler's principle, the apparent frequency *increasing* if the motion is *toward* the observer and *decreasing* if the motion is *away* from the observer. Only for those atoms which have no component of velocity in the direction of the observer will the observed frequency of the emitted light be equal to the actual frequency.

In a luminous gas, such as the mercury vapor in the mercury-arc lamp, the atoms are moving with a maxwellian distribution of velocity, the average velocity increasing with temperature. It is obvious, therefore, that a spectral line emitted by a gas must comprise, as observed, a range of frequencies symmetrically distributed about the frequency emitted by the atom when at rest and, further, that this range should increase with increasing temperature. The distribution of intensity throughout the line is determined by Maxwell's distribution of velocities. According to Rayleigh,[1] the brightness of the line at a distance $\lambda' - \lambda$ from the center is proportional to

$$e^{-b(\lambda'-\lambda)^2}$$

where b is a constant depending on the temperature and on the mass of the atom, and $e = 2.718$. From this formula and the value of b it follows that the width Δ defined as above, if it is due entirely to the Doppler effect, should be

$$\Delta = 0.72 \times 10^{-6}\lambda \sqrt{\frac{T}{M}} \qquad \text{wavelength units}$$

where T is the absolute temperature and M is the atomic or molecular weight of the radiating atom or molecule.[2]

Careful studies of the breadth of lines in the spectra of the rare gases were made by Fabry and Buisson,[3] using an interferometer method. They confirmed the formula for Δ as written above. At liquid-air temperatures the breadth of the krypton line $\lambda = 5,570$ A was found to be only 0.006 A, practically all of which could be ascribed to the Doppler effect resulting from thermal agitation at that temperature.

b. Pressure. Using the light from a single unresolved spectral line, it is possible, under favorable conditions, to produce interference fringes when the difference in the path of the two beams is as much as several hundred thousand wavelengths. In terms of classical theory, this fact was interpreted to mean that the wave train sent out by any particular atom is continuous, i.e., without change of phase, for at least that number of vibrations. In order that the atom may emit wave trains of this length, it must be "free from interruptions" for a corresponding period

[1] Rayleigh, *Phil. Mag.*, vol. 27, p. 298, 1889.

[2] Cf. H. E. White, "Introduction to Atomic Spectra," p. 419, 1935.

[3] Fabry and Buisson, *J. phys.*, vol. 2, p. 442, 1912.

of time.   This means that the *mean free time* between collisions with other atoms must, on the average, exceed the time required to emit a complete wave train, since it may be assumed that a collision would cause either a change of phase or excessive damping.   Analogous conclusions are deduced from wave mechanics.

Now, collisions between atoms become more frequent the higher the pressure of the gas for a given temperature.   The higher the pressure, the shorter, therefore, should be the wave trains and the more frequent the abrupt changes of phase.   An increase of temperature, at given density, increases both the collision rate and the pressure.   Thus in general, at high gas pressure, not only should there be a broadening of the line due to the Doppler effect but also an additional broadening due to the increasing frequency of phase changes resulting from collisions. Michelson confirmed this by showing, from measurements with the interferometer, that below a pressure of the order of a millimeter, the breadth of the hydrogen line $\lambda = 6,563$ A is almost entirely due to the Doppler effect; but that at higher pressures the line becomes considerably broader.

The observed broadening is enhanced further by direct disturbances of the energy levels, or of the radiation process itself, when another molecule comes close to the radiating atom.

c. Natural Line Breadth.   According to wave-mechanical theory, a line ought also to exhibit a small "natural" width even when emitted by an atom at rest.   As an analogy, a classical oscillator, radiating energy, would decrease continually in amplitude; it would emit, therefore, a damped wave train of finite effective length.   It can be shown that a damped train of sine waves is equivalent to the superposition of a large number of perfectly regular trains of great length, with slightly differing frequencies.   Such radiation, observed as a spectral line, would, therefore, be broadened slightly.   In the visible region, the natural line breadth is mostly much less than 0.001 A and so is not detectable.   It is easily observable, on the other hand, in the case of x-rays.

Natural line breadth is associated with an indeterminateness in the atomic energies.   Apparently, the principle of the conservation of energy will always be found to hold in so far as it can be tested; but measurement of the energy takes time, and the precision of the result is thereby limited. If Δt denotes the time available for measurement or establishment of an energy, and if ΔW denotes the indefiniteness in the energy, then, roughly, as another example of the indetermination principle

$$\Delta W \, \Delta t \geqq \frac{h}{2\pi}$$

For an atomic or molecular energy level, we may take $\Delta t = \tau$, where τ is the mean life of the level (Sec. 108), whether limited by radiative processes or otherwise, as by Auger transitions (Sec. 163).   Thus

$$\Delta W = \frac{h}{2\pi\tau}$$

The quantity ΔW is sometimes regarded as a natural level width.   For a spectral transition into or out of the normal state, for which $\tau = \infty$ and $\Delta W = 0$, theory gives for the natural line breadth $\Delta \nu = \Delta W/h = 1/2\pi\tau$, where τ refers to the other state that is involved in the transition; thus $\Delta = \Delta\lambda = \Delta(c/\nu) = \lambda^2/2\pi c\tau$.   In general, if τ_1 and τ_2 refer to the two levels, respectively,

$$\Delta = \frac{\lambda^2}{2\pi c}\left(\frac{1}{\tau_1} + \frac{1}{\tau_2}\right)$$

The formula $\nu = (W_1 - W_2)/h$ refers to the center of the line

d. *Incipient Stark Effect.*   In the spectra emitted by discharge tubes, a common cause of broadening is the production of a small Stark effect by strong electric fields, which are not great enough to produce an observable splitting of the line but are sufficient to make it appear perceptibly broader than it otherwise would.

138. Molecular Spectra.   In preceding sections of this chapter we have considered only spectra emitted by *atoms*.   There are other spectra in vast variety which are believed on good evidence to be emitted by *molecules* containing two or more atoms.

Thus, in the visible part of the spectrum emitted by a discharge tube containing hydrogen, only three or four lines belonging to the Balmer series are emitted by free atoms, which have been produced by the dissociation of molecules.   Many other lines are observed, however, mostly fainter, which are ascribed to emission by the undissociated molecules themselves.   Again, if one looks at the spectrum of the carbon arc with a spectroscope of moderate resolving power, one will observe, at the extreme (violet) edge of the visible part of the spectrum, "bands," which are sharply defined and brightest on the long-wavelength edge and which fade out gradually toward shorter wavelengths.   With higher resolving power, these bands are seen to be composed of a large number of lines which are crowded together at the long-wavelength edge, called the "head" of the band, and are separated farther and farther toward the short-wavelength side, the lines, however, being so close together as to appear, under low resolving power, like a *continuous* spectrum.   These bands are ascribed to molecules of cyanogen, CN.   There are also many groups or bands of lines in the infrared which have been found to have a molecular origin.

In the space available here we can discuss only a few of the features

of molecular spectra, referring the student to other books or to the literature for further information.[1]

In general, the spectrum emitted by any given kind of molecule can
be divided into *three spectral ranges* which correspond to different types
of transition between molecular quantum states.   The principal exception is that the spectrum of some molecules is confined to only one of these
ranges.   Simple reasoning in terms of familiar classical assumptions concerning molecular structure leads us to expect such a feature in molecular
spectra, and the reasoning needs only to be translated into wave-mechanical terms in order to constitute a correct theoretical approach to the
subject.

a. Rotation Spectra.   Suppose a molecule were a rigid structure but
contained electric charges so disposed that the molecule possessed an
electric moment.   If such a molecule were to rotate, according to classical
theory, it would emit radiation for essentially the same reason that an
electron revolving in a circle would radiate.   It is readily seen that the
radiation would consist of sine waves having a single frequency, viz., the
frequency of rotation.   Conversely, radiation falling upon such a molecule would tend to set it into rotation, energy of the radiation being at
the same time absorbed.

A few spectral lines corresponding to this simple picture have been
observed in the far infrared and are said to constitute "rotation spectra."

b. Vibration-rotation Spectra.   If the molecule were not rigid but contained atoms capable of vibration under elastic forces about equilibrium
positions, and if the chemical binding were of the ionic type (Sec. 113),
so that some atoms contained an excess of positive charge and others an
excess of negative, then according to classical theory radiation would be
emitted by the vibrating atoms as they move back and forth.   Unless
the molecule were at the same time rotating, the frequency emitted would
be that of the atomic vibration.   If the molecule were rotating, however,
the emitted line would be divided into two lines having frequencies respectively greater or less than the frequency of the atomic vibration, in essentially the same way as, in the classical theory of the Zeeman effect (Sec.
46), a magnetic field modifies the frequencies emitted by a vibrating
electron.

Furthermore, it would be anticipated that, if the amplitude of vibration
became large, the atomic vibrations, although still periodic, would no
longer be simple harmonic.   This is true even in the familiar example of

[1] G. Herzberg, "Molecular Spectra and Molecular Structure," 2d ed., vol. I,
"Spectra of Diatomic Molecules," 1950, also "Infrared and Raman Spectra of
Polyatomic Molecules," 1947; Ruark and Urey, "Atoms, Molecules and Quanta";
Weizel, "Bandenspektren," 1931; R. C. Johnson, "Introduction to Molecular
Spectra," 1949.

the vibrations of a pendulum. The radiation emitted could then be resolved by Fourier analysis into wave trains with frequencies representing the fundamental and the harmonic overtones of the atomic vibrations. Each of these separate frequencies would then be split up further by rotation of the molecule.

Many spectra corresponding roughly to this classical picture are known in the infrared and are called "vibration-rotation spectra."

c. *Electronic Spectra.* Finally, according to classical ideas, an electron in the molecule might vibrate by itself and so radiate. The emitted radiation would be affected, however, both by the vibrations of the atoms in the molecule and by the rotation of the molecule as a whole. It would probably be one of the outer electrons that radiated in the optical region of the spectrum, and its frequency would be much affected by the instantaneous position and motion of the nuclei. The rotation of the molecule would tend to split up the emitted lines as in the emission of the vibration-rotation spectrum. Molecular bands in the visible and ultraviolet, such as the cyanogen bands described above, are believed to correspond roughly to this third classical picture.

The three types of molecular spectra thus characterized will be taken up in succession for a brief discussion.

139. Rotation Spectra. As a simple model to illustrate certain features of the behavior of actual molecules, we may imagine a molecule to consist of several mass points held rigidly at fixed distances from each other. The quantum states for such a molecule, according to wave mechanics, would be characterized by fixed values for the angular momentum, in the same way as are the states of an atom (Sec. 115). The corresponding quantum number J, however, is confined here to integral values (zero included). The discussion will be restricted hereafter almost entirely to *diatomic molecules.* If there are only two mass points in the molecule, the line joining them is an axis of symmetry, and only rotation about an axis perpendicular to this line has significance; furthermore, the moment of inertia about all such perpendicular axes will have the same value.

The relation between angular momentum and energy is found to be the same according to wave mechanics as in classical theory. For the angular momentum G and energy W, we shall have, therefore, in terms of the angular velocity ω and moment of inertia I,

$$G = I\omega \qquad W = \tfrac{1}{2}I\omega^2 \qquad \therefore W = \frac{G^2}{2I}$$

Inserting here the wave-mechanical value of G^2 (Sec. 115), we have

$$G^2 = \frac{J(J+1)h^2}{4\pi^2}$$

$$W = J(J+1)\frac{h^2}{8\pi^2 I} \tag{189}$$

Such a molecule can radiate by dipole emission only if it possesses an electric moment, which will be the case, for example, if one mass point has associated with it a positive charge and the other an equal negative charge.   The selection rule for J is then found to be the same as that for the quantum number l of a single electron in a central field:

$$\Delta J = \pm 1$$

Since in the present case W and J increase or decrease together, $\Delta J = -1$ will correspond to emission of energy and $\Delta J = +1$ to absorption.   In a transition from state J to state $J - 1$, the emitted frequency will be

$$\nu = \frac{\Delta W}{h} = 2BJ \qquad B = \frac{h}{8\pi^2 I} \qquad (190a,b)$$

since

$$J(J + 1) - (J - 1)(J - 1 + 1) = 2J$$

Thus a molecule of the type under consideration will emit a spectrum consisting of *equally spaced lines, with frequencies equal to a multiple of a fixed number, B.*   For an emission line, J refers to the initial state for the molecular transition; for an absorption line, to the final state.   The corresponding type of energy-level diagram is illustrated in Fig. 104.   The arrows pointing downward refer to transitions for emission, those pointing upward to transitions for absorption.

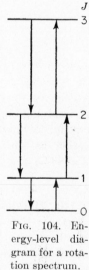

FIG. 104. Energy-level diagram for a rotation spectrum.

We may form some idea of the spectral region in which such lines may be expected to occur by estimating the probable magnitude of I from other considerations. The molecule HCl, for example, might be expected to have an electric moment, since it is strongly ionized in solution.   In the formula $I = \Sigma m r^2$, in which r denotes distance from the center of mass of the molecule, the Cl atom will contribute little because it is so close to the center of mass.   The mass of a hydrogen atom will be approximately the reciprocal of the Avogadro number (Sec. 66).   Hence, if we assume $r = 10^{-8}$ cm for the H atom, we have

$$I = \frac{10^{-16}}{6 \times 10^{23}} = 1.7 \times 10^{-40} \text{ cgs unit}$$

Thus, for the constant B in Eq. (190a), if we also divide by c to obtain it in wave-number units, we find, roughly,

$$B = \frac{6.6 \times 10^{-27}}{8\pi^2 \times 1.7 \times 10^{-40} \times 3 \times 10^{10}} = 17 \text{ cm}^{-1}$$

For $J = 10$, we find $\tilde{\nu} = 2BJ = 340$ cm^{-1}, or $\lambda = 0.029$ mm $= 29$ μ.

Now all the hydrogen halides in the gaseous state show broad absorption lines in the far infrared which are nearly equally spaced and whose wave numbers are nearly multiples of a constant quantity These lines are believed to result from transitions in which the rotational state of the molecule alone changes, almost according to the simple theory just described. Thus for HCl, Czerny[1] found a series of absorption maxima at wavelengths ranging from 120 μ to 44 μ. The corresponding wave numbers are listed as $\bar{\nu}$ in Table 7-8. Under the heading J is given the

TABLE 7-8. ABSORPTION SPECTRUM OF HCl IN THE FAR INFRARED

J	$\bar{\nu}$	$\Delta\bar{\nu}$
4	83.03	
5	. . . . . .	(41.27)
6	124.30	20.73
7	145.03	20.48
8	165.51	20.35
9	185.86	20.52
10	206.38	20.12
11	226.50	

larger of the two values of J assigned to each transition. We note that the spacing of the maxima is almost uniform but shows a slight trend. A decrease in $\Delta\bar{\nu}$ as J increases, and hence also in the apparent value of B, implying an increase in I, is what would be expected if the atoms are not tightly bound together but become slightly pulled apart by centrifugal action as the speed of rotation increases. Substituting in $(190a,b)$ $\nu = 83.03 \times 3 \times 10^{10}$, $J = 4$, $h = 6.625 \times 10^{-27}$, we find

$$I = 2.70 \times 10^{-40} \text{ Gram cm}^2$$

140. Vibration-rotation Spectra. *a. Approximate Theory of a Vibrating Diatomic Molecule.* To obtain a simple model of a diatomic molecule in which atomic vibrations can occur, suppose the atoms are themselves point masses but that, instead of being rigidly bound together, they are held by a force that varies with the distance between them. Let this force correspond to a potential energy V, which, plotted as a function of the distance r between atomic centers, is represented by a curve of the type of that marked V in Fig. 105. The potential has been arbitrarily taken to be zero at $r = \infty$. The force exerted by either atom on the other will be proportional to the slope of this curve; it is represented by the curve marked F in Fig. 105. From the point r_0 at which V has its minimum value outward, the force is attractive; for $r < r_0$, it is repulsive, rising rapidly to high values. Under the influence of such a force, accord-

[1] Czerny, Z. Physik, vol. 34, p. 227, 1925.

ing to classical theory, the atoms could be at rest and in equilibrium at the distance r_0. If disturbed moderately, they would vibrate about this point; if given kinetic energy exceeding $-V_0$, however, where V_0 is the value of V at $r = r_0$, they would fly apart entirely, i.e., dissociation of the molecule would ensue. Such a picture corresponds to the observed properties of molecules, and it is also suggested by wave-mechanical theory.

According to wave mechanics, however, there would be a set of *discrete quantum states* for the positions of the atoms relative to each other, with energies as suggested by the horizontal lines in Fig. 105. The lowest of these quantum states would correspond to an energy a little greater than V_0—it might be said, therefore, that even in their lowest state the atoms have a certain amount of kinetic energy, analogous to the zero-point energy $h\nu/2$ of a harmonic oscillator. Thus the interatomic distance is not quite fixed even when the molecule is in this state, although the most probable value of the interatomic distance will be close to r_0. Let us number the quantum states in the order of increasing energy, denoting the number of a state by $v \geqq 0$. Let the corresponding energy be denoted by W_v. The

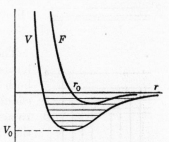

FIG. 105. The mutual potential energy V and force F, measured positively as a repulsion, between two atoms in a diatomic molecule.

values of W_v are all negative, zero energy belonging to a state in which the atoms are at rest at infinity. Thus, $-W_v$ represents the energy of dissociation of the molecule when it is in state number v and not rotating. The total number of the discrete states may be finite or infinite, depending upon the form of the potential curve.

The wave functions and energies for the first few states should resemble those for a harmonic oscillator. For, if we expand V in a Taylor series about $r = r_0$ and note that $dV/dr = 0$ at $r = r_0$, we obtain

$$V = V_0 + \frac{1}{2}\left(\frac{d^2V}{dr^2}\right)_{r=r_0}(r - r_0)^2 + \frac{1}{6}\left(\frac{d^3V}{dr^3}\right)_{r=r_0}(r + r_0)^3 + \cdots$$

and the first two terms of this series represent a potential function of the same type as that for a harmonic oscillator (Sec. 102).[1] The wave functions and energies for the higher states, however, must depart considerably from those for an oscillator, owing to the influence of the remaining terms of the series. Thus the selection rule for the harmonic oscillator,

[1] The wave functions for the first few states should be practically zero for values of $r - r_0$ that are large enough to give appreciable magnitude to terms of the series beyond the first two.

$\Delta v = \pm 1$, cannot be expected to hold, in general, for a diatomic molecule, even $\Delta v = 0$ being possible. The probability of a jump may be expected, however, to fall off rather rapidly as $|\nabla v|$ increases above 1.

To obtain quantum states for the whole molecule, allowance must then be made for rotation of the line joining the atoms. If we suppose that, to a sufficient approximation, the energies of rotation and of vibration are additive, we may write for the total energy, by Eq. (189) above,

$$W = W_v + J(J + 1)Bh \qquad B = \frac{h}{8\pi^2 I} \qquad (191a,b)$$

The various values of W_v are called *vibrational* levels of the molecule; the energies represented by both terms on the right in Eq. (191a) are called *vibration-rotation* levels, or simply *rotational* levels. In actual cases Bh is usually very small relative to the difference between successive values of W_v; hence, the rotational levels belonging to each vibrational level form a closely spaced group. The general arrangement of the rotation-vibration levels is illustrated in Fig. 106, in which, however, the relative spacing of the rotational levels is enormously exaggerated and only a few of these levels are shown.

Because of the relative smallness of B, all lines arising from transitions between two given vibrational levels will lie close together; they are said to constitute a *band*, because with low resolving power they appear as a continuous streak in the spectrum. Bands arising from transitions in which only the vibrational and perhaps rotational energies of the molecule change are called *vibration-rotation* bands.

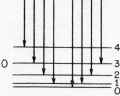

FIG. 106. The energy levels for a rigid diatomic molecule (the relative magnitude of the rotational separations being enormously exaggerated), and a few of the transitions for the first band.

For a molecule composed of two point masses, the selection rule for J is found to be, as for the pure rotation lines,

$$\Delta J = \pm 1$$

For many molecules of more complicated structure, $\Delta J = 0$ is also allowed. A few transitions allowed by the rule $\Delta J = \pm 1$ are indicated in Fig. 106.

From the approximate expression for the energy in Eq. (191), we find, since

$$J(J + 1) - (J - 1)(J - 1 + 1) = 2J$$

for the frequencies emitted in a transition between levels v', $J - 1$ and v'', J, or between v', J and v'', $J - 1$, respectively,

v', $J - 1$; v'', J: $\nu = \nu_{v'v''} - 2BJ$ $J = 1, 2, 3, \ldots$ (192a)

v', J; v'', $J - 1$: $\nu = \nu_{v'v''} + 2BJ$ $J = 1, 2, 3, \ldots$ (192b)

$$\nu_{v'v''} = \frac{W_{v'} - W_{v''}}{h}$$ (192c)

It is assumed here that $v' > v''$ and $W_{v'} > W_{v''}$.[1]

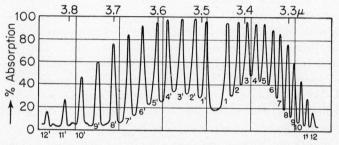

Fig. 107. The principal absorption band of HCl in the near infrared (*after E. S. Imes*) The numbers on the lines give the larger J for the transition, those for which ΔJ is opposite in sign to Δv being primed. (*Reprinted by courtesy of Prentice-Hall, Inc., New York; from G. Herzberg, "Molecular Spectra and Molecular Structure," 1939.*)

According to Eqs. (192a,b), the lines in a given vibration-rotation band emitted by a diatomic molecule should be equally spaced in frequency, with a separation $2B$.   It is clear, however, that the value $\nu = \nu_{v'v''}$ cannot occur, so that there is no line corresponding to pure vibration.   The nearest frequencies to this are $\nu = \nu_{v'v''} + 2B$ and $\nu_{v'v''} - 2B$.   The central line of the band should thus appear to be missing, as is illustrated in Fig. 106.

b. Observed Absorption Bands of Vibration-rotation Type.   Absorption bands answering the foregoing description were observed long ago in the near-infrared regions of the spectra of the hydrogen halides.   The band of HCl at 3.5 μ is shown, as observed by Imes,[2] in Fig. 107, per cent of absorption being plotted against wavelength.   In order to obtain this curve, Imes passed the radiation from a Nernst glower through 15 cm of HCl gas at atmospheric pressure and then through a spectrometer con-

[1] In absorption, therefore, v' refers to the *final* state into which the molecule is raised by the absorption of a quantum.   In considering the spectrum, however, it is simplest to think only of numerical energy differences, without bothering to remember which state is the initial or final one in the radiative process.

[2] Imes, *Astrophys. J.*, vol. 50, p. 251, 1919

taining a prism of rock salt, and measured the transmitted radiation with a thermopile and a galvanometer. The band in question had been observed by Burmeister in 1913 as a continuous band with a double top and was thought to be capable of explanation in terms of classical theory. The molecules were assumed to possess a maxwellian distribution of rotational velocities, so that according to classical theory the effect described in Sec. 137a would be expected to spread the vibrational line out into a broad, continuous band. When later workers observed a succession of *maxima* in the band, it was realized that an explanation could only be found in terms of a discrete set of rotational quantum states.

The anticipated absence of the central line is very evident in Fig. 107. The lines show some approach to equal spacing, but a considerable systematic variation occurs.

c. *Relation between Rotation and Vibration-rotation Bands.* It is obvious that there should exist a relation between the vibration-rotation bands and the pure rotation spectrum of a given substance; indeed, the rotation spectrum is simply a band arising from transitions in which $\Delta v = 0$. If we put $\nu_{v'v''} = 0$ in Eq. (192b), we obtain $\nu = 2BJ$, in agreement with (190a) in the last section. Thus, according to the simplest type of theory, the *separations of the lines should be the same in the rotation and in the vibration-rotation parts* of the spectrum, being equal to $2B$ in both cases. This conclusion is easily tested. According to (192a,b), the separation of the innermost two lines ($J = 1$) in a vibration-rotation band is $4B$. In the HCl band just described, this separation is 41.60 cm^{-1}. Half of this, or 20.8, agrees very well with $\Delta \bar{\nu}$ as shown in Table 7-8.

d. *Bands of Higher Order, and the Heat of Dissociation.* Besides the relation between the two kinds of bands, another theoretical point that can be tested is the prediction that, although transitions for $\Delta v > 1$ are to be expected, the resulting bands should be relatively weak. If the vibrational levels were equally spaced, as for the harmonic oscillator [Eqs. (126a,b) in Sec. 102], the vibrational frequencies of the bands for $\Delta v \geqq 1$ would be proportional to 1, 2, 3, . . . , just as they are for the harmonic overtones of a classical vibrating system. Thus, if we assume that the HCl band at 3.46 μ arises from a transition between the lowest two vibrational levels ($v'' = 0$, $v' = 1$), we should expect to find bands diminishing progressively in intensity at about 1.73, 1.15, 0.865 μ, etc. Actually, by observing the absorption through very thick layers of HCl gas, bands have been observed at 1.76, 1.20, and 0.916 μ, the last mentioned being 10,000 times weaker than the 3.46 band.[1]

The occurrence of these "harmonic" bands with the expected variation

[1] Herzberg and Spinks, *Z. Physik*, vol. 89, p. 474, 1934; Cleaves and Edwards, *Phys. Rev.*, vol. 48, p. 850, 1935.

in strength, and the agreement of the spacing in all bands, including the rotation spectrum, with theoretical expectations, constitute strong evidence that our interpretation of these infrared absorption spectra is essentially correct. A further check is furnished by a connection with the *heat of dissociation* of the molecule. The heat of dissociation represents the energy that must be added to a molecule in its lowest quantum state in order to separate the atoms and leave them at rest an infinite distance apart. Obviously, the energy of the molecule in any possible quantum state must be less than the energy of the separated atoms, else the molecule would dissociate spontaneously. Hence, the quantity $h\nu$ for any molecular line, representing the difference in energy between two molecular states, must be less than the heat of dissociation. For the HCl band at $\lambda = 0.916\ \mu$,

$$h\nu = 6.6 \times 10^{-27} \times \frac{3 \times 10^{10}}{0.906 \times 10^{-4}} = 2.2 \times 10^{-12}\ \text{erg}$$

In the "International Critical Tables," the heat of dissociation of a gram-molecule of HCl, for dissociation into H_2 and Cl_2, is given as 92 kilojoules, whereas the heats of combination of a gram-atom of H or Cl into H_2 or Cl_2 are, respectively, 211 and 120.3 kilojoules. Hence to dissociate one molecule of HCl into H and Cl requires

$$(92 + 211 + 120.3) \times \frac{10^{10}}{6.02 \times 10^{23}} = 7.0 \times 10^{-12}\ \text{erg}$$

This is more than three times the value of $h\nu$ as just calculated for the highest-frequency vibration band of HCl that has been observed, so that the theoretical expectation is confirmed.

e. Effect of Thermal Agitation upon Infrared Bands. No absorption bands are observed for which $v'' > 0$ in the spectrum of HCl. This is explained as a consequence of the wide spacing of the vibrational levels relative to the quantity kT. Molecules are seldom thrown by thermal agitation into a vibrational level which can serve as the initial level for an absorption band with $v'' > 0$. Even for $\lambda = 3.5\ \mu$, we find $h\nu = 5.7 \times 10^{-13}$ erg; whereas, at $T = 288°\text{K}\ (15°\text{C})$,

$$kT = 288 \times 1.38 \times 10^{-16} = 4 \times 10^{-14}\ \text{erg}$$

If W_0, W_1 are the energies of the two states involved in the production of $\lambda = 3.5\ \mu$, the ratio of the number of atoms in the upper of these two states to that in the lower will be the ratio of their Boltzmann factors or, according to Eq. (94) in Sec. 88,

$$\frac{n_1}{n_0} = e^{-(W_1 - W_0)/kT} = e^{-h\nu/kT} = e^{-57/4} = 10^{-6.2}$$

This is so small that practically all molecules of HCl will be in their lowest vibrational states ($v = 0$) at ordinary temperatures. Hence only the absorption band for which $v'' = 0$ can be observed; and the observed rotation spectrum is the $0 - 0$ vibration-rotation band ($v = 0$ to $v = 0$).

Among the various *rotational* levels, on the other hand, a wide distribution of the molecules occurs even at room temperature. The experimental value of B, $20.6/2$ cm^{-1}, makes Bhc equal to

$$6.6 \times 10^{-27} \times 3 \times 10^{10} \times \frac{20.6}{2} = 2.0 \times 10^{-15} \text{ erg}$$

Thus, for these states, if the energy of the lowest is taken as zero,

$$W = J(J + 1) \times 2 \times 10^{-15} \text{ erg}$$

which is much smaller than kT. For $J = 10$, we find

$$e^{-W/kT} = e^{-5.5} = 0.0041$$

Furthermore, there are $(2J + 1)$ fundamental states for each J (with $M = -J, \ldots, J$), so that even states with J as large as 10 will occur $(2 \times 10 + 1) \times 0.0041$ or 0.086 times as often as states with $J = 0$. This result agrees nicely with the number of lines that are actually observed in the HCl band at $3.5\ \mu$.

In some other substances, such as I_2, an appreciable fraction of the molecules are normally in higher vibrational states, and other bands can occur in absorption or in the rotation spectrum.

f. Infrared Bands of Other Types of Molecules. Vibration-rotation spectra are known for many other molecules. Their structure is often more complex than that described above; in many cases transitions for $\Delta J = 0$ are permitted, so that an additional sequence of lines occurs and there is no gap in the center of the band. Thus the absorption spectrum of CO_2 shows many vibration-rotation bands in the region from $1.46\ \mu$ to $15.50\ \mu$, and that of water vapor shows many from 0.69 to $6.26\ \mu$;[*] these bands, together with the rotation lines of water vapor, are responsible for the marked infrared absorption of the earth's atmosphere.

In order to exhibit vibration-rotation and rotation spectra of appreciable intensity, a molecule must possess an electric moment. *Homonuclear* diatomic molecules, such as O_2, N_2, H_2, Cl_2, possess no moments and, hence, have no spectra of these two types. Gases composed of such molecules are entirely transparent in the infrared.

141. General Theory of Molecular Quantum States. Up to this point, the *electrons* in the molecule have been ignored. Actually, the wave function for a molecule must contain the coordinates and spins of all the electrons as well as the coordinates of the nuclei. When atoms unite into

---

[*] Weizel, *op. cit.*

a molecule, the inner electrons in each atom can be regarded as remaining associated, more or less, with the nucleus of that atom; but the outer electrons come to belong to the molecule as a whole rather than to any individual nucleus.

a. Approximate Separation of Electronic and Nuclear Motions. In many cases, especially for the diatomic molecules, the wave function can be separated approximately into two factors, of which one has reference to the electrons whereas the second factor represents vibrations of the nuclei and rotation of the molecule as a whole. The first factor then represents the electrons as being in a certain *electronic quantum state.* Both the energy and the wave function of the electronic state will depend upon the relative positions of the nuclei; in this respect the situation in a molecule is quite different from that in an atom. The mutual electrostatic energy of the nuclei is commonly included in the energy of the electronic state. The electronic energy as so defined possesses a minimum value for certain relative positions of the nuclei; if they move closer together, or move farther apart, the electronic energy rises, and hence, so does the energy of the molecule. Thus the energy of the electronic state functions as a potential energy tending to hold the atoms together in definite relative positions of equilibrium. It is in this way that a potential energy such as was sketched in Fig. 105 comes to exist in a diatomic molecule.

In this same approximation, the energy W of the molecule can be written as the sum of two parts, a negative part W_e, representing roughly the average of the electronic energy but including also the electrostatic energy due to the mutual repulsion of the nuclei, and a much smaller positive part W_{rv}, which is associated with vibration of the atoms relative to each other and with rotation of the molecule as a whole. Thus $W = W_e + W_{rv}$. For a diatomic molecule, the energy W_{rv} is what was denoted by W in Sec. 140, as in Eq. (191).

For a detailed discussion of electronic states we must refer the student to other books, but something may be said here by way of explanation of the notation that the student will meet. Only *diatomic* molecules will be discussed.

b. ΛS Coupling. As in the theory of atomic states, electronic spin may be treated in different ways according to circumstances. If the *electronic spin-orbit effects are small*, an analog of LS coupling occurs. It is possible, as a first approximation, to assign a fixed value to the component of the orbital angular momentum of the electrons about the nuclear line, or line joining the two nuclei, which is an axis of symmetry. The magnitude of this momentum is denoted by $\Lambda h/2\pi$, where Λ is a positive integer or zero; the molecular quantum number Λ corresponds to L or M_L in atomic theory. In a diatomic molecule a unique choice of axis is supplied by the nuclear line. The *total* orbital momentum of the electrons cannot have a fixed value in a molecule, however, hence there can be no quantum number L. Spectroscopically, Λ plays a role analogous to L, since states corresponding to different values of Λ have different energies; hence, in imitation of the atomic notation for LS coupling, states with $\Lambda = 0, 1, 2, 3, \ldots$ are indicated by the letters Σ, Π, Δ, Φ, $\ldots$, respectively.

The electronic spins are then coupled with the introduction of a quantum number S. The value of $2S + 1$ is written as a superscript. Thus, we obtain a set of ΛS electronic states represented by such symbols as

$$^1\Sigma, \ ^3\Sigma, \ ^1\Pi, \ ^3\Pi, \ \ldots \qquad ^2\Sigma, \ ^4\Sigma, \ ^2\Pi, \ ^4\Pi, \ \ldots$$

As with atoms, an important significance of the quantum numbers lies in the associated selection rules. There is a strong tendency for transitions to be limited to those for which

$$\Delta\Lambda = 0 \text{ or } \pm 1 \qquad \Delta S = 0$$

Instead of introducing next the electronic spin-orbit effects, however, we now turn to the consideration of the *nuclear* motions, the effect of which upon the energy we are assuming to be much larger than the electronic spin-orbit effects. Each electronic state of the molecule may be combined with any one of the vibrational states for the nuclei, which may be numbered off as before with a quantum number $v = 0, 1, 2, \ldots$. The orbital angular momentum of the electrons is then added vectorially to the angular momentum of rotation of the nuclei about axes perpendicular to the nuclear line. This results in the introduction of a rotational quantum number K, which may have any integral value such that

$$K \geqq \Lambda$$

It is not possible for K to be less than Λ because in a diatomic molecule the two angular momenta are necessarily perpendicular to each other. The general selection rule for K is that

$$\Delta K = 0 \text{ or } \pm 1$$

We obtain in this way a set of *electronic-vibration-rotation states* for the molecule, numbered with quantum numbers $\Lambda \ S \ v \ K$.

The *electronic spin-orbit effect* must then be considered. In preparation for its introduction, we add the total orbital angular momentum of electrons and nuclei, represented by K, to the total angular momentum due to electronic spin, represented by S, thus obtaining a grand resultant angular momentum, for which we will introduce the usual quantum numbers J and M. The possible values of J are integrally spaced from $K + S$ down to $|K - S|$. The effect of the electronic spin-orbit interaction is then, as in atomic LS coupling, to separate states having different values of J. Thus a *fine structure*, analogous to the LS multiplet structure, is introduced into the electronic-vibration-rotation levels. The superscript in such a symbol as $^3\Pi$ refers to the (normal) number of J levels in this fine structure.

In singlet levels, with $S = 0$, there is no fine structure, just as in atoms. For such levels, $J = K$, and the quantum number K need not be used. The HCl molecule, for example, is normally in a $^1\Sigma$ electronic state; hence, the discussion of the vibrational and rotational states of this molecule as given above was adequate.

c. Ω Coupling. When the electronic spin-orbit effects are not smaller than the effects of molecular rotation, other modes of approach by means of perturbation theory become appropriate. We shall mention only one of them, briefly. If the *spin-orbit* effect is actually *large*, we have the analog of *jj* coupling in atoms. In this case, the electronic orbital and spin momenta about the nuclear line are first added together, their magnitude being represented by a quantum number Ω. The values of Ω are integral or half-integral according as the number of electrons in the molecule is even or odd. Each electronic state, characterized by a value of Ω, is then combined with a vibrational state represented by quantum numbers v and J. Thus in this form of coupling, as when $S = 0$, the rotational levels correspond to the value of J.

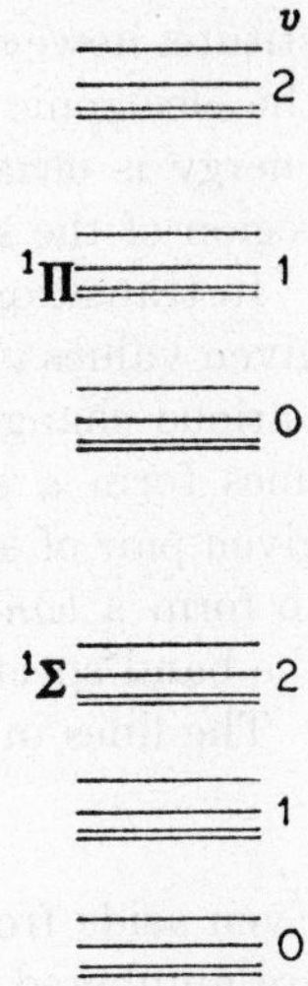

d. The *energy of a molecular state* thus depends in the case of ΛS coupling upon five quantum numbers, $\Lambda S v K J$, or in the case of Ω coupling upon three, $\Omega v J$. Its variation with the various numbers presents, however, several different orders of magnitude. The variation with K or J is comparatively small. Spectral lines that differ only in the K values for the initial and final states lie close together and form a band, similar to the vibration-rotation bands that have been described. In such cases, if $J \neq K$, the energy varies still less with J, the effect of this variation being only to introduce a fine structure into the lines of the band. In the case of Ω coupling,

Fig. 108. Diagram illustrating general arrangement of molecular levels. To make the scale correct, the rotational levels (numbered by $K = J$) should be drawn much closer together, and the $^1\Pi$ and $^1\Sigma$ groups should lie much farther apart.

on the other hand, the lines of a band arise from differences in the values of J. The energy varies much more rapidly with v than it does with K or J. Each pair of values of v, one for the initial and one for the final state, gives rise to a possible band. The electronic states, finally, characterized by various values of Λ and S, or of Ω, are separated in energy by differences of the order of those between atomic LS terms.

These general features of the array of molecular levels are illustrated for a simple case in Fig. 108.

142. Electronic Bands. The most general type of transition between molecular states is one in which changes occur in the electronic state of the molecule as well as in its nuclear vibration-rotation state. The spectra hitherto discussed, of rotational or vibrational type, represent special cases in which the electronic state does not change. Such spectra constitute, however, only a small fraction of all known band spectra. When the electronic state does change in a transition, the resulting change in energy is usually so large that the band lies in the visible or ultraviolet region of the spectrum. Such bands may be called *electronic* bands.

In transitions characterized by a given pair of electronic states and by given values v' and v'' of v, representing a fixed pair of vibrational states, various changes of J (and of K, if $K \neq J$) may occur. The resulting lines form a single *band*. All the bands due to transitions between a given pair of electronic states, for all possible values of v' and v'', are said to form a *band system*. Because various electronic jumps are possible, the band spectrum of any molecule consists of many band systems.

The lines in a given electronic band are limited by the selection rules

$$\Delta K = 0 \text{ or } \pm 1 \qquad \Delta J = 0 \text{ or } \pm 1$$

Even aside from the fine structure that exists when the rotational levels are numbered by a quantum number K which is different from J, electronic bands are commonly more complicated than the simple type of vibration-rotation band described above because transitions for $\Delta K = 0$ (or $\Delta J = 0$) are allowed. Lines for which ΔK (or ΔJ if there is no fine structure) has the opposite sign to Δv are said to constitute the P *branch* of the band; those for $\Delta K = 0$ (or $\Delta J = 0$) constitute the Q *branch;* those for which ΔK (or ΔJ) is in the same direction as Δv form the R *branch*. The Q branch is frequently missing, however, for special reasons, e.g., in all bands arising from a $\Sigma \rightarrow \Sigma$ electronic transition. When $K \neq J$, what is regarded as a single band sometimes contains more than one branch of each type.

A good approximate expression for the energies of the molecular levels is often obtained if we employ for the vibration-rotation part an expression like that in Eq. (191a) but allow B to vary with v. We have then for the molecular energy, in cm^{-1},

$$\tilde{W} = \tilde{W}_e + \tilde{W}_v + B_v K(K + 1) \cdots \tag{193}$$

where B_v is positive. Thus, for the levels belonging to two different electronic states, we may write

$$\tilde{W}' = \tilde{W}'_e + \tilde{W}'_{v'} + B'_v K(K + 1)$$
$$\tilde{W}'' = \tilde{W}''_e + \tilde{W}'''_{v''} + B''_{v''} K(K + 1)$$

and we then find for the three branches of the band:

$$P: v',K - 1; v'',K: \qquad \tilde{\nu} = \tilde{\nu}_e + \tilde{\nu}_{v'v''} - (B'_{v'} + B''_{v''})K$$
$$+ (B'_{v'} - B''_{v''})K^2 \qquad (194a)$$
$$Q: v',K; v'',K: \qquad \tilde{\nu} = \tilde{\nu}_e + \tilde{\nu}_{v'v''} + (B'_{v'} - B''_{v''})K(K + 1) \qquad (194b)$$
$$R: v',K; v'',K - 1: \qquad \tilde{\nu} = \tilde{\nu}_e + \tilde{\nu}_{v'v''} + (B'_{v'} + B''_{v''})K$$
$$+ (B'_{v'} - B''_{v''})K^2 \qquad (194c)$$

Here K refers in each case to the larger of the two values of K concerned in the transition. If the quantum number K does not exist for the levels in question, K is to be replaced by J in all equations from (193) to (194c). The symbol $\tilde{\nu}_e = (\bar{W}'_e - \bar{W}''_e)/h$ and represents the frequency that would arise from the electronic transition alone; whereas $\tilde{\nu}_{v'v''} = (\bar{W}'_{v'} - \bar{W}''_{v''})/h$, and it is assumed that $v' \geqq v''$.

Since the quantities $B'_{v'}$ and $B''_{v''}$ in Eqs. (194a,b,c) refer to different electronic states, they may be expected to differ considerably. We may suppose the forces between the atoms to be quite different in the two cases; hence, their positions of equilibrium and the values of the moment of inertia of the molecule are also different. This is in contrast to the case of the vibration-rotation bands, where B_v varies only a little from one level to another. The quadratic terms in (194a,b,c), therefore, will soon make themselves felt. As K increases, the trend of $\tilde{\nu}$ in one branch will soon be reversed, in the P branch if $B'_{v'} > B''_{v''}$, in the R branch if $B'_{v'} < B''_{v''}$. It is thus a general characteristic of electronic bands that one branch is folded back on itself and on top of the others. At the point in the spectrum where a branch turns back, the lines are crowded together, forming a *band head*. The band appears to shade away from the head; some bands are shaded in this way toward the red, some toward the violet. When a Q branch is present, it may form a second head, although such behavior is not obviously predicted by Eq. (194b).

A band of this type is often represented graphically by means of a Fortrat diagram, on which each line is represented by a point or circle, the ordinate representing K (or J) and the abscissa, $\tilde{\nu}$. Such a diagram is shown in Fig. 109 for the CuH band λ 4,280 A, which has no Q branch; a spectrogram of this band due to Professor R. Mecke is shown in Fig. 110. The band is shaded toward the red from a head which is plainly shown in the spectrogram. The electronic transition is $^1\Sigma \rightarrow {}^1\Sigma$.

The *number of different bands in a band system*, all arising from the same electronic transition but with various values of v' and v'', may be very large. The change in v, $v' - v''$, however, although not confined to ± 1 as for a harmonic oscillator, tends to be restricted to moderate values. A spectrogram showing parts of three such band systems is reproduced in Fig. 111. Extremely low dispersion was used in order to include a wide spectral range; hence each *band* appears as a single *line* in the figure;

the groups that seem to the eye to stand out are groups of bands having in each case the same value of the difference $v' - v''$. The values of v', v'' (e.g., 6 − 3) are shown for a few bands. The Swan bands of C_2 result from a $^3\Pi \rightarrow {}^3\Pi$ electronic transition; the violet CN bands, from $^2\Sigma \rightarrow {}^2\Sigma$; the red CN bands, from a $^2\Pi \rightarrow {}^2\Sigma$ transition.

The band spectra of molecules containing *different isotopes* of the same element are slightly different, because of the difference in nuclear mass. Extra lines due to this cause in band spectra as observed have sometimes led to the discovery of rare isotopes, such as the oxygen isotope of atomic weight 18, present in only about 1/500th as great concentration as O^{16}.[1]

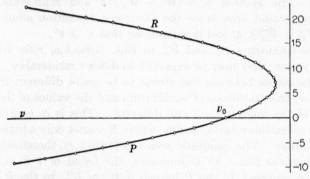

FIG. 109. Fortrat diagram for the CuH band λ 4,280 A. The lines are represented by circles, the ordinate representing the larger J value for the transition. $\nu_0 = \nu_{v'v''}$.

143. The Raman Effect. At this point a slight digression may conveniently be made to describe the Raman effect, which can occur in atomic spectra but is of greatest interest in relation to band spectra.

When light passes through a "transparent" substance, solid, liquid, or gaseous, a certain part of the light is scattered in all directions (the Tyndall effect). The most familiar example is the light from a clear sky. Rayleigh ascribed such effects to scattering by the individual molecules, or by groups of molecules much smaller in linear dimension than the wavelength of the light. If the incident light is monochromatic, the scattered light is ordinarily observed to be unchanged in frequency, in accordance with Rayleigh's theory.

It was shown in 1925 by Kramers and Heisenberg,[2] however, that, according to classical electromagnetic theory, if the scattering electrons in an atom or molecule are in motion, the scattered light should contain other frequencies in addition to that of the incident light. Failure to notice this implication of classical theory had been due to the common

[1] Giauque and Johnston, *Nature*, vol. 123, p. 318, 1929; Mecke and Childs, *Z. Physik*, vol. 68, p. 362, 1931.

[2] Kramers and Heisenberg, *Z. Physik*, vol. 31, p. 681, 1925.

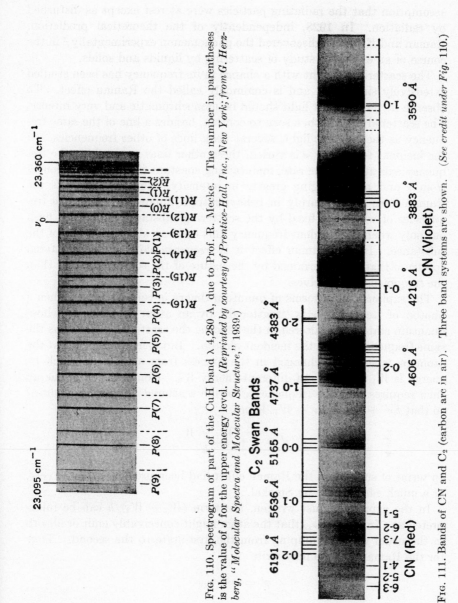

23,360 cm⁻¹

ν_0

23,095 cm⁻¹

R(2)
R(1)
R(0)
R(12)
R(13) P(1)
R(14) P(2)
R(15) P(3)
R(16) P(4)
P(5)
P(6)
P(7)
P(8)
P(9)

FIG. 110. Spectrogram of part of the CuH band λ 4,280 A, due to Prof. R. Mecke. The number in parentheses is the value of J for the upper energy level. (Reprinted by courtesy of Prentice-Hall, Inc., New York; from G. Herzberg, "Molecular Spectra and Molecular Structure," 1939.)

C₂ Swan Bands

6191 Å 5636 Å 5165 Å 4737 Å 4383 Å
2·0 1·0 0·0 1·0 2·0

0·1
0·2

CN (Red)
5·1
6·2
7·3
4·1
5·2
6·3

CN (Violet)

4606 Å 4216 Å 3883 Å 3590 Å
0·2 0·1 0·0 1·0

FIG. 111. Bands of CN and C₂ (carbon arc in air). Three band systems are shown. (See credit under Fig. 110.)

331

assumption that the radiating particles were at rest except as disturbed by radiation. In 1928, independently of the theoretical prediction, Raman and Krishnan discovered the phenomenon experimentally,[1] in the course of an extensive study of scattering by liquids and solids.

The scattering of light with a change in its frequency has been studied extensively since then and is commonly called the Raman effect. To observe it, the incident light should be monochromatic and very intense. The scattered light is then seen to contain, besides a line of the same frequency as the incident light, several weak lines of other frequencies. If the incident frequency ν is varied, these other lines move along the frequency axis at the same rate, maintaining constant frequency differences from ν and not changing greatly in intensity. In these respects the Raman lines differ sharply in behavior from fluorescent lines, the frequencies of which are fixed by the scattering substance and which flash out only when the incident frequency falls upon an absorption line of the substance. In the Raman effect it is *frequency shifts* in the scattered spectrum that are determined by the nature of the scatterer rather than the frequencies themselves.

The explanation in terms of quantum theory is very simple. When a photon of frequency ν is "scattered" by an atom or molecule whose quantum state is not altered in the process, the scattered photon has the same frequency as had the incident photon. But it may happen that the atom or molecule is changed in the process from a state in which its energy is W_1 to a state of different energy W_2. Conservation of energy then requires that the frequency ν' of the scattered photon be modified so that $h\nu' + W_2 = h\nu + W_1$; hence,

$$\nu' = \nu + \frac{W_1 - W_2}{h}$$

In terms of such ideas the Raman effect had been predicted, tentatively, at a much earlier date by Smekal.

In the expression just written, the term $(W_1 - W_2)/h$ can be interpreted as a frequency ν_{12} that the atom might conceivably emit or absorb in the usual way, in jumping from the first state to the second. Thus for the Raman line we may write

$$\nu' = \nu + \nu_{12}$$

The difference between the frequency of each Raman line and the frequency of the incident light is thus equal to the frequency of some conceivable emission or absorption line of the scattering atom or molecule.

[1] Raman and Krishnan, *Nature*, vol. 121, p. 501, 1928; Raman, *Indian J. Phys.*, vol. 2, p. 387, 1928.

The *intensity* of a Raman line has nothing to do, however, with the intensity of the emission or absorption line that is thus correlated with it. The selection rules for the two are quite different; transitions that are forbidden in ordinary spectra may occur freely in the Raman effect. This is one reason for its great theoretical interest. According to wave mechanics, *a Raman jump is possible between two atomic or molecular levels A and B only when there exists at least one third level, C, such that ordinary radiative transitions are allowed between A and C and between B and C.* It is almost as if the atom or molecule actually jumped first from A to C and then from C to B. The relative probabilities of the various processes do not correspond to this simple picture, however, nor can it be said that the atom or molecule exists for any definite time in state C, as it does in the production of fluorescence.

In light scattered by *polyatomic molecules*, for example, there may be Raman lines correlated in this manner with energetically possible lines in either the rotational or the vibration-rotational or the electronic spectra of the molecule. It does not matter whether these spectra can actually be observed or are prevented from direct occurrence by a selection rule.

In the common type of rotation spectrum, the selection rule is $\Delta J = \pm 1$ (Sec. 139). For the Raman lines associated with this spectrum, therefore, the selection rule will be either $\Delta J = 0$ (that is, $J \to J \pm 1$ for a jump from A to C and $J \pm 1 \to J$, from B to C) or $\Delta J = \pm 2$ (for example, $J \to J + 1$ and $J + 1 \to J + 2$). The case $\Delta J = 0$, however, involves no change in the molecular energy and hence merely contributes to the ordinary, or Rayleigh, scattering. Thus, effectively, for Raman lines of purely rotational origin, we must have

$$\Delta J = \pm 2$$

The incident line, as seen in the spectrum of the scattered light, should thus be accompanied on each side by several lines spaced twice as far apart on the frequency scale as are the lines of the rotational spectrum itself. From Eq. (189) it is seen that the displacements of the Raman lines from the incident line will be proportional to $J(J + 1) - (J - 2)(J - 1)$, or to $2(2J - 1)$, J referring to the upper rotational level. Hence, since $J \geqq 2$, the displacements are proportional to 6, 10, 14, . . . ; thus the distance from the unmodified line to the first Raman line is 1.5 times the mutual spacing of the Raman lines themselves. The origin of the lines is illustrated diagrammatically in Fig. 112.

Besides these *rotational* Raman lines, there may also appear, at a much greater distance and usually only on the long-wave side, a band corresponding to the ordinary *vibration-rotation* spectrum. For this band the selection rule is easily seen to be

$$\Delta J = 0 \text{ or } \pm 2$$

Lines for which $\Delta J = 0$, involving almost no change in rotational energy, coalesce into an intense line in the approximate position of the missing central line of frequency $\nu_{v'v''}$ or ν_{10} in the vibration-rotation band. With low resolving power, only this line may be seen. On each side of this line, however, there are much fainter lines for $\Delta J = \pm 2$. In this band the vibrational change is from $v = 0$ to $v = 1$, as for absorption. In case the vibrational level for $v = 1$ lies so low that a considerable fraction of the molecules are maintained in this state by thermal agitation, a similar weaker Raman band should be observed on the short-wave side of the exciting line as well, associated with the transition from $v = 1$ to $v = 0$.

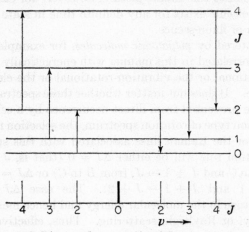

FIG. 112. Diagram for a rotational Raman spectrum.

Many Raman spectra have been observed. They constitute a valuable source of information concerning molecular quantum states. In an early observation, the light scattered by HCl gas when strongly illuminated by light from a mercury arc in glass was studied by Wood and Dieke.[1] They found a line at 4,581.8 A which they interpreted as the single intense line in a vibration-rotation Raman spectrum excited by the Hg line at 4,047 A. The frequency difference between these two lines is 2,886.0 cm^{-1}, which is in excellent agreement with the frequency of the missing central line in the 3.5-μ band from HCl, viz., 2,885.4 cm^{-1} (Sec. 140). Much closer to the exciting line and on both sides of it there were also a number of lines which they interpreted as a rotational Raman spectrum. In the corresponding spectrum adjacent to the mercury line at 4,358 A, the measured spacings between the lines lay mostly between 41 and 42 cm^{-1}, in good agreement with double the spacing in the ordinary rotation spectrum of HCl, as shown in Table 7-8.

[1] Wood and Dieke, *Phys. Rev.*, vol. 35, p. 1355, 1930.

A more complete Raman spectrum for HCl, photographed by Andry-chuk, is shown in Herzberg's book[1] and is diagramed on a wavelength scale in Fig. 113, with little suggestion of relative intensities. The exciting line was the Hg line at 2,536.5 A.

Even homonuclear molecules such as O_2 and N_2 give Raman spectra corresponding to vibration-rotation and rotational spectra, although the latter cannot be observed directly. Such molecules deserve special discussion.

144. Homonuclear Molecules. Molecules that contain at least two *similar* nuclei have certain peculiar and sometimes astonishing properties. Thus, it was early observed that in certain bands from such molecules alternate lines were weaker or perhaps missing entirely. After the advent

2536.5A   2737A
Exciting Line   Vibration Band

FIG. 113. Diagram of a Raman spectrum from HCl (as observed by Andrychuk).

of wave mechanics, it was shown by Hund that this phenomenon could be explained as an effect of nuclear spin.[2] The effect is essentially statistical in nature, and in discussing it no account need be taken of the nuclear magnetic moments or of other minor forms of nuclear interaction, which serve only to produce, as in atomic spectra, a minute hyperfine structure. Diatomic molecules only will be considered here.

a. Ortho and Para States. The wave function ψ for a molecule must contain as variables the coordinates of the nuclei and, in general, an allowance for nuclear spin. The spin numbers I and M_I were described in Sec. 135. All the known facts are consistent with the assumption that ψ is always *symmetric* in the coordinates and spins of any two similar nuclei for which I is *integral or zero* (the Bose-Einstein type), whereas if I is *half-integral* (Fermi-Dirac type) the wave function is *antisymmetric*. That is, interchange of the spatial coordinates and of the values of M_I for any two similar nuclei leaves ψ unchanged if I is integral or zero, but reverses the sign of ψ, as in the case of electrons, if I is half-integral.

As with electrons, so long as spin energies can be ignored, *spatial* symmetry and *spin* symmetry can be treated separately. States for a pair of similar nuclei that are *symmetric* in the nuclear spins have been called *ortho* states, those antisymmetric in the spins, *para* states. ("Ortho" means right or proper, i.e. ordinary; "para," alongside of, i.e. a variant, the less common variety.) Since M_I has $(2I + 1)$ possible different

[1] G. Herzberg, "Spectra of Diatomic Molecules," p. 62, 1950.
[2] F. Hund, Z. *Physik*, vol. 42, p. 93, 1927.

values, there are, for two similar nuclei, $(2I + 1)^2$ possible spin states in all. Of these, the states in which M_I has the same value for both nuclei are symmetric in the nuclear spins; there are $(2I + 1)$ such states. Then, each combination of two different values of M_I yields both a symmetric and an antisymmetric state, in analogy with the $\alpha\beta$ combination for two electrons as described in Sec. 107. There are $(2I + 1)I$ such possible combinations. The number N_p of antisymmetric or para states will thus have the value $(2I + 1)I$, whereas the total number of symmetric or ortho states is $N_o = (2I + 1)I + (2I + 1) = (2I + 1)(I + 1)$. Thus we have the statistical ratio

$$\frac{N_p}{N_o} = \frac{I}{I + 1} \tag{195}$$

The ortho states have always the greater statistical weight; if $I = 0$, the para states are missing altogether.

The *spatial* symmetry of ψ relative to nuclear exchange, i.e., for exchange of only the spatial coordinates of the particles, must then be considered. Sometimes this is referred to simply as the "symmetry" of ψ. A wave function will have the required grand symmetry when I is *integral* provided the spin factor by itself is symmetric and the spatial factor is also symmetric, i.e., remains unaltered when the coordinates of the nuclei are interchanged; or, both factors may be antisymmetric. Thus, for integral or zero I, the ortho states have spatially symmetric wave functions, whereas the para states have spatially antisymmetric functions. Conversely, for *half-integral* I, the ortho states are those with spatially antisymmetric wave functions, while the para states are symmetrical in the spatial coordinates.

No general rules can be given for predicting with certainty the spatial symmetry of ψ. Usually a good approximate form for ψ, with nuclear spin omitted, is

$$\psi = \psi_e \psi_v \psi_J$$

where ψ_e, ψ_v, and ψ_J stand for electronic, vibrational, and rotational factors corresponding to the division of the molecular energy into three parts as described in Secs. 140 and 141. The vibrational factor ψ_v is always symmetric for nuclear exchange, essentially because a vibration of similar nuclei looks the same seen from either end. The rotational factor ψ_J is even for even values of J and odd for odd J. But ψ_e, although often symmetric in states with $\Lambda = 0$, may be either symmetric or antisymmetric for nuclear exchange. Thus the ortho states are the even-J rotational states in some cases but the odd-J states in others.

An important *selection rule* exists in this connection, paralleling that for the different S states of atoms. If the nuclei had no spin-dependent form of interaction in addition to their Coulomb fields, the ortho and para states would never combine at all; a molecule in one type of state would remain in states of that type forever. If $I = 0$, the molecules do remain permanently in ortho states. If $I > 0$, however, conversion from ortho to para or vice versa can take place, as a result of slight non-Coulomb nuclear forces, but this process is very slow, requiring perhaps months or years.

  b. *Effects on Band Spectra.* The selection rule just stated effectively limits spectral transitions to those between two ortho states or between two para states. Since a certain type of spatial symmetry accompanies each type of spin state, dependent upon the parity of I, it follows also that the *spatial* symmetry of ψ for nuclear exchange cannot change in a radiative transition. These restrictions result in two major peculiarities in the bands from homonuclear diatomic molecules.

  In the first place, since in a purely rotational or vibration-rotational transition the electronic state of the molecule does not change, to preserve the symmetry of ψ the spatial symmetry (for exchange) of the rotational factor ψ_J cannot change. Thus transitions of this kind can occur only between two even values of J or between two odd values. But for such bands there is also a spectral selection rule that $\Delta J = \pm 1$. It follows that, so far as dipole radiation is concerned, *homonuclear diatomic molecules cannot have any purely rotational or vibration-rotational spectra at all!* As was noted at the end of Sec. 140, the absence of such spectra may also be regarded as due to the absence of a molecular electric moment in such molecules. In Raman spectra, on the other hand, frequency shifts corresponding to such transitions may occur, since for Raman lines the usual selection rule is that $\Delta J = \pm 2$.

  The second major consequence of exchange symmetry concerns the *relative intensity* of the lines composing a given band. Ordinarily, some of the molecules will be in ortho states while others are in para states, and in one of these states transitions will occur only between even values of J while in the other they occur only between odd values. The relative intensity of the even-J and odd-J lines will thus depend upon the relative population of the ortho and para states. If a substance has been for a long time at a given temperature, it may be assumed that all *fundamental* states will be populated in proportion to a Boltzmann factor $e^{-\epsilon_i/kT}$ [cf. Eq. (94)]. Thus the intensity of a spectral line as observed will be proportional to (1) the Boltzmann factor for the initial state, (2) the transition probability, and (3) the nuclear statistical weight of the initial state, which is proportional, for successive values of J, alternately to I or to $I + 1$. Since the factors (1) and (2) do not usually vary rapidly from line to line, the observed lines will appear to alternate in intensity. If quantitative allowance can be made from theory for the first two factors, the magnitude of I for the nucleus can be inferred with certainty from measurements of the relative intensities of the lines. Furthermore, if $I = 0$, there are no para states and no para lines at all, so that either the even-J or the odd-J lines are missing altogether.

Many examples of these phenomena are known, and they all agree with the theoretical predictions provided the right value of I is assumed. Such observations are regarded as a reliable source of information concerning I. Thus, O_2 has no rotation or vibration-rotation bands, and in its Raman spectra the even-J lines are missing. It is concluded that $I = 0$ for the O nucleus.

Perhaps the most famous case is that of N_2. A photograph showing alternating intensities in a Raman spectrum from nitrogen is shown in Fig. 114. The spectrum is a rotational one excited by the mercury line at 2,536.5 A, photographed by F. Rasetti.[1] Careful measurements had also been made much earlier by Ornstein and van Wijk on four electronic bands of nitrogen (at 3,984, 4,278, 3,884, 4,237 A).[2] After correcting for the Boltzmann factor and the transition probabilities, they found a ratio of statistical weights for even-J states to odd-J states very close to $\frac{1}{2}$. Equating $\frac{1}{2}$ to $I/(I + 1)$, we find $I = 1$ for the nitrogen nucleus.

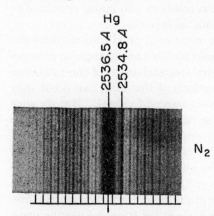

FIG. 114. Alternating intensities in a rotational Raman spectrum of N_2. (*From "Molecular Spectra and Molecular Structure," vol. I—"Spectra of Diatomic Molecules," G. Herzberg, 2d ed., D. Van Nostrand Co., 1950.*)

These observations were published in 1928, and at that time a value $I = 1$ for nitrogen was "extraordinarily surprising."[3] It was supposed then that the nitrogen nucleus must consist of 14 protons and 7 electrons and that an odd number of fundamental particles should require a half-integral value of I. The difficulty was resolved after the discovery of the neutron had led to the view that the nitrogen nucleus is composed of 7 protons and 7 neutrons.

c. *Effects on Other Physical Properties.* The different statistical weights of the ortho and para states must be taken account of in dealing with any physical property, such as specific heat, that depends upon the distribution of the molecules among their quantum states. The question may also be raised as to the possibility of a mass separation of molecules in the two states.

[1] F. Rasetti, *Z. Physik*, vol. 61, p. 598, 1930.

[2] L. S. Ornstein and W. R. van Wijk, *Z. Physik*, vol. 49, p. 315, 1928.

[3] W. Heitler and G. Herzberg, *Naturwiss.*, vol. 17, p. 673, 1929.

These features have been studied extensively only in the famous case of hydrogen.[1] This gas is a mixture of orthohydrogen with molecules rotating in odd-J states and parahydrogen in even-J states, the latter including the state of no rotation with $J = 0$. Here $I = \frac{1}{2}$ for the protons, and the electronic state is symmetric for nuclear exchange; hence odd J's must go with the ortho spin. If all fundamental I, M_I states occurred with equal frequency, the ratio of para to ortho would be $I/(I + 1) = \frac{1}{3}$. At room temperature, it is calculated that ordinary hydrogen should be about 25.1 per cent para. In ordinary experimentation there is not time for appreciable change to occur in the para-ortho ratio; nevertheless, the difference in statistical weights should have some effect on the observed specific heat at low temperatures because of the unequal representation of the even-J and odd-J rotational states.

A more remarkable fact is that it was found possible to accelerate the rate of interconversion between the two forms by adsorbing the gas onto charcoal, so that at 20°K it becomes almost pure parahydrogen, in the state $J = 0$, within a few hours. In this way the special properties of parahydrogen could be studied, especially its specific heat as a function of temperature, and agreement with theoretical predictions was found. The properties of pure orthohydrogen were then inferred by comparison with those of the normal mixture (Fig. 115). Orthodeuterium (H_2^2) has also been prepared; here $I = 1$, $N_p/N_o = \frac{1}{2}$, and it is the ortho states that have even values of J.

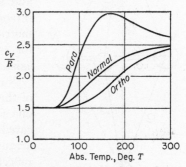

Fig. 115. Specific heat of three forms of hydrogen.

145. The Ammonia Inversion Spectrum. The band spectra of *poly-atomic* molecules are complicated, and few of them are well understood. Several or many different modes of vibration of the molecule are possible, and, if these modes involve oscillating electric moments, they give rise to easily observable vibration-rotation bands. The qualitative features to be expected in simple cases were worked out in 1927 by Hund.[2] We have space here only to describe one feature of special interest, which is well represented in the spectrum of gaseous ammonia.[3]

In the ammonia molecule NH_3 the nuclei may be thought of as lying at the corners of a low pyramid, N at the apex and H at the corners of

[1] Cf. L. Farkas, "Orthohydrogen, Parahydrogen and Heavy Hydrogen," 1935; E. H. Kennard, "Kinetic Theory of Gases," 1938.

[2] F. Hund, *Z. Physik*, vol. 43, p. 805, 1927.

[3] See D. M. Dennison, *Revs. Mod. Phys.*, vol. 3, p. 280, 1931, and vol. 12, p. 175, 1940.

an equilateral triangular base (Fig. 116). It is calculated that the N nucleus is about 0.36 A distant from the H_3 plane, the NH distance being about 1.01 A and HH, 1.63 A; the HNH angles are about 108°. In a vibration of the molecule, the nuclei move only short distances from their positions of equilibrium. A system of four particles will have a total of 12 degrees of freedom, but three of these belong to their common center of gravity and three more correspond to rigid rotations, leaving six degrees of vibrational freedom. Because of symmetry, however,

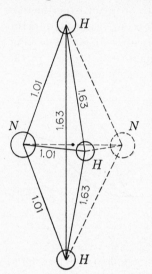

degeneracies occur so that only four distinct vibrational frequencies are observed in the ammonia spectrum, namely: $\bar{\nu}_1 = 3,336$ cm^{-1} and $\bar{\nu}_2 = 3,414$ cm^{-1}, the latter weak, and both near $\lambda = 3$ μ; $\bar{\nu}_3 = 949.9$ cm^{-1} (10.5 μ) and $\bar{\nu}_4 = 1627.5$ cm^{-1} (6.2 μ), the latter very intense. In $\bar{\nu}_1$ and $\bar{\nu}_3$ the nuclei move symmetrically relative to the axis of the pyramid; for $\bar{\nu}_2$ and also for $\bar{\nu}_4$, two independent modes exist, so that there are six modes in all.

Now it will be noted that, for given positions of the protons, the N nucleus may lie either on one side of the H_3 plane or on the other, as indicated in Fig. (116). These two alternative arrangements are related to each other as if by reflection in a mirror placed parallel to the H_3 plane; and one of them cannot be converted into the other by a pure rotation. It is easily seen, however, that they *can* be interconverted by a rotation plus interchange of two of the protons; and, since all protons have the same properties,

FIG. 116. The ammonia molecule NH_3. Numbers represent distances between atoms in angstroms.

it follows *in classical mechanics* that these two forms of the NH_3 molecule, once formed, must be physically indistinguishable. In such situations, however, wave mechanics introduces a nonclassical distinction.

Consider the variation of the potential energy V of the molecule as N moves along a line perpendicular to the H_3 plane, x being its distance from this plane. The curve for V will be symmetrical in x; there will be two similar minima M_1 and M_2, representing two possible positions of stable equilibrium for N relative to the H atoms, separated by a potential "hill." If the protons stand still while N moves, the hill is very high, as illustrated qualitatively by the incomplete curve V_1 drawn in Fig. 117(a); if, however, they move first outward and then inward, as if slipping round the N atom at a nearly constant distance, there is reason to believe that the potential hill is quite low, perhaps less than 3,000 cm^{-1} above the minima (curve V_2 in the figure).

Now in classical mechanics the N atom would simply be located in *one or the other* of the two hollows M_1 and M_2. The wave function for a quantum state, on the other hand, is in such cases either symmetric or antisymmetric relative to the center of symmetry of V, and thus represents simultaneous *equal probabilities* of finding N in one minimum or the other. If the potential hill were very low or very narrow, the energies of the quantum states would in general be widely separated, but, when the hill is high and wide, they come almost together in pairs, a symmetric and an antisymmetric state close together. That they do not quite coincide is connected with the fact that, contrary to the classical case,

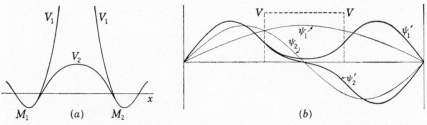

FIG. 117. (a) Schematic illustration of the inversion potential in NH_3. (b) Wave functions for a particle in a box.

$|\psi|^2$ represents a small probability, different for the two functions, that N might be found *inside the hill*, perhaps even in the same plane with H_3.

This characteristic wave-mechanical effect can readily be explored in the simple case of a particle in a box described in Sec. 102. A square potential hill may be assumed to occupy, say, the central third of the space between the walls. It is easy to solve the wave equation for this case, with use of exponentials instead of sines or cosines in the hill and with coefficients adjusted to preserve continuity of ψ and $\partial\psi/\partial x$ at the sides of the hill. A case is illustrated in Fig. 117(b). Here the curves labeled ψ_1 and ψ_2 represent roughly the first two wave functions when $V = 0$ for $0 < x < L$, with respective energies W_0 and $4W_0$; introduction of the hill represented by curve V on the same diagram replaces ψ_1 and ψ_2 by ψ_1' and ψ_2' as drawn and changes the energies so that $W_1' = 6.31W_0$ and $W_2' = 6.36W_0$.

In ammonia the result of this "inversion" effect is that each of the vibration-rotation states of the molecule appears to be doubled. The lowest two levels, one of them being the normal state of lowest energy, lie only about 0.66 cm^{-1} apart. The lowest pair of excited states connected with the ν_3 vibration, on the other hand, are 35.7 cm^{-1} apart.

The effect on the band spectra should be to convert all vibration-rotation or rotational lines into doublets, the selection rules being such that the doublet separation $\Delta\nu$ is the sum of the inversion separations in the initial and final states.   This theoretically predicted effect was sought and found by Dennison and Hardy[1] in the ν_1 band; the vibration-rotation lines were observed as doublets spaced 1.3 cm^{-1} apart.   Soon thereafter Wright and Randall[2] found a split averaging 1.3 cm^{-1} in the purely *rotational* lines at 71, 83, and 100 μ, observed in absorption.

Finally—and of greatest interest—radiative transitions between the lowest two molecular levels themselves should be possible, corresponding to a calculated frequency $\bar{\nu} = 0.66$ cm^{-1} or a wavelength $\lambda = 1.5$ cm. This, too, called the NH_3 inversion line, has been found, by Cleeton and Williams.[3]   As a source, they used a magnetostatic oscillator, whose

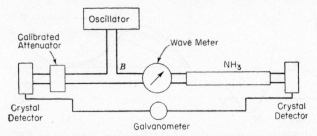

FIG. 118. Diagram of Good's setup for measuring absorption by ammonia.

frequency depends primarily upon the time of flight of electrons between cathode and anode.   Their spectrometer consisted of two brass mirrors 3 ft in diameter and an echelette grating of corresponding size. They observed a clear-cut peak in the absorption spectrum of NH_3 at $\lambda = 1.25$ cm (0.8 cm^{-1}).

Even a *fine structure* in the inversion line, caused by differences in the various rotational states of the molecule, has been detected,[4] as predicted from theory.[5]   W. E. Good found 30 inversion-rotation lines spread over a range of 6,000 Mc per sec or 0.20 cm^{-1}.   The principal components of his apparatus are diagramed in Fig. 118.   Electromagnetic waves from an oscillator are conducted by a wave-guide tube, made of highly conducting metal, past a branch point B and right and left to two crystal detectors, which are connected in opposition to a galvanometer or oscilloscope.   One arm contained a closed section 2.5 meters long that could be either evacuated or filled with NH_3 gas.   Measurements were made either by a null method, the attenuator in one branch being adjusted to balance the absorption due to the NH_3 gas in the other branch, or by

[1] D. M. Dennison and J. D. Hardy, *Phys. Rev.*, vol. 39, p. 938, 1932.

[2] N. Wright and H. M. Randall, *Phys. Rev.*, vol. 44, p. 391, 1933.

[3] C. E. Cleeton and N. H. Williams, *Phys. Rev.*, vol. 45, p. 234, 1934.

[4] B. Bleaney and R. P. Penrose, *Nature*, vol. 157, p. 339, 1946; W. E. Good, *Phys. Rev.*, vol. 70, p. 213, 1946.

[5] H. Y. Sheng, E. F. Barker, and D. M. Dennison, *Phys. Rev.*, vol. 60, p. 786, 1941.

sweeping the oscillator frequency and so obtaining a curve of absorption versus frequency as a trace on an oscilloscope screen. The 30 lines as observed at 24°C are plotted in Fig. 119, labeled with values of J and K for the rotational state of the molecule, which does not change during a transition.

Finally, even a *hyperfine* structure was noted by Good in certain lines. For example, at very low gas pressures two faint lines could be seen on each side of the main peak of the (3,3) line near 24×10^9, whose half-intensity width was about 7×10^5 cycles per sec. This fine structure was studied in detail by Coles and Good,[1] using separated isotopes, and

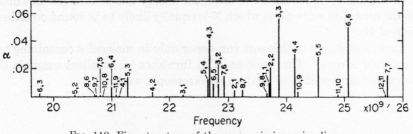

FIG. 119. Fine structure of the ammonia inversion line.

was found, with a width of a few megacycles per second or roughly 10^{-4} cm^{-1}, in most of the lines due to N^{14}H$_3$ but not in those due to N^{15}H$_3$. The splitting was ascribed to a slight local departure of the nuclear field of N^{14} from the Coulomb form, representable by an electric quadrupole moment. The effect of this moment on the energy levels varies for different coupling states of the nuclear spin with other spins. This interpretation was confirmed by later theoretical analysis.[2] Quadrupole splitting should occur only with a nucleus having $I > \frac{1}{2}$; for N^{14}, $I = 1$, for N^{15}, $I = \frac{1}{2}$. It may be imagined that, if $I = 0$, the direction of the quadrupole axis would be indeterminate, whereas, although with $I = \frac{1}{2}$ two opposite orientations are possible, a quadrupole looks the same when turned end for end.

Perhaps, in conclusion, the interest of the inversion phenomenon itself may warrant the following remark. Thermal collisions should freely induce transitions between the inversion states, usually leaving the molecule in a mixed wave-mechanical state. As a special case, after a collision, Ψ might have the form

$$\Psi = C(\psi_1 e^{-2\pi i W_1 t/h} + \psi_2 e^{-2\pi i W_2 t/h})$$

ψ_1 and W_1 referring to one inversion state and ψ_2, W_2 to the other. Then, at time $t = 0$, $\Psi = C(\psi_1 + \psi_2)$ and, because of the contrasting sym-

[1] D. K. Coles and W. E. Good, *Phys. Rev.*, vol. 70, p. 979, 1946.
[2] See *Phys. Rev.*, vol. 70, p. 984, 1946, and vol. 71, p. 468, 1947.

metries of ψ_1 and ψ_2, Ψ represents N as being pretty definitely on one side of H_3, ψ_1 and ψ_2 almost canceling on the opposite side. At the later time $t = \tau/2$, however, where $\tau = h/(W_2 - W_1)$,

$$\Psi = Ce^{-\pi i W_1 \tau/h}(\psi_1 - \psi_2)$$

since $W_2\tau/h = W_1\tau/h + (W_2 - W_1)\tau/h = W_1\tau/h + 1$ and $e^{-\pi i} = -1$. Now N is on the other side of H_3. Thus, so long as further collisions do not intervene, the molecule spontaneously goes back and forth between the two states, at the inversion frequency $\nu = (W_2 - W_1)/h$. This represents a very special case, however; and, in any case, a radiative transition will soon remove the state of higher energy and reduce the molecule to the quantum state ψ_1, in which N is equally likely to be found on either side of H_3.

Inversion states of this sort can occur only in molecules containing at least four atoms. The work on NH_3 furnishes an excellent example of the amazing precision of modern spectroscopic work.

CHAPTER 8

X-RAYS

There is probably no subject in all science which illustrates better than x-rays the importance to the entire world of research in pure science. Within 3 months after Roentgen's fortuitous discovery, x-rays were being put to practical use in a hospital in Vienna in connection with surgical operations. The use of this new aid to surgery soon spread rapidly. Since Roentgen's time, x-rays have completely revolutionized certain phases of medical practice. However, had Roentgen deliberately set about to discover some means of assisting surgeons in reducing fractures, *it is almost certain that he would never have been working with the evacuated tubes, induction coils, and the like, which led to his famous discovery.*

In many other fields of applied science, both biological and physical, important uses have been found for x-rays. Transcending these uses in applied science are the applications of x-rays to such problems as the atomic and the molecular structure of matter and the mechanism of the interaction of radiation with matter. X-rays provide us with a kind of supermicroscope, by means of which we can "see" not only atoms and their arrangement in crystals but also even the interior of the atom itself. Roentgen's discovery must be ranked with the most important scientific discoveries.

In this chapter a brief account will be given of the history and properties of x-rays.

EARLY, MOSTLY QUALITATIVE DEVELOPMENTS (1895–1912)

146. The Discovery of X-rays. In the autumn of 1895, Wilhelm Konrad Roentgen, professor of physics at Würzburg, was studying that fascinating phenomenon, the discharge of electricity through rarefied gases. A large induction coil was connected to a rather highly evacuated tube (Fig. 120), the cathode C being at one end and the anode A at the side. The tube was covered "with a somewhat closely fitting mantle of thin black cardboard."[1] With the apparatus in a completely darkened

---

[1] Quotations from papers by Roentgen, *Electrician*, vol. 36, pp. 415, 850, 1896.

room, he made the accidental observation that "a paper screen washed with barium-platino-cyanide lights up brilliantly and fluoresces equally well whether the treated side or the other be turned toward the discharge tube." The fluorescence was observable 2 meters away from the apparatus. Roentgen soon convinced himself that the agency which caused the fluorescence originated at that point in the discharge tube where the glass walls were struck by the cathode stream in the tube.

Realizing the importance of his discovery, Roentgen at once proceeded to study the properties of these new rays—the unknown nature of which he indicated by calling them "x-rays." In his first communications he recorded, among others, the following observations:

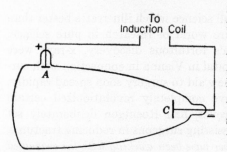

Fig. 120. Diagram of the tube with which Roentgen discovered x-rays.

1. All substances are more or less transparent to x-rays. For example, wood 2 to 3 cm thick is very transparent. Aluminum 15 mm thick "weakens the effect considerably, though it does not entirely destroy the fluorescence." Lead glass is quite opaque, but other glass of the same thickness is much more transparent. "If the hand is held between the discharge tube and the screen the dark shadow of the bones is visible within the slightly dark shadow of the hand."

2. Many other substances besides barium-platino-cyanide fluoresce—calcium compounds, uranium glass, rock salt, etc.

3. Photographic plates and films "show themselves susceptible to x-rays." Hence, photography provides a valuable method of studying the effects of x-rays.

4. X-rays are neither reflected nor refracted (so far as Roentgen could discover). Hence, "x-rays cannot be concentrated by lenses."

5. Unlike cathode rays, x-rays are not deflected by a magnetic field. They travel in straight lines, as Roentgen showed by means of "pinhole" photographs.

6. X-rays discharge electrified bodies, whether the electrification is positive or negative.

7. X-rays are generated when the cathode rays of the discharge tube strike any solid body. A heavier element, such as platinum, however, is much more efficient as a generator of x-rays than is a lighter element, such as aluminum.

It is a stirring tribute to Roentgen's masterly thoroughness that most of the basic properties of x-rays were described in the paper in which the discovery was first announced. His discovery excited intense interest, and work on x-rays began at once in many laboratories both in America and in Europe.[1]   This early work is beautifully illustrative of the qualitative phase of development of a typical field of physics.

An important additional property of x-rays was discovered immediately.   In an attempt to discover the reflection of x-rays, Imbert and Bertin-Sans[2] arranged apparatus as shown diagrammatically in Fig. 121. Between the source S of the rays and the photographic plate P was placed a thick copper screen AA.   A plane mirror M was so placed that a beam of rays, if reflected, would pass to the photographic plate P, on which would appear an image or shadow of an obstacle B.   Such a shadow was

obtained *irrespective of the angular position* of the mirror M.   Indeed, a plate of paraffin was just as effective as the mirror.   From these facts it was concluded that, instead of being reflected, the rays were diffused or scattered by M, somewhat as light is scattered by fog particles.

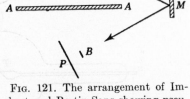

Fig. 121. The arrangement of Imbert and Bertin-Sans showing pseudoreflection (scattering) of x-rays from the mirror M.

Evidence for the *diffraction* of x-rays was reported in 1899 by Haga and Wind,[3] from which they concluded that the wavelength of the rays must be of the order of 10^{-8} cm.   They used wedge-shaped slits only a few thousandths of a millimeter wide and observed a slight broadening of the image on a photographic plate.

147. Production and Measurement of X-rays.   Until 1913, tubes for the production of x-rays were similar to a form suggested by Roentgen [Fig. 122(a)].   A residual gas pressure of the order of 10^{-3} mm Hg provides, when voltage is applied, a few electrons and positive ions.   These positive ions, bombarding the cathode C, release electrons which, hurled against the anode A, give rise to x-rays.   A curved cathode converges the electrons into a focal spot on A of desired shape and size.   In this type of tube, known as the "gas" tube, the anode current, applied voltage, and gas pressure are more or less interdependent, and it is essential that the gas pressure be maintained at the desired value.   Various ingenious devices were introduced for accomplishing this.   In 1913, however, an important improvement was introduced by Coolidge.   He evacuated the tube to the highest attainable vacuum and incorporated in the cathode a hot spiral filament of tungsten to serve as a source of electrons [F in Fig. 122(b)].   The filament was heated by an adjustable current from a battery.   Thus the current of electrons in the tube could be controlled independently of the applied voltage.

[1] *Beibl. Ann. Physik* for 1896 contains 400 titles on x-rays.
[2] Bertin-Sans, *Compt. rend.*, vol. 122, p. 524, 1896.
[3] Haga and Wind, *Ann. Physik*, vol. 68, p. 884, 1899.

For quantitative measurements, the ionization method was early adopted. The discharging effect of x-rays upon charged bodies was traced to ionization of the molecules of the surrounding gas. The effect was found to increase rapidly with density, and also to depend on the nature of the gas, the following being increasingly active in the order given: H_2, CO, air, CO_2, ether vapor, CS_2. At first the rate of discharge of an electroscope was used in measuring the intensity of an x-ray beam,

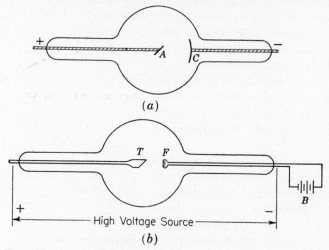

Fig. 122. (a) An early form of x-ray tube; (b) the Coolidge tube.

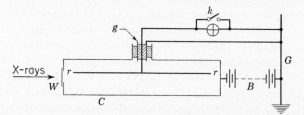

Fig. 123. An ionization chamber used for measuring electrically the intensity of a beam of x-rays.

but later an "ionization chamber" was introduced. This is shown schematically in Fig. 123. C is a metal tube several centimeters in diameter, from about 20 to 100 cm long, and closed at both ends except for an opening or "window" W, over which may be placed a thin sheet of Cellophane or aluminum for admitting the x-rays. A rod rr suitably supported by good insulating material, such as amber or quartz, is connected to an electrometer. An electric field is maintained between the rod rr and the cylinder C by a battery B, of about 100 volts, one end of which is connected to the ground wire G. An earthed guard ring g prevents leakage from the cylinder to the rod rr.   The cylinder may be filled with a heavy gas to make the arrangement more sensitive; argon or methyl bromide is often used.   When x-rays enter the window W, the gas within the cylinder is made conducting, and, on account of the electric field between the cylinder and the rod, the latter acquires a charge at a rate which can be measured by the electrometer.   This rate is a measure of the intensity of the x-ray beam.

Nowadays the electrometer is often replaced by a vacuum-tube amplifier and a galvanometer.   For very low x-ray intensities, a Geiger counter with appropriate vacuum-tube circuit may supplant the ionization chamber.

148. The Classical Pulse Theory of X-rays.   Concurrently with the discovery of x-rays, it was shown that the cathode rays consist of negative electrons.   This fact suggested that x-rays may consist of short pulses of electromagnetic radiation emitted as the electrons are suddenly brought to rest in the target.[1]

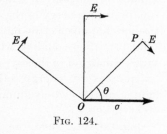

FIG. 124.

The necessary conclusions from electromagnetic theory for the description of such pulses are summarized in Secs. 227 and 228 of Appendix I.   If an electron moving at a speed small relative to the velocity of light is given a vector acceleration **a**, then the electric vector **E** in the emitted wave, as this wave passes any point P, lies in a plane containing both the direction of **a** and the line OP drawn from P to the position O occupied by the electron when it emitted the wave (Fig. 124).   The vector **E** is perpendicular to the line OP and so oriented as to have a component in the direction of **a**; and its magnitude in electrostatic units is

$$E = \frac{ea}{cr} \sin \theta \tag{196}$$

Here e is the numerical charge on the electron in electrostatic units, a the magnitude of **a**, c the speed of light, and r the distance OP, all in centimeters and seconds as units, and θ is the angle between OP and a line drawn through the electron and parallel to **a**.   Since the intensity of an electromagnetic wave is proportional to E^2, it follows that the intensity of the emitted pulse is proportional to $\sin^2 \theta$; thus the intensity vanishes at points in line with the vector acceleration **a**.   The total instantaneous rate of emission of radiation by the electron is readily calculated to be

$$\Omega = \frac{2}{3} \frac{e^2 a^2}{c^3} \qquad \text{ergs per sec} \tag{197}$$

[1] Cf. J. J. Thomson, "Conduction of Electricity through Gases," 2d ed., p. 321.

Thus, if, for example, an electron moving at speed $v_0 \ll c$ is brought to rest with uniform acceleration a during a time v_0/a, while traveling a distance $s = v_0^2/2a$, the total energy in the emitted pulse will be

$$W = \Omega(v_0/a)$$

or
$$W = \frac{2}{3} \frac{e^2 v_0 a}{c^3} = \frac{e^2 v_0^3}{3c^3 s} \tag{198}$$

This formula predicts that the energy radiated will increase very rapidly with the initial velocity of the electron and will be inversely proportional to the distance within which the electron is stopped. Qualitatively, these same features might be expected to hold when an electron is brought to rest by an atom, although in that case the acceleration would not, of course, be uniform. Experiment shows that the intensity of the radiation from a given x-ray target increases roughly as v_0^4, that is, as the square of the energy of the cathode ray. Furthermore, it is reasonable to assume that an electron moving with a given velocity will be stopped more suddenly when colliding with a heavy atom than with a lighter one. A target made of a heavy metal like platinum should, therefore, give out more x-ray energy, other things being equal, than one made of a lighter metal such as aluminum. This is in agreement with Roentgen's observations.

Qualitatively, therefore, the classical theory of x-ray production was fairly successful. Quantitatively, however, it was destined to meet with serious difficulties. It still retains an interest, although we now know that it has reference only to one part of the x-ray spectrum (the "continuous" spectrum) and, for accuracy, must be replaced even in dealing with that part by a more abstract theory, wave-mechanical in nature.

In later work other charged particles besides electrons were found to be effective for the production of x-rays, such as α-rays,[1] protons, and deuterons.[2]

The *scattering* of x-rays, also, was treated by J. J. Thomson with some success on the pulse theory. As a pulse passes over an electron of mass m, the electric vector **E** will give the electron an acceleration eE/m and will cause it to radiate energy at a rate, from Eq. (197),

$$\Omega = \frac{2}{3} \frac{e^4 E^2}{m^2 c^3} \tag{199a}$$

This energy is abstracted from the primary beam and reradiated or scattered as a secondary beam. Its magnitude is most usefully expressed in terms of the instantaneous intensity I_1 of the primary beam, defined as the energy crossing unit area per second. By a slight generalization

[1] Chadwick, *Phil. Mag.*, vol. 25, p. 193, 1913.
[2] Cork, *Phys. Rev.*, vol. 59, p. 957, 1941.

of Eq. (307a), $I_1 = cE^2/4\pi$ ergs per cm^2 per sec (in vacuum). Hence we can write

$$\Omega = \frac{8\pi}{3} \frac{e^4}{m^2 c^4} I_1 \tag{199b}$$

The ratio Ω/I_1, which will be denoted by σ_e, is called the *classical scattering cross section* or *coefficient* for a free electron. As much of the incident energy is scattered as passes through an area of magnitude σ_e drawn perpendicular to the incident beam. Inserting $e = 4.803 \times 10^{-10}$, $m = 0.9109 \times 10^{-27}$, $c = 2.998 \times 10^{10}$, we find

$$\sigma_e = 6.65 \times 10^{-25} \text{ cm}^2 \tag{200}$$

The classical theory of x-ray scattering has, however, only limited validity. At least three important features have been left out of account: the fact that the electrons in matter are mostly not free but are bound in atoms; interference effects between waves scattered by neighboring electrons; and the modifications of the scattering process introduced by wave mechanics and described as the Compton effect. We shall return to the subject of scattering in Secs. 159 and 160.

Number of Electrons in an Atom. The classical formula just mentioned was employed by Barkla and his collaborators[1] as a basis for estimating the number of electrons in an atom of the lighter elements. They concluded that this number was about equal to half the atomic weight; for example, an atom of carbon was correctly inferred to contain six electrons. This result was of great historical importance. It should be remarked, however, that, if Barkla had used considerably different wavelengths in his observations, the results of the computation might have been less satisfactory.

149. Polarization, Absorption, and Fluorescence of X-rays. *a. Polarization.* If x-rays are electromagnetic waves, they should exhibit the phenomenon of polarization. This property cannot be studied by the usual optical methods because x-rays are so hard to reflect or refract, but a method was devised by Barkla for interpreting the results of certain scattering experiments in such a way as to reveal the polarization of the rays.[2]

Let a stream of cathode rays proceeding in the direction of zO (Fig. 125) impinge on a target at O, and consider the primary beam of x-rays proceeding from the target in the direction Ox_1, perpendicular to Oz. If the cathode-ray electrons are all accelerated in the direction Oz, this primary beam will be plane-polarized with the electric vector as indicated by the

---

[1] Barkla and Sadler, *Phil. Mag.*, vol. 17, p. 739, 1909; C. G. Barkla, *Phil. Mag.*, vol. 21, p. 648, 1911.

[2] C. G. Barkla, *Proc. Roy. Soc. (London)*, vol. 77, p. 247, 1906.

vector Z drawn in the figure.   Let a piece of scattering material be located at P_1.   Then the electrons in this material will all be accelerated by the primary beam in the direction P_1z_1', and, according to Eq. (196), the intensity in the scattered beam will vary from a maximum in the direction P_1P_2 to zero in directions P_1z_1 or P_1z_1'.

In his experiments Barkla found that the intensity of the radiation scattered in the direction P_1z_1, although not zero, was considerably less than the intensity in the direction P_1P_2.   This indicates that the beam is *partially* polarized.   A little further consideration shows that this is really what we should expect.   For the electrons will usually pursue a zigzag path in the target, colliding with many atoms before being brought

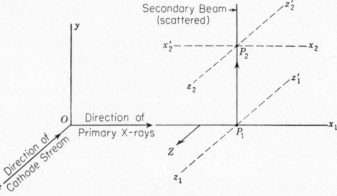

FIG. 125.

to rest.   The electric vector in the primary x-ray beam, therefore, although favoring directions near P_1z_1, may also have any other direction in the plane $z_1P_2z_1'$.

With the *secondary* scattered beam of x-rays proceeding in the direction P_1P_2, however, the situation is quite different.   Being produced by electronic accelerations lying in the plane $z_1P_2z_1'$, the electric vector in the secondary beam at P_2 must always have a direction parallel to z_2z_2', so that this beam will be entirely plane-polarized.   If, then, *this* beam is scattered in turn by a *second* scatterer placed at P_2, the intensity of the tertiary radiation sent out from P_2 should vary from *zero* in the direction P_2z_2 to a maximum in directions such as P_2x_2.

Barkla's experiments testing this conclusion indicated that the secondary rays were 70 per cent polarized, instead of the predicted 100 per cent.   A similar experiment was performed much later by Compton and Hagenow[1] in which a more intense primary beam was employed, thereby allowing (1) better collimation, i.e., greater definition of the scattering angle, and (2) the use of smaller scatterers so as to decrease multiple

[1] Compton and Hagenow, J.O.S.A., *Rev. Sci. Instr.*, vol. 8, p. 487, 1924.

scattering, i.e., successive scatterings at angles other than 90°. It was found that within the limit of error of the measurements the intensity of the tertiary radiation scattered in the direction $P_2 z_2$ is zero. The prediction of the classical theory is thus verified.

b. Absorption of X-rays. In 1897 Buguet made the significant observation that the opacity of a given material to x-rays varied with the thickness of the material previously traversed by the beam.[1] This was explained by assuming that his beams were a mixture of components having different absorbabilities, so that the composition of the beam changed as it traversed an absorber. For many years the only available measure of the quality of an x-ray beam was its absorbability in some standard material, usually aluminum. Beams were called "hard" or "soft" according as their absorbability was low or high. It was early suspected, and later verified, that, in general, greater hardness is associated with higher frequencies (or shorter wavelengths) of the rays. In describing this early work done before wavelengths could be measured, we shall continue to use the term hardness, but in every case the word frequency may be substituted.

c. Characteristic or Fluorescent X-rays. A new type of phenomenon was revealed as early as 1896 by an important observation made by Winkelmann and Straubel.[2] A beam of x-rays was passed *through* a photographic plate P (Fig. 126), the emulsion being on the rear side. Behind a part of the plate was a piece of fluor spar F. On developing the plate, it was found that the film was much denser in the neighborhood of F, as if F had reflected the rays. A similar observation had been made by Roentgen. But Winkelmann and Straubel showed that the phenomenon was not one of true reflection, for they repeated the experiment with a thin sheet of paper AA between F and P and found

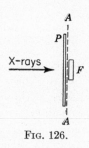

Fig. 126.

that the intensifying action of F was almost but not entirely destroyed, although the paper was very transparent to the incident beam. From this, they concluded that the quality of the rays had been altered by the spar in such a way as to make the beam of rays returned by F more absorbable in paper than was the original beam. In other words, the primary rays, incident on the spar, had been transformed into characteristic "spar" rays.

Barkla and his collaborators made a thorough study of this phenomenon.[3] Let a primary beam of hard x-rays from a target T (Fig. 127),

[1] Buguet, *Compt. rend.*, vol. 125, p. 398, 1897.

[2] *Jenaisch. Z. Naturwiss.*, vol. 30, 1896.

[3] Cf. *Phil. Mag.*, vol. 16, p. 550, 1908; vol. 22, p. 396, 1911; vol. 23, p. 987; *Proc Cambridge Phil. Soc.*, vol. 15, p. 257, 1908–1912.

after passing through holes in lead screens S_1S_1, fall upon the secondary emitter E.   Let the secondary beam, taken off at right angles to the primary beam, after passing screens S_2S_2, enter the ionization chamber C, by means of which the intensity of the secondary beam can be measured either with or without slabs of absorbing material placed at A or at B. When the secondary emitter E is of some light material, such as carbon, an aluminum absorbing screen placed at B absorbs (nearly) the same fraction of the secondary beam as it does of the primary beam when placed at A.   This shows that the hardness (or frequency) of the secondary beam as measured by its absorption in aluminum is (nearly) the same as

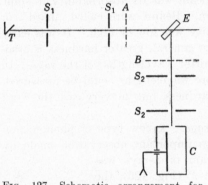

that of the primary beam.   The primary beam has thus merely been scattered by the emitter E, in accord with Thomson's theory.

If, however, a heavier material, such as silver, is substituted for the carbon at E, the absorption coefficient of the secondary beam in aluminum is found to be *greater* than that of the primary beam.   Thus the x-rays are considerably softened (or decreased in frequency) by the process of apparent scattering.

FIG. 127. Schematic arrangement for studying secondary radiation.

Barkla found that the hardness of the secondary beam, as measured by its coefficient of absorption in aluminum, is characteristic of the material used as secondary emitter, and, almost without exception, increases with increasing atomic weight of the secondary emitter.   He called secondary beams of this kind *characteristic* radiations.

Barkla then used other absorbers of greater atomic weight than aluminum, and, for each one, he compared its absorption coefficients for a series of characteristic radiations obtained from different kinds of secondary emitters.   Using iron, for example, as an absorber, he found that, as the hardness of the incident characteristic radiation increased, its absorption in iron decreased, until, at a hardness about equal to that of the characteristic radiation from an iron emitter, the absorption in iron jumped suddenly to a much higher value; as the hardness was still further increased, the absorption again decreased.   Similar results were obtained with other absorbing materials in place of iron.

From his results Barkla concluded that a secondary emitter, besides scattering the primary beam, also emits a fluorescent radiation characteristic of the emitter, *provided* the hardness (or frequency) of the primary beam exceeds the hardness of this fluorescent radiation.   Barkla called the latter the "K fluorescent radiation" of the emitter. For the heavier emitters two discontinuities in the absorption curve were observed, indicating that two types of fluorescent radiation were emitted; he designated the softer of the two by L. The occurrence of fluorescence is accompanied by a marked increase in the absorption of the primary beam. Barkla recognized that these K and L radiations must constitute lines or groups of lines in fluorescent spectra of the secondary emitters.

These experiments have been described at some length because of their interest as work in which x-rays of differing wavelengths were compared before any methods corresponding to those used in ordinary spectroscopy had become available.

X-RAY SPECTRA

150. The Crystal Diffraction Grating. *a.* The first practical method for resolving x-ray beams according to wavelength developed out of a brilliant suggestion by Laue. The order of magnitude of x-ray wavelengths, as revealed by the diffraction experiments described above, is the same as the order of magnitude of the spacing of the atoms in crystals. Laue suggested, therefore, that a crystal, with its regular three-dimensional array of atoms, might behave toward a beam of x-rays in somewhat the same way as does a ruled diffraction grating toward a beam of ordinary light.

Let it be assumed that plane electromagnetic waves traveling in a given direction fall upon a crystal. Then each atom will scatter some of the incident radiation. If the crystal is perfectly regular, the wavelets scattered by different atoms will combine, in general, in all sorts of phases and so will destroy each other by interference. Laue argued, however, that for certain wavelengths and in certain directions the wavelets should combine in phase and so produce a strong diffracted beam.[1] It would be expected, therefore, that such diffracted beams might be observed upon passing a heterogeneous x-ray beam through a crystal.

b. Such an experiment was performed by Friedrich and Knipping in 1913.[2] By means of suitable screens a narrow pencil of x-rays was allowed to pass through a crystal beyond which was a photographic plate. After an exposure of many hours, it was found on developing the plate that, in addition to the interior central image where the direct beam struck the plate, there were present on the plate many fainter but regularly arranged spots, indicating that the incident x-ray beam had been

[1] See for example A. H. Compton and S. K. Allison, "X-rays in Theory and Experiment," 1935.

[2] Friedrich, Knipping, and Laue, *Bayer Akad. Wiss.*, 1912; *Le Radium*, vol. 10, p. 47, 1913.

diffracted by the crystal in certain special directions, just as Laue had predicted.   Figure 128 shows such a photograph, taken by Dr. George L. Clark,[1] of an iron crystal.   In their original paper, Friedrich, Knipping, and Laue, from an analysis of a series of photographs of a crystal of zinc blende oriented at various angles with respect to the incident pencil, concluded that there were present in the x-ray beam wavelengths varying between 1.27×10^{-9} and 4.83×10^{-9} cm.   This positive result seemed

FIG. 128. Laue photograph of an iron crystal.   (*Photograph by Dr. George L. Clark. Used by permission.*)

to prove the correctness of the *two* postulates underlying the experiment: (1) that x-rays are electromagnetic waves of definite wavelengths, and (2) that the atoms of a crystal are arranged in regular three-dimensional order, as suggested by the external symmetry of crystals.

This experiment marked the beginning of a new era in the technique of x-ray measurement and in x-ray theory.   Two new fields of investigation were at once opened up: (1) in x-rays, the study of spectra and the use of homogeneous beams in experiments on scattering, absorption, etc.; (2) the study of the arrangements of atoms or molecules in crystals.   In the following sections, we shall confine our discussion to some of the more important aspects of the former field.

[1] This photograph is used by permission of Dr. Clark.

c. A very simple and convenient way of looking at the process of diffraction by a crystal grating was proposed by Bragg.[1] He pointed out that through any crystal a set of equidistant parallel planes can be drawn which, among them, pass through *all* the atoms (or similar groups of atoms) which compose the crystal. Indeed, a great many such families

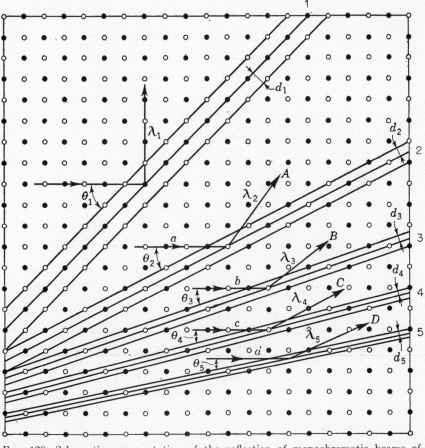

FIG. 129. Schematic representation of the reflection of monochromatic beams of x-rays by a crystal of NaCl when a heterochromatic beam is incident upon it.

of planes may be drawn, the planes of each family being separated from each other by a characteristic distance. Such planes are called *Bragg planes,* and their separations, *Bragg spacings.* Traces of five families of Bragg planes are shown in Fig. 129.

If plane monochromatic waves fall upon the atoms in a Bragg plane, a wavelet of scattered radiation spreads out from each atom in all direc-

[1] W. L. Bragg, *Proc. Cambridge Phil. Soc.,* vol. 17, p. 43, 1912.

tions. There is just one direction in which, irrespective of the atomic
distribution in the plane, the scattered wavelets will meet in the same
phase and will constructively interfere with each other, viz., the direction
of *specular reflection* from the plane. This follows from the ordinary
Huygens construction as used for the reflection from a mirror. The
beam scattered in this direction may be thought of as reflected from the
Bragg plane. But, now, we note that each Bragg plane is one of many
regularly spaced parallel planes. The beams reflected from these various
parallel planes will combine, in general, in different phases and so will
destroy each other by interference. Only if certain conditions as to wavelength and angle of incidence of the beam on the planes are satisfied will

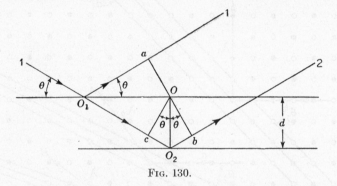

FIG. 130.

the waves *from different planes* combine in the same phase and reinforce
each other. The necessary conditions are easily found.

In Fig. 130, let the horizontal lines represent the traces of two successive Bragg planes spaced d apart. Denote by θ the angle between the
direction of propagation of the incident beam and the planes; this angle
is called the *glancing angle* of the beam on these planes. Let a ray meet
the two planes at O_1 and O_2, respectively, and let a line drawn from O_2
perpendicular to the planes cut the other plane at O. Draw $O_1 1$ and $O_2 2$
representing rays specularly reflected from the two planes, and draw
aOb perpendicular to $O_1 1$ and $O_2 2$ to represent a wave front of the reflected
beam. Then constructive interference will occur if the path $O_1 O_2 b$, taken
by waves scattered at O_2, exceeds the path $O_1 a$ for waves scattered at O_1
by an integral number of wavelengths. Draw Oc perpendicular to $O_1 O_2$.
Then $O_1 a = O_1 c$; hence the difference in path is $cO_2 b = 2d \sin \theta$. The
conditions that there should be a reflected beam are, therefore,

$$\theta = \theta'$$
and
$$n\lambda = 2d \sin \theta \qquad (201)$$

where n is an integer, called the "order of the reflection," and θ' is the
angle between the Bragg planes and the direction of the diffracted rays.

These two conditions are known as *Bragg's law* for x-ray reflection. The first condition is often omitted in the statement of Bragg's law with the understanding that it is implied by the term "reflection."

Suppose, now, that a parallel wave train, containing a *continuous spectrum* of wavelengths, is incident upon a crystal, as represented by the parallel arrows a, b, c, d in Fig. 129. In the figure, traces of five families of Bragg planes are shown, numbered 1, 2, 3, 4, 5, with their characteristic spacings d_1, d_2, ... Many other families of planes might be imagined, some perpendicular and some not perpendicular to the plane of the paper. Suppose that in the incident beam there is a wavelength λ_2 such that

$$n\lambda_2 = 2d_2 \sin \theta_2$$

where n is an integer, d_2 is the distance between the set of planes numbered 2, and θ_2 is the glancing angle between the direction of the incident radiation and these planes. Then there will be reflected from this group of planes a beam A, of wavelength λ_2, which will proceed in the direction of the arrow A. Similarly, we may have reflected beams B, C, D, . . . in different directions in the plane of the paper, and also many other beams reflected from other families of planes in directions not in the plane of the paper. Each "Laue spot" in the experiment of Friedrich and Knipping may be interpreted as produced by such a reflected beam. In general, the most intense spots correspond to reflections from Bragg planes containing the greatest number of atoms on each plane.

The crystal represented in Fig. 129 is one of a very simple type, but the conception of Bragg planes is applicable to all types of crystals. It should be pointed out, however, that it is not necessary to draw the Bragg planes actually *through* the atoms; instead of a given family of these planes, any other set of planes parallel to them and spaced the same distance apart could be employed and would lead to the same conditions for strong reflection.

It should be pointed out also that the Bragg equation (201) does not give a complete solution to the interference problems of x-rays scattered from a crystal. The equation predicts only the position of the center of the expected diffraction pattern for a given wavelength and family of Bragg planes; nothing is said about the intensity distribution in this diffraction pattern.

151. The X-ray Spectrometer. Immediately following the announcement by Friedrich, Knipping, and Laue of their successful experiment, many investigators took up the study of the new phenomenon. Among these were W. H. and W. L. Bragg,[1] to whom we are chiefly indebted for the early development of the x-ray spectrometer.

[1] W. L. Bragg, *Nature*, vol. 90, p. 410, 1912; W. H. Bragg and W. L. Bragg, *Proc. Roy. Soc.* (*London*), vol. 88, p. 428, 1913; W. H. Bragg, *Nature*, vol. 91, p. 477, 1913.

A spectrometer of the Bragg type is shown diagrammatically in Fig. 131(a). X-rays from the target T of an x-ray tube pass through two narrow slits S_1 and S_2, a few hundredths or tenths of a millimeter wide, the edges of which are made of some material, such as lead or gold, which is very opaque to x-rays. This ribbon-shaped incident beam of x-rays I falls at a glancing angle θ on the cleavage face of a crystal K—rock salt, calcite, mica, gypsum, quartz, etc.—which is mounted on a table D, the angular position of which can be accurately read by verniers or

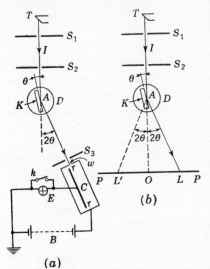

micrometer microscopes. The reflected beam of x-rays, which makes an angle 2θ with the incident beam, enters, through the "window" w, an ionization chamber C by means of which the intensity of the reflected beam may be measured. By suitably turning the table D about the axis A, the incident beam may be made to strike the face of the crystal at any glancing angle θ. The ionization chamber C is mounted on an arm (not shown) by means of which the chamber can be rotated about the axis A so as to admit the reflected beam through the window w. For protection against stray scattered radiation, a third slit S_3 is attached to the chamber.

FIG. 131. The x-ray spectrometer using (a) the ionization method, (b) the photographic method.

For photographic registration, the ionization chamber may be replaced by a photographic plate PP [Fig. 131(b)]. With the crystal set at a glancing angle θ, the reflected beam will strike the plate at L (or at L', if the crystal is "reversed"). From the position O at which the direct beam strikes the plate, the distances OL and OA and hence the angles 2θ and θ may be determined. The wavelength λ is then obtained from the Bragg formula, $n\lambda = 2d \sin \theta$.

The distance d between the reflecting planes of a crystal such as NaCl is determined as follows. From his investigations, Bragg showed[1] that, in the rock-salt crystal, the Na and the Cl atoms or ions occupy alternate positions at the corners of elementary cubes in the cubic lattice characteristic of the crystal, the arrangement being similar to that shown in Fig. 129, which represents one plane of atoms. Taking the atomic weight of chlorine as 35.46 and of sodium as 23.00, we find the molecular weight of

[1] See W. H. Bragg and W. L. Bragg, "The Crystalline State," vol. I, 1933.

NaCl to be 58.46.   Therefore, 58.46 grams of the NaCl contain $2N_0$
atoms, viz., N_0 atoms of Na and N_0 atoms of Cl, where N_0 is Avogadro's
number.   Thus we find for the number of atoms n in 1 cm^3 of rock salt
$2N_0\rho/58.46$, where $\rho = 2.163$, the density of crystalline NaCl.   If d is
the distance between the center of one atom and the next along the edge
of the cube, $1/d$ is the number of atoms in a row of atoms 1 cm long, and
$n = 1/d^3$.   From these two equations d can be calculated, provided N_0
is known.

Until about 1930 the most accurate value of N_0 was obtained by dividing the faraday by the electronic charge as measured in Millikan's oil-
drop experiment.   Using Millikan's original value of e for this purpose
($e = 4.774 \times 10^{-10}$ esu), it was calculated that, for the distance between
the cleavage planes in NaCl, $d = 2.814 \times 10^{-8}$ cm (old value).

The value of d as thus determined was dependent both on N_0 and on ρ,
the density of rock salt; and neither of these constants was known to
much better than 0.1 per cent.   Since x-ray wavelengths can be *compared* to a much greater precision than this, it was considered expedient
to adopt a new unit length, called the "X unit" or "X.U.," which was
very nearly 1×10^{-11} cm but which was accurately defined by taking the
grating space of NaCl at 18°C as exactly 2,814.00 X.U.   The grating
space of any other crystal could then be determined from this arbitrarily
chosen standard as follows.   Let θ_{NaCl} be the angle at which a line of
given wavelength is reflected from a rock-salt crystal, and θ_c the angle
at which the same line is reflected from some other crystal of unknown
grating space d_c.   Then, from Bragg's law (Eq. 201), we have

$$n\lambda = 2d_{NaCl} \sin \theta_{NaCl} = 2d_c \sin \theta_c$$

from which d_c may be determined.   In later work, calcite was adopted
as the best crystal for practical use, and its grating space at 18°C was
calculated to be 3,029.45 X.U.

When precise measurement of x-ray wavelengths by means of ruled
gratings had been accomplished, however, it was noted that wavelengths so measured were 0.20 per cent greater than the same wavelengths
as calculated from crystal diffraction.   As was stated in Sec. 48, an error
in the oil-drop value of e was then discovered, whose correction brought
the two sets of wavelengths into satisfactory agreement.   A new value,
$d = 2,820 \times 10^{-11}$ cm, was thus obtained for the grating space of rock
salt, and $d = 3,035.60 \times 10^{-11}$ cm for calcite (at 18°C).   The proposal
was then made to redefine the X unit as *exactly* 10^{-11} cm.   Objection was
raised, however, by Siegbahn[1] on the ground that the accuracy attainable
in the *comparison* of x-ray wavelengths by means of crystals will probably

[1] M. Siegbahn, *Nature*, vol. 151, p. 502, 1943.

exceed the accuracy attainable with a grating for a long time to come. It has been considered preferable, therefore, by Siegbahn and others, to retain an artificial X unit based on the old assumed value of the grating space of calcite, and to express all wavelengths that are measured with crystals in terms of this unit. The true wavelength in terms of 10^{-11} cm as the unit can then always be found by multiplying values in X units by a standard conversion ratio. The ratio 1.002020 has been recommended, but perhaps 1.002063 would be better.[1] At the present time both units are in use, so that in stating x-ray wavelengths the unit should always be specified.

In Table 8-1 are listed some of the crystals commonly used in x-ray spectroscopy together with their grating spaces. In the second column the spaces are listed as given by Siegbahn;[2] in the column headed "corrected," these values are multipled by 1.00202 to bring them into harmony with the grating wavelengths.

Using crystal gratings, x-ray wavelengths may be compared with a precision of a few parts in 10^5. In such work, however, correction must be made for thermal expansion of the crystal and for the slight refraction of

TABLE 8-1. GRATING SPACES OF SOME CRYSTALS USED IN X-RAY SPECTROSCOPY

Crystal	Grating space d at 18°C		Change in d per degree centigrade, X.U. or 10^{-11} cm
	Siegbahn, X.U.	Corrected, $\times 10^{-11}$ cm	
Rock salt (NaCl)....................	2,814.00	2,819.68	0.11
Calcite (CaCO₃).....................	3,029.45	3,035.57	0.03
Quartz (SiO₂).......................	4,246.02	4,254.60	0.04
Gypsum (CaSO₂·2H₂O)..............	7,584.70	7,600.0	0.29
Mica...............................	9,942.72	9,962.8	0.15

the rays in it. According to Eq. (201) the maximum wavelength measurable with a given crystal is $2d$, but the practical limit is somewhat smaller, since the glancing angle cannot usefully exceed about 70°. In general, crystals are now used up to about 25 A and gratings from somewhat below 20 A up. Various special types of crystal spectrometers have been developed; some use transmission and "internal reflection," some use two crystals in succession, and some use a bent crystal to focus the reflected rays.

152. Monochromatic Characteristic Radiations. With a beam of x-rays from a platinum target incident on the cleavage face of a rock-salt

---

[1] J. W. M. DuMond and E. R. Cohen, *Revs. Mod. Phys.*, vol. 25, p. 691, 1953.
[2] Siegbahn, *loc. cit.*

crystal, W. H. Bragg[1] rotated the crystal in steps of $\Delta\theta$ and the ionization chamber in steps of $2\ \Delta\theta$. He plotted the curve of ionization current against glancing angle θ and found that the current or x-ray intensity did not vary uniformly with angle but rose at certain angles to a sharp maximum. A curve similar to that shown in Fig. 132 was obtained. A group of three maxima, a_1, b_1, and c_1, was observed at the respective angles θ of 9.9, 11.6, and 13.6°. A second group of three maxima, a_2, b_2, and c_2, was observed at approximately double these angles. This second group is similar, as to relative intensities of the maxima, to the first group. Bragg interpreted the maxima a_1, b_1, and c_1 as three monochromatic lines; and

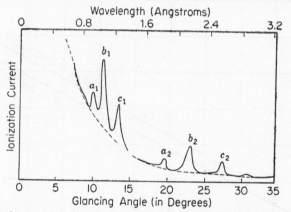

FIG. 132. Bragg's curve for the energy distribution in an x-ray spectrum, showing the characteristic lines a, b, c.

the second group of maxima a_2, b_2, and c_2 as second-order reflections of the lines a_1, b_1, and c_1. He computed their wavelengths by the formula $n\lambda = 2d\sin\theta$, taking $n = 1$ for the "lines" a_1, b_1, and c_1 and $n = 2$ for the second-order lines a_2, b_2, and c_2, and obtained wavelengths of 0.97, 1.13, 1.32 A, respectively.

Curves similar to Fig. 132 were obtained with other crystals, the only difference being that the maxima occurred at different glancing angles, indicating that each crystal had a characteristic grating space d. Bragg convinced himself, however, that these respective maxima for different crystals always represented the same monochromatic radiation, since, for example, the absorption in aluminum of peak b_1 was always the same, whatever the crystal used. In short, the peaks of the curve in Fig. 132 represent *spectral lines* the wavelengths of which are *characteristic of the target emitting the rays*. These monochromatic lines are superimposed on a *continuous* spectrum represented by the partially dotted line in the figure. Curves of the type shown in Fig. 132, therefore, represent (subject to certain corrections to be mentioned later) the distribution of

[1] *Nature*, Jan. 23, 1913.

energy in the x-ray spectrum, continuous and characteristic combined, of an element.

153. Moseley's Law.   In two classic papers,[1] Moseley presented a systematic study of the characteristic radiations emitted by various targets, using a photographic method similar in principle to that shown in Fig. 131(*b*).   He found a larger number of characteristic lines than Bragg and, also, that these lines could, in general, be classified into two groups: (1) a group of shorter wavelengths, which, by means of the value of

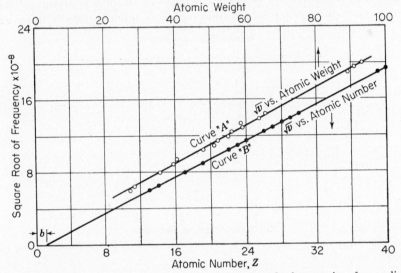

FIG. 133. Moseley's curve showing the relation between the frequencies of x-ray lines and atomic number.

absorption coefficients in aluminum, he identified with Barkla's characteristic *K* secondary radiations and (2) a group of lines of longer wavelength, similarly identified with Barkla's *L* radiation.

Unlike the optical spectra, however, the x-ray characteristic spectra of the elements were found to be similar from element to element, homologous lines occurring, in general, at shorter wavelengths the greater the atomic weight of the element in which the lines originate.   In searching for a relation between the frequency of a given line, say the $K\alpha$ line, and some property of the atom in which the line originated, Moseley first observed that the frequency did not vary uniformly with the atomic weight, as is shown by curve *A*, Fig. 133, in which the square root of the frequency is plotted against the atomic weight.   In Bohr's theory of the origin of spectra, however, which at that time had recently been proposed, the *charge on the nucleus* played a fundamental role.   Accord-

[1] Moseley, *Phil. Mag.*, vol. 26, p. 1024, 1913; vol. 27, p. 703, 1914.

ing to Bohr's theory, the frequency ν of a spectral line is given by

$$\nu = Z^2 \frac{2\pi^2 m e^4}{h^3}\left(\frac{1}{n_2{}^2} - \frac{1}{n_1{}^2}\right) \tag{202}$$

[Eq. (87a)], Z being the atomic number. Rutherford had shown, from his experiments on the scattering of α-particles, that the value of the nuclear charge, for a given atom, is approximately one-half the atomic weight; and Barkla had shown, from experiments on the scattering of x-rays, that the number of electrons surrounding the nucleus is also approximately one-half the atomic weight. Guided by these considerations, Moseley assigned atomic numbers Z to the elements he had investigated and then plotted a curve between $\sqrt{\nu}$ and Z. Such a plot of Moseley's data for the $K\alpha$ line is shown in Fig. 133, curve B. The graph is seen to be a straight line, with a small intercept $b = 1$ on the Z axis. It is obvious from a comparison of the two curves A and B of Fig. 133 that, as far as the determination of the *frequency of characteristic lines is concerned, atomic number* is a much more fundamental quantity than atomic *weight*.

Curve B in Fig. 133 is represented by the equation

$$\nu = 0.248 \times 10^{16}(Z - 1)^2$$

If we set $n_2 = 1$ and $n_1 = 2$ in Eq. (202), we obtain

$$\nu = 0.246 \times 10^{16}Z^2$$

by inserting the numerical values of m, e, and h. Except for the slight correction to Z, *the last two equations are seen to be almost identical.* This agreement suggests the hypothesis described in the next section as to the origin of the $K\alpha$ line.

154. The Origin of X-ray Lines. *a. Emission Spectra.* In Sec. 110, we have seen that in an atom there are just two electrons corresponding to the electronic quantum number $n = 1$. These electrons, which constitute the K shell and may be called the K electrons, have (in the zero-order stage of perturbation theory) one-electron wave functions whose values are very small except close to the nucleus. The electrons in question are, therefore, very unlikely to be found at any considerable distance from the nucleus and may be regarded as the innermost electrons in the atom. In any neutral atom of atomic number $Z > 2$, there exist also one or more, *up to a maximum of eight*, electrons in quantum states with $n = 2$, called "L electrons." Their wave functions extend effectively to much greater distances from the nucleus than those of the K electrons, so that, although any one of the L electrons might be found closer to the nucleus than the K electrons, they are most likely to be found at much greater distances. Then, if Z is large enough, there may occur, also, M

electrons, with $n = 3$, characterized by wave functions extending still farther out, and so on, until all the circumnuclear electrons are accounted for.

Now suppose an atom in the target of an x-ray tube is bombarded by an energetic cathode ray and that one of the two K electrons is "knocked out" of the atom. The atom is thereby converted into an ion, and the ion is left in a quantum state characterized by the absence of one K electron. This state of the ion may be called a K *quantum state of the ion*. Subsequently an L electron may "drop" into the K vacancy, i.e., change from an electronic state with $n = 2$ to one with $n = 1$. The ion thereby undergoes a transition from a K state to an L state, its excess energy being emitted as a quantum of radiant energy. Atomic processes of this sort are assumed to give rise to the $K\alpha$ line. According to this assumption, the quantum $h\nu$ of $K\alpha$ radiant energy is equal to the difference in energy between the K and the L quantum states or levels of the ionized atom.

In a similar way, the $K\beta$ line is assumed to originate when an M electron, with quantum number $n = 3$, drops from the M shell into the K vacancy; i.e., when there occurs an atomic (ionic) transition from a K state to an M state. The picture may be extended to account for, or to predict, any one of a large number of characteristic emission lines. A line may be expected corresponding to any atomic (actually ionic) transition from an initial state characterized by the absence of an electron of quantum number n to a final state corresponding to the absence of any electron of quantum number greater than n. Of course, in an actual target in an x-ray tube many atoms are simultaneously involved and many lines are emitted simultaneously.

This picture suggests, also, an explanation, at least qualitative, of the appearance of the factor $(Z - 1)^2$ instead of Z^2 in Moseley's equation. When, as a result of bombardment by the cathode stream, one of the K electrons is removed from an atom, there is one K electron left near the nucleus. This electron "screens" the nucleus and makes its *effective* nuclear charge about 1 unit less; hence, the factor $(Z - 1)^2$. Further work has shown, however, that Moseley's law holds only as a first approximation.

Following and extending the notation of Barkla, x-ray lines are classified into series known as the K, L, M, N, etc., series, respectively; the letter designating a series refers to the initial atomic (ionic) state in the transitions giving rise to the lines in question. The principal lines in the K series and L series from tungsten are plotted in Fig. 134, as explained under the figure. Each series of lines contains several strong lines and numerous faint ones. To illustrate further the appearance of x-ray spectra, there is shown in Fig. 135 a section of the L series of silver, as recorded with a two-crystal ionization spectrometer of high resolving

power and dispersion.   It is to be noted that the phrase "series of lines"
as used in x-ray spectroscopy refers to a group of lines arising from a
common *initial* atomic state, whereas in the part of spectroscopy that
deals with the outermost electrons of the atom the term "series" is
applied to a group of lines having a common *final* atomic state.

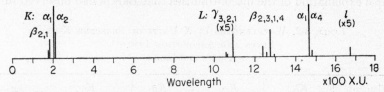

FIG. 134. Plot of the principal K and L lines of tungsten against wavelength.   The
relative intensity of the lines, when observed under certain conditions, is indicated
roughly by the heights of the lines on the plot, the heights for the $L\gamma$ and l lines
being increased in the ratio 1:5.

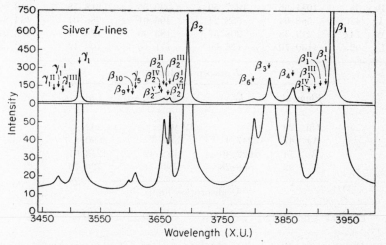

FIG. 135. Distribution of intensity on an arbitrary scale, as measured with an ioniza
tion chamber from a target of silver, in the $L\beta$ region.   The three groups of lines
β^I_1 to β^{IV}_1, β^I_2 to β^{VI}_2, and γ^I_1 to γ^{III}_1, are satellite lines (Sec. 163).   (*From L. G. Parratt
Phys. Rev., vol. 54, p. 99, 1938.*)

In Table 8-2 are listed the wavelengths of the four principal lines of the
K series, the α_1, α_2, β, and γ lines, for a number of elements.

It is more convenient from the theoretical standpoint, however, to
work with quantities proportional to the frequencies of the lines instead
of with their wavelengths; for this purpose values of ν/R are commonly
employed, ν being the frequency and R denoting the Rydberg constant
for an atom of infinite mass (in the same units as ν).   As an example,
for the $K\beta$ line of sulfur, $\nu/R = 181.49$; for the $K\alpha_2$ line of U, it is 8,550.

Many faint x-ray lines, called "satellite lines," originate in atomic transitions between states of double ionization and will be discussed in more detail in a later section (163a). Except in that section, the discussion will be confined to "first-order lines," arising in the manner just described from transitions between states of *single* ionization.

b. Absorption Spectra. This picture just described furnishes also a simple explanation of the discontinuities that Barkla had observed in the

TABLE 8-2. WAVELENGTHS IN X UNITS OF SELECTED X-RAY
LINES AND ABSORPTION LIMITS*

K lines and limits

Element		$K\alpha_2$	$K\alpha_1$	$K\beta_1$	$K\gamma$	λ_K
Al	13	8323.82	8321.37	7965.		7935.1
Ca	20	3354.81	3351.48	3083.4		3063.97
Cu	29	1541.22	1537.40	1389.36	1378.24	1377.65
Br	35	1041.66	1037.59	930.85	918.78	918.09
Ag	47	562.64	558.24	496.01	486.01	484.84
W	74	213.38	208.57	183.99	179.14	178.01
U	92	130.70	125.69	111.16	108.42	106.58

L absorption limits

Element		L_I	L_{II}	L_{III}
Cu	29		12,984.	13,262.
Ag	47	3247.4	3506.7	3690.8
W	74	1022.40	1072.42	1213.01
U	92	568.28	590.71	720.76

M absorption limits

Element		M_I	M_{II}	M_{III}	M_{IV}	M_V
Cu	29	110.7 A	159.5 A	166.0 A		
W	74	4365	4800	5430	6487	6702
U	92	2228	2385	2877	3327	3491

* $K\beta_1$ is really a close doublet, resolved for the heavier elements. $K\gamma$ is also a doublet. Three limits are given in angstroms (A).

SOURCE: Data from Y. Cauchois and H. Hulubei, "Longueurs d'onde des émissions X et des discontinuités d'absorption X," Herman & Cie, Paris, 1947.

absorption coefficient of various materials. Absorption being the reverse of emission, it should be possible for a photon of the right frequency to be absorbed by an atom while one of the K electrons is raised into an L-shell —provided there is a vacancy in the L shell to receive it. As we have seen, however, in atoms with $Z > 10$ the L shell is normally full. Hence for such atoms the $K\alpha$ lines cannot actually be observed as absorption lines. The same is true of all of the x-ray emission lines that are commonly observed. A photon *can* be absorbed, however, if it has enough energy to remove an inner electron from the atom entirely. Let W_K denote the energy required to remove a K electron and to leave it at rest outside the atom. Then a photon of frequency ν can eject a K electron provided $\nu \geqq \nu_K$, where

$$h\nu_K = W_K$$

The explanation of Barkla's absorption curves is now clear. As ν is progressively increased, at the frequency $\nu = \nu_K$ the absorption suddenly increases because absorption in the K shell then begins; and thereafter this absorption continues for all larger values of ν. The curve for the absorption coefficient plotted against frequency or wavelength, therefore, will show a sudden rise toward the side of shorter wavelength at $\nu = \nu_K$. The critical wavelength λ_K or frequency ν_K at which absorption in the K shell begins is called the *K absorption limit*. Some values of λ_K are listed in the last column of Table 8-2. Since the energy W_K required to remove a K electron is somewhat greater than the energy change when the ionized atom undergoes a transition between its K state and another of its discrete quantum states, it is to be expected that λ_K will be somewhat less than the wavelength of any of the K lines. This conclusion is in agreement with observation.

The intimate connection between the emission lines of the K series and the K absorption limit is further shown by the critical voltage which must be applied to the x-ray tube in order to generate these lines. The critical voltage V_K is found to be determined by the relation

$$eV_K = h\nu_K$$

where ν_K is the frequency of the K absorption limit for the material of which the target is composed, h is Planck's constant, and e is the (numerical) electronic charge. Furthermore, *all the lines of the K series are excited at the same critical voltage V_K*, and, as the voltage is increased above V_K, these lines all increase in intensity at exactly the same rate. In the case of tungsten, for example, for which $\lambda_K = 178.01$ X.U., we find from the last equation, or from Eq. (91b) in Sec. 83, that $V_K = 69,500$ volts. When voltages higher than this are applied to a tungsten-target x-ray tube, all the K-series lines of tungsten appear.

Similar facts and interpretations hold for each of the other series. A significant difference, however, is that here more than one absorption limit exists in each case. Thus, *three L absorption limits are found*, denoted, in order of decreasing frequency, by L_I, L_{II}, and L_{III}. There are *five M limits*, *seven N limits*, etc. The theoretical reason for the existence of these multiple limits will be discussed in Sec. 155. The N

and O limits have very long wavelengths, however, and can be observed only for the heaviest atoms.   A few L and M absorption limits in terms of wavelength are listed in Table 8-2.

  c. Fluorescent Spectra.   Finally, the explanation of the fluorescent radiation observed by Barkla is obvious.   After an electron has been removed from the K shell by absorption of a photon, an electron from the L shell or any outer shell may drop into the K shell, accompanied by the emission of a photon belonging to one of the K series of lines.   Thus, as with cathode-ray excitation, the entire series of lines will appear in fluorescence whenever any member of the series appears. Similar statements hold for excitation in outer shells. The frequency of the fluorescent radiation will always be lower than the frequency of the original incident radiation, in agreement with observation.   Fluorescence is a comparatively unusual phenomenon in the visible region, but in the case of x-rays it is very common.

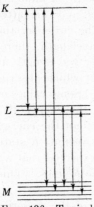

FIG. 136. Typical arrangement of the higher x-ray energy levels.

155. X-ray Energy Levels and Selection Rules. The energies of the various states produced by ionization in an inner shell constitute a set of high-lying *energy levels* for the ionized atom, lying far above the levels encountered in ordinary spectroscopy.   The highest is the K level; below it, corresponding to the three L absorption limits, there must be three L levels, which are denoted, in order of decreasing energy, as the L_I, L_{II}, L_{III} levels; below these, in heavy atoms, are five M levels, M_I, M_{II}, M_{III}, M_{IV}, M_V; and so on.   See Fig. 136.   The energy $h\nu$ for critical absorption that leaves the atom in one of these levels is equal to the difference between the energy of the atom when ionized in that level and the energy of the un-ionized atom in its normal state.   The complete x-ray energy-level diagram for ionized uranium is shown in Fig. 137, energy being plotted on a logarithmic scale.   In lighter atoms, as Z decreases, the lower levels tend to disappear one after the other.

  Lines indicating transitions between x-ray levels are often drawn, as in Figs. 136 and 137, with an arrowhead at each end, to indicate that, in a sense, an electron moves upward on the diagram as the atom moves downward.   Thus, in the emission of a $K\alpha$ line, as the atom drops from its K level to one of its L levels, an electron simultaneously moves from the L shell to the K shell; and so on.   It is not advantageous, however, to think of the diagram as representing a set of levels for an *electron*. For example, if an atom ionized in its K level drops first into one of the L levels and then further into an M level, with the emission of two photons, the electron that moves from the M shell into the L shell during the

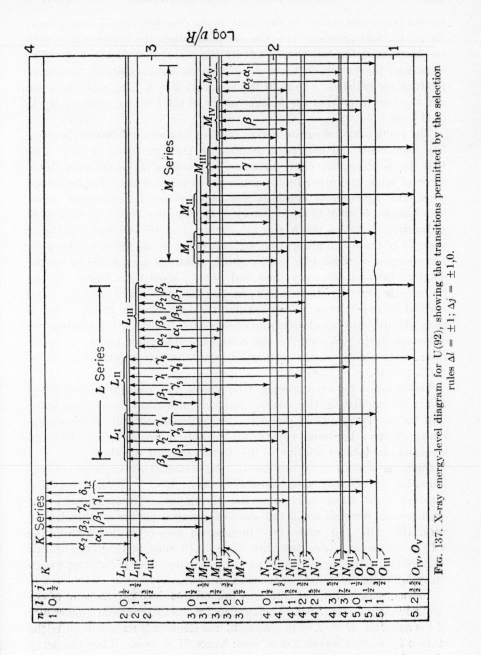

FIG. 137. X-ray energy-level diagram for U(92), showing the transitions permitted by the selection rules $\Delta l = \pm 1$; $\Delta j = \pm 1, 0$.

371

second transition cannot be the same as the one that moved from L to K during the first process.   It is simpler to correlate the atomic states with the location of the *hole* that is left by the removal of an electron.   The atom and the hole both move downward on the diagram as successive photons are emitted.   Thus in the emission of a K line, both the atom and the hole drop from the K level to one of the L levels, or to an M, N, or O level.

The energy-level diagram makes obvious important relations between *line frequencies* and *absorption limits*.   In the first place, it is obvious that the K absorption limit functions as a sort of series limit for the K series of lines, and other limits similarly for other series.   In the second place, the *difference in frequency between the K and L_{II} absorption limits*, for example, *is equal to the frequency of the $K\alpha_2$ line*, which is emitted in a transition between the K and L_{II} levels.   For, the difference in the $h\nu$ energies of these two absorption limits is equal to the difference between the energies of these two levels.   Such relations are predicted by the diagram between all x-ray lines and related absorption limits, and, so far as experimental check has been possible, this conclusion has been verified by experiment.   For example, the ν/R value of the $K\alpha_1$ line of molybdenum was calculated from observation to be 1,287.4, whereas the difference in the ν/R values of the K and L_{III} absorption limits was found from observations of the absorption spectrum of molybdenum to be $1,473.4 - 185.8 = 1,287.6$.

This relation between spectral frequencies and absorption limits is of utility in calculating the *relative* positions of certain absorption limits that cannot be measured directly.   Actual measurement of absorption limits, on the other hand, constitutes the only means by which the x-ray levels can be located relative to the normal state of the atom.

Quantum Theory of X-ray Levels.   No satisfactory explanation was found for the occurrence of *several different L, M, . . .* levels lying close together until wave mechanics was developed.   To understand this explanation, we may recall the wave-mechanical picture as sketched in Secs. 109, 110, 115, and 118.   Because of spin-orbit interaction, the $n\ l\ j\ m$ electronic states described in Sec. 118 must be employed in this connection.   However, it must not be concluded that jj coupling necessarily holds for the inner electrons in an atom.

As was remarked in Sec. 115, any full subshell has Σm, the sum of the electronic m's, equal to 0, and hence also, for the total angular momentum of the subshell, $M = J = 0$.   If, now, one electron is removed out of the state $n\ l\ j\ m$, this leaves $\Sigma m = -m$; hence $M = -m$.   Thus the array of possible values of M resulting from removal of an electron in an $n\ l\ j$ state is the same as the array of possible values of m, and consequently for the resulting ionized state of the subshell we have $J = j$.   Obviously there is an exact correspondence between the states of a singly ionized subshell and those of a single valence electron (Sec. 116). For this reason the x-ray levels are usually labeled with the letter j rather than J. The value of j is the same as that of the removed electron, but it is perhaps better to associate it with the hole that is left behind. The spectroscopic notation customarily employed for a single valence electron is sometimes used also for the corresponding x-ray levels.

The *selection rule* for configurations requires that, in a radiative transition between singly ionized subshells, $\Delta l = \pm 1$; and the general rule for J becomes here a rule for j. Thus for such transitions, giving rise to what are called *diagram lines*, the selection rules are

$$\Delta l = \pm 1 \qquad \Delta j = 0 \text{ or } \pm 1$$

For the innermost shell, $n = 1$, $l = 0$; hence, when it is singly ionized, we have $j = \frac{1}{2}$ and only one energy level. Hence there can be only a single K level. In the L shell, however, $n = 2$ and $l = 0$ or 1. The subshell with $l = 0$ again gives rise to a single level; but that with $l = 1$ gives rise to two levels, with $j = \frac{1}{2}$ or $\frac{3}{2}$. Thus the three L levels are accounted for. Similarly, the theory predicts the existence of five M levels, and so on, in agreement with observation.

Identification of the levels thus inferred with those previously denoted by such symbols as L_I, L_{II} is made as follows. The selection rule for l shows that the $K\alpha$ doublet must arise from transitions into the two L levels with $l = 1, j = \frac{1}{2}$ and $l = 1, j = \frac{3}{2}$, in analogy with the D lines of sodium. Thus these two levels must be L_{II} and L_{III}, the $(0, \frac{1}{2})$ level being therefore L_I. Comparison of the selection rules with other lines similarly identifies L_{II} as having $j = \frac{1}{2}$, so that L_{III} has $j = \frac{3}{2}$. Furthermore, since the spin-orbit effect of one electron is *subtracted* when a subshell is ionized, it would be expected that the order of the levels would be inverted as compared with the alkali fine-structure levels; for example, the $j = \frac{3}{2}$ level should lie below that for $j = \frac{1}{2}$ in the same doublet. This is in agreement with the order already inferred for the L levels. Use of this principle together with the selection rules results in the remaining identifications shown in Fig. 137.

Certain predictions as to the *relative intensity* of x-ray lines may also be derived from the theory. Lines in which l and j change in the same sense should be stronger than those in which l and j change in opposite directions; and the lines for the largest values of l and j should be, as a rule, the strongest. These conclusions from the approximate theory agree, in a general way, with the data. The order of the subscripts commonly used in designating lines, α, β, γ, δ, . . . , indicates, in general, decreasing intensity; lines such as η and l are very weak. In the case of lines that start from a common initial level, furthermore, the theory leads to *quantitative* predictions concerning the relative intensities. When the initial level is the same for two lines, uncertainties in regard to the relative probabilities of excitation do not arise. Thus, theoretically, $K\alpha_1$ should be twice as strong as $K\alpha_2$; and experimentally this is at least very nearly true. Experimental work on the relative intensities of x-ray lines is, however, usually very difficult, because of the numerous troublesome corrections that have to be made to the observed intensities.[1]

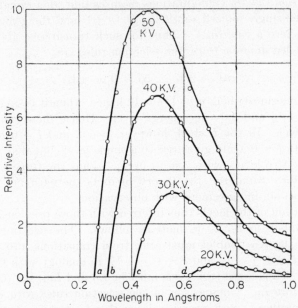

FIG. 138. Ulrey's curves for the distribution of energy in the continuous x-ray spectrum of tungsten at various voltages.

It should be remarked in conclusion that the dipole selection rules, employed above, do not hold in all cases, in agreement again with theoretical predictions. Many weak lines "forbidden" by these rules have been observed; especially in the spectra of the heavier elements, lines have been reported[2] corresponding to transitions $L_{III} \rightarrow N_{II}$ and $L_{III} \rightarrow N_{III}$, for each of which $\Delta l = 0$. Such lines are called "quadrupole" lines. They are subject to a different set of selection rules (for example, $\Delta l = 0$ or ± 2).

156. The Continuous X-ray Spectrum. The characteristic line spectrum emitted by an x-ray target as observed is superposed upon a *continuous spectrum*. This appears clearly, for example, in Fig. 132. The

[1] L. G. Parratt, *Phys. Rev.*, vol. 54, p. 99, 1938.

[2] Idei, *Tôhoku Univ., Sci. & Technol. Reports*, vol. 19, p. 559, 1930; Kaufman, *Phys. Rev.*, vol. 40, p. 116, 1932.

positions, i.e., wavelengths, of the *lines* are determined solely by the material of the target; their *intensity* is determined, for a given target material and tube current, by the voltage applied to the tube. On the other hand, the *wavelength* characteristics of the *continuous* spectrum are quite independent of the material of the target but are determined by the voltage applied to the tube. The intensity of the continuous spectrum, for a given tube current, is dependent both on the target material and on the applied voltage, as well as on the thickness of the target.

A series of four spectral-energy distribution curves, recorded with an ionization spectrometer for the radiation from a tungsten target, and for applied voltages of 20,000, 30,000, 40,000, and 50,000 volts, respectively, is shown in Fig. 138.[1] The spectral region of this figure lies between the *K*- and *L*-series lines of tungsten. Starting at the long-wavelength side, the curves rise to a maximum and then drop rapidly toward zero; the position of the maximum depends on the applied voltage. The curves are seen to meet the axis at finite angles, as is shown at the intersections *a*, *b*, *c*, and *d*, respectively. The intersections come at shorter wavelengths, the higher the voltage.

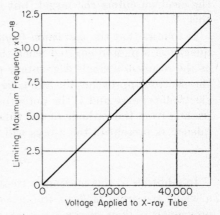

Fig. 139. Relation between the limiting frequency and the applied voltage.

A very simple relation exists between these limiting frequencies and the applied voltage; it is shown graphically in Fig. 139, in which limiting frequencies are plotted as ordinates against applied voltages as abscissas. It will be seen that the limiting frequency is strictly proportional to the applied voltage.

The existence of this sharp "cutoff" is hard to explain on the basis of classical theory. The continuous spectrum is believed to be emitted as a consequence of the deflection of the cathode electrons by the strong fields surrounding the nuclei of the atoms of the target itself. According to classical theory, acceleration of an electron causes the emission of a pulse of radiation. According to quantum theory, however, our conception of the process by which acceleration of a cathode-ray electron produces radiation requires the same sort of modification that is necessary in the case of a spectral line emitted by an atomic electron. A cathode electron passing through the strong electric field near the nucleus of an atom is

[1] These curves are from the measurements of Ulrey, *Phys. Rev.*, vol. 11, p. 401, 1918. They are subject to certain corrections.

not to be thought of as undergoing continuous acceleration, accompanied by the continuous emission of radiation. The process is essentially one of alternative probabilities. The electron may actually pass through the field undeviated in direction; it is much more likely, however, to issue from the atom in a different direction from its direction of approach. It may suffer no change in its energy, being merely deflected or "scattered"; and in this case no radiation is emitted. Or, it may suffer a decrease ΔW in energy; in this latter case the energy lost is emitted as a photon of frequency ν given by Einstein's equation, $h\nu = \Delta W$. The amount of energy lost cannot exceed the total kinetic energy with which the electron enters the target, but it may have any value smaller than this.

It follows that the *maximum frequency* ν_0 of the x-rays will be the frequency of a photon emitted when the electron is brought entirely to rest as the result of a single elementary process. For the energy with which the electron approaches the atom, we can write eV, e being the (numerical) electronic charge and V the potential difference through which it falls in passing from the cathode of the tube to the target. The maximum frequency ν_0 present in the x-rays will thus be determined by the equation

$$h\nu_0 = eV \tag{203}$$

In addition to this maximum frequency ν_0, we should then expect also a whole spectrum of *lower* frequencies, emitted by electrons which lose only a part of their energy in a single encounter with a nucleus, in the form of a smaller quantum $h\nu$. A further reason for the emission of frequencies lower than ν_0 lies in the fact that, in the vast majority of cases, an electron will experience many collisions with atoms of the target before being brought to rest, and at each of these collisions some of the initial energy eV is dissipated. Thus, a great deal of radiation is emitted by electrons which impinge upon atoms with incident energy less than eV. If the target is sufficiently thin, however—say of very thin gold foil—only a few of the electrons of the incident cathode stream will collide with atoms in it, most of them passing through the target undeviated. Thus slowly moving electrons will not be present in a *thin* target to the same degree as in a *thick* one. Accordingly, we should expect that a greater proportion of the energy in the continuous spectrum from thin targets should lie near the ν_0 limit than from thick targets. This is in agreement with experiment.

In the continuous spectrum from a *very thin* target, as a matter of fact, experiment indicates, in agreement with the wave-mechanical computation of Sommerfeld, that the maximum of the energy-distribution curve occurs *at the limiting wavelength λ_0 itself*. On the short-wave side of λ_0, the curve drops abruptly to the axis of abscissas, whereas toward longer waves it falls nearly in proportion to $1/\lambda^2$, as illustrated in Fig. 140. The curves for a thick target, as in Fig. 138, can be regarded as arising from the superposition of many elementary curves, such as that in Fig. 140 with various values of λ_0. In such a target it might be expected that there would be a *most probable* type of collision which would correspond to the peak or maximum of the energy-distribution curve.

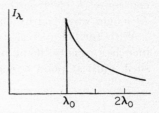

Observations of the limiting frequency ν_0 are a good source of data from which to calculate h, or rather h/e (Sec. 48). For a time, values of h so obtained did not agree quite as well as might be expected with values derived from other sources. It was discovered, however,

Fig. 140. Approximate distribution of energy in the continuous x-ray spectrum from a very thin target, near the short-wavelength limit.

that a slight bend in the curves close to the limit of vanishing intensity had not been revealed by the earlier work, and when allowance was made for this bend the difficulty disappeared.[1]

INTERACTIONS OF X-RAYS WITH ATOMS

157. The Absorption of X-rays. In this section a few further details will be given concerning the absorption of x-rays in matter. In contrast with the apparently chaotic state of affairs in regard to the absorption of light in the visible or near-visible portions of the spectrum, we find comparative simplicity in the laws for the absorption of x-rays. Measurements of the absorption coefficient for a monochromatic beam of parallel rays are readily made by use of the ionization spectrometer [Fig. 131(a)]. It is necessary to use such a tube voltage as to eliminate second-order reflections. For a given crystal angle θ and, therefore, wavelength λ, the ionization current is measured both with and without a sheet of absorbing material of known density ρ and thickness x placed in the path of the beam, say between the two slits S_1 and S_2. These measurements give, respectively, I and I_0 in the equation

$$I = I_0 e^{-\mu x} = I_0 e^{-(\mu/\rho)\rho x} \tag{204}$$

from which either the *linear absorption coefficient* μ or the *mass absorption coefficient* μ/ρ may be computed.

a. Properties of μ/ρ. Figure 141 shows roughly the mass absorption coefficient of lead in the wavelength range $0.1 < \lambda < 1.2$ A. Beginning at point o, μ/ρ rises rapidly with increasing wavelength until point a, corresponding to $\lambda = 0.1405$ A and $\mu/\rho = 8$ (about), is reached, at which

[1] Panofsky, Green, and DuMond, *Phys. Rev.*, vol. 62, p. 217, 1942.

the value of μ/ρ suddenly drops to point a'. This is the K absorption limit (Secs. 149 and 154). Up to this point, absorption accompanied by ejection of K electrons has constituted the major part of the absorption. At longer wavelengths, this K absorption does not occur at all.

With further increase in wavelength, however, the absorption again increases rapidly, being mostly due now to ionization of atoms in the L shell, until at point b, corresponding to $\lambda = 0.780$ A, the L_I absorption

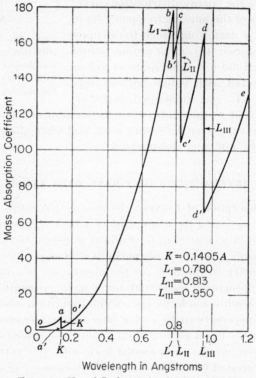

FIG. 141. K and L absorption limits of lead.

limit is reached, at which there occurs another drop in the absorption to point b'. From b' to c, absorption still occurs owing to processes which leave the ionized atoms in L_{II} or L_{III} states; i.e., the atoms are raised to their L_{II} or L_{III} energy levels. None, however, is raised to the L_I level. Similar drops or "breaks" occur at cc' ($\lambda = 0.813$ A) and at dd' ($\lambda = 0.950$ A), the L_{II} and L_{III} limits, respectively; from c' to d, absorption into the L_{III} state is still occurring, but beyond d' absorption with ionization in the L shell ceases altogether. Beyond point d', however, the absorption again increases rapidly. If we could follow, by direct measurement, the absorption beyond point e, we should find that, in the region $3.2 < \lambda < 5.0$ A, a group of five "breaks" occurs, representing the five M absorption limits; beginning at about 14 A, there would come the group of seven N limits; etc.

Curves similar to Fig. 141 are obtained for the absorption of x-rays in other substances, the respective discontinuities or limits occurring at longer wavelengths, the lower the atomic number of the absorber. In fact, a curve plotted between the square root of the frequency of a given limit and the atomic number is nearly a straight line, similar to Moseley's curve (Fig. 133) for line spectra.

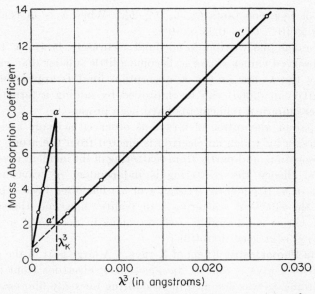

Fig. 142. Mass absorption coefficients of lead as a function of wavelength, showing the K discontinuity and the linear relation between μ/ρ and λ^3.

In Fig. 142 is shown the mass absorption coefficient of lead as measured by Richtmyer[1] in the region o to o' of Fig. 141, plotted as a function of the cube of the wavelength. The two parts of the graph on each side of the K absorption limit aa' are seen to be *straight lines*, with nearly equal intercepts at $\lambda = 0$. We can write, therefore, in the regions ao and $a'o'$, respectively,

$$\frac{\mu}{\rho} = k\lambda^3 + b \qquad \frac{\mu}{\rho} = k'\lambda^3 + b \qquad\qquad (205a,b)$$

k, k', and b denoting empirical constants.

A further striking relation becomes evident when Eqs. (205a,b) are divided through by the number of atoms per gram or N_0/A where N_0 is Avogadro's number and A is the atomic weight. The left-hand mem-

[1] F. K. Richtmyer, *Phys. Rev.*, vol. 27, p. 1, 1925.

ber then becomes the *atomic* absorption coefficient, or coefficient of absorption per atom, $\mu_a = \mu A / N_0 \rho$. The new coefficients of λ^3 are then found to be *nearly proportional to the fourth power of Z*, the atomic number of the absorbing atoms. Thus we can also write, as approximate empirical equations, with λ_K and λ_L denoting, respectively, the K and L absorption limits,

$$\lambda < \lambda_K: \qquad \mu_a = C_a Z^4 \lambda^3 + b_a \qquad (206a)$$
$$\lambda_K < \lambda < \lambda_L: \qquad \mu_a = C_a' Z^4 \lambda^3 + b_a' \qquad (206b)$$

in terms of new constants C_a, b_a, C_a', b_a'. When λ is in centimeters, $C_a = 2.25 \times 10^{-2}$, $C_a' = 0.33 \times 10^{-2}$.

The formulas just written do not hold accurately, however; for example, the observed values of μ or μ_a become a little smaller than values calculated by the λ^3 law as the K absorption limit is approached. The formula given in (206a) can be improved by adding a term $-DZ^6 \lambda^4$; and further empirical refinements have been proposed.[1]

The apparent absorption of x-rays as observed actually arises partly from processes by which an electron is ejected from the atom, resulting in true absorption, and partly from scattering of the incident rays. Since in classical theory the scattering is independent of wavelength, the constant b or b_a (frequently written σ or σ_a) has often been supposed to represent the effect of scattering. In reality, however, the scattering coefficient varies considerably with wavelength (Sec. 159), so that this identification is at least doubtful.

158. The Photoelectric Effect of X-rays. A large part of the apparent absorption of x-rays is due to the ejection of electrons from the inner shells of atoms, as was assumed in accounting for x-ray fluorescence. It should be possible to observe these electrons as photoelectrons. When an electron is ejected from the K shell by x-rays of frequency ν, the amount of energy absorbed from the radiation is $h\nu$; but work equal to $h\nu_K$ must be done by the electron in escaping from the atom, ν_K being the frequency of the K absorption limit. Hence the electron will emerge from the atom with kinetic energy equal to $h\nu - h\nu_K$. If the atom lies on the surface of the absorbing material, the electron may escape into the surrounding space with this amount of energy [more exactly with energy $h\nu - h\nu_K - \omega_0$ (Sec. 52), but ω_0 is usually negligibly small]. Otherwise it may lose part of its energy in passing through a layer of matter. Thus the *maximum* kinetic energy with which photoelectrons produced by absorption in the K shell may emerge from the absorbing material is, effectively,

$$\tfrac{1}{2} m v_m^2 = h(\nu - \nu_K) \qquad (207)$$

---

[1] Victoreen, *J. Appl. Phys.*, vol. 14, p. 95, 1943; vol. 19, p. 855, 1948; vol. 20, p. 1141, 1949.

If $\nu < \nu_K$, no photoelectrons at all can be ejected from the K shell. As ν increases above ν_K, the maximum energy of the photoelectrons increases linearly, just as in the ordinary photoelectric effect. The *number* of photoelectrons ejected from the K shell decreases, however, as ν increases, thereby causing the known decrease in the absorption coefficient as ν recedes from ν_K. The number of photoelectrons is strictly proportional to the intensity of the x-rays.

Similar statements hold for the photoelectrons ejected from the L shell, which consist of three slightly different groups with maximum energies corresponding to the three L absorption limits, ν_{L_I}, $\nu_{L_{II}}$, $\nu_{L_{III}}$.

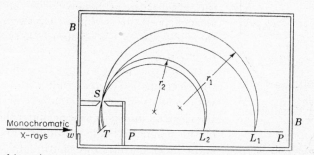

Fig. 143. Robinson's magnetic spectrograph for studying the photoelectric action of x-rays.

The differences in these maximum energies arise from differences in the quantum state in which the remaining L electrons are left. Similarly, from the M shell there are five groups; and so on. If we start with x-rays of very high frequency, photoelectrons of all kinds are produced. If the frequency is then decreased, as it passes ν_K, the K photoelectrons disappear; as it passes the L limits, the three groups of L photoelectrons disappear in turn; and so on.

Among the experiments demonstrating these facts may be mentioned those of Robinson and his collaborators,[1] whose apparatus is shown diagrammatically in Fig. 143. A beam of x-rays of frequency[2] ν enters through a thin window W a highly evacuated brass box BB and falls

[1] Robinson et al., *Phil. Mag.*, vol. 28, p. 277, 1914; *Proc. Roy. Soc. (London)*, vol. 104, p. 455, 1923; *Phil. Mag.*, vol. 50, p. 241, 1925; *Proc. Roy. Soc. (London)*, vol. 128, p. 92, 1930.

[2] It is extremely difficult by present experimental means to get a strictly monochromatic beam of x-rays of sufficient intensity for such an experiment as this. Accordingly, use is made of the fact that, with suitable exciting voltage, the $K\alpha$ lines from an x-ray target are much more intense than the accompanying radiation of the other wavelengths and, therefore, serve effectively as a "monochromatic" beam, particularly if the beam is first passed through a filter of suitable thickness, the wavelength of whose K limit is just shorter than the wavelength of the $K\alpha$ lines. (See Hull, *Phys. Rev.*, vol. 10, p. 661, 1917.)

upon a target T of the material under investigation. Photoelectrons are expelled from the surface of T in all directions and with various velocities. The whole apparatus is placed in a known magnetic field B, at right angles to the plane of the paper, which can be varied at will; the photoelectrons describe circles in this field. Some of them pass through the narrow slit S and eventually strike the photographic plate PP. If the electrons leaving T have velocities $v_1, v_2, \ldots$, they will move in circles of radii $r_1, r_2, \ldots$ and will strike the plate at points $L_1, L_2, \ldots$. As shown

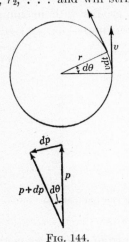

in the figure, the arrangement is such as to "focus" electrons leaving the different parts of the target with the same velocity onto the plate at such positions as L_1 and L_2, the diameter of the circle being the distance between S and L_1 or L_2.

In an experiment such as this, the velocity of the electrons is so great that variation of mass with velocity must be taken into account. As the electron moves in a circle under the influence of the magnetic field, its momentum p is constant in magnitude but continually changes in direction. We can imagine that the electron receives continually vector increments of momentum directed toward the center of the circle.

FIG. 144.

As the direction of motion changes by $d\theta$ an increment dp of momentum must be added of magnitude (Fig. 144) $dp = p\,d\theta$. The force on the electron is evB, e being the electronic charge in electromagnetic units and v its velocity. Hence during a time dt the electron receives momentum[1]

$$dp = evB\,dt$$

But, also, $dp = p\,d\theta$; and $d\theta = v\,dt/r$. Hence

$$p = erB \qquad\qquad (208)$$

Furthermore, from Eq. (9)

$$\frac{p^2}{m^2 c^2} = \frac{v^2/c^2}{1 - v^2/c^2} \qquad \therefore \frac{p^2}{m^2 c^2} + 1 = \frac{1}{1 - v^2/c^2}$$

[1] Equations relating to the motion of charged particles in given electric or magnetic fields are valid without change in esu, emu, or mks units, provided all quantities are expressed in the same system. Since the magnetic induction B is seldom expressed in esu, the emu or mks units are generally preferred when magnetic deflection is involved. The mixed, "Gaussian" system that is frequently used requires electric quantities to be expressed in esu and magnetic quantities in emu; the force relation is then $\mathbf{F} = e\mathbf{E} + (e/c)\mathbf{v} \times \mathbf{B}$. In the mks, or practical, system, lengths are expressed in meters, masses in kilograms and energy in joules. See Appendix I.

Hence we can also write Eq. (10) for the kinetic energy of the electron in the form[1]

$$T = mc^2 \left[\left(1 + \frac{p^2}{m^2c^2} \right)^{\frac{1}{2}} - 1 \right] \qquad (209)$$

and for an electron revolving in a magnetic field, by (208),

$$T = mc^2 \left[\left(1 + \frac{e^2r^2B^2}{m^2c^2} \right)^{\frac{1}{2}} - 1 \right] \qquad (210)$$

Here m is the electronic rest mass.

By means of this last formula, values of the kinetic energy T of the photoelectrons can be calculated from measured values of r, for comparison with $h(\nu - \nu_A)$, where ν_A is any absorption limit. If losses of energy by the electrons within the absorber are negligible, we can substitute values of T so found in the photoelectric equation

$$T = h(\nu - \nu_A)$$

and, knowing ν, can obtain values of the absorption limit ν_A, for comparison with values measured spectroscopically.

Robinson found on his plates a number of "lines" representing groups of photoelectrons. The corresponding absorption limits, calculated in the manner just described, were in complete agreement with values determined spectroscopically. He found *one K* level, *three L* levels, *five M* levels, and, in the case of U 92, five of the seven N levels, the pairs of levels $N_{IV,V}$ and $N_{VI,VII}$ being too close together to be resolved in his apparatus.

The technique of measuring the velocities of photoelectrons ejected by x-rays has been developed to the point that this method is now one of the most reliable for the precise determination of physical constants.[2]

159. The Scattering of X-rays. *a. The Total Scattering Coefficient.* When a beam of monochromatic x-rays of intensity I traverses a thickness dx of scattering material, part of the incident energy is scattered, for which we may write $\sigma I \, dx$. The coefficient σ thus defined is called the *total linear scattering coefficient* for x-rays of that wavelength. According to the simple classical theory described in Sec. 148 and based on the two assumptions (1) that the electrons scatter as if they were free and (2) interference between the wavelets scattered by different electrons may be ignored, the value of σ can be found by multiplying the scattering

---

[1] Calculations from such formulas are most easily made thus:

$$T = mc^2 \left[\left(\cos \tan^{-1} \frac{p}{mc} \right)^{-1} - 1 \right]$$

[2] Robinson et al., *Phil. Mag.*, vol. 22, p. 1129, 1936; *Proc. Roy. Soc. (London)*, vol. 173A, p. 192, 1939, and 176A, p. 28, 1940.

coefficient σ_e for a single electron, as given in Eq. (200), by n, the number of electrons per cubic centimeter of the material. If we also divide by ρ, the density of the material, we find thus for the *classical mass scattering coefficient*

$$\frac{\sigma_0}{\rho} = \frac{n\sigma_e}{\rho} = \frac{8\pi}{3} \frac{e^4}{m^2c^4} \frac{n}{\rho} \tag{211}$$

Thus, if we assume that $\sigma = \sigma_0$, σ/ρ should be independent of wavelength, and it should not vary greatly with the material, since n is roughly

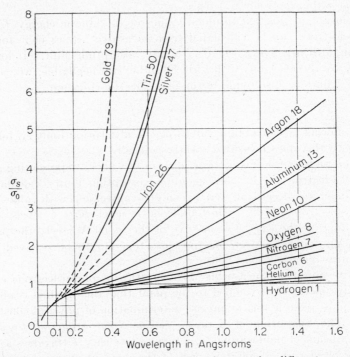

Fig. 145. Scattering coefficients σ_s of various elements for different wavelengths relative to the classical value σ_0. (*Reproduced by courtesy of D. Van Nostrand Company, Inc., from Fig. III-3 in A. H. Compton and S. K. Allison, "X-rays in Theory and Experiment," 1935.*)

proportional to ρ (the number of electrons per atom being about half the atomic weight); it should, in fact, be nearly equal to 0.2, as may be verified by putting into Eq. (211) the numerical values of the constants e, m, and c and the values of n and ρ for some scattering material, such as carbon or aluminum. In Fig. 145 are shown data on scattering for a number of elementary substances; the ordinates represent the ratio of the scattering coefficient σ for the substance, denoted by σ_s in the figure, to the value σ_0 as given in Eq. (211). We note from the figure that for light scattering materials and for x-rays of $\lambda > 0.2$ A the scattering coefficients approximate to the classical free-electron value σ_0. Otherwise, there are wide departures.

For heavier materials, and especially at longer wavelengths, σ greatly exceeds σ_0. This excessive scattering is easily explained classically. When the wavelength becomes comparable with the distances between the electrons in the atoms, they no longer scatter independently; the waves scattered by different electrons become superposed on each other more or less in the same phase, and constructive interference occurs. If the wavelength is actually long as compared to the distances between the N electrons in a given atom, the relative phase differences of the waves are all small, consequently the amplitude of the resultant scattered wave is approximately proportional to N, and the intensity of the scattered radiation is proportional to N^2. For a heavy atom, the difference is enormous.

The decrease of σ at short wavelengths which is evident from Fig. 145, on the other hand, is impossible of explanation by classical theory. For $\lambda = 0.1$ A, the observed scattering coefficient is only about 0.15, instead of the value of about 0.2 deduced above. For γ-rays, the wavelengths of which are of the order of 0.02 A or less, the total absorption coefficient of carbon, including photoelectric absorption as well as that due to scattering, is only about 0.06. For such short waves, however, the assumption that the electrons scatter independently, and approximately at the same rate as if they were free, should certainly be justified; for, on classical theory, they will not move far enough from their equilibrium positions to call appreciable elastic forces into play. Wave mechanics, on the other hand, furnishes a complicated formula that agrees very well with observations in this region of short wavelengths.[1]

b. *The Angular Distribution of Scattered X-ray Energy.* According to Thomson's simple pulse theory (Sec. 148), the intensity of x-rays scattered out of an unpolarized beam should be twice as great in directions at 0° or 180° from the direction of the incident beam as at 90°, varying with scattering angle as shown by a curve in Fig. 146. The extreme difference mentioned is due to the fact that at a scattering angle of 90° the component of electronic acceleration parallel to the direction of scattering contributes nothing to the scattered beam. In Fig. 146 are shown also the observed relative intensities at different angles for x-rays of wavelength $\lambda = 0.71$ A scattered from liquid mesitylene $C_6H_3(CH_3)_3$, and for rays with $\lambda = 0.017$ A scattered from iron. At the longer wavelength some agreement with Thomson's theory will be noted, but the scattering of very short waves is much less than that predicted by classical theory, and the scattered radiation is also heavily concentrated in

[1] W. Heitler, "The Quantum Theory of Radiation," 2d ed., p. 157, 1944.

the forward direction.   Both these features, likewise, are in quantitative agreement with the wave-mechanical theory.

160. The Compton Effect.   *a. The Modified Line.*   It was early found that secondary radiation is usually *less* penetrating than the primary radiation.   This fact was later explained as due to the presence in the secondary beam, not only of scattered radiation, but also of the *characteristic fluorescent* radiation, which, as we have seen, is always of longer wavelength and therefore less penetrating than the primary beam.   It

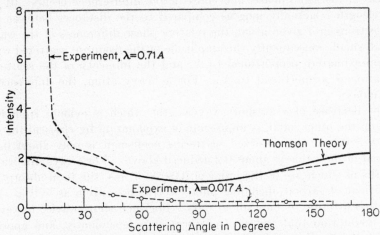

FIG. 146. Relative scattered intensity at various angles of scattering, for x-rays of λ 0.71 A scattered by mesitylene, and for x-rays of λ 0.017 A scattered by iron. (*Reproduced by courtesy of D. Van Nostrand Company, Inc., from Fig. III-4 in A. H. Compton and S. K. Allison, "X-rays in Theory and Experiment," 1935.*)

was found, however, that this explanation was not adequate in all cases. For example, a scattering material of very low atomic number, such as carbon, emits fluorescent radiation of such long wavelength as to be absorbed by even a thin film of air.   Yet, even with carbon immersed in air as the scatterer, the secondary beam was found to be somewhat less penetrating and presumably therefore of somewhat longer mean wavelength than the primary.

The explanation of such cases was discovered by A. H. Compton. He showed[1] that, when *monochromatic* primary radiation is used, the scattered beam is composed of *two lines*, one corresponding in wavelength to that of the primary beam and the other being of definitely longer wavelength.   Figure 147 shows the spectrum of radiation scattered at 90° from a carbon scatterer when irradiated by the $K\alpha$ line of molybdenum. The vertical line *aa* indicates the wavelength of the primary radiation.

[1] A. H. Compton, *Phys. Rev.*, vol. 21, p. 715; vol. 22, p. 409, 1923.

There are seen to be two maxima, or lines, one of which, P, corresponds exactly to the primary radiation, whereas the other, S, is "shifted" toward longer wavelengths, the difference in wavelength being 0.0236 A.

In order to explain the occurrence of the shifted component, Compton boldly applied the extreme quantum picture of radiant energy. He assumed that the scattering process could be treated as an elastic collision between a photon and an electron and that this collision is governed by the two laws of mechanics: (1) the conservation of energy, and (2) the conservation of momentum.

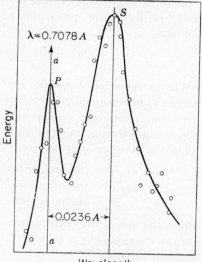

Let an incident photon containing energy $E_0 = h\nu_0$ rebound from an electron of rest mass m_0, initially at rest at the point a (Fig. 148). After the collision, let the electron move in a direction making an angle ϕ with the initial direction of motion of the photon, while the photon itself moves in a direction making an angle θ with its initial direction. Qualitatively, one sees at once that the energy E_θ of the photon after collision and, therefore, also the frequency must be less than that of the photon before collision, since some of its energy must have been given to the electron.

FIG. 147. The spectrum of scattered x-rays, showing the unmodified line P and the modified or "shifted" line S. (*Compton.*)

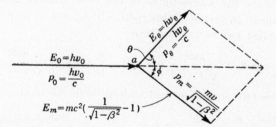

FIG. 148. Vector diagram showing the conservation of momentum when a photon is scattered by an electron.

If E_m is the kinetic energy of the electron after the collision, we have, from the law of the conservation of energy,

$$E_0 = E_\theta + E_m$$

Using the relativistic formula, Eq. (10), we have

$$E_m = mc^2 \left(\frac{1}{\sqrt{1 - \beta^2}} - 1 \right) \qquad \beta = \frac{v}{c} \tag{212a,b}$$

v denoting the velocity of the electron after the collision. Inserting this value of E_m in the preceding equation, and also $E_0 = h\nu_0$, $E_\theta = h\nu_\theta$, we have

$$h\nu_0 = h\nu_\theta + mc^2 \left(\frac{1}{\sqrt{1 - \beta^2}} - 1 \right) \tag{213}$$

Furthermore, as stated in Sec. 226, a beam of radiation in free space carries momentum equal to the energy carried by it divided by c. Hence a photon, containing energy $h\nu$, carries momentum $h\nu/c$. The momentum of an electron moving with speed v is given by Eq. (9) in Sec. 37. Thus for the momenta we have

$h\nu_0/c$ = the momentum of the photon before the collision
$h\nu_\theta/c$ = the momentum of the photon after the collision
$mv/\sqrt{1 - \beta^2}$ = the momentum of the electron (after the collision)

From the law of the conservation of momentum, therefore, we can write for the x component of momentum (in the direction of propagation of the incident photon)

$$\frac{h\nu_0}{c} = \frac{h\nu_\theta}{c} \cos\theta + \frac{m\beta c}{\sqrt{1 - \beta^2}} \cos\phi$$

and for the y component, in the plane containing the directions of motion of both the scattered photon and the electron,

$$0 = \frac{h\nu_\theta}{c} \sin\theta - \frac{m\beta c}{\sqrt{1 - \beta^2}} \sin\phi$$

If we introduce the wavelengths of the two photons (whatever wavelength may mean in terms of this picture!), $\lambda_0 = c/\nu_0$ and $\lambda_\theta = c/\nu_\theta$, we can write the last two equations thus:

$$\frac{h}{\lambda_0} - \frac{h}{\lambda_\theta} \cos\theta = \frac{m\beta c}{\sqrt{1 - \beta^2}} \cos\phi \qquad \frac{h}{\lambda_\theta} \sin\theta = \frac{m\beta c}{\sqrt{1 - \beta^2}} \sin\phi$$

Squaring these two equations and adding them, we have

$$\frac{h^2}{\lambda_0{}^2} + \frac{h^2}{\lambda_\theta{}^2} - \frac{2h^2}{\lambda_0\lambda_\theta} \cos\theta = \frac{m^2\beta^2c^2}{1 - \beta^2} = \frac{m^2c^2}{1 - \beta^2} - m^2c^2 \tag{214}$$

Similarly Eq. (213) can be written, after dividing it through by c,

$$\frac{h}{\lambda_0} - \frac{h}{\lambda_\theta} + mc = \frac{mc}{\sqrt{1 - \beta^2}}$$

$$\therefore \frac{h^2}{\lambda_0{}^2} + \frac{h^2}{\lambda_\theta{}^2} - \frac{2h^2}{\lambda_0\lambda_\theta} + 2mch \left(\frac{1}{\lambda_0} - \frac{1}{\lambda_\theta} \right) + m^2c^2 = \frac{m^2c^2}{1 - \beta^2}$$

Subtracting Eq. (214) from the last equation, we obtain

$$\frac{2h^2}{\lambda_0 \lambda_\theta} (\cos \theta - 1) + 2mch \left(\frac{1}{\lambda_0} - \frac{1}{\lambda_\theta}\right) = 0$$

$$\therefore \lambda_\theta - \lambda_0 = \frac{h}{mc} (1 - \cos \theta) \qquad (215a)$$

If we insert here the values $h = 6.625 \times 10^{-27}$, $m = 0.9108 \times 10^{-27}$, $c = 2.998 \times 10^{10}$, and multiply by 10^8, we have

$$\lambda_\theta - \lambda_0 = 0.0243(1 - \cos \theta) \qquad \text{angstrom} \qquad (215b)$$

This equation states that *when incident radiation of wavelength λ_0 is scattered by a free electron at an angle θ, the wavelength λ_θ of the scattered radiation should be greater than that of the incident radiation by the quantity* $0.0243(1 - \cos \theta)$ A, which, for a given angle θ, is constant whatever the incident wavelength. When the scattering angle is 90°, the "shift" in wavelength between the primary and the scattered beam should be 0.0243 A. Further, the shift should be entirely independent of the material of the scatterer, and for various angles θ of scattering it should be proportional to $(1 - \cos \theta)$. To a first approximation these predictions were soon confirmed by further investigations. The predicted recoil electrons, as they are called, were immediately detected by C. T. R. Wilson[1] and W. Bothe.[2] Furthermore, by the method of the magnetic spectrograph, described in Sec. 158, Bless showed that the observed values of E for the recoil electrons are in agreement with the theory.[3]

b. The Unmodified Line. The presence of the unmodified line (P in Fig. 147) may be accounted for as follows. In setting up our equations, it was assumed that the electron with which the photon collides is free. This assumption should be approximately justified if the energy given to the electron is much larger than the work necessary to detach it from the atom. It is possible, however, that another type of collision may occur in which the electron remains bound to the atom. Such a collision may be regarded as taking place between the photon and the atom as a whole, the mass of which is far greater than that of the electron. If the mass of the atom itself is substituted for m in Eq. (215a), the computed change of wavelength is found to be so small as to be beyond the possibility of detection. It may well be that, in the scattering of photons, the electron sometimes behaves as if bound to the atom and sometimes as if free.

[1] C. T. R. Wilson, *Proc. Roy. Soc. (London)*, vol. 104, p. 1, 1923.

[2] W. Bothe, *Z. Physik*, vol. 20, p. 237, 1923.

[3] A. A. Bless, *Phys. Rev.*, vol. 29, p. 918, 1927.

To refine the theory by taking account of the nuclear field that holds the electrons in the atoms, resort must be had to the methods of wave mechanics. The following conclusions are reached,[1] which, as far as tested, are confirmed by experiment. At very low frequencies, the scattered radiation has the same frequency as the frequency ν of the incident radiation, constituting an unmodified scattered line. As the wavelength becomes comparable with the dimensions of the electronic shells in the atoms, however, the intensity of the radiation thus scattered diminishes, especially at the larger angles of scattering. Then, as ν becomes larger than the absorption limits for any given atomic shell, Compton scattering accompanied by the ejection of recoil electrons out of this shell sets in; and, at considerably greater frequencies, the modified line due to this type of scattering becomes easily observable.

The Compton or modified line is very broad at comparatively low frequencies. This breadth can be thought of as caused by the motion of the electrons in the atom. In our simple deduction of the Compton effect, the electron was assumed to be initially at rest; if it is assumed to have a component of velocity, positive or negative, in the direction of the incident radiation, the wavelength shift is different. Wave mechanics furnishes a probability distribution for the velocities of the atomic electrons, from which the broadening can be computed, in agreement with experiment.[2] A microphotometer curve showing Mo K radiation as scattered by a block of graphite is shown in Fig. 149.[3]

As ν is then increased further, the Compton line becomes narrower. Eventually, in any direction of scattering other than that of the incident beam, the unmodified line becomes weaker than the Compton line, sooner at large angles of scattering than at small angles, and sooner for heavy atoms than for light ones. Finally, only the modified line remains in appreciable intensity; this happens, for example, in light scattered at right angles to the incident beam, for $\nu/\nu_K > 300$ in the case of carbon or $\nu/\nu_K > 50$ in the case of lead, ν_K being the absorption limit for the K shell. The modified line is then fairly sharp and approximately the same in all respects as it would be if the electrons in the atom were free and at rest. According to theory, the modified line should exhibit the same features as to polarization as the unmodified line, except at extremely high frequencies.

[1] Cf. Bloch, *Phys. Rev.*, vol. 46, p. 674, 1934; W. Heitler, "Quantum Theory of Radiation," 2d ed., 1944.

[2] DuMond, *Phys. Rev.*, vol. 5, p. 1, 1933; Burkhardt, *Ann. Physik*, vol. 26, p. 567, 1936.

[3] Kirkpatrick and DuMond, *Phys. Rev.*, vol. 54, p. 802, 1938. See also *Phys. Rev.*, vol. 52, p. 419, 1937; DuMond, *Revs. Mod. Phys.*, vol. 5, p. 1, 1933, and *Phys. Rev.*, vol. 33, p. 643, 1929.

According to the theory, the other process by which x-rays may eject electrons from atoms, that of photoelectric absorption, should likewise decrease rapidly with increasing frequency of the incident radiation and should be relatively less important in light atoms than in heavy ones. The probability of the ejection of a photoelectron should become equal to that of the ejection of a Compton electron at about $\lambda = 0.5$ A or $\nu/\nu_K = 85$ in carbon, or $\lambda = 0.025$ A or $\nu/\nu_K = 6$ in lead. At much higher frequencies the ejection of Compton recoil electrons should constitute effectively the only form of action of radiation upon the electrons in matter.

It may be remarked that only the *unmodified* scattered radiation contributes to the beams that are reflected (or diffracted) in certain char-

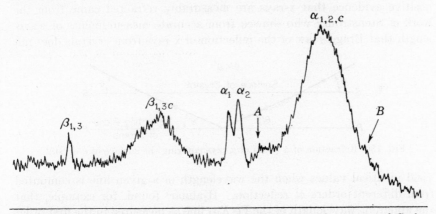

Fig. 149. Microphotometer curve of Mo K radiation scattered by orientated Ceylon graphite with its diamagnetic axis normal to the natural reference axis of the scattering experiment. (*Kirkpatrick and DuMond.*)

acteristic directions by crystals or gratings and upon which x-ray spectroscopy depends. Only to this part of the radiation can we apply the classical conception of scattered waves which are coherent with the incident waves, so that the waves scattered by different atoms possess definite relations of phase to one another and are capable of interfering constructively. The waves representing the Compton scattering must be supposed to be completely incoherent.

c. Time Relations in Compton Scattering. Reference should be made to another experiment, performed much later, which further heightened the contrast between classical and quantum theory by demonstrating that the recoil electron and the scattered photon are produced *at the same instant.*[1] The scattered photon was detected by observing in a cloud chamber the track of a photoelectron released by it at some other point

[1] Bothe and Geiger, Z. *Physik*, vol. 26, p. 44, 1924; vol. 32, p. 639, 1925.

in the scattering material, which was a gas. Recoil tracks and photo-electron tracks due to scattered x-rays were observed to occur simultane-ously. This observation shows very clearly the discontinuous nature of the scattering process, which, according to classical theory, should be continuous. Most of the time nothing is happening in the scattering material. At irregular instants, however, a recoil electron is projected from one of the molecules, and almost simultaneously (presumably slightly later owing to the time it takes light to pass from one point to the other) a photoelectron is ejected from another molecule. At such instants, we say that an x-ray photon has been "scattered" by the first molecule and absorbed by the second.

161. Refraction and Reflection of X-rays. *a. Refraction.* The first positive evidence that x-rays are measurably refracted came from the work of Stenström,[1] who showed from accurate measurements of wave-length that Bragg's law of the reflection of x-rays from crystals does not

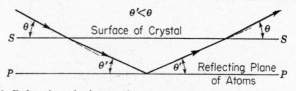

FIG. 150. Refraction of a beam of x-rays entering the surface of a crystal.

yield identical values when the wavelength of a given line is computed from different orders of reflection. Hjalmar[2] found, for example, that the apparent wavelength of the Fe $K\alpha_1$ line as measured in the first order by reflection from a gypsum crystal ($2d = 15.155$ A) was 1.9341 A; while measurements in the sixth order gave 1.9306 A, nearly 0.2 per cent less.

This apparent failure of the Bragg formula was shown to be due to refraction of the rays on entering the crystal, the index of refraction being *less than unity.* In Fig. 150 is shown the path of a ray entering at glancing angle θ and incident on the Bragg plane PP at an angle θ'. Bragg's law in the form

$$n\lambda' = 2d \sin \theta' \tag{216}$$

where λ' is the wavelength *in the crystal,* gives the true law of reflection *at the crystal plane.* To obtain the relation between θ and λ, the wave-length in air, we use the law of optics, $\mu = \lambda/\lambda' = \cos \theta/\cos \theta'$, μ being the refractive index from air to crystal. Substituting values of λ' and of $\sin \theta' = (1 - \cos^2 \theta')^{1/2}$ in Eq. (216), expanding in powers of the very

[1] Stenström, Dissertation, Lund, 1919.
[2] Hjalmar, *Z. Physik*, vol. 15, p. 65, 1923.

small quantity $1 - \mu$ and keeping only the first power of this quantity, it is found that

$$n\lambda = 2d \sin \theta \left(1 - \frac{1-\mu}{\sin^2 \theta}\right) \qquad (217)$$

A few values of $1 - \mu$ or δ obtained with use of this formula by Larsson, from observations in which different orders of diffraction were compared, are as follows:[1]

λ, A	1.537	2.499	3.447	5.166	7.111	8.320
$\delta \times 10^6$, mica	8.94	24.6	49.1	103	182	262
$\delta \times 10^6$, calcite	8.8	22.4	41.9			

Good values of $1 - \mu$ have also been obtained by refraction through a prism[2] and by measuring the critical angle for total reflection.[3]

b. *Reflection from Ruled Gratings.* With the discovery of the total reflection of x-rays, the possibility arose that a ruled grating might be used to measure x-ray wavelengths in exactly the same way that a grating is used in the optical region, provided that the glancing angle between the x-ray beam and the ruled surface is less than the critical angle for total reflection. Compton and Doan[4] were the first to make measurements of this kind. Using a grating of speculum metal with 50 lines per millimeter, they found the wavelength of the $K\alpha_1$ line of molybdenum to be $\lambda = 0.707 \pm 0.003$ A. Ten years later Bearden, using gratings having 100 or 300 lines per millimeter ruled on glass sputtered with gold, measured the wavelength of the Cu $K\alpha_1$ line (1.5406 A) to an accuracy better than 0.01 per cent.[5]

Measurements made with ruled gratings afford the most reliable means of determining the absolute magnitudes of x-ray wavelengths, since they involve no assumptions as to the homogeneity of a crystal; in fact, the only elements that enter into the determination by this method are the wave theory of light as propagated in a vacuum and such well-tested operations as the measurement of angles and the counting of lines under a micrometer microscope.

162. The Nature of Electromagnetic Radiation. The question as to the true nature of electromagnetic radiation, left unanswered at the end of Sec. 55, arises in its sharpest form in contemplating the contrasting properties of x-rays. How can an entity exhibit, on the one hand, the

[1] Quoted in Siegbahn, *loc. cit.*
[2] Cf. Bearden, *Phys. Rev.*, vol. 54, p. 698, 1938.
[3] Cf. Doan, *Phil. Mag.*, vol. 4, p. 100, 1927.
[4] Compton and Doan, *Proc. Natl. Acad. Sci.*, vol. 11, p. 598, 1925.
[5] Bearden, *Phys. Rev.*, vol. 48. p. 385, 1935.

wave behavior that is evidenced in the diffraction of x-rays by crystals and, on the other hand, the particle properties that are revealed by the Compton effect?

According to quantum mechanics, as interpreted by Bohr and other theoretical physicists, the riddle can be solved only by extending to radiation the same limitation upon the use of ordinary space-time conceptions that was found to be necessary in dealing with electrons. Bohr insists that whenever an observation of any sort is made, its *immediate* results will always be expressible in terms of familiar ideas of space and time, since these ideas have been developed out of human experience and any observation necessarily includes as its primary stage a certain experience by a human observer. But it does not follow that it will always be possible to construct a picture of the physical reality that causes these experiences, in the same way in which we picture everyday objects. In classical theory, an electromagnetic field was assumed to have a certain character at every point in space and at every instant of time, as represented by certain values of the electric and magnetic vectors. According to the new view, such a conception of the electromagnetic field is valid at best as an approximation, and only in certain cases.

The essential significance of what we call a radiation field lies in its effects upon the motion of charged particles. In describing this motion we encounter the limitations that are expressed in the indeterminacy principle as described in Sec. 99; and these limitations make it possible for the field to exhibit contrasting characteristics under different circumstances.

At one extreme, the action of the field takes the form with which we have become familiar in the Compton effect. Here a photon appears to bounce off an electron, thereby changing the momentum of the electron suddenly and discontinuously. The change of momentum δp cannot exceed twice the momentum of the photon, or $2h\nu/c$, however. Furthermore, this change of momentum will be definitely observable and measurable by the physicist only if it considerably exceeds the range of indeterminateness of the momentum already possessed by the particle, which cannot be less than Δp as given by Eq. (110) or $\Delta p = h/2\pi\Delta x$. The maximum possible ratio of δp to Δp is thus

$$\frac{\delta p}{\Delta p} = \frac{2h\nu/c}{h/2\pi\Delta x} = 4\pi \frac{\Delta x}{\lambda} \tag{218}$$

where $\lambda = c/\nu$ and represents the wavelength of the radiation, whereas Δx measures the indeterminateness in position of the particle.

From the last equation it is evident that a clear-cut scattering process of the Compton type can occur only when, to make $\delta p/\Delta p$ large, *the wavelength of the radiation is shorter than the diameter of the region in which the particle may be supposed to be effectively located.* For an electron in an atom, this condition can be met only for wavelengths considerably shorter than the atomic diameter, such as the wavelengths of hard x-rays or γ-rays.

In the Compton process there is no feature that can be regarded as a manifestation of an electric intensity in the wave. In order to obtain, at the opposite extreme, an action of radiation that can be interpreted in terms of the familiar electric and magnetic vectors, two conditions must be met. The experimental conditions must be such that it is possible to follow the test particle in effectively continuous motion along a path, so that its acceleration can be determined. It is also necessary that a segment of path which is sufficiently long to permit an adequate determination of the acceleration shall yet be short enough so that along it the field vectors do not vary appreciably in value. The first condition requires that the segment of path shall be many times as long as Δx; and the second requires that it must be much shorter than λ. It follows that necessarily Δx is much shorter than λ.

Thus *the familiar action ascribable to electric and magnetic fields in the radiation is obtained only when the particle acted on is definitely located within a region much smaller than a wavelength.*

This latter condition is satisfied, for example, by the electrons in a wire held parallel to the electric vector in long electromagnetic waves. In such a wire alternating electric current is observed to be produced, varying in phase with the electric vector. Ions in the upper atmosphere acted on by such waves furnish another example.

In such cases the *magnetic* field in the waves will also act upon the current or on the moving ions. It thus comes about that the *average* result is a force in the direction of propagation of the waves. This force constitutes an example of light pressure, and it can be regarded as analogous to the Compton recoil that occurs under other circumstances; but here there is a continuous rather than a discontinuous action. It might be thought that the photons are simply too small to be detected individually, but a better view is probably that in such cases there are no photons at all. The photon is thus an apparition that is evident under some circumstances but not under others.

In intermediate cases it will be impossible to obtain clear-cut evidence either for the occurrence of photons and of Compton recoils, or for action by electric and magnetic vectors; the difference between these two modes of action will be more or less concealed under statistical variations which are closely related to the indeterminacy of motion of the particle.

Thus we are in part prevented by indeterminacy of particle motion from even asking those questions concerning the nature of radiation that are naturally suggested by classical lines of thought. It seems probable that these questions really have no complete answers, and that the radiation field cannot be pictured in the full space-time detail with which we form, for example, a picture of the waves on the sea. One kind of picture is appropriate to one phenomenon, another kind to another phenomenon; but in no case can the picture be filled in completely without going beyond observable phenomena, and no one type of picture will cover all cases.

SOME LATER DEVELOPMENTS IN X-RAY SPECTROSCOPY

163. Multiple Ionization of Inner Shells. *a. Satellites or Second-order Lines.* It was perhaps fortunate that the spectral apparatus available

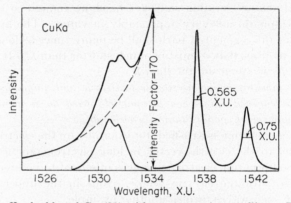

FIG. 151. The $K\alpha$ doublet of Cu (29) with accompanying satellites. The left-hand half of the curve is plotted on a scale 170 times larger than the right-hand half, and below it is plotted the intensity due to the satellites alone, obtained by subtracting the presumable intensity due to other lines as represented by the dotted curve.

to Moseley and the early workers did not have the sensitivity and resolving power of present-day spectrometers. The lines which they observed were the more intense and more easily resolvable lines of x-ray spectra. These are the lines which are represented on the conventional energy-level diagram; they are due to transitions between states of *single ionization* and are called *first-order* lines.

With improvements in technique, many other lines were subsequently discovered which did not fit into the conventional diagram.[1] The majority of these lines were rather faint, were usually found close to and on the short-wavelength side of the more intense "diagram" lines, and hence were called "satellite" lines. A typical spectral curve of the satellite structure accompanying the $K\alpha$ lines of copper is reproduced[2] in Fig. 151. The satellites accompanying the $L\beta_1$, $L\beta_2$, and $L\gamma_1$ lines for Ag (47) are

[1] For a more detailed discussion than that given here see Richtmyer, *Revs. Mod Phys.*, vol. 9, p. 391, 1937.

[2] Parratt, *Phys. Rev.*, vol. 50, p. 1, 1936.

designated by superscripts in Fig. 135. As illustrated in these figures, the satellite structure is observed to be very complex, containing numerous component lines of various intensities. Most (if not all) first-order lines are accompanied by such satellite structure, varying from line to line as well as from element to element. The total number of satellite lines now known far exceeds the number of diagram lines.

In seeking a plausible interpretation of the origin of satellite lines, we may focus our attention upon such key characteristics as the following: (1) the minimum excitation voltage, or, if the lines are observed in fluorescence, the minimum photon energy for excitation; (2) wavelength positions of the lines; (3) variation in the relative intensities of the satellite lines with the atomic number of the radiating material, or with the voltage and current in the x-ray tube.

Because of the low intensity of the satellites, reliable experimental information on such characteristics is extremely difficult to obtain. The excitation voltage of certain satellites, however, has been definitely shown to be somewhat greater than the excitation voltage of the accompanying first-order or parent line.[1] In the case of the type of K satellites that is illustrated in Fig. 151, the energy of excitation is found to be equal to the energy required to eject a K electron and *in addition* an L electron from the atom, the energies required to eject these electrons being calculated from the corresponding absorption limits. Hence, we may assume that the initial state for the emission of these satellite lines is a state of *double ionization,* in which the atom has an electronic vacancy in both the K shell and the L shell. Such a state of the atom may be called a "KL atomic state." In a similar way, other states of double ionization, such as KK, KM, LM, etc., should be possible.[2]

An atom in a KL state may undergo a radiative transition into any one of a number of other states of double ionization, e.g., $KL \rightarrow KM$ (an electron dropping from the M shell into the L shell), or $KL \rightarrow LL$ (an electron dropping from the L shell into the K shell). Estimates of the atomic energy indicate that the loss of energy should be slightly greater in the transition $KL \rightarrow LL$ than in the diagram transition $K \rightarrow L$, which gives rise to the $K\alpha$ lines; hence, the former transition should give rise to satellites close on the short-wave side of the $K\alpha$ lines. Similarly, the transition $KL \rightarrow LM$ should give rise to satellites on the short-wave side of the $K\beta$ lines. In a doubly ionized atom, the two vacancies would function spectroscopically in much the same way as would two valence electrons (Sec. 126). Furthermore, the vacancies may have different l values corre-

[1] See for example Druyvesteyn, *Z. Physik,* vol. 43, p. 707, 1927; Parratt, *Phys. Rev.,* vol. 49, p. 132, 1934; Coster, Kuipers, and Huizinga, *Physica,* vol. 2, p. 870, 1935.

[2] This theory of satellites was proposed by Wentzel, *Ann. Physik,* vol. 66, p. 437, 1921, and modified by Druyvesteyn, *Z. Physik,* vol. 43, p. 707, 1927.

sponding to the various subshells; for example, the satellites associated with the $L\alpha$ diagram line are assumed to originate in transitions between the levels L_{III}, M_{IV} or L_{III}, M_V (written compactly as $L_{III}M_{IV,V}$) and the levels $M_{IV}M_{IV}$, $M_{IV}M_V$, M_VM_V (or $M_{IV,V}M_{IV,V}$).

In this way we may explain the multiplicity of the observed satellite structures. As far as it has been possible to make approximate theoretical calculations, the predictions of wave mechanics lend support to the explanation.[1] Some satellites have been reported which are believed to originate in transitions between states of *triply* ionized atoms.

b. The Auger Effect. In the discussion of satellites, we assumed the atom to be doubly ionized without considering how this state might be brought about. Presumably, it is possible for a cathode-ray electron to eject two electrons at once from an atom. If this is the origin of the doubly ionized atoms, theoretical estimates indicate that the intensity of satellites relative to the parent lines should decrease in a continuous manner with increasing atomic number. Such a variation with atomic number is found by experiment to hold for K satellites, i.e., those accompanying lines of the K series, but not for L or M satellites. *The intensity of the satellites accompanying the $L\alpha$ line, for example, is observed to decrease rather abruptly as the atomic number increases from 47 to 50 and to increase again rather abruptly at about 75; between atomic numbers 50 and 75, $L\alpha$ satellites are practically unobservable.* This anomalous behavior as to intensity prevented for a time the universal acceptance of the Wentzel-Druyvesteyn theory of satellite origin. The difficulty was resolved when Coster and Kronig pointed out the importance, in this connection, of another physical process known as the "Auger effect."[2]

Under certain conditions of energy, an atom in a state of single ionization may undergo spontaneously an *Auger transition* which leaves it in a state of double ionization. The electron released in such a transition is expelled from the atom and left with an amount of kinetic energy E given by

$$E = E_i - E_f \tag{219}$$

where E_i is the initial energy of the singly ionized atom and E_f is the final energy of the doubly ionized atom. This type of atomic transition does not involve the emission of a photon and, therefore, is often called a "nonradiative" transition. Nonradiative transitions are possible, in general, only when an electron can be ejected from the atom; and for this to be possible it is necessary that E as defined by Eq. (219) be equal to

[1] For discussion and references, see Richtmyer and Ramberg, *Phys. Rev.*, vol. 51, p. 925, 1937.

[2] Coster and Kronig, *Physica*, vol. 2, p. 13, 1935.

or greater than zero.[1]   Electrons ejected by such radiationless transitions
were observed by Auger, who detected the short, fat tracks made by
them in the gas of a cloud chamber irradiated with x-rays.[2]

The effect of Auger transitions upon the occurrence of satellites may
be illustrated in the case of the L satellites just mentioned.   Let E_i refer
to the L_I state of an atom of atomic number Z, that is, E_i is the energy
of the L_I absorption limit.   If the final state for an Auger transition is
$L_{III}M_{IV}$, the value of E_f is the sum of the energies required to remove,
first, an electron from the L_{III} shell and, then, a second electron from the
M_{IV} shell.   Of these two energies, the first is that corresponding to the
L_{III} absorption limit of the atom of atomic number Z; the second is practically equal to the energy corresponding to the M_{IV} absorption limit of
an atom of atomic number $Z + 1$, since the absence of the L_{III} electron
will cause the atomic field acting on the M shell of electrons to resemble
more closely that in an atom of nuclear charge increased by unity.
Hence, as a good approximation, we may write as the energy equation
for the transition $L_I \rightarrow L_{III}M_{IV}$

$$E = (E_{LI})_Z - (E_{LIII})_Z - (E_{MIV})_{Z+1}$$

In order that the Auger transition $L_I \rightarrow L_{III}M_{IV}$ may occur, the right-
hand member of this equation must be positive, since $E > 0$.   The
range of elements for which this condition is satisfied, as determined from
a table of energies, is as follows: $Z < 50$ and $Z > 75$ (about).   These
are just the regions in which $L\alpha$ satellites are observed.   Hence, if we
suppose that few atoms in the states $L_{III}M_{IV,V}$ are produced directly by
the cathode-ray bombardment, so that such states are produced chiefly
by Auger transitions, the absence of $L\alpha$ satellites from $Z = 50$ to $Z = 75$
is explained.

The occurrence of Auger transitions should also have an effect upon
the intensities of certain *diagram* lines.   Thus, transitions for which L_I
is the initial state should be weakened by removal of atoms from the L_I
state through Auger transitions, and hence should undergo a rather
abrupt change in intensity at $Z = 50$ and $Z = 75$ (about), in agreement
with experiment.[3]   Finally, it may be mentioned that the Auger effect

[1] It may be remarked that atomic states from which an Auger transition is possible
do not represent true stationary states, or quantum states, of the atomic system.   The
atom in such a state cannot be represented by a Ψ function of the type of that written
in Eq. (111) but must be represented by a Ψ or wave packet of a more general form,
perhaps as in Eq. (113).   As time goes on, Ψ changes, slowly or rapidly, into a form
representing an additional electron of the atom as free and the others as remaining
in the atom, which is in a new state of higher ionization.

[2] Auger, *Compt. rend.*, vol. 180, p. 65, 1925.

[3] J. N. Cooper, *Phys. Rev.*, vol. 59, p. 473, 1941.

furnishes an explanation, which cannot be discussed further here, of the great broadness of all lines except those of the K series.[1]

164. X-ray Spectra and the Outer Part of the Atom. X-ray spectra are related primarily to the *inner* atomic structure. Concurrent changes that may occur elsewhere in the atom can largely be ignored because these changes have relatively little effect upon the energy levels arising from vacancies in the innermost shells. Certain finer features of x-ray spectra, however, involve in their explanation a consideration of the outer part of the atom, or even, in a solid or liquid, of the surrounding material.

In *emission* spectra from isolated atoms, nothing more is to be expected than the usual multiplicity of lines resulting from the existence of several L, M, . . . levels. In *absorption*, however, further possibilities exist. We have assumed hitherto that, when an x-ray photon is absorbed, an electron is removed entirely from the absorbing atom. If the atom is isolated, however, as in a monatomic gas, it should be possible for the electron to stop in some outer vacancy in the atom; the absorbed energy $h\nu$ would then be less than if the electron were removed to infinity.

With an electron removed from an inner shell, the ion will be surrounded by a field, due to the nucleus and the remaining electrons, approximating that of a hydrogen nucleus, and in this field there will exist a discrete set of quantum states. An electron removed from the K shell, for example, may stop in one of these states. Thus, below the true K energy level or absorption limit, there should exist also a discrete but closely spaced set of levels, often called *resonance* levels. These levels belong to the neutral atom, but they lie far above the ordinary spectroscopic levels because of the displacement of an electron out of the K shell. The K level itself corresponds to ionization with the ejected electron at rest at infinity, and above the K level there lies the usual continuum of levels representing ionization with an excess of kinetic energy given to the ejected electron; these energy levels may be regarded as belonging to the combined system of ion and ejected electron. The upper part of Fig. 153(a) will illustrate such an array of levels for a gaseous atom if the band labeled KV_e is replaced by an additional line below the K level.

The *absorption* curve should show, therefore, in addition to the photoelectric absorption extending toward higher frequencies from the K absorption edge, a series of absorption lines on the long-wave side of this edge, resulting from atomic transitions into one of the K resonance levels. These lines should be closely spaced, however; for the energy differences between the levels should be of the same order of magnitude as the differences between the ordinary optical levels, i.e., a few electron-volts or less.

[1] Cf. Richtmyer, Barnes, and Ramberg, *Phys. Rev.*, vol. 46, p. 836, 1934; Parratt, *Phys. Rev.*, vol. 54, p. 99, 1938; Cooper, *Phys. Rev.*, vol. 61, p. 234, 1941.

The spacing of the levels that are associated with a vacancy in one of the inner shells of an atom of atomic number Z ought, in fact, to be almost the same as that of the ordinary optical levels for a neutral atom of atomic number $Z + 1$; for the number of electrons in the outer part of the atom is the same in the two cases and the modification of the electronic motion that results from the removal of an inner (negative) electron should be almost the same as that caused by an increase of the (positive) nuclear

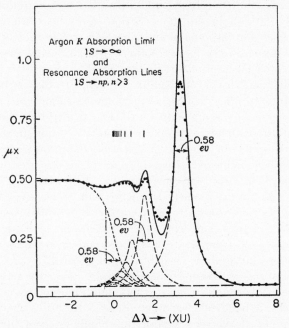

FIG. 152. The K absorption edge of argon and its interpretation in terms of a series of resonance lines and the continuous photoelectric K absorption band. (*Illustration furnished by courtesy of Professor L. G. Parratt.*)

charge by 1 unit. A similar structure is to be expected at all the absorption limits.

In Fig. 152 is shown an absorption curve for argon near its K limit,[1] as observed with a spectrometer of very high resolving power. There is clear evidence of the type of resonance absorption structure just described, but the absorption lines are so broad that there is great overlapping. The electronic configuration for argon ($Z = 18$), $1s^2 2s^2 2p^6 3s^2 3p^6$, will be altered in nonionizing absorption to $1s 2s^2 2p^6 3s^2 3p^6 np$, a p state being the only kind to which an electron can change from a $1s$ state in accord-

[1] Parratt, *Phys. Rev.*, vol. 56, p. 295, 1935. Resonance absorption structure, also found for polyatomic gases, was first identified by Kossel, *Z. Physik*, vol. 1, p. 119, 1920.

ance with the selection rules. The spacing of the atomic levels under discussion will thus be almost the same as that of the optical P levels of potassium ($Z = 19$). Hence, if we ascribe the most intense line in Fig. 152 to the electronic transition $1s \rightarrow 4p$, we can locate the positions of the other resonance lines and of their series limit by using the known optical P terms for potassium. The photoelectric absorption edge should have a finite "width" when observed with such high resolving power; theory indicates that the shape should be given by an arctangent curve, whose width is due to the same factors that cause the width of each of the absorption lines and also of the emission lines. The theoretical absorption edge is drawn in the figure as the left-hand dotted curve, centered at the calculated position of the P-series limit.

165. X-ray Spectroscopy of Solids. When an atom is brought into close proximity to other atoms, as in compound molecules or in solids, x-ray phenomena involving only ionization in an inner shell are little affected but those involving also the atomic exterior are considerably modified. A number of cases have been studied, but only a partial understanding has been achieved. Details tend to be obscured by the great natural breadth of x-ray lines, especially if the wavelength is less than about 5 A,[1] and only two illustrative cases will be described here.

In a solid, the outermost atomic electrons come to be associated with the entire solid rather than with individual atoms, and essentially continuous bands of electronic states may be supposed to replace the discrete atomic states so far as these electrons are concerned.

The simplest case is that of the alkali metals. Here the set of electronic states for the valence electrons in their individual atoms is replaced in the crystal by a band of electronic states 5 to 20 ev wide in energy. Displacement of an electron within this band, or from this band into another band, is associated in simple cases with an equal change in the crystal energy. In the alkali metals, however, the number of valence electrons is only sufficient to fill the valence band half full, the remainder of the band being normally empty. In Fig. 153(b) the full and the empty halves of the valence band are represented by V_f and V_e, respectively. The lines labeled K and L represent the K and L shells, respectively, and S represents the surface of the metal. Part (b) of Fig. 153 represents six out of many possible electronic conditions, state G being the normal or "ground" state; part (a) represents diagrammatically certain associated energy levels of the crystal.

As an example of an associated spectrum, the L *emission* from solid sodium, corresponding to the L lines ($M \rightarrow L$) from heavy atoms, is observed as a wedge-shaped band about 3 volts wide; the band begins at

---

[1] Skinner, *Repts. Progr. in Phys.*, vol. 5, p. 257, 1939, and references. See also reports by J. A. Bearden and collaborators, *Phys. Rev.*, vol. 58, pp. 387, 396, 400, 1940.

about 450 A and rises almost linearly to a maximum near 390 A, where the intensity drops within 0.1 volt to zero. In the initial state of the crystal for the transitions that give rise to this band, an electron has been removed from the L shell of one of the atoms and has at least left the neighborhood of this atom. This condition is illustrated by state L in Fig. 153(b), the ejected electron being represented by a solid circle and the hole left in the L shell by an open circle. An electron then drops from any position in the full half-band V_f into the L shell, producing crystal

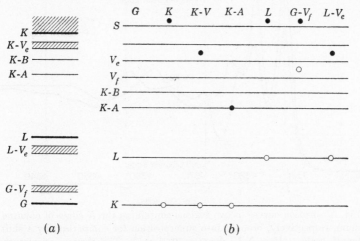

$$(a) \qquad\qquad (b)$$

FIG. 153. Diagram showing (a) crystal energy levels and (b) electronic positions.

state G-V_f and causing emission of an L photon. The transition may be denoted thus:

$$\text{Crystal, } L \rightarrow G\text{-}V_f$$
$$\text{Electron, } V_f \rightarrow L$$

The width of the L emission band should thus be equivalent to the width in energy of the V_f half-band of electronic valence levels. This width, in turn, should be comparable with the total depth in energy of the Sommerfeld distribution (Secs. 56 and 174). It is found, in fact, that the widths of the soft x-ray emission bands of metals belonging to the first two groups of the periodic table agree fairly exactly with values of E_m calculated from the formula given in Sec. 56 [or ζ_0 as calculated from Eq. (240)].

In the *absorption* spectrum of sodium, on the other hand, production of the state L out of the normal state G of the crystal by the absorption of a photon results in absorption at the L limit. As an alternative, however, the electron removed from the L shell may stop at some point in the empty V_e half of the valence band, producing a crystal state and level

L-V_e; this transition is

Crystal, $G \rightarrow L$-V_e

Electron, $L \rightarrow V_e$

Thus there should also exist a rather broad resonance absorption band below the L limit.[1]   In the spectrum, this band should lie above the emission band previously described, since V_e lies above V_f.   The two bands,

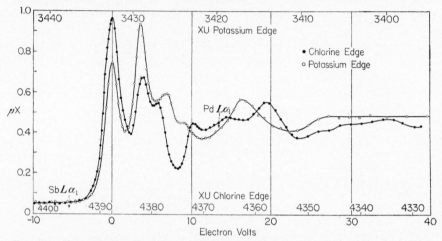

FIG. 154. Absorption curves in two regions containing the K edges of chlorine and of potassium, respectively, brought into superposition for comparison by a shift of the wavelength scale.   (Here X.U. denotes 10^{-11} cm.)   The abscissa represents energy in electron-volts, measured from an arbitrary zero.   The ordinate represents μx in the factor $e^{-\mu x}$, to which the transmitted intensity is proportional, x denoting distance along the beam.   (*After Trischka, Phys. Rev., vol. 67, p. 318, 1945. See also L. G. Parratt and E. L. Jossem, K Spectra of Potassium Chloride, Tech. Report no. 1, Physics Dept., Cornell University, 1954.*)

however, should be contiguous; for, at the long-wave edge of the absorption band the electron just reaches the bottom of V_e, which is also the top of V_f; and the corresponding electronic transition in absorption is just the reverse of the transition out of the top of V_f in emission.   Hence the short-wave emission edge should coincide with the long-wave absorption edge.   Such a coincidence of emission and absorption edges has been found experimentally in a few cases.

As a final example, absorption curves showing the K regions for chlorine and potassium in KCl are plotted in Fig. 154.   The curves give evidence of two resonance levels, diagrammed as K-A and K-B in Fig. 153(a), and perhaps also of absorption due to electronic transitions from the K shell into the V_e band.   It is difficult, however, to be sure of the reasons for all the details in such curves.

[1] L. G. Parratt and E. L. Jossem, *Phys. Rev.*, vol. 85, p. 729, 1952.

CHAPTER 9

WAVE MECHANICS OF MATTER IN BULK

Wave mechanics has been most successful in representing the properties of single atoms or molecules, and also the behavior of matter in bulk in those few cases in which the molecules act independently of each other. A notable example is a gas at low densities. The classical kinetic theory of gases scored many successes, but certain difficulties concerning specific heats were not overcome until quantum principles were introduced. A wave-mechanical theory for the equation of state of a gas is easily worked out; it predicts certain striking departures from classical behavior but only under such conditions that these departures are scarcely within reach of observation. The most important application of the wave-mechanical theory of gases is to the free electrons in metals.

The cooperative action of molecules in the more condensed phases of matter presents a much more difficult problem. The theory of liquids and of amorphous solids, in particular, has not progressed far. In crystals, on the other hand, the regular arrangement of the molecules introduces certain simplifying features into the theory that can be worked out mathematically, and by means of these general features considerable progress has been made toward understanding the properties of crystalline substances, including the metals.

In this chapter a short account will be given of the most notable successes of quantum theory and of wave mechanics in dealing with gases and with crystalline solids. As in other chapters, no attempt will be made to develop the mathematical theory, and few mathematical details will be given. Attention will be focused rather upon the ideas involved and upon the physical aspects of the conclusions.

THE QUANTUM THEORY OF SPECIFIC HEATS

166. The Specific Heats of Ideal Gases. *a. Theory.* The classical argument concerning the specific heats of gases was as follows. As was stated in Sec. 66, the kinetic energy of translation E_t of all the molecules in a mole or gram-molecule of gas will have the value $E_t = \frac{3}{2}RT$, R being the general gas constant and T the absolute temperature. If the molecules had no other energy, as might reasonably be supposed to be the case for monatomic gases at low density, it follows that the molar specific heat at constant volume C_v, or the heat required to raise 1 mole of the gas 1°C, would be

$$C_v = \frac{d}{dT} E_t = 1.5R$$

Here C_v is expressed in the same set of units that is used for R, for example, ergs per gram per degree or joules per kilogram per degree. Since in the former units $R = 8.314 \times 10^7$, the thermal value of R is

$$8.314 \times \frac{10^7}{4.19 \times 10^7} = 1.98 \text{ cal per deg C}$$

Molecules of the dumbbell type (Sec. 66) would then have five degrees of freedom instead of three, so that for them $C_v = 2.5R$; a diatomic molecule in which the atoms vibrate relative to each other but in which rotation about the axis of symmetry is lacking would have $C_v = 3.5R$, the additional energy for a vibratory degree being kT; a rigid triatomic molecule with noncollinear molecules would have $C_v = 3R$; and so on.

Values of C_v/R calculated from observed values of C_v for a few gases at room temperature are as follows:

He	A	H_2	HCl	N_2	O_2	Cl_2	H_2O	SO_2
1.52	1.51	2.44	2.54	2.45	2.50	3.02	3.3	3.79

As is illustrated by these figures, classical theory was fairly successful in the case of the simplest molecules. Chlorine, however, presented a problem; if the two atoms in the molecule were rigidly connected, C_v should be $2.5R$, as is nearly true for H_2, O_2, and N_2, whereas an added vibration of the atoms would raise C_v to $3.5R$.

All major difficulties disappeared when the internal energy of the molecules was described in terms of the quantum states that play such an important role in the theory of band spectra (Secs. 138 to 142). The molecules will be distributed statistically among these quantum states, as was described in Sec. 88. Grouping together states having the same energy, as in Eq. (96), we can write Eq. (95) for the number of molecules in a gram of gas that are in composite state number τ,

$$N_\tau = \frac{N_0 w_\tau e^{-\epsilon_\tau/kT}}{\sum_\kappa w_\kappa e^{-\epsilon_\kappa/kT}} \tag{220}$$

Here w_τ is the statistical weight of the composite state, or the number of fundamental states composing it, and ϵ_τ is the internal energy of a molecule when in one of these states. This energy may be associated with rotation of the molecule, with vibration of the atoms within it, or, at least in principle, to electronic excitation (which includes rotational energy of the atoms themselves). The total internal energy of the molecules will then be

$$E_i = \sum_\tau N_\tau \epsilon_\tau = N_0 \sum_\tau \epsilon_\tau w_\tau e^{-\epsilon_\tau / kT} \left(\sum w_\kappa e^{-\epsilon_\kappa / kT} \right)^{-1} \tag{221}$$

Adding the translational energy E_t and calculating C_v as $d(E_t + E_i)/dT$, we obtain as the general formula for the molar specific heat at constant volume of an ideal gas, in terms of degrees centigrade and the same mechanical units as those used for R,

$$C_v = \frac{3}{2} R + N_0 \frac{d}{dT} \frac{\Sigma \epsilon_\kappa w_\kappa e^{-\epsilon_\kappa / kT}}{\Sigma w_\kappa e^{-\epsilon_\kappa / kT}} \tag{222}$$

It should now be possible to take values of ϵ_τ derived from a study of band spectra and to calculate C_v from them by means of the last equation. Thus *a specific heat would be calculated from spectroscopic data.* This has actually been done with complete success in a number of cases. Such calculations constitute a striking confirmation of the correctness of the general quantum theory of molecular structure.

Equation (222) predicts a certain mode of variation of the specific heat of an ideal gas with temperature. When T is very small, the exponential factor referring to the state of lowest energy will be much larger than the exponentials referring to all other states, so that for an approximation the latter can be dropped. Both sums then reduce to a single term, out of which the exponential factor can be canceled in numerator and denominator, with the result that the fraction becomes a constant. Thus, at sufficiently low temperatures, $C_v = 1.5R$, approximately.

As the temperature rises, however, molecules will pass by thermal agitation into other quantum states, beginning in the case of polyatomic molecules with the rotational levels associated with the lowest vibrational and electronic states. Let kT_{15} denote the value of kT at 15°C, which also equals two-thirds of the mean kinetic energy of a molecule at that temperature. Then comparison with experimental data shows that in general the second rotational level lies from 0.1 to $0.3kT_{15}$ above the first, whereas the first step upward in vibration requires from 1 to $10kT_{15}$ and the first step in electronic excitation requires at least $100kT_{15}$. It is clear, therefore, that at ordinary temperatures the molecules should be rather widely distributed among the first set of rotational levels; and under such conditions it can be shown that the average rotational energy per molecule approximates the classical value, which is kT for a diatomic molecule or $\frac{3}{2}kT$ for a molecule composed of three or more noncollinear atoms. Thus we can understand the approximate success of classical theory in dealing with the simpler types of molecules.

At higher temperatures, vibrational energy will contribute appreciably to C_v, eventually to the extent of kT for each vibrational level; and at temperatures well above 10,000°C contributions may be expected from the higher electronic levels as well.

b. Comparison with Observation. Data on the specific heat of hydrogen, plotted as circles in Fig. 155, are in good agreement with the theoretical predictions. Below 60°K, $C_v = 1.5R$, whereas from 300 to 500°K, $C_v = 2.5R$ very closely, but from 600° upward it is clear that vibration of the molecule begins to play a part. Thus it might be said that the apparent constancy of the specific heat of hydrogen as found by early experimenters was accidental. The complete theory of a molecule composed of two *similar* atoms is more complicated than as here described,

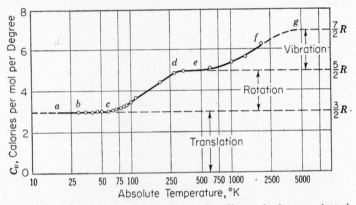

FIG. 155. Specific heat at constant volume of ordinary hydrogen plotted against temperature on a logarithmic scale.

however; and in the case of hydrogen it has been possible to verify experimentally the remarkable conclusions that follow from the theory, as was described briefly in Sec. 144.

In further illustration of the use of quantum theory, we may return to the problem of chlorine. Whereas the second vibrational state ($v = 1$) for gases such as N_2 or H_2 lies far above the first ($v = 0$), for chlorine it lies only 560 cm^{-1} above the first, as may be inferred from a study of the electronic band system that extends in the absorption spectrum from 4,800 to 5,800 A.[1]

The difference in energy between these two states is thus

$$\epsilon_1 - \epsilon_0 = h\nu = 6.62 \times 10^{-27} \times 560 \times 3 \times 10^{10} = 1.110 \times 10^{-13} \text{ erg}$$

Since $k = 1.380 \times 10^{-16}$, at $T = 288°K$ the ratio of the Boltzmann factors for the two states is $e^{-(\epsilon_1-\epsilon_0)/kT} = e^{-2.794} = 0.0611$. Thus, 0.061 times as many molecules will be in the second vibrational state as in the

[1] Kuhn, *Z. Physik*, vol. 39, p. 77, 1926.

first. For a rough estimate, we may suppose that this fraction of *all* the molecules are in the second state. Then the excess vibrational energy due to this cause, in a gram of gas containing N molecules, will be

$$N(\epsilon_1 - \epsilon_0)e^{-(\epsilon_1-\epsilon_0)/kT}$$

The derivative of this expression with respect to T gives for the contribution of the excess energy to C_v

$$N \frac{(\epsilon_1 - \epsilon_0)^2}{kT^2} e^{-(\epsilon_1-\epsilon_0)/kT} = R\left(\frac{\epsilon_1 - \epsilon_0}{kT}\right)^2 e^{-(\epsilon_1-\epsilon_0)/kT} = 0.48R$$

where $R = Nk$. Thus $C_v = (2.5 + 0.48)R = 2.98R$, in fair agreement with the observed value, $3.02R$. A more exact calculation using Eq. (222)[1] gives $C_v = 3.06R$.

When a similar calculation is made for HCl, whose vibration-rotation band at $3.4~\mu$ or $2,886~cm^{-1}$ (Sec. 140) indicates that

$$\epsilon_1 - \epsilon_0 = 5.73 \times 10^{-13}~erg$$

the ratio of the Boltzmann factors is found to be only

$$e^{-(\epsilon_1-\epsilon_0)/kT} = 5 \times 10^{-7}$$

Thus molecular vibration can make no appreciable contributin to the specific heat of HCl. For O_2, $\epsilon_1 - \epsilon_0 = 1,556~cm^{-1}$ and vibration may contribute about $0.026R$ to C_v. Other variations in C_v may be due to quantum corrections on the rotational energy.

167. The Specific Heats of Simple Solids. Over 100 years ago, Dulong and Petit, as a result of measurements made on a number of elements in solid form, concluded that "the product of the atomic weight and the specific heat is the same for all elementary (solid) substances." The product mentioned, called the *atomic heat*, also represents the specific heat of a gram-atom. At ordinary temperatures this "law of Dulong and Petit" holds roughly for many substances, the atomic heats for 58 elements ranging from 5.38 to 6.93 cal per gram-atom, with an average of 6.15.

A few striking exceptions occur, however, notably boron, with atomic heat 3.34; beryllium, 3.85; diamond (carbon), 1.46; silicon, 4.95. These are all light elements with high melting points. Their specific heats were the subject of extended research, and it was early discovered that the specific heats of such substances vary rapidly with temperature. Thus, in 1872, Weber observed that the specific heat of diamond increases threefold between 0 and 200°C. Later it was found that the specific heats of *all* substances decrease rapidly if the temperature is lowered sufficiently, tending toward zero at the absolute zero of temperature.

[1] Trautz and Ader, *Z. Physik*, vol, 89, p. 15, 1934.

Typical curves are shown in Fig. 156. The curves for elementary substances are actually, in a sense, all of the same form; that is, they can be brought (almost) into coincidence by making a suitable choice of the temperature scale for each. Such a striking regularity must have its source in a simple general principle.

Classical theory suggested the following explanation for the observed uniformity of the atomic heats. In a solid the atoms should merely vibrate about certain mean positions, instead of wandering about as in a fluid, and they should thus behave rather like harmonic oscillators having three degrees of freedom. The atomic heat should, therefore, be

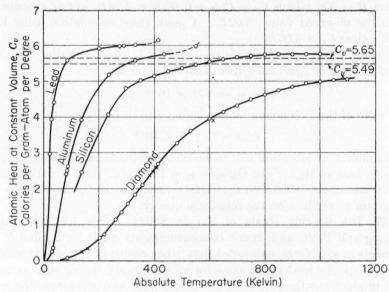

FIG. 156. Variation of atomic heat at constant volume with temperature.

$3R$ (Sec. 66) or $3 \times 1.98 = 5.94$ cal per gram-atom, in approximate agreement with many observations. However, classical theory could offer no reason for the observed rapid decrease of all specific heats at low temperatures.

A long step toward an explanation of the temperature variation was taken by Einstein in 1907.[1] He replaced the classical value kT for the mean energy of an oscillator by the value derived from Planck's new quantum theory. Multiplying the mean energy $\bar{\epsilon}$ as given in Eq. (65) by N_0 and by 3, since the oscillators here are three-dimensional, we have as the energy of a gram-atom according to Einstein's assumption

$$E_0 = \frac{3N_0 h\nu}{e^{h\nu/kT} - 1}$$

[1] *Ann. Physik*, vol. 22, p. 180, 1907.

and for the specific heat of a gram-atom

$$C_v = \frac{dE_0}{dT} = 3R \left[\frac{e^{h\nu/kT}}{(e^{h\nu/kT} - 1)^2} \left(\frac{h\nu}{kT}\right)^2 \right] \tag{223}$$

since $N_0 k = R$. At sufficiently high temperatures this expression reduces to the classical value, $3R$, but at low temperatures the exponential becomes large and C_v decreases rapidly. The formula was found to fit the data remarkably well, as is illustrated by the lower curve in Fig. 157.

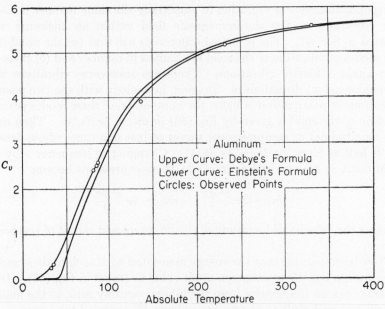

FIG. 157. Comparison of specific-heat formulas with experiment.

At *very* low temperatures, however, the roughly exponential shape of the curve is definitely wrong.

Einstein's expression for C_v contains, in the frequency ν, a single constant characteristic of a given substance. Several attempts were made to derive values of ν from other properties of the substance. Einstein derived such values from compressibilities,[1] Lindemann from melting points, on the assumption that at the melting point the amplitude of vibration, calculated classically to correspond to the energy kT, is equal to the average distance apart of the atoms.[2] Others, using the formulas as an approximation even for simple solid salts, identified ν with the frequency of the "residual rays," a frequency in the infrared at which a

[1] *Ann. Physik*, vol. 34, pp. 170, 590, 1911.
[2] *Physik. Z.*, vol. 11, p. 609, 1910.

crystal exhibits strong selective reflection. It is remarkable that frequencies derived in such different ways commonly agreed within 10 to 20 (or 30) per cent with the frequency that was found to give the best fit with the thermal data!

A different approach was used by Debye, whose theory is still the best available. Any solid is capable of vibrating elastically in many different modes, the frequencies varying from one mode to another. Debye considered the temperature vibrations of the atoms to be equivalent to a complex of such vibrations superposed, and calculated the number of independent modes of vibration in essentially the same manner in which the vibrations of the electromagnetic field within an enclosure were treated in Sec. 67. The principal differences are that (a) the number of the modes of vibration of the solid are limited in number and (b) there are two kinds of elastic vibrations. There are transverse vibrations with two independent directions of vibration, in analogy with the two possible directions of polarization of light; the number dn_t of these modes per unit volume of the solid is given by Eq. (56) or $dn_t = 8\pi \, d\lambda/\lambda^4$. Then there are longitudinal or compressional waves of just one type, whose density dn_l is half as large, or $dn_l = 4\pi \, d\lambda/\lambda^4$. Changing to frequency ν by the relations $\lambda = v/\nu$ and $|d\lambda| = (v/\nu^2) \, d\nu$, these expressions became

$$dn_t = 8\pi \frac{\nu^2 \, d\nu}{v_t^3} \qquad dn_l = 4\pi \frac{\nu^2 \, d\nu}{v_l^3}$$

v_l being the velocity of longitudinal elastic waves and v_t that of transverse waves.

Now let us assume that the energy associated with each of these modes of vibration has the average quantum value as stated in Eq. (65). Integrating over all frequencies from the lowest, sensibly zero, to the highest possible ν_m and multiplying by the volume V_0 occupied by a gram-atom of the substance, we thus find for the thermal energy of a gram-atom

$$E_0 = 4\pi V_0 \left(\frac{1}{v_l^3} + \frac{2}{v_t^3} \right) \int_0^{\nu_m} \frac{h\nu}{e^{h\nu/kT} - 1} \nu^2 \, d\nu \qquad (224)$$

The true value of ν_m is difficult to determine; hence Debye used an approximate value derived from the condition that the total number of modes of vibration of a gram-atom must be equal to the number of degrees of freedom of all the atoms, or to $3N_0$. On this assumption

$$3N_0 = 4\pi V_0 \left(\frac{1}{v_l^3} + \frac{2}{v_t^3} \right) \int_0^{\nu_m} \nu^2 \, d\nu = \tfrac{4}{3}\pi V_0 \left(\frac{1}{v_l^3} + \frac{2}{v_t^3} \right) \nu_m^3 \quad (225)$$

By means of this result, Eq. (224) can be written

$$E_0 = \frac{9N_0}{\nu_m^3} \int_0^{\nu_m} \frac{h\nu}{e^{h\nu/kT} - 1} \nu^2 \, d\nu \qquad (226)$$

The qualitative features of the formula are better seen, however, if the variable of integration is changed from ν to the dimensionless variable x, where

$$x = \frac{h\nu}{kT} \qquad \therefore \; \nu = \frac{kT}{h} x \qquad d\nu = \frac{kT}{h} dx$$

It is convenient also to introduce a characteristic temperature T_c defined as $T_c = h\nu_m/k$, so that $\nu_m = kT_c/h$. With these substitutions, and with $N_0 k$ replaced by R, Eq. (226) becomes

$$E_0 = 9R \frac{T^4}{T_s^3} \int_0^{T_c/T} \frac{x^3}{e^x - 1} dx \qquad (227)$$

and the specific heat is

$$C_v = \frac{dE_0}{dT} = 9R \left[4 \left(\frac{T}{T_c} \right)^3 \int_0^{T_c/T} \frac{x^3 \, dx}{e^x - 1} - \frac{T_c}{T} \frac{1}{e^{T_c/T} - 1} \right] \qquad (228)$$

At *high temperatures*, C_v as given by Eq. (228) approaches the classical value, $3R$. (To prove this, expand the exponentials in series.) At *very low temperatures*, on the other hand, the exponentials become large, so that the last term in Eq. (228) can be neglected; the upper limit in the integral can also be replaced by ∞ with little error. It is known that[1]

$$\int_0^\infty \frac{x^3 \, dx}{e^x - 1} = \frac{\pi^4}{15}$$

Hence Eq. (228) becomes, approximately,

$$C_v = \tfrac{12}{5}\pi^4 R \left(\frac{T}{T_c} \right)^3 = 234R \left(\frac{T}{T_c} \right)^3 \qquad (229)$$

Thus, at temperatures much below the characteristic temperature T_c, the atomic heat of a simple solid should be *proportional to the cube* of the absolute temperature. This has been confirmed by experiment (e.g., for lead up to 8°K, Si to 50°, CaF_2 to 40°).

It will be noted that variation of the specific heat as T^3 implies a finite value of the entropy ($\int C_v \, dT/T$) at absolute zero—an example of the Nernst heat theorem or the "third law of thermodynamics." According to classical theory the entropy of a solid at 0°K would be negatively infinite.

For intermediate temperatures, it is necessary to evaluate the integral in (227) numerically. Tables for this purpose have been published.[2] Good agreement with observation has been found for many substances

---

[1] Cf. Bierens de Hahn, "Nouvelle Table d'Intégrales Définies," no. 4, p. 124, where $B_{2a-1} = \tfrac{1}{30}$.

[2] *Nernst*, "The New Heat Theorem," pp. 246–254, 1924; Beattie, *J. Math. Phys.*, vol. 6, p. 1, 1926.

when T_c is chosen for best fit with the data,[1] and even when T_c is calculated from the elastic constants with the use of Eq. (225).[2]   The curve for aluminum, with T_c taken as 398° for the best fit, is shown in Fig. 157.

The data for many crystalline compounds can be fitted by adding one or more terms of the Einstein type to represent, in effect, internal vibrations of the atoms within each crystal cell.

THE WAVE MECHANICS OF IDEAL GASES

168. The Ideal Gas.   The kinetic theory of gases as developed by Clausius, Maxwell, and others in terms of classical mechanics was strikingly successful in dealing with those properties of gases that depend only upon the translatory motion of the molecules.   The results of the theory refer, strictly speaking, only to ideal gases, in which the molecules interact with each other only during a small part of the time, but all real gases behave more and more nearly like an ideal gas as their density decreases.   When wave mechanics was developed, it was soon seen that the classical kinetic theory should usually hold with sufficient accuracy for gases at sufficiently low density or sufficiently high temperature, but that under certain imaginable circumstances wide departures from classical behavior should occur.   Since the wave-mechanical theory for such cases is of interest in dealing with the theory of electrons in solids, a short description of certain features of the theory will be given here.[3]

The translational motion of a single molecule confined within a closed vessel may be treated by the theory of a "particle in a box" as described in Sec. 102.   Let the vessel have the form of a rectangular parallelepiped with edges l_1, l_2, l_3.   Then, with the axes of coordinates suitably chosen, the wave function for a quantum state has the form

$$\psi = C \sin\left(\pi k_1 \frac{x}{l_1}\right) \sin\left(\pi k_2 \frac{y}{l_2}\right) \sin\left(\pi k_3 \frac{z}{l_3}\right) \tag{230}$$

where k_1, k_2, k_3 are any set of three positive integers and C is a constant. The corresponding translational kinetic energy ζ of the molecule, denoted by W in Eq. (124), is

$$\zeta = \frac{h^2}{8m}\left(\frac{k_1{}^2}{l_1{}^2} + \frac{k_2{}^2}{l_2{}^2} + \frac{k_3{}^2}{l_3{}^2}\right) \tag{231}$$

Each set of k's defines a translational state for the molecule.

When many molecules are present together in the vessel, so long as they do not interact, each one can be assumed to be in a certain one of

[1] R. H. Fowler and E. A. Guggenheim, "Statistical Thermodynamics," 2d ed., where data for Al, C, Na, Zn, Ag, Pb, I, NaCl, KCl, CaF$_2$ are shown.

[2] Allen, *Proc. Roy. Soc. (London)*, vol. 94, p. 100, 1918.

[3] Cf. E. H. Kennard, "Kinetic Theory of Gases," chaps. IX, X.

these molecular states, and the chosen set of molecular states represents a quantum state for the gas as a whole. The next step might then be to employ perturbation theory (Sec. 103) in order to ascertain the modifications of the gaseous quantum states and the associated energies that result from a slight interaction between the molecules. We shall assume, however, that the density of the gas is sufficiently low so that its properties can be adequately investigated without taking account of molecular interaction.

The wave function for a single translational molecular state does not represent the molecule as localized in one part of the vessel or as moving in a definite direction. It is noteworthy, however, that any ψ as given by Eq. (230) can be written as the sum of eight terms, each of the form

$$\pm \frac{1}{8i} \, C e^{i\pi(\pm k_1 x/l_1 \pm k_2 y/l_2 \pm k_3 z/l_3)}$$

by means of the formula $\sin u = (e^{iu} - e^{-iu})/2i$. Each of these terms can be regarded, by an extension of the interpretation of Eq. (107), as a wave train which represents the molecule as traveling in a certain direction with speed $v = \sqrt{2\zeta/m}$. The eight wave trains can then be thought of as generating ψ by repeated reflection at the walls of the vessel. It can be shown that, if one molecule collides with another, it will collide as if it were moving in one of these directions, with equal probability for each of the eight. It is also possible, as in Eq. (113) in Sec. 100, to construct a wave packet that is composed of wave functions for many quantum states and represents the molecule as localized in a small part of the vessel and moving with a fairly definite velocity. In such ways the groundwork can be laid for the treatment of transport phenomena in gases.

Here, however, we shall consider only gases in thermal equilibrium and shall be interested chiefly in the equation of state of the gas and in the statistical distribution of energy among its molecules.

The Two Wave-mechanical Kinds of Gases. In assigning molecular quantum states, two kinds of molecules must be distinguished. *Similar* molecules composed of an *odd* number of particles—protons, neutrons, or electrons—must be assigned each to a different molecular state. This rule is analogous to that for the electrons in an atom. Such gases are said to exhibit "Fermi-Dirac statistical" behavior.[1] An example is monatomic beryllium vapor. For similar molecules composed of an *even* number of particles, on the other hand, no such restriction exists. Such gases exhibit "Bose-Einstein statistical" behavior, which was first studied in the case of photons.[2]

[1] E. Fermi, *Z. Physik*, vol. 36, p. 902, 1926; P. A. M. Dirac, *Proc. Roy. Soc. (London)*, vol. 112, p. 661, 1926.

[2] S. N. Bose, *Z. Physik*, vol. 26, p. 178, 1924; A. Einstein, *Berl. Ber.*, 1924, p. 261.

For both types of molecules, as with the particles discussed in Sec. 106, interchange of molecules among the molecular states has no significance, so that an assignment of a sufficient number of molecular states to accommodate all the molecules specifies a single quantum state for the gas as a whole.

At extremely low temperatures or at high densities, the two types of gas should have different physical properties, but the difference tends to be obscured by the effects of molecular interaction. The formulas for the Fermi-Dirac type, however, are of interest also in the electron theory of metals. For these reasons, although most actual gases are of the Bose-Einstein type, only the theory of the Fermi-Dirac type will be considered in detail.

169. Gaseous Pressure. A simple expression for the pressure in an ideal gas of either type can be derived very easily. Consider a molecule in one of its quantum states within a cubical vessel of side l, with kinetic energy given by Eq. (231) or, in the present case,

$$\zeta = \frac{h^2}{8ml^2} (k_1{}^2 + k_2{}^2 + k_3{}^2) \tag{232}$$

Let l be increased extremely slowly by a small amount dl. During this process, the molecule will remain in the quantum state characterized by k_1, k_2, k_3, and ζ will decrease in proportion to $1/l^2$. This is an example of Ehrenfest's adiabatic principle, according to which, when a parameter characterizing a system is changed very slowly, the system, if initially in a definite quantum state, remains in the corresponding quantum state under the new conditions, provided the quantum states themselves do not become degenerate and ambiguous. The energy thus lost by the molecule must appear as work done by a pressure p exerted by the gas on the walls of the vessel. The volume of the vessel being l^3, the work will be $p \, d(l^3) = 3pl^2 \, dl$; hence

$$3pl^2 \, dl = -d\zeta = \frac{h^2 \, dl}{4ml^3} (k_1{}^2 + k_2{}^2 + k_3{}^2) = \frac{2\zeta}{l} \, dl$$

$$p = \frac{2}{3} \frac{\zeta}{l^3} \tag{233}$$

This conclusion is immediately applicable to any number of molecules in the vessel, provided the molecular density is very low. Thus the pressure due to an ideal gas is equal to $\frac{2}{3}$ of the translational kinetic energy of the molecules in unit volume, just as in classical theory. The actual value of the pressure can be calculated for a Fermi-Dirac gas from expressions given in the next section for the energy.

170. The Fermi-Dirac Gas. We have not space to reproduce here the argument from statistical mechanics by which the distribution of energy among the molecules is determined; we can only write down the formula and trace its significance.   For this purpose it is necessary to treat separately the molecules in each of the internal rotation-vibration-electronic states.   Let w denote the multiplicity of any given internal state, and let $n_\zeta \, d\zeta$ denote the number of the molecules in unit volume that are in this internal state and that also have translational kinetic energies lying between ζ and $\zeta + d\zeta$.   It is assumed that the molecules are distributed among so many different states that ζ may be treated as a continuous variable.   Then, for a Fermi-Dirac gas in thermal equilibrium at absolute temperature T,

$$n_\zeta = \frac{2\pi}{h^3} \, (2m)^{3/2} \, \frac{w\zeta^{1/2}}{Be^{\zeta/kT} + 1} \tag{234}$$

Here m is the mass of a molecule, k is Boltzmann's constant, and B is a constant whose value is determined by the total number n of molecules in the given (multiple) internal state in unit volume of the gas or by the equation

$$\int_0^\infty n_\zeta \, d\zeta = n \tag{235}$$

The Classical Distribution as a Limit.   If $B \gg 1$, the 1 can be dropped in the denominator of Eq. (234) without great error and the equation can be written in the approximate form

$$n_\zeta = \frac{2\pi}{h^3 B} \, (2m)^{3/2} w\zeta^{1/2} e^{-\zeta/kT} \tag{236}$$

For this case, a simple relation can be found connecting B with other quantities.   Upon substituting n_ζ as given by Eq. (236) in Eq. (235) and then changing the variable of integration to $x = (\zeta/kT)^{1/2}$, so that $\zeta = kTx^2$ and $d\zeta = 2kTx \, dx$, it is found that,

$$\int_0^\infty n_\zeta \, d\zeta = \frac{4\pi w}{h^3 B} \, (2mkT)^{3/2} \int_0^\infty x^2 e^{-x^2} \, dx = n$$

Integrating by parts

$$\int_0^\infty x^2 e^{-x^2} \, dx = -\frac{1}{2} \, xe^{-x^2} \Big|_0^\infty + \frac{1}{2} \int_0^\infty e^{-x^2} \, dx = \frac{\sqrt{\pi}}{4}$$

since the integrated term vanishes and $\int_0^\infty e^{-x^2} \, dx = \sqrt{\pi}/2$.   Thus, solving for B, the condition that $B \gg 1$ can also be written, as an approximation,

$$B = \frac{1}{h^3} \, (2\pi mkT)^{3/2} \frac{w}{n} \gg 1 \tag{237}$$

Equation (236), taken together with the statement that the molecules are moving with equal probability in all directions, is easily seen to constitute a statement of Maxwell's law for the distribution of the molecular velocities (at least for molecules in the given internal state). Thus, whenever the condition represented by the inequality in Eq. (237) is satisfied, the classical distribution law holds to a close approximation. The condition can be realized at any given density n provided the temperature is high enough, or, conversely, at any given temperature provided the density is made low enough.

It may be remarked that, for a Bose-Einstein gas, the only change required in the equations so far written is to replace $+1$ in the denominator in Eq. (234) by -1. In this case n_ζ varies with temperature in the same way as does the energy density in an isothermal enclosure [cf. Eq. (67)]. Planck's law can, in fact, be deduced by assuming that the radiation consists of photons behaving statistically like a Bose-Einstein gas.[1]

It is interesting that the condition for the approximate validity of classical theory can be given a simple physical meaning; it is roughly equivalent to the requirement that the mean de Broglie wavelength of the molecules in the given internal state shall be much less than the mean distance between the molecules themselves. To see this, we recall first that, if v is the root-mean-square velocity of the molecules, then for a molecule having this velocity and also momentum p equal to mv, according to the classical law

$$\frac{1}{2}mv^2 = \frac{p^2}{2m} = \frac{3}{2}kT$$

The corresponding de Broglie wavelength λ is given by the equation $p = h/\lambda$. Finally, if we imagine the molecules arranged at the corners of cubes of equal edge δ, the number in unit volume is seen to be $1/\delta^3$, so that $n = 1/\delta^3$. By means of these relations, kT, m, h, and n can all be eliminated from the inequality (237) with the result

$$\left(\frac{\lambda}{\delta}\right)^3 \ll (\tfrac{2}{3}\pi)^{3/2}w$$

Thus the ratio λ/δ must be small.

The State of High Degeneracy of a Fermi-Dirac Gas. At the opposite extreme of a very low temperature, or a very high molecular density, or both, marked departures from classical conditions occur and the gas is said to be degenerate. For this case it is convenient to define a critical energy ζ_1, by the equation $B = e^{-\zeta_1/kT}$, so that Eq. (234) becomes

$$n_\zeta = \frac{2\pi}{h^3}(2m)^{3/2}\frac{w\zeta^{1/2}}{e^{(\zeta - \zeta_1)/kT} + 1} \tag{238}$$

The value of ζ_1, like that of B, is fixed by Eq. (235).

---

[1] Bose. *loc. cit.*

If, now, the temperature T is very low, as ζ increases from zero, the exponential in (238) remains negligible until ζ approaches the value ζ_1 and then quickly rises to high values. Thus n_ζ is almost constant for $\zeta < \zeta_1$ and almost zero for $\zeta > \zeta_1$, except near ζ_1 itself.

At absolute zero we can regard n_ζ as actually having a constant value $n_{\zeta 0}$, where

$$n_{\zeta 0} = \frac{2\pi}{h^3}(2m)^{3/2}w\zeta^{1/2} \tag{239}$$

up to a certain limit ζ_0, and the value zero for $\zeta > \zeta_0$. The value of ζ_0 is fixed by Eq. (235), which becomes, if $T = 0$,

$$\int_0^{\zeta_0} n_\zeta \, d\zeta = \frac{2\pi}{h^3}(2m)^{3/2}w \int_0^{\zeta_0} \zeta^{1/2} \, d\zeta = n$$

whence, since $\int_0^{\zeta_0} \zeta^{1/2} \, d\zeta = \frac{2}{3}\zeta_0^{3/2}$,

$$\zeta_0 = \left(\frac{3}{4\pi}\right)^{2/3} \frac{h^2}{2m}\left(\frac{n}{w}\right)^{2/3} \tag{240}$$

The molecules are now in the lowest translational quantum states into which they can get. Since, however, in a Fermi-Dirac gas the exclusion principle prevents two molecules from occupying the same state, the molecules are spread out over a considerable range of states. Thus, in strong contrast with the conclusion from classical theory, even at the absolute zero of temperature the gas possesses a considerable amount of energy, called "zero-point" energy; its average value per molecule in the given internal state is $\frac{3}{5}\zeta_0$, since

$$\frac{1}{n}\int_0^{\zeta_0} \zeta n_\zeta \, d\zeta = \frac{2\pi}{nh^3}(2m)^{3/2}w \int_0^{\zeta_0} \zeta^{3/2} \, d\zeta = \frac{3}{5}\zeta_0$$

Curves for n_ζ corresponding to three different values of the ratio kT/ζ_0 were shown, effectively, in Fig. 18. The small nonzero value of n_ζ for $\zeta > \zeta_1$ and $T > 0$ is expressed approximately by Eq. (236), since the exponential term in (234) predominates heavily over unity. Thus, at any temperature except $T = 0$, the molecular distribution in the highly degenerate gas has a "tail" of classical or maxwellian form.

For small values of kT/ζ_0, useful series expansions can be found. Thus, E_0 denoting the energy of a gram-molecule containing N_0 molecules in a given internal state, it can be shown that

$$\zeta_1 = \zeta_0\left[1 - \frac{\pi^2}{12}\left(\frac{kT}{\zeta_0}\right)^2 \cdots\right]$$

$$E_0 = \frac{3}{5}N_0\zeta_0\left[1 + \frac{5}{12}\pi^2\left(\frac{kT}{\zeta_0}\right)^2 \cdots\right] \tag{241a,b}$$

Also, for the translational specific heat C_v of a gram-molecule,

$$C_v = \frac{dE_0}{dT} = \frac{\pi^2}{2} \frac{kT}{\zeta_0} R \cdots \tag{242}$$

in terms of the gas constant $R = N_0 k$. It follows that, as T increases from zero, the specific heat increases at first linearly with T. Subsequently it approaches its classical value $\frac{3}{2}R$ asymptotically as kT/ζ_0 becomes comparable with unity or larger.

Starting at the other extreme, the first departure from classical behavior as degeneracy begins to be manifest may be exhibited by the following formulas, in which the factor before the bracket represents in each case the classical value:

$$E_0 = \frac{3}{2}RT \left[1 + \frac{h^3}{16(\pi mk)^{3/2}} \frac{n}{wT^{3/2}} \cdots \right] \tag{243}$$

$$C_v = \frac{3}{2}R \left[1 - \frac{h^3}{32(\pi mk)^{3/2}} \frac{n}{wT^{3/2}} \cdots \right] \tag{244}$$

It should be noted that all these formulas apply separately to the set of molecules in each internal quantum state; those in a given internal state constitute in effect an independent gas behaving as if the others were absent. The molecular density, energy, and specific heat of the whole gas will then be the sum of the values of n_ζ, E_0, and C_v for all components.

To illustrate the difficulty of observing quantum effects in gases, it may be remarked that even for a gas of protons at 10 times normal density or at $n = 2.7 \times 10^{20}$ molecules per cubic centimeter, but at a temperature of $4°K$, the bracket in Eq. (244), in which $w = 1$, is less than unity by only 0.016. An interesting effect appears to occur, however, in liquid helium. It has been found possible to concentrate the isotope He^3 that is found in minute quantity in ordinary helium by utilizing a special differential flow of He^3 and He^4 molecules that occurs in a temperature gradient below $2.19°K$. This differential flow has been tentatively ascribed to the fact that He^3 is of Fermi-Dirac type and He^4 of Bose-Einstein type. Only He^4 atoms are believed to exhibit, below the "λ-point," or $2.19°K$, the curious phenomenon of superfluidity (helium II),[1] characterized by evanescent viscosity and a tendency of the liquid helium to crawl over solid surfaces.

CRYSTALLINE SOLIDS

Because of the regular arrangement of the atoms in crystals, it has been possible to achieve a partial theoretical understanding of their properties.

[1] Cf. Soller, Fairbank, and Crowell, *Phys. Rev.*, vol. 91, p. 1058, 1953.

No inclusive survey of this field can be attempted here; only a brief description will be given of the application of wave-mechanical principles to a few topics for whose understanding the new conceptions have been especially useful. Nothing will be said, furthermore, concerning the cohesion of crystals, on which work was begun as early as 1909 and was continued after 1935 with the help of wave-mechanical ideas concerning the interactions between the atoms.[1]

Two approaches to a wave-mechanical theory have been used. In one, the crystal is regarded as made up of atoms in mutual interaction; in the other, the crystal is regarded as composed of nuclei and electrons. Each approach has its advantages but neither has furnished a clear picture covering everything. It seems best, therefore, in spite of the resulting confusion, to say something about both approaches.

171. The Atomic Approach in the Wave Mechanics of Crystals. In certain phenomena the atoms comprising a solid or liquid appear to act more or less individually, somewhat as they do in a gas. For example, it was early observed that the x-ray spectrum characteristic of an element is little affected by the presence of other elements either combined chemically with the first or mixed with it in solid form. This is particularly true of x-ray lines involving only inner shells of the atom, such as the K lines from atoms heavier than neon, or L lines from atoms heavier than argon. Lines involving both an inner shell and the peripheral shell of the atom, on the other hand, are at least broadened when the substance is in solid form.

The most satisfactory approach in attempting to construct a theory of such phenomena has been to imagine the atoms or molecules to be at first widely separated from each other and then brought together to form a condensed phase. We shall speak specifically only of atomic crystals, in which the atoms are not grouped into identifiable molecules, since only this case has been extensively studied, but the same approach is possible in principle for any solid or liquid body.

When the atoms are very far apart, each one may be assumed to be in a certain atomic quantum state; an assignment of these atomic states then specifies a quantum state of the assembly as a whole, and its energy

---

[1] The application of wave mechanics to crystalline solids has been described in several books, but no treatment yet published is entirely clear to a nonspecialist. Classical and wave-mechanical ideas are freely intermingled, and statements are sometimes made concerning wave mechanics that are at least ambiguous. The following books may be mentioned: N. F. Mott and H. Jones, "Theory of the Properties of Metals and Alloys," 1936; F. Seitz, "Modern Theory of Solids," 1940; N. F. Mott and R. W. Gurney, "Electronic Processes in Ionic Crystals," 2d ed., 1948; N. F. Mott and I. N. Sneddon, "Wave Mechanics and its Applications," 1948; W. Shockley, "Electrons and Holes in Semi-conductors," 1950; A. H. Wilson, "Theory of Metals," 2d ed.. 1953.

when in this state is the sum of the atomic energies. The most important feature of such a dispersed assembly is that its energy levels are apt to be *highly degenerate*. In the first place, the atomic states themselves may be degenerate; for example, a $^2S_{\frac{1}{2}}$ atomic state has a multiplicity of 2. An assembly of N similar atoms in similar states, each having multiplicity w, will be in a state of multiplicity w^N. In the second place, if one of the atoms is in a *special* state, being excited or perhaps ionized, then *additional* degeneracy of a new type occurs; for any one of the N atoms may be the selected one. The actual wave function for the assembly will not, to be sure, represent a *particular* atom as being in the special state, but there will be N different wave functions all corresponding to the same energy of the assembly.

The significance of these degeneracies lies in the fact that, when the atoms are brought together, interaction between them tends to separate degenerate energy levels. In this way each degenerate level for the dispersed assembly becomes converted, in general, into a *band*, wide or narrow, of immensely numerous and very closely spaced energy levels for the crystal. The individual bands may happen to be separated by empty gaps, representing energies of the crystal that cannot occur, or they may

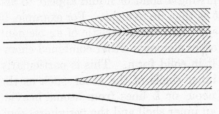

Dispersed   Crystal

Fig. 158. Schematic illustration of bands of crystal energies.

touch each other, or they may overlap. In addition, there may be other states of the assembly that are not degenerate and do not split at all. Such possibilities are illustrated diagrammatically in Fig. 158. Rough estimates of the width of a band may be made by means of perturbation theory.

The most important energy bands are those arising out of states of the dispersed assembly in which the atoms are in their *normal states*, except perhaps for one or a few atoms which are peripherally excited or ionized. The lowest bands of this series are estimated to be a few electron-volts wide, perhaps never more than 20 ev. In x-ray phenomena, on the other hand, *another series* of initial states is involved in which *one atom* has lost an *internal* electron, perhaps from the K or L shell. These bands are broadened in much the same way as the series first mentioned, but they lie as a whole very much higher in energy. They may be called *deep-excitation* levels, or (after Frenkel) *ionization* levels if the electron removed from an inner atomic shell has actually left the crystal.

It appears that the lower bands of the deep-excitation series may resemble what are called in the x-ray theory of the atom "resonance levels" (Sec. 164). An atom that has lost an electron is surrounded by an electric field like that due to a hydrogen nucleus. It is believed reasonable to imagine that this field persists when the atoms are brought together in the crystal, but in a weaker form. In an insulator the effect of neighboring atoms on this field is thought to be roughly equivalent to the ordinary dielectric effect of the material in mass, that is, the field is weakened nearly in inverse proportion to the ordinary dielectric constant K. In a hydrogenlike field modified in this manner there would be an infinite series of possible quantum states for an electron, with energies more closely spaced and wave functions more widely spread out than in the hydrogen atom; in Eq. (80), Z would be replaced by Z/K, so that the lowest two levels would be spaced about $10.19/K^2$ ev apart instead of 10.19 ev as in hydrogen. In the crystal, however, only a few of the lowest of these levels can be realized; they represent discrete levels or bands of levels lying below another, broader band in which the electron has been effectively lost from the ionized atom. See Fig. 153, which was drawn to illustrate a case of deep-excitation levels in the theory of x-rays.

The combination of a positive "hole" formed by removal of an electron from an atom and an electron trapped in the field of this hole was called by Frenkel an *exciton*. It is thought that excitons may sometimes be produced by absorption of a quantum of ordinary light; perhaps this process is responsible for the ultraviolet absorption bands of crystalline alkali halides. It should be noted that an exciton, or any similar local feature, is capable of wandering through a crystal lattice. To represent such a feature as localized in a particular spot, a wave packet must be constructed consisting of a series of stationary-state wave functions, in analogy with Eq. (113). Since the time factor $e^{-2\pi i W t/h}$ associated with these wave functions differs slightly from one function to another because of differences in the energy W, the wave packet spreads out as time passes, and this spreading represents migration of the structure.

172. Conductors and Insulators. One of the most important properties of solids is electrical conductivity. This varies enormously; the conductivity of silver, for example, is about 10^{20} times that of diamond. In some cases, as in chlorides at high temperatures, the conduction is electrolytic, involving a transport of atomic ions, but usually only electrons are actually transported.

Now how can wave mechanics account for electronic conductivity? When a physical body is in a pure quantum state, $|\Psi|^2$ is constant and hence the distribution of the electrons cannot change with time. The answer is that an electric current can exist only in a physical body that is in a *mixed* wave-mechanical state composed of many elementary quantum states, in analogy with Eq. (113). A body can be thrown into such a mixed state by the application of a weak electric field provided the component states lie very close together in energy, their levels belonging either to a single band or to adjacent or overlapping bands. Thus high electronic conductivity will be a property only of those bodies whose quantum state of lowest energy lies at the bottom of a band of closely spaced levels. Several possibilities are illustrated diagrammatically in Fig. 159.

Such a situation should occur in a crystal whenever the normal states of the constituent atoms are themselves degenerate, resulting in an associated *band* of levels for the crystal. The most striking examples are the alkali metals. Here the atoms are normally in $^2S_{1/2}$ states with twofold degeneracy ($J = \frac{1}{2}$, $M = \pm\frac{1}{2}$). Such atoms condense into crystals of the atomic type; and these are in fact excellent conductors of electricity. The atoms of the rare gases, on the other hand, are in nondegenerate

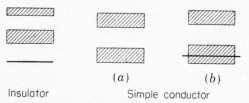

$$(a) \qquad\qquad (b)$$

Insulator   Simple conductor

FIG. 159. Schematic illustration of the relations between crystal energy levels for insulators and for simple conductors.

$^1S_0$ states and, at extremely low temperatures, form a crystal in an isolated nondegenerate crystal state. These crystals are good insulators.

Looking farther, however, it will be noted that many divalent atoms such as zinc are also normally in $^1S_0$ states, yet they form highly conducting atomic crystals. It has been surmised, although not actually deduced from the theory, that in such cases the single state arising out of the $^1S_0$ atomic states actually lies higher than the bottom of a band of states that arises out of superficially excited atomic states, and that the conductivity is due to this latter band [Fig. 159(b)]. (See also Sec. 174.)

An interesting and instructive case is that of the alkali halides, which form insulating crystals of the simple cubic type; NaCl is a typical example. When the sodium and chlorine atoms are widely separated, the state of lowest energy for the assembly is one in which the atoms are electrically neutral; for it requires 5.2 ev of work to remove an electron from a sodium atom and only 3.8 ev of this work is recovered if the electron is subsequently attached to a chlorine atom, which has an affinity for an extra electron. As the atoms approach each other, however, the situation becomes reversed. Imagine the atoms, while still neutral, to be brought into their proper crystal positions. If an electron is now transferred from each sodium atom to a chlorine atom, an electrostatic field is created, and it will be noted that each negatively charged chlorine

atom has six positive sodium ions as its nearest neighbors and is, therefore, at a point of comparatively high potential in this field, whereas,
similarly, each sodium ion is at a point of relatively low potential (due to
all other atoms).   See Fig. 160.   Calculation shows that the electrostatic
energy of the crystal has thus been lowered to the extent of 17.9 ev per
electron transferred.   Even when account is taken of the net work
required to remove each electron from a sodium atom and attach it to
a chlorine atom, a net release of energy in the amount 17.9 − 5.2 + 3.8
or 16.5 ev is seen to occur.   The *stable* configuration in the *crystal* will
thus be an assembly, not of neutral atoms, but of sodium and chlorine
ions.

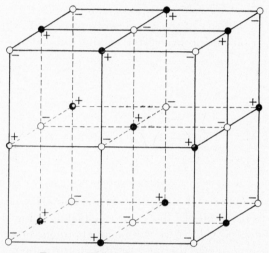

FIG. 160. The sodium chloride lattice.

Now the crystal might also have been constructed by the alternative
procedure of bringing the *ions* together.   Since both ions have closed
shells and are in nondegenerate $^1S_0$ states, the lowest state for the crystal,
like that of a rare gas, will be nondegenerate.   Estimates indicate, furthermore, that in this case all other energy levels lie considerably higher.
Hence electronic conduction should not occur in an uncharged sodium
chloride crystal, in agreement with observation.   It should be remarked,
however, that the further diversity of crystal states representing *thermal*
vibrations of the crystal lattice has been ignored in this simplified description of the theory.

The atomic approach thus gives a satisfactory *qualitative* picture of the
distinction between insulators and conductors.   For *quantitative* calculations, however, this approach is scarcely practical because of the enormous
influence of atomic interaction when the atoms are brought so close
together.   We shall return to the subject of conductors in Sec. 174.

173. The Collective-electron Approach.   An alternative approach to the wave-mechanical theory of crystals was initiated by F. Bloch in 1928. It can be regarded as an extension to crystals of the modified-field method that proved so successful in atomic theory (Sec. 109).

In this method the atomic nuclei are assumed to be placed at once in their proper crystal positions, and the average effect of mutual electronic repulsions is allowed for by adding a suitable continuously distributed negative charge cloud.   The total electric potential ϕ due to the nuclei and to the charge cloud then provides a field of potential $V = -e\phi$ to which each electron is assumed to be subjected.   (Here either electrostatic or practical units may be used; if ϕ is in volts, $-\phi$ also represents V measured in electron-volts.)   In a crystal composed of similar atoms, because of the periodicity of the atomic arrangement, V will be a periodic function of position within the crystal, sinking quickly to very low values

FIG. 161. Schematic diagram of periodic potential energy of an electron in a crystal.

in the neighborhood of each nucleus.   At the boundary of the crystal, V rises several electron-volts to the value 0 outside (cf. Fig. 161).

In such a potential field there will be an enormous number of possible quantum states for an electron; and because of the periodicity of the field a good deal can be inferred concerning these quantum states.   Each electronic wave function extends over the entire crystal, but in the vicinity of each nucleus it resembles one of the wave functions for a single atom. The most important conclusion obtained from the theory is that the corresponding *electronic* energy levels must fall into almost continuous bands, which may either overlap or merely touch or be separated by gaps representing impossible values of the electronic energy.   The highest band that is normally occupied, with wave functions resembling near the nuclei a function for one of the outermost atomic electrons, is called the valence band and has in the case of metals a width between 3 and 15 ev.   The number of levels in each band is easily found by an argument rather similar to that used in Sec. 67 in counting the degrees of freedom of the electromagnetic field in an enclosure, the number of levels being doubled here to allow for the two possible values of electronic spin.

An assignment of sufficient electronic levels to contain all the electrons that are present in the crystal then defines, in this approximation, a quantum state for the crystal as a whole. The uppermost band that contains any electrons at all may be either full or partly full; lower bands will normally be full. Final refinement of the theory could then be made, as in atomic theory, by taking into account more accurately the interactions between the electrons.

In this way the same bands of *crystal* states and energy levels are ultimately obtained as by the atomic approach. The crystal levels and the electronic levels should not be indiscriminately confused; for the significance of the *electronic* levels is limited. So long as only the uppermost electrons are disturbed, there should be a fair agreement between changes of electronic energy and changes of crystal energy. On the other hand, to deal with those deeply excited or ionized states of the crystal which are involved in x-ray phenomena, it would be necessary, in the collective-electron approach, to start from a *different potential field*, namely one whose periodicity is interrupted near one nucleus because of the absence of an electron. In this field a *different set of electronic states and levels* would be obtained. This particular series of crystal states, however, is more easily treated by means of the atomic approach.

A few words should be added concerning the actual mathematical procedure that is commonly followed in using the collective-electron approach. If the periodic potential field V is assumed to be unlimited in spatial extent, it can be shown that the allowed solutions of the Schrödinger amplitude equation (112a) have the form

$$\psi = e^{i\mathbf{k}\cdot\mathbf{r}}u(\mathbf{r}) \tag{245}$$

where $\mathbf{k}$ is a constant vector, $\mathbf{r}$ is the position vector of the electron, $\mathbf{k}\cdot\mathbf{r}$ denotes the scalar product, and u is a periodic function of the space coordinates having the three-dimensional symmetry of the crystal lattice. All values of $\mathbf{k}$ are allowed. Such a ψ represents the electron as moving through the crystal with a certain vector velocity, depending both upon $\mathbf{k}$ and upon u. Although a ψ of this form cannot represent a stationary state for a finite crystal, the same electronic energy bands and the same mathematical results in general are obtained as would be obtained with use of the true wave functions for the finite crystal, provided closely spaced values of $\mathbf{k}$ are chosen in a proper manner.

174. Metals and Nonmetals. Essentially the same distinction between conductors and insulators results from the collective-electron approach as from the atomic approach; the statement is merely phrased here in terms of the more concrete imagery of *electronic* states and levels.

In some crystals the uppermost occupied band is exactly full of electrons and this band is separated in energy from the next higher empty band by a gap of several electron-volts. In such a crystal, neither an applied electric field nor thermal agitation can appreciably disturb the electronic distribution. The crystal is therefore an electrical insulator; and the electrons also play no role in the conduction of heat, so that the thermal conductivity is relatively low. Such a crystal is nonmetallic.

In other crystals the uppermost occupied band is only partly full of electrons, or this band may overlap in energy another band which is only partly full. Such a crystal exhibits the high thermal and electronic conductivities that are characteristic of a metal. The loose statement is usually made that, whereas normally as many electrons are moving in any one direction as in the opposite direction, an applied electric field will throw some electrons into states of higher energy and, in doing so, will favor those states in which electrons are moving in the opposite direction to that of the field, thereby generating a current. Obviously this cannot happen in a full band. A more accurate wave-mechanical explanation would be phrased in terms of mixed quantum states, in analogy with the explanation given in terms of crystal states in Sec. 172.

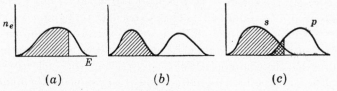

(a) (b) (c)

FIG. 162. Diagram showing three among many possible relations between electronic bands in a crystal.

Three possible cases are illustrated in Fig. 162, in which n_e, the number of electronic levels per unit of electronic energy E, is shown qualitatively as a function of E. The horizontal shading represents the part of a band or bands that is normally filled. Case a, that of the isolated, partly full band, includes the alkali metals already mentioned in Sec. 172, and also, among others, Cu, Ag, and Au. In these metals there are N valence electrons for N atoms but the valence band contains $2N$ levels because of the two possible spin orientations for each electron. Case c is believed to hold for divalent metals such as Mg, Ca, Zn, Hg. Here the $2N$ valence electrons are just numerous enough to fill the s band, but the p band (with electronic functions of the p type near the nuclei) overlaps the s band. The resulting conductivity, however, is considerably smaller than that of the monovalent metals.

In other cases the situation is more complicated. Two bands just touching, as in Fig. 162(b), may result in a low conductivity in some cases, perhaps, for example, in graphite. In "transition metals" such as iron, cobalt, and nickel, a band related to the unfilled atomic d levels also overlaps the s and p bands. On the other hand, the low conductivity of at least some semiconductors appears to be due chiefly to electrons released into a conduction band from impurity centers in the crystal lattice. In ZnO the impurity may consist of a few excess atoms of Zn (perhaps one in 10^4) lodged interstitially in the crystal lattice, in the form of positive ions. In a crystal of Cu_2O containing excess oxygen, a few Cu^+ ions are replaced by oxygen atoms; the resulting local deficit of positive charge is balanced by an electronic deficit nearby, which can be regarded as a diffuse positive "hole." Such holes may remain trapped near the oxygen atoms or they may move in an electric field; if they move, however, they are equivalent to a current of *positive* electricity, so that the Hall coefficient of the crystal has the opposite sign from its values for ordinary metals.

Free-electron Theory of the Conduction Band. Even simpler electronic functions may frequently be employed with success. If the potential field V is smoothed out into a constant average value, then the electrons behave in it just like the molecules of a Fermi-Dirac gas, as described in Sec. 170. We are thus led to the treatment of the valence electrons that was described in Sec. 56. The widths in energy of the occupied parts of the valence bands of the metals in the first two groups of the periodic table, as inferred from x-ray phenomena (Sec. 165), are found to agree closely with the free-electron value as represented by ζ_0 in Eq. (240).

Magnitude of the Electrical Conductivity. Calculations of electrical conductivity by means of wave mechanics are usually attempted with functions of the type shown in Eq. (245). First, a calculation is made of the rate at which an applied electric field transfers electrons into levels with functions representing motion in the direction opposite to the field. In a perfect crystal of infinite extent this motion, once created, would persist indefinitely; in actual crystals, imperfections in the crystal lattice and thermal displacements of the nuclei both tend to "scatter the waves" and so to destroy the current generated by the field. In more exact terms, the theoretical wave functions possess approximate validity only for the perfect lattice, and any departure from perfect periodicity can be treated as a perturbation tending to induce electronic transfers into other functions. By equating expressions for these two opposing actions, an expression for the equilibrium magnitude of the current and thence for the conductivity is obtained.

The following results obtained from the theory are noteworthy.

a. VARIATION WITH TEMPERATURE. It was observed long ago that the electrical resistance of pure metals is nearly proportional to the absolute temperature T. This fact was hard to explain in the classical electron theory; it was necessary to assume that, as the temperature decreases, either the number of the free electrons becomes greater or their mean free path increases, and neither assumption seemed plausible. According to wave mechanics it is in a sense the "mean free path" that increases. The wave-mechanical argument may be paraphrased by saying that the amplitude of the electronic wave that is scattered by an atom displaced through a distance x from its proper position is proportional to x, and the intensity of the scattered wave is therefore proportional to x^2; but, on the average, for displacements due to thermal agitation, x^2 is proportional to T. The resistance itself is, therefore, proportional to T.

At extremely low temperatures, however, the wave-mechanical theory predicts proportionality between the resistance and T^5, and this conclusion has been widely confirmed experimentally. The peculiar phenomenon of superconductivity, on the other hand, has not yet been adequately explained.

b. ABSOLUTE VALUES. The results of long calculations of the conductivity for the monovalent metals have given, in terms of a unit corresponding to a resistance of 10^{-4} ohm in a 1-cm cube: Li 28, Na 23, K 20, as compared to observed values of 11.8, 23.4, 16.4, respectively; but 174 was obtained for Cu and 143 for Ag as compared with 64 and 66. This limited degree of agreement should probably be considered encouraging, but it also illustrates the difficulty of obtaining quantitative results in the theory of solids comparable with those that have been achieved in atomic theory.

c. ALLOYS. As a rule, the resistance of alloys is much greater than that of the constituent pure metals, and it varies relatively slowly with temperature. For example, the addition of one atom of tin per 100 atoms of copper more than doubles the resistivity. In such cases the excess resistance is ascribed to scattering of the electronic waves by irregularities in the crystal lattice resulting from the intermingling of two different kinds of atoms.

CHAPTER 10

THE NUCLEUS

We have seen in previous chapters how the development of the quantum theory led in such a striking way to an essentially complete solution of the atomic problem. From a mass of apparently unrelated observations and a number of puzzling regularities, atomic spectroscopy blossomed forth in the course of a decade or so into a subject in which one could say with some confidence that all the principles and perhaps most of the interesting ramifications were well understood. The nucleus has been somewhat less tractable in this regard; although there has been accumulated a large store of facts about nuclei and although we have even had some success in harnessing the nucleus in a practical sense, we have as yet found no simple framework into which to fit our information, and the answers to many fundamental questions are lacking. We have, for example, only the crudest phenomenological description of the forces which act between the constituents of nuclei; we are not even sure to what extent we may justifiably regard the "particles" that we talk about in the nucleus as elementary, or incapable of further division. The solution to these and many other problems of the most fundamental nature must await further developments along both experimental and theoretical lines. In the meantime, there are a good many of the grosser features of nuclei and nuclear processes which can be understood without this information, and in the interpretation of which the quantum mechanics has been conspicuously successful. It will be the object of the present chapter to set down some of these facts and principles, together with an account of the experiments which brought them to light.

NATURAL RADIOACTIVITY

The discovery of radioactivity by Henri Becquerel in 1896 marks the starting point of nuclear physics. As a result of his work and of the investigations along the same lines by the Curies, by Rutherford and his collaborators, and by many others, it became evident within a few years that this comparatively innocent-looking phenomenon represented the operation of forces of quite a different order of magnitude from any which were familiar to chemists or physicists of that time, and that one was in fact dealing here with the actual transmutation of the elements, for which men had searched in vain since the time of the Egyptians. As a direct outgrowth of these studies came the identification of a whole host of materials possessing the remarkable property of spontaneously transforming one into another, and with the unraveling of these successive transformations came the first clue to the intimate relation between the elements. Exploitation of the enormously energetic radiations which these substances emitted led to the discovery of the nucleus itself, and finally to the artificially induced transmutation of the stable elements. Nuclear physics has progressed greatly since the time of these early experiments, and the startling developments in the field have properly deserved the epithet "spectacular" on several occasions since, but there are few periods which seem in retrospect quite as exciting as these first years must have been.

175. The Discovery of Radioactivity.[1] Becquerel's discovery was directly connected with the discovery of x-rays announced by Roentgen only a few months earlier. The fact that the production of x-rays seemed to be associated with a fluorescence of the glass envelope of the x-ray tube suggested that substances which were naturally fluorescent or phosphorescent might also produce such a penetrating radiation after exposure to light. As a part of a program to investigate this possibility, Becquerel prepared in February of 1896 a sample of the double sulfate of potassium and uranium, a well-known phosphorescent material, and placed it on a photographic plate enveloped in black paper, intending to expose it to sunlight. After waiting in vain for sunshine for some days, he decided to develop the plate, since the package had been exposed to some diffuse light and would therefore not be suitable for his experiment. Much to his surprise, the image of the crystals stood out clearly on the plate, much more clearly than it had in any of his previous tests. Further experiments showed that the blackening of the plate was quite independent of exposure to light or of the previous treatment of the materials, and even compounds which exhibited no fluorescence could produce the effect, so long as they contained uranium. The magnitude of the effect was shown to be directly proportional to the atomic content of uranium in the compound, and extreme variations of temperature had no demonstrable influence. It was these observations which led to the conclusion that "radioactivity," as it was later named by Mme. M. Curie, was not a molecular effect, but had something to do with an atomic process, the like of which had not been seen in any chemical reaction.

---

[1] E. Rutherford, "Radioactivity," Cambridge, London, 1904, and E. Rutherford, J. Chadwick, and C. D. Ellis, "Radiations from Radioactive Substances," Cambridge, London, 1931. Becquerel's papers appeared in *Compt. rend.*, vol. 122, 1896. See also W. F. Magie, "A Source Book in Physics," McGraw-Hill, New York, 1935.

The announcement of these results led, naturally enough, to an intensive search for other substances possessing the same properties, and in 1898 Mme. Curie discovered two new substances, which she named "polonium" and "radium." These materials, which were found in uranium minerals, were many times more active than uranium itself; radium is in fact so active that its compounds are able to maintain themselves several degrees above the temperature of their surroundings. The radioactivity of thorium was found by Schmidt, and independently by Mme. Curie, in 1898, and in 1900 the radioactive gases thoron and radon emanating from thorium and radium were reported by Rutherford and Dorn, respectively.

176. Radiations from Radioactive Substances. It was soon found that the rays from these various substances were mainly of two kinds—one a "soft" radiation which could penetrate only very thin paper, which

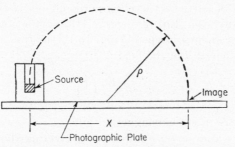

FIG. 163. Arrangement used by Becquerel to determine the deflection of β-rays in a magnetic field. Rays coming from the source are deflected in a semicircular arc by a magnetic field perpendicular to the plane of the figure.

was in fact stopped in only a few centimeters of air, and another which traveled some tens or hundreds of centimeters in air and could even penetrate thin foils of metal. These two radiations were called alpha-rays and beta-rays, respectively. The existence of still a third, much more penetrating component, called gamma-radiation, was discovered by Villard in 1900. The α- and β-rays were shown by Becquerel to be capable of rendering air conducting and of discharging a gold-leaf electroscope just as Roentgen had shown to be the case for x-rays.

a. Identification of the Beta-particle. In 1899 Giesel and, independently, Becquerel found that the β-rays could be easily deflected in a magnetic field. The arrangement used by Becquerel is illustrated in Fig. 163. A small lead container, open at the top and containing a radioactive preparation, is placed on a photographic plate with a magnetic field parallel to the surface of the plate (perpendicular to the plane of Fig. 163). Beta-rays emerging from the container in the plane of the figure are deflected by the field through semicircles and register on the plate at various distances, depending on their momenta. From the law of magnetic deflection, it may be seen that the distance at which particles of a given momentum and charge strike the plate is

$$x = 2\rho = 2 \frac{mv}{eB}$$

where v is the velocity of the β-particle, and B is the magnetic induction; e and B are in electromagnetic units. The quantity $B\rho$, called the *magnetic rigidity*, is a measure of the momentum divided by the charge. Becquerel found a wide variation in $B\rho$ even for a thin source, indicating that the β-rays are not homogeneous. By placing absorbing foils on the plate, he found that the most easily deflected β-particles were the most easily absorbed. He soon found that the β-particles could also be deflected electrostatically, and set out to determine their specific charge (e/m) by a comparison of the magnetic and electric deflections. If we imagine a beam of particles traveling perpendicularly to an electrostatic field E, it is easily seen [Eq. (25), Sec. 47] that, for not-too-large deflections, the displacement y perpendicular to the motion after the particles have traveled a length l in the field is

$$y = \frac{1}{2} \frac{Ee}{m} \left(\frac{l}{v}\right)^2$$

where E and e are in electromagnetic units.

Inserting the value of $B\rho$ for the rays (selecting the least absorbable components) Becquerel could obtain v, and hence also e/m. He found a velocity of more than half the speed of light and obtained a value for e/m of about 10^7 emu per gram (the charge was negative). This observation suggested that the β-rays were to be identified with the electrons observed as the cathode rays by Thomson (only 3 years earlier), but showed that their velocities greatly exceed those of the cathode rays. Later work, by Kaufmann in 1902, who used simultaneous electric and magnetic deflections, gave a more accurate value of e/m, and showed the variation of mass with velocity that was later to be explained by the special theory of relativity. The enormous velocities observed, up to $0.96c$, emphasized again that radioactivity was no ordinary chemical phenomenon.

b. Alpha-particles. The magnetic deflection of the α-rays was first demonstrated by Rutherford, in 1903. How difficult they were to deflect may be judged from Rutherford's own figures, according to which, in a field of 10,000 gauss, the radius of curvature was some 39 cm, while that of the cathode rays from an ordinary tube would be only 0.01 cm! The sense of the deflection indicated a positive charge. Applying the methods of magnetic and electrostatic deflection, Rutherford obtained values of $v = 2.5 \times 10^9$ cm per sec and $e/m = 6 \times 10^3$ emu per gram for the

α-particles of radium[1] (actually, RaC′, a derivative of radium).   Unlike the β-particles, the α-particles turned out to occur in groups with discrete velocities.   The value of e/m for hydrogen ions was known from the work of Faraday, for

$$\frac{e}{m} = \frac{F}{M} = \frac{9,650}{1.008} = 0.96 \times 10^4 \text{ emu per gram}$$

where F is the amount of charge required to produce 1 gram-atom, $M = 1.008$ grams, of hydrogen in an electrolytic cell (Sec. 45).   If the charge of the α-particle is the same as that of the hydrogen ion, the mass is about twice that of hydrogen; if the charge is twice as great, an identification with helium seems indicated.   The suggestion that the α-particles might be helium ions was particularly attractive since it was well known that helium is always present in radioactive minerals.

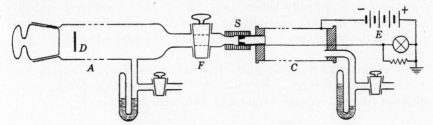

FIG. 164. Apparatus of Rutherford and Geiger for counting the number of α-particles emitted by radium.   Those particles from the source D which pass through the aperture S are registered in the counter C.   (*Adapted from Rutherford, Chadwick, and Ellis, "Radiations from Radioactive Substances," Cambridge University Press, 1931.*)

In a series of experiments reported in 1908, Rutherford and Geiger[2] measured directly the number of α-particles emitted per gram of radium and the total charge carried by them, thus making possible a determination of the charge of the α-particle.   The apparatus for the first measurement is illustrated in Fig. 164.   An evacuated vessel A contains a thin deposit of radium on a holder D.   When the stopcock F is opened, the α-particles pass through an aperture S, which is covered by a thin mica foil, into the "counter" C.   The counter consists of a brass tube, provided with ebonite plugs through which a fine center wire passes. The tube is connected to the negative side of a high-voltage battery, the positive end of which is grounded, and the center wire is connected to an electrometer E provided with a high-resistance leak to ground.   With the counter exhausted to a few centimeters pressure, the passage of a single α-particle produces a momentary discharge which causes the elec-

---

[1] These numbers were later revised to 1.922×10^9 cm per sec and 4,826 emu per gram.

[2] E. Rutherford and H. Geiger, *Proc. Roy. Soc. (London)*, vol. 81, p. 141, 1908.

trometer to deflect.   With this instrument, Rutherford and Geiger found
that 3.4×10^{10} α-particles were expelled per gram of radium per second
(actually, from the amount of RaC′ in equilibrium with 1 gram of
radium).   In the second experiment,[1] they determined by direct measurement the amount of charge collected on a plate suspended above the
preparation in an evacuated vessel.   Beta-rays and secondary electrons
were eliminated by putting the apparatus in a strong transverse magnetic
field.   The result was 31.6 esu per gram per sec.   Dividing this number
by the total number of α-particles gave for the charge per α-particle
9.3×10^{-10} esu, which they concluded must correspond to two elementary charges.   They could then divide one-half the e/m value for the
α-particles, which Rutherford had recently redetermined as 5,070 emu
per gram, by the value for hydrogen ions, obtaining an atomic weight of
3.8 relative to hydrogen.   Thus there could be little doubt that the
α-particles were actually helium ions.   Even more conclusive evidence
was obtained in 1909 when Rutherford and Royds[2] detected spectroscopically the helium gas formed when α-particles pass into a closed glass
vessel.

The velocity obtained by Rutherford for the α-particles from radium
(C′) implies a very high energy indeed.   The mass of the helium atom,
obtained from the atomic weight and Avogadro's number, is

$$M = \frac{4.00}{6.02} \times 10^{-23} = 6.64 \times 10^{-24} \text{ gram}$$

The kinetic energy is then $\frac{1}{2}mv^2 = 12.3 \times 10^{-6}$ erg, or

$$\frac{12.3 \times 10^{-6}}{1.6 \times 10^{-12}} = 7.7 \times 10^6 \text{ ev}$$

Thus the emission of each α-particle involves an energy change of several
million times the energy release in a chemical reaction!   It was pointed
out by Rutherford and Soddy that the presence of only a few times 10^{-14}
parts by weight of radium in the earth would compensate for the heat
lost from the earth by radiation.   They also suggested that the heat of
the sun might be derived from radioactive substances.   Actually we now
have a more sophisticated theory of the source of solar and stellar energy
(Sec. 204), but the heat of the earth probably is due to radioactive
materials.

   c. *Gamma-rays.*   The third component of the radioactive radiations,
the γ-rays, proved much less amenable to study than were the α- and
β-rays.   The γ-rays are much more penetrating and they are not deflected

[1] *Ibid.*, p. 162.
[2] E. Rutherford and T. Royds, *Phil. Mag.*, vol. 17, p. 281, 1909.

by electric or magnetic fields.   They are, however, able to produce ionization in air by secondary processes, and it is by this means that they
are ordinarily detected.   It was conjectured rather early that they might
be a form of electromagnetic radiation, like the x-rays, but the proof of
this hypothesis had to await development of a much more complete
understanding of the interaction of electromagnetic radiation with matter.   We shall return to a discussion of the γ-rays later on, in connection
with the spectra of radioactive disintegrations (Sec. 179).

177. Radioactive Transformations.[1]   The hypothesis that there exists
a genetic relation between some of the radioactive elements was first

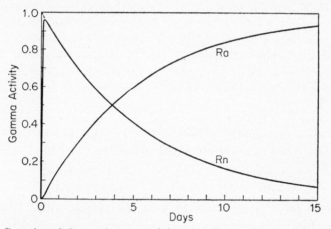

FIG. 165. Growth and decay of γ-ray activity of radium and radon, as a function of
time after chemical separation.   The initial transient due to the growth of radium A,
B, and C is exaggerated in the figure.

advanced by Rutherford and Soddy in 1903, on the basis of their work
on the decay and production of chemically separable activities.   A typical example is afforded by a study of the γ-rays of radium.   Radium
solutions continually evolve a gas, called radon.   If the radon gas is
completely pumped away from a radium source which has been standing
in a sealed vessel, it is found that after a short time the gas exhibits all the
γ-activity (measured by absorbing out the α- and β-components), while
the solution has none.   If the vessels containing the radon and the
radium are left standing separately for a few weeks, it is found that the
latter now is γ-active again and the former is not.   More detailed measurements of the γ-ray activity of the two samples as a function of time
lead to the curves shown in Fig. 165, where it may be seen that, aside from
certain transient effects at the very beginning, the activity of the radon
falls exponentially, reaching half-value in about 3.8 days.   The activity

[1] Cf. Rutherford, Chadwick, and Ellis, *op. cit.*; D. S. Halliday, "Introductory
Nuclear Physics," Wiley, New York, 1950.

of the radium sample rises exponentially and also reaches half-value in 3.8 days; the sum of the two curves is constant in time.   That two activity curves relating to chemically quite different substances should bear such close similarity argues strongly that there must be some very close relation between them, and it was this observation which suggested the hypothesis that one member is produced by a spontaneous transmutation of the other.

a. Theory of Spontaneous Transformations.   The essential feature of the transformation theory lies in the assumption that each radioactive atom has a definite probability of disintegrating in a given time, a probability which depends on the kind of atom but which is constant for all atoms of a given kind.   If we have N such atoms, the number disintegrating in a time dt is $dN = -N\lambda\, dt$, where λ is the *disintegration constant* and the minus sign indicates that N is decreasing with time.   If the sample is isolated, i.e., if no new atoms are being added, the number of atoms of the original kind remaining after time t is

$$N(t) = N(0)e^{-\lambda t} \tag{246}$$

where $N(0)$ is the number present at $t = 0$.   The time at which half of the original atoms have disintegrated, called the "half-life," is given by

$$\frac{N(t_{1/2})}{N(0)} = \tfrac{1}{2} = e^{-\lambda t_{1/2}} \qquad t_{1/2} = \frac{\ln 2}{\lambda} = \frac{0.693}{\lambda}$$

The "mean life," or life expectancy of the average atom, is given by (cf. Sec. 108)

$$t_m = \frac{\displaystyle\int_0^\infty te^{-\lambda t}\, dt}{\displaystyle\int_0^\infty e^{-\lambda t}\, dt} = \frac{1}{\lambda}$$

The behavior of an isolated radon sample with a given initial number of atoms is thus accounted for by a simple decay, with disintegration constant $\lambda(Rn) = 0.693/t_{1/2} = 0.21 \times 10^{-5}$ sec^{-1}.

If now we consider instead the production of radon in the vessel containing radium, we have a somewhat different situation.   The number of radium atoms disintegrating in time dt is $dN_1 = -\lambda_1 N_1\, dt$, where λ_1 is the disintegration constant of radium.   Each of these disintegrations produces a radon atom; in the same time, however, a number $\lambda_2 N_2\, dt$ of radon atoms will disintegrate (the subscript 2 refers to radon), so the total change in the amount of radon is

$$dN_2 = +\lambda_1 N_1\, dt - \lambda_2 N_2\, dt = [\lambda_1 N_1(0)e^{-\lambda_1 t} - \lambda_2 N_2]\, dt$$

If at time $t = 0$ there is no radon present, the integral of this equation is

$$N_2(t) = N_1(0)\, \frac{\lambda_1}{\lambda_2 - \lambda_1}\, (e^{-\lambda_1 t} - e^{-\lambda_2 t}) \tag{247}$$

In the present case the parent, radium, has a relatively long half-life (1,622 years) so we may ignore λ_1 compared to λ_2. We then obtain

$$N_2(t) = N_1(t) \frac{\lambda_1}{\lambda_2} (1 - e^{-\lambda_2 t}) \tag{248}$$

From this relation we see that the growth of radon from radium will exhibit a time constant characteristic of the decay of radon, and that the sum of the activities in the two separated samples of Fig. 165 will remain practically constant. Actually the γ-rays in this case come not from the radon itself, but from radium C, which appears only after several subsequent disintegrations. The least rapid of the successive stages has a half-life of about 27 min so there is a transient effect of about this magnitude in the growth and decay curves of Fig. 165.

After a time long compared to $1/\lambda_2$, the amount of radon in equilibrium with radium will approach the constant value $N_2 = N_1\lambda_1/\lambda_2$; thus

$$N_2\lambda_2 = N_1\lambda_1 \tag{249}$$

This relation, which is general for any radioactive chain, provided only that the system has been undisturbed for a time long compared with the half-life of any of the products, merely expresses the fact that, at equilibrium, the rate of decay of any radioactive product is just equal to its rate of production from the previous member of the chain. A system which has reached this condition is said to be in "secular equilibrium."

The picture of the radioactive chains which thus emerged from Rutherford and Soddy's considerations is the following. A radioactive atom disintegrates by the emission of an α-particle, thereby losing four units of mass and changing its chemical properties. The product then further disintegrates either by α- or β-emission, each disintegration leading to a different element, until finally a stable substance is formed, ending the chain. A little later, when the importance of the nuclear charge in determining the chemical behavior of an element was realized, it was established that the α-transformation removes four units of mass and two units of charge, producing an element two steps down in the periodic table, while the β-disintegration removes one negative charge, and essentially no mass, producing an element one step higher in the table. This picture has found ample confirmation in studies of the chemical properties of the various products. Although the amounts of material available for such studies are ordinarily too minute for conventional analytical techniques, the fact that the substances are radioactive makes it possible to carry out the usual chemical manipulations and to trace the material under investigation through the various stages by means of the radiation emitted. Thus, Rutherford and his coworkers were able in 1903 to determine the chemical and physical properties of radon gas, including its condensation temperature, with samples amounting to small fractions of a microgram.

b. Radioactive Isotopes.[1] Further investigations of the radioactive transformations of one element into another led to the identification of a great number of such successive transformations and to the discovery of many new radioactive substances. A particularly important result of this work was the observation for the first time of "isotopes," atoms having identical chemical properties but differing in their atomic weights. The discovery of isotopes came incidentally to a search for the origin of radium. The fact that radium has a half-life which is short on a geological time scale suggested that it must be a product of some longer-lived material, probably uranium, since radium is always found in uranium minerals. In the course of a search for this connection, Boltwood discovered in 1906 a long-lived substance which appeared to be the intermediate between uranium and radium. The interesting feature of his report was that this substance, which he named "ionium," appeared to be chemically very similar to thorium. The matter was followed up by Marckwald and Keetman in 1909, and later by v. Welsbach, with the astonishing result that ionium and thorium are in fact chemically identical, although their radioactive properties are quite different. Within the next year several other such cases were found and it was established that the difference in radioactive properties was associated with a difference in atomic weight. The importance of these findings was emphasized by Soddy in 1910, when he pointed out that the existence among radioactive elements—and, as he presumed to be the case, among stable elements as well—of atoms having various masses but identical chemical properties provided a natural explanation of the nonintegral atomic weights of certain elements, and reopened the question of whether all atoms might not be built out of some common constituents.

The hypothesis that the elements are constructed from hydrogen atoms had been advanced by the English chemist Prout in 1816, only ten years after Dalton's formulation of the atomic hypothesis, from the observation that many atomic weights appeared to be integral multiples of that of hydrogen. Prout's suggestion fell into disrepute, however, when with more precise measurements it developed that there were deviations from the whole-number relation in many cases. Finally, when the atomic weight of chlorine (35.5) was shown to deviate by a full half-integer, further discussion of the point was generally abandoned.[2] With the discovery of isotopes, such deviations as that of chlorine could be simply accounted for by assuming an appropriate mixture, and one could again

[1] F. W. Aston, "Mass Spectra and Isotopes," Longmans, London, 1933.

[2] Most chemical atomic weights are actually determined relative to oxygen, and until 1900 the atomic weight of hydrogen was believed to be just $\frac{1}{16}$ that of oxygen.

consider the possibility of some elemental constituents of atoms. As
we shall see later, the masses of isotopes are in fact very nearly (though
not quite) integral multiples of a single number, and there is now good
evidence that the hydrogen nucleus (not the atom) is one of the building
blocks of nuclei.

In modern terminology, each nucleus is characterized by a definite
charge number Z, a multiple of the protonic charge, and a definite mass

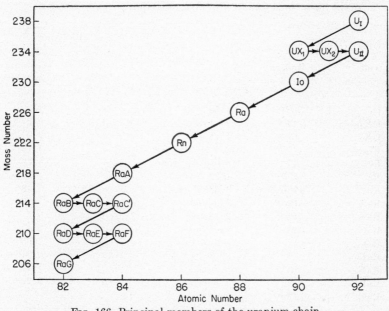

FIG. 166. Principal members of the uranium chain.

number A. The mass number is the integer nearest the actual isotopic
mass, expressed in a scale where the mass of the most abundant oxygen
isotope equals 16 exactly (see Sec. 181c). The nuclear charge determines
the number of electrons in the neutral atom and hence the gross atomic
properties (Sec. 79), but such specifically nuclear properties as radioactivity depend just as much on A as on Z. A nuclear species with a
given Z and A is called a "nuclide"; nuclides with the same Z and different A are "isotopes," those with the same A but different Z are called
"isobars." It is becoming general practice to replace the original names
of the various radioelements with designations more consistent with their
known chemical properties: thus ionium, mesothorium I, and thorium X
appear in much current literature as $_{90}Th^{230}$, $_{88}Ra^{228}$, and $_{88}Ra^{224}$. In
these symbols, the letters refer to the chemical name, the subscript gives
the atomic number and the superscript the mass number. The subscript
is of course redundant and is often omitted entirely.

c. *Radioactive Chains.* There are now known to exist in nature, among the heavy elements, three independent radioactive chains, the uranium, thorium, and actinium series. The first of these starts with $_{92}U^{238}$ and ends with RaG, an isotope of lead, $_{82}Pb^{206}$. The successive steps in this chain are illustrated in Fig. 166, and some properties of the various members are listed in Table 10-1. There have recently been discovered a number of new substances which decay into members of this series, and

TABLE 10-1. THE URANIUM SERIES OF RADIOACTIVE SUBSTANCES

Nuclide		Half-life	Radiation	
Old designation	Modern designation		Type	Maximum energy, Mev
U$_I$	$_{92}U^{238}$	4.50×10^9 years	α	4.2
UX$_1$	$_{90}Th^{234}$	24.1 days	β	0.2
UX$_2$	$_{91}Pa^{234}$	1.18 min	β	2.3
U$_{II}$	$_{92}U^{234}$	2.5×10^5 years	α	4.76
Io	$_{90}Th^{230}$	8.0×10^4 years	α	4.68
Ra	$_{88}Ra^{226}$	1622 years	α	4.777
Rn	$_{86}Em^{222}$	3.825 days	α	5.486
RaA	$_{84}Po^{218}$	3.05 min	α*	5.998
RaB	$_{82}Pb^{214}$	26.8 min	β	0.7
RaC	$_{83}Bi^{214}$	19.7 min	β†	3.17
RaC'	$_{84}Po^{214}$	1.6×10^{-4} sec	α	7.683
RaD	$_{82}Pb^{210}$	22 years	β	0.018
RaE	$_{83}Bi^{210}$	5.0 days	β‡	1.17
RaF	$_{84}Po^{210}$	138 days	α	5.298
RaG	$_{82}Pb^{206}$	stable		

* An 0.03 per cent β-branch leads to $_{85}At^{218}$, which decays by α-emission to RaC.

† An 0.04 per cent α-branch leads to RaC''($_{81}Tl^{210}$), which decays by β-emission to RaD. The RaC-RaC' transition is the source of the γ-radiation of interest in medical applications.

‡ A 5×10^{-5} per cent α-branch leads to $_{81}Tl^{206}$, which decays by β-emission to RaG.

in addition an entirely new chain, the neptunium series, has been identified, but since all these substances must be artificially produced, we shall not discuss them here.[1] As found in ordinary uranium minerals which have not been subjected to chemical separation, a given chain is in secular equilibrium and the number of atoms of any radioactive product present is simply proportional to its half-life. For example, the amount of Ra^{226} per gram of U^{238} in any ore is

$$\frac{1{,}622 \times 226}{4.5 \times 10^9 \times 238} = 3.4 \times 10^{-7} \text{ gram}$$

[1] Cf. J. M. Hollander, I. Perlman, and G. T. Seaborg, *Revs. Mod. Phys.*, vol. 25, p. 469, 1953.

In the chemical reduction of the ore, radium is separated both from the uranium and from all other members of the series, and the secular equilibrium is destroyed. In the course of a few days, the next product, Rn, is built up again, and with it, all the short-lived products, RaA, B, and C. The half-life of RaD, however, is 22 years, so only quite old radium samples will contain equilibrium amounts of RaD, E, and F.

d. Half-life of Radium. The half-life of such a long-lived substance as radium is rather difficult to determine directly: instead, the disintegration constant is measured by counting the number of disintegrations per second from a known number of Ra atoms. In the early experiments of Rutherford and Geiger described in Sec. 176, the number of α-particles emitted per second from the RaC' in equilibrium with the radon drawn off a known quantity of radium was counted (α-particles from the other members of the chain have lower energies and can be cut out by an absorbing foil). In a more recent measurement[1] the number of α-particles emitted per second by a thin, weighed deposit of freshly separated radium was determined directly and the value corrected for the growth of the decay products during the experiment. The number of disintegrations obtained was $3.608 \pm 0.028 \times 10^{10}$ α-particles per second per gram, giving

$$\lambda = \frac{3.608 \times 10^{10} \times 226.096}{6.0247 \times 10^{23}} = 1.354 \times 10^{-11} \text{ sec}^{-1}$$

and $t_{1/2} = 0.693/\lambda = 1,622 \pm 13$ years. The standard unit of radioactivity is the "curie," formerly defined as the amount (i.e., the activity) of radon in equilibrium with 1 gram of radium. With the general application of the term in recent years to activities of other substances, the definition of the curie has been changed to mean an activity of exactly 3.7×10^{10} disintegrations per second. Another unit, the "rutherford," which was proposed to mean exactly 10^6 disintegrations per second, has failed of general adoption.

e. Age of Minerals.[2] The half-life of U^{238}, determined by the same procedure as that just described, is 4.50×10^9 years: as it is reasonably certain that U^{238} is not itself derived from a longer-lived material, it would appear that this substance—and presumably all other elements as well—was formed not very many times this number of years ago. It is possible, in fact, to make fairly accurate determinations of the age of uranium-containing minerals by several independent methods. To illustrate the principle involved, we consider the production of helium from U^{238}. For each atom of U^{238} which has decayed since the mineral was formed,

[1] T. P. Kohman, D. P. Ames, and J. Sedlet, "The Transuranium Elements," Paper 22.60, National Nuclear Energy Series, McGraw-Hill, New York, 1949.

[2] R. L. Burling, *Nucleonics*, p. 30, May, 1952.

eight helium atoms will have been produced, presumably remaining occluded in the mineral. If the number of atoms of U^{238} originally present was N_0, and the number present at time t is N, the number of helium atoms produced is

$$N(\text{He}) = 8(N_0 - N) = 8N(e^{\lambda t} - 1)$$

where λ is the disintegration constant of U^{238}. A measurement of the ratio of helium to U^{238} content then permits calculation of t. In practice it is of course necessary to take into account the production of He by other radioactive materials present, such as U^{235} and Th^{232}. Also the loss of helium is a serious problem in rocks containing high concentrations of uranium. Other methods, involving measurement of the isotopic composition of the lead in uranium-containing minerals, are less subject to this difficulty. The age of the earth, i.e., the time which has elapsed since the oldest known minerals were formed, as estimated from such determinations, appears to be 4.5×10^9 years.

f. Light Radioelements. In the periodic table of the naturally occurring elements there appear two gaps, at $Z = 43$ (technetium) and 61 (promethium). All the isotopes of promethium from mass number 141 to 151 have been produced by artificial means, and the longest-lived of these has a half-life of only 30 years. It is quite certain that a stable isotope, if it existed, would have a mass number within this range (Sec. 187g). Isotopes of technetium have also been produced with mass numbers from 92 to 102, with the single exception of 98, and all are radioactive. Technetium 99 has a half-life of 2×10^5 years, and Tc^{97} is reported as "approximately 10^4–10^5 years," but it is not impossible that either Tc^{97} or the unidentified Tc^{98} has a sufficiently long half-life to exist in nature.[1] This question has particular interest in view of the existence of strong technetium lines in certain red giant stars.[2] Several other naturally occurring nuclides, among them K^{40}, Rb^{87}, Sm^{152}, Lu^{176}, and Re^{187}, are actually radioactive, with half-lives lying between 10^9 and 10^{12} years.

178. Detection of Individual Charged Particles.[3] In most detecting devices, the passage of a charged particle is manifested by its ionization of the medium through which it passes. An α-particle, for example, in passing through a gas will both ionize and excite the atoms along its path by the action of its electric field on the atomic electrons, producing free electrons and positive ions. In many gases—oxygen and chlorine are examples—the electrons so released immediately attach themselves to

---

[1] E. Segrè, *Il Nuovo cimento*, vol. 9, p. 1008, 1952.

[2] P. W. Merrill, *Science*, vol. 115, p. 484, 1952.

[3] B. B. Rossi and H. H. Staub, "Ionization Chambers and Counters," National Nuclear Energy Series, McGraw-Hill, New York, 1949; E. Segrè, "Experimental Nuclear Physics," vol. I, article by H. H. Staub, Wiley, New York, 1953; S. A. Korff, "Electron and Nuclear Counters," Van Nostrand, New York, 1946.

neutral atoms and form negative ions; in others, like the noble gases, the electrons may travel by themselves. On the average, a charged particle loses about 33 ev of energy for each ion pair that is formed. The probability per unit path length for formation of an ion is approximately proportional to Z^2/v^2, where Z is the effective charge of the particle and v its velocity. From this fact it may be seen that, for a given energy, β-particles (electrons) will make many fewer ion pairs per unit path and hence will travel much farther than α-particles.

Gamma-rays are, like x-rays, a form of electromagnetic radiation, generally of relatively short wavelengths. In fact the only distinction lies in the source of the radiation: if it is produced in an extranuclear process, like the abrupt acceleration of an electron in the nuclear Coulomb field, it is called an x-ray; radiation which is produced by radiative transitions within the nucleus is called γ-radiation (similarly, electrons which are derived from atomic processes are called "electrons" while those which are produced in nuclear processes are called β-particles). Gamma-rays and x-rays may be detected through their interaction with atoms: in the photoelectric or Compton processes, for example, part of the energy of the radiation is converted into kinetic energy of an electron, and the electron is then detected through its ionizing power.

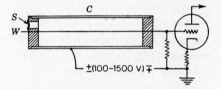

FIG. 167. Schematic diagram of a detector for charged particles. Ions formed by passage of a charged particle through the counter are collected by the insulated central wire W, giving rise to a change in potential which may be amplified as necessary. Depending on the voltage and gas pressure, the device may act as an ionization chamber, proportional counter, or a Geiger counter.

a. Ionization Chambers and Counters. In electrical detection methods, the ions produced by the passage of a charged particle are separated by means of an electrostatic field. The ions move toward the electrodes and on arrival are registered by an electrometer or some type of vacuum-tube amplifier. A typical arrangement is shown in Fig. 167, where C represents a metal cylinder, provided with an insulated axial wire W. The cylinder is connected to a source of potential, and the wire is connected to the first grid of a vacuum-tube amplifier. Particles may enter through the thin window S, or, in the case of γ-rays, secondary electrons may be ejected from the wall. If a 5-Mev[1] α-particle, for example, is stopped in the gas of the chamber, it will produce about $5 \times 10^6/33 = 150,000$ ions, each ion carrying a charge of 4.8×10^{-10} esu or 1.6×10^{-19} coulomb. Supposing the wire and measuring system to have a capacity of 10 micromicrofarads, the potential of the wire will be changed by

[1] "Mev" = million electron-volts: 1 Mev = 1.6×10^{-6} erg.

$$\frac{1.5 \times 10^5 \times 1.6 \times 10^{-19}}{10^{-11}} = 0.0024 \text{ volts}$$

With a reasonably good amplifier, a pulse of this size is easily detectable. It is ordinarily preferable to use a noble gas since electrons move much more rapidly in the collecting field than do negative ions, and recombination of ions in the gas is minimized.

With a sufficiently fine wire and high positive voltage on the wire, it is possible to obtain so strong a field that electrons nearing the wire are accelerated to the point where they may produce further ions. The new electrons so formed are again accelerated and produce still more ions, resulting in a multiplication of the original charge by a factor which may in practical cases be as much as 1,000. Under these conditions the device is called a "proportional" counter, since the pulse size is proportional to the original ionization. The counter used by Rutherford and Geiger in their determination of the number of α-particles from radium (Fig. 164) was of this type. At still higher voltages, the so-called "Geiger-counting" region is reached; in this condition the rate of multiplication is so great that the discharge spreads through the whole of the counter, giving rise to a current which is limited only by the power supply. In practice, a limiting resistance is inserted in the circuit to lower the voltage and quench the discharge. The pulse output represents then merely a count, and its magnitude bears no relation to the number of original ions. A Geiger counter will easily respond to individual β-particles.

b. Scintillation Counters.[1] Many of Rutherford's early experiments on charged particles were made by counting scintillations in a zinc sulfide screen. When an ionizing particle passes through a crystal lattice such as that of zinc sulfide it excites electrons in the lattice, and in the course of rearrangement the lattice may reemit some of the absorbed energy in the form of light. It is important that the emitted radiation be of a wavelength which is not strongly absorbed by the lattice. The action in the case of zinc sulfide is dependent on a trace of impurity such as Cu or Ag. A number of other substances, both inorganic and organic, have the same property. In modern applications a photomultiplier tube is used to detect the scintillations, and a response which is directly proportional to the energy loss in the scintillator can be obtained. A typical arrangement is shown in Fig. 168. The light emitted by the scintillator is collected on a photosensitive surface which comprises the cathode of the photomultiplier tube. The photoelectrons are accelerated by an electric field to the first electrode: at this electrode each impinging elec-

[1] O. R. Frisch, "Progress in Nuclear Physics," vol. 2, article by G. F. J. Garlick, Pergamon Press, 1952; W. H. Jordan, "Annual Review of Nuclear Science," vol. I, p. 207, 1952.

tron produces two or three secondaries, and these in turn travel to the second electrode, there multiplying again. The whole process, which may continue through 10 or more stages, requires less than 10^{-8} sec, and the amplification is sufficient to allow direct display of the pulse on an oscilloscope screen.

c. Cloud Chamber. The path of an ionizing particle through a gas may be made visible by means of the cloud chamber, invented by C. T. R. Wilson in 1912. This device consists essentially of a cylindrical or rectangular chamber, provided with transparent windows and closed at the bottom by a movable piston or a flexible diaphragm. In the chamber are contained a gas and a supply of some liquid which has a reasonable vapor pressure at room temperature: a mixture of ethyl alcohol and water is often used. After the vapor has reached equilibrium, the chamber is suddenly expanded by pulling out the piston or diaphragm, and the gas is rapidly cooled, producing a condition of supersaturation of the vapor. In the absence of any condensation nuclei, the supersaturation can persist for a long time, but if any ions are present, they act as centers on which droplets of liquid can grow. Thus, with suitable illumination the trail of ions which mark the path

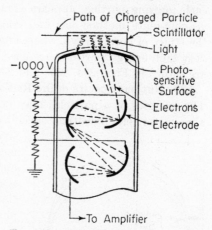

FIG. 168. Scintillation counter (schematic diagram). Passage of a charged particle through the scintillator gives rise to light pulses which in turn eject electrons from the photosensitive surface of the photomultiplier tube. The electrons are accelerated to the first electrode where they produce secondaries which are further accelerated and multiplied at successive electrodes.

may be seen and photographed. Examples of cloud-chamber photographs are shown in Figs. 180 and 190. If a magnetic field is provided, the tracks are curved, and from a measurement of the reprojected images the magnetic rigidity can be determined. If the particle velocity is nonrelativistic, i.e., not too near the velocity of light, the density of droplets per unit path length can be used to estimate Z/v.

d. Photographic Plate. One of the earliest detection methods—and with some modifications, one of the most modern—makes use of the photographic plate. Roentgen's and Becquerel's initial investigations were based on the blackening of the photographic plates by charged particles. For reasons which are not yet completely understood, the production of a few hundred ions in the neighborhood of a silver halide grain in the emulsion renders the grain developable. When a large number of such events have occurred in a small region of a plate, that region is blackened in the development process. Ordinary emulsions contain only a small amount of silver compared to the other components present, and hence many ionizing events may be required to produce a detectable effect. With recent development of emulsions containing over 80 per cent silver halide by weight, however, the sensitivity is much increased, and under microscopic examination of the developed plate, the path of each ionizing particle appears as a track of silver grains. The photographic-plate method has had considerable application, particularly in the study of cosmic rays, where emulsions sufficiently thick to stop even very high energy particles are used (Sec. 216). Some microphotographs are shown in Figs. 234, 237, and 244.

179. Nuclear Spectra of the Radioelements. *a. Alpha-particle Spectra.* The energies of α-particles may be determined from their deflection in a magnetic field, once their specific charge (e/m) is known. If the inten-

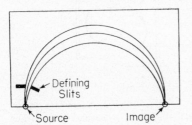

FIG. 169. Principle of the magnetic spectrograph with semicircular focusing. There is a uniform magnetic field perpendicular to the plane of the figure.

sity of the source suffices, the measurement can be made in a straightforward manner, defining a narrow beam with a system of slits and observing the deflection in a uniform field by means of a photographic plate. For a precision determination, a very thin source must be used, in order to minimize the energy loss of the particles in emerging from the source. Magnetic spectrographs employing special geometry or specially shaped fields which focus rays emerging from the source over a range of angles are often used when only weak sources are available. A simple example of this type, the semicircular spectrograph, is illustrated in Fig. 169. With a uniform field perpendicular to the plane of the figure, trajectories starting at angles differing even by several degrees come together again after 180° deflection and a reasonably sharp line image of the point source is formed. If the magnetic field is made to vary as the inverse square root of the radius, rays emerging in a cone are brought to a point focus after a 255° deflection.

The *range* of α-particles, i.e., the distance they travel in a specified material before stopping, can also be used for energy determinations, once the range-energy relation has been established by measuring ranges of α-particles with selected known velocities. A range-energy curve, derived mainly from a few fixed points, with interpolation by a theoretical formula[1] is shown in Fig. 170.

[1] E. Segrè, "Experimental Nuclear Physics," vol. I, article by H. A. Bethe and J. Ashkin, Wiley, New York, 1953.

It was discovered rather early that α-particles from radioactive substances occur in groups, each quite homogeneous in energy. In Fig. 171 is shown, for example, the magnetic spectrum of Rn, RaA, and RaC' obtained with a radon source. For a time it was thought that all

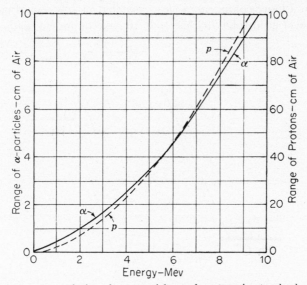

FIG. 170. Range-energy relations for α-particles and protons in standard air (760 mm, 15°C). (*Data from E. Segrè, "Experimental Nuclear Physics," vol. I*, Wiley, New York, 1953.)

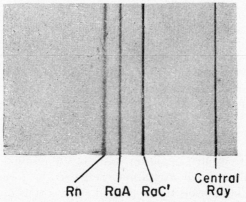

FIG. 171. Magnetic spectrum of α-particles from a radon source, recorded on a photographic plate. The line at the right is from the undeflected beam, obtained without magnetic field. (*S. Rosenblum, J. phys. radium, vol. 1, p. 438, 1930.*)

α-particles from a given radioactive species had the same energy, and the observed complexity was attributed to the presence of several members of a radioactive chain in the source. Later work showed, however, that this was not the case, and that many nuclides emit more than one group.

In the simpler case, where only one group is emitted—radon is an example
—the α-particle is believed to result from a transition from the normal or
ground state of the parent nucleus to that of the daughter, with a release
of energy equal to the kinetic energy of the α-particle plus the energy of
recoil.   In a more complicated case, like that of ThC (see Fig. 172), the
appearance of groups having less than the maximum energy is attributed

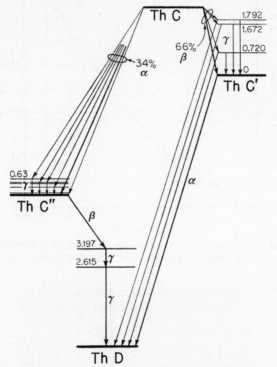

FIG. 172. Radiations observed in the two branches of the ThC-ThD chain.   The
vertical scale is proportional to the kinetic energy released.   Strong transitions are
indicated by heavy arrows; light horizontal lines represent excited quantum states of
the nuclei.

to transitions to excited quantum states of the residual nucleus (ThC'')
which then release their excitation energy in the form of γ-radiation.
The decay of these levels to the ground state is thus quite analogous to
the decay of excited atomic states, and the γ-spectrum corresponds to
the line spectrum emitted by an excited atom.   The correctness of this
conclusion can be established by comparing the γ-ray energies and
α-energies: a short-range α-particle should be accompanied by one or
more γ-rays, such that the total energy equals that of the longest-range
α-particles.   Such a comparison is exhibited in Table 10-2, and the rela-

tions of the various radiations observed in the decay of ThC are illustrated in Fig. 172.

In ThC′ (Po^{212}), formed by β-decay of ThC, there occur, in addition to the main group of 8.776-Mev α-particles which are believed to represent transitions between the ground states of ThC′ and ThD, a very few α-particles of considerably higher energy. These long-range α-particles come from excited states of the *parent* nucleus, ThC′, which decays in this manner in preference to emitting γ-radiation. This behavior results from the fact that γ-radiation is a relatively slow process on a

TABLE 10-2. ALPHA-PARTICLES AND GAMMA-RAYS* OF ThC

α-particle energy, Mev	Disintegration energy, Mev	γ-ray energy, Mev	Sum, Mev
6.0837	6.2007		6.2007
6.0445	6.1607	0.03995	6.2007
5.7621	5.8729	0.3267	6.1996
5.6202	5.7283	0.4709	6.1992
5.6012	5.7089	0.4908	6.1997

* W. B. Lewis and B. V. Bowden, *Proc. Roy. Soc.* (*London*), vol. 145, p. 235, 1934; C. D. Ellis, *Proc. Roy. Soc.* (*London*), vol. 138, p. 318, 1932; J. Surugue, *Ann. phys.*, ser. 11, vol. 8, p. 484, 1937. In the second column a correction has been made for the kinetic energy of the recoil nucleus.

nuclear time scale, and, given sufficient energy, the α-particles can escape before the parent nucleus can become deexcited. The lifetime of ThC′ is only a fraction of a microsecond.

b. Gamma-rays. Nuclear γ-ray spectra consist typically of sharp lines:[1] in the naturally radioactive elements they are invariably associated either with α- or β-emission. Because γ-rays interact relatively weakly with matter they are not easy to detect, and it is sometimes difficult to achieve high precision in γ-ray spectroscopy. For not too hard—i.e., not too energetic—radiation, a measurement of the absorption coefficient in some suitable material provides a rough determination of the energy (Secs. 157 and 160). Considerably higher precision can be obtained by the method described in Sec. 158, in which the γ-rays are allowed to fall on a thin foil, called the converter, from which secondary electrons are ejected. From the observed energy of the secondary electrons, determined by magnetic deflection, the γ-ray energy can be calculated.

With relatively strong sources, the Bragg crystal spectrometer may be used (Sec. 151), as was done first by Rutherford and Andrade in 1914. Development of this technique, particularly by DuMond and his col-

[1] A few examples of γ-lines of measurable breadth occur among the light nuclei.

laborators,[1] has resulted in a number of energy determinations with a precision of 1 part in 10,000 or better.

The scintillator-photomultiplier combination discussed in Sec. 178 provides a most sensitive γ-ray spectrometer of fair precision. In this application, a large mass of scintillating material is used, sufficient to absorb an appreciable fraction of the incident γ-radiation. The secondary electrons produced in the scintillator give rise to light pulses whose magnitude is proportional to the electron energy, and from the pulse spectrum the γ-ray energy may be determined. With a sodium iodide crystal a few centimeters on a side, an efficiency for γ-ray detection of some tens of per cent and a resolution in energy of 6 to 8 per cent can be attained.

Particularly in elements of high atomic number, it occurs not infrequently that the energy released in the transition between two nuclear quantum states is taken up directly by an atomic electron, without the intervention of a γ-ray.[2] In this process, called *internal conversion*, the oscillating electromagnetic field associated with the nuclear transition interacts with the atomic electrons, resulting in the ionization of the atom. Just as in the ordinary photoelectric effect, the transition energy is given by the sum of the observed energy of the ejected electron plus its binding energy in the atom. The electron lines so produced are very sharp, and they have been much used in determining the energy levels of the heavy elements. By comparing two internal-conversion electron lines from the same transition, for example lines due to conversion by K- and L-shell electrons, one can determine the difference in the atomic binding energies and by comparing with the known values from x-ray data, one can identify (as to Z) the radiating atom. This procedure has been used to ascertain whether the transition in question follows or precedes the disintegration. The ratio of the number of transitions of a given energy which result in internal conversion to the number which yield γ-rays is called the internal conversion coefficient α. In the natural radioactive elements, α normally lies in the range 10^{-4} to 10^{-1}. In a few cases, however, where the γ-radiation is forbidden or strongly discouraged, as for example when the angular momenta of the initial and final states differ by several units, the internal conversion coefficient may be much larger than 1. It is possible by means of the quantum theory to calculate the internal conversion coefficients to be expected for various values of the angular-momentum change in any given transition, so the experimental determination of α can yield important information on the nuclear quantum states involved. A case of some interest occurs in

[1] D. E. Muller, H. C. Hoyt, D. J. Klein, and J. W. M. DuMond, *Phys. Rev.*, vol. 88, p. 775, 1952.

[2] W. Heitler, "Quantum Theory of Radiation," Oxford, London, 1944; F. Rasetti, "Elements of Nuclear Physics," Prentice-Hall, New York, 1936.

RaC′, where an excited state, at 1.41 Mev, makes a transition to the ground state entirely through internal conversion: no corresponding γ-ray is observed at all.   There is reason to believe that this situation occurs because both the initial and final states have total angular momentum zero, single-quantum electromagnetic transitions between spin zero states being strictly forbidden.

   c. Beta-rays.   The β-rays, again, may be analyzed crudely by the absorption technique.   Since β-rays generally follow extremely tortuous paths through matter, their range is not a well-defined quantity, even for an initially homogeneous group, so the derivation of a β-spectrum from an absorption curve is not an easy matter.   If the intensity of the source suffices, a magnetic spectrograph is far preferable.   It is important that a thin source be used because the spectrum may otherwise be seriously distorted.

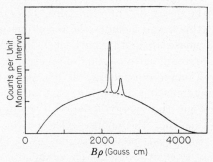

   A typical magnetic spectrum of the β-rays from Au[198] (an artificially produced radioisotope) is shown in Fig. 173, where the number of β-particles per unit momentum interval is exhibited as a function of the momentum.   The curve shows a broad distribution on which are superposed two sharp peaks.

FIG. 173. Beta spectrum of Au[198], showing internal conversion lines.   (*Adapted from D. Saxon and R. Heller, Phys. Rev., vol. 75, p. 909, 1949.*)

The latter are the internal-conversion lines just discussed, and are associated in this example with a single 411-kev γ-ray which follows the β-disintegration.   The fact that the β-spectrum itself is not homogeneous in energy but has a broad distribution has occasioned no little perplexity.   It might of course have been thought that this distribution merely represented β-transitions to a large number of excited quantum states of the daughter nucleus, but then the corresponding γ-spectrum would be expected to exhibit a continuous distribution, whereas the γ-rays are in fact discrete.   Furthermore, β-spectra entirely unaccompanied by γ-rays are not at all rare.   It was early suggested that the observed β-spectrum was distorted in some way; for example, it could be conceived that the β-particles were actually homogeneous as they left the nucleus, but that they lost varying amounts of energy as they went through the atomic electron cloud.   That this is not a tenable hypothesis was established by calorimetric measurements by Ellis and Wooster[1] in 1927.   Using a calorimeter with walls sufficiently thick that no radiation could be detected outside, they established that the

[1] C. D. Ellis and W. A. Wooster, *Proc. Roy. Soc. (London)*, vol. 117A, p. 109, 1927.

energy absorbed in the calorimeter per disintegration corresponded not
to the maximum β-ray energy, but to the average. Thus they were
forced to conclude either that the β-transitions leading to values other
than the average violate the principle of conservation of energy, or that
some particle is emitted which is neither absorbed in the calorimeter
nor detectable outside. The first suggestion was seriously discussed
by Bohr on the assumption that the conservation of energy might apply
only in a statistical sense to nuclear processes. This distasteful hypothesis met its fate in an analysis by Ellis[1] of the ThC-ThD disintegration energies. This transition, shown in Fig. 172, can occur in two ways:
ThC goes to ThC′ by β-emission, with a maximum energy of 2.253 Mev;
the decay of ThC′ then proceeds mainly by an α-transition of 8.946 Mev
(this figure includes the recoil energy), giving a total (maximum) energy
release along this path of 11.199 Mev. On the other branch we have
first an α-transition, of energy 6.203 Mev, followed by a β-particle[2]
of maximum energy 1.798 Mev, followed by γ-transitions (in ThD)
aggregating 3.197 Mev, giving a total energy change of 11.198 Mev.
Thus the energy balance is accurately accounted for by the assumption that the energy release in a β-decay process corresponds always
to the *maximum* β-ray energy. This result has been amply confirmed
in later experiments on artificially produced radioactive nuclei. In the
β-decay of B^{12} to C^{12}, for example, the known mass difference implies an
energy release of 13.370 Mev, in reasonable agreement with the observed
maximum β-ray energy of 13.43 $\pm$ 0.06 Mev. The average β-ray energy
in this case is less than 7 Mev. It has also been established that not
only energy, but also linear momentum and angular momentum are
inadequately accounted for by the observed β-particles.[3]

A part of the difficulty in understanding the β-decay process has been
resolved by the introduction of a new particle, the neutrino, first suggested
by Pauli in 1930. In the present picture of β-decay, as developed first
by Fermi,[4] a neutrino and a β-particle are considered to be emitted simultaneously, sharing the available energy in such a way that, on the average,
only about half is taken by the electron. The neutrino is assumed to
have a rest mass very small compared to that of the electron, and no
charge: it is so cleverly contrived that it has practically no interaction
with matter and hence cannot be detected by any ordinary means. From
many points of view, the neutrino is the least satisfactory of all the
"particles" of nuclear physics, and its lamentable intransigence has

[1] C. D. Ellis, "International Conference on Physics," London, 1934.

[2] Other β-transitions occur to higher states of ThD, but these do not affect the
present argument.

[3] Cf. H. R. Crane, *Revs. Mod. Phys.*, vol. 20, p. 278, 1948.

[4] E. Fermi, *Z. Physik*, vol. 88, p. 161, 1934.

caused many physicists to question whether it is in fact anything more than a name to conceal our ignorance.   However, certain experiments,[1] involving extremely sensitive detecting apparatus, appear to indicate that the neutrino can stimulate positron decay of the proton and thus make its presence known.

MASSES OF ATOMS

From the point of view of the nuclear physicist the mass of a nucleus is quite as interesting as its charge, for, while the charge determines practically all the gross properties of the atom and of the larger structures of which the atom is a subunit, the mass is of major importance in determining the properties of the nucleus itself.   We have already seen examples among the radioactive elements where two chemically identical species may have entirely different radioactive properties, clearly connected with a difference in mass.   In the following sections we shall see that stable elements also have isotopes, and we shall discuss how their masses may be measured.

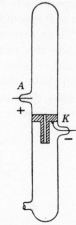

FIG. 174. Schematic diagram of Goldstein's discharge tube. The discharge takes place between the anode A and cathode K; a positive-ion beam issues d o w n w a r d through the channel in K.

180. Positive Rays.[2]   The first step in the development of direct, precision mass-measuring techniques for atomic masses came with the discovery of the "canal" rays in the Crookes discharge tube, by Goldstein in 1886. Goldstein's tube is schematically illustrated in Fig. 174. In a glass envelope are provided two electrodes: the anode A, a simple side connection, and the cathode K, which is perforated by a long canal.   When the tube is evacuated to the point where the Crookes dark space is well developed, one sees the cathode rays streaming upward and, in addition, a stream of rays issuing downward from the canal in the cathode. If the residual gas in the tube is neon, the ionization due to the cathode rays produces a pale-blue light, while the canal rays are a brilliant red. Unlike the cathode rays (electrons) the canal rays are quite difficult to deflect with a magnetic field.   It was not, in fact, until 1898 that Wien exhibited the effect with a powerful electromagnet, and showed, by simultaneous application of electrostatic and magnetic deflections, that the values of e/m were of the order of those observed for ions in electrolytic cells, or about 10^{-4} emu per gram.   Because he operated at too high pres-

[1] F. Reines and C. L. Cowan, *Phys. Rev.*, vol. 92, p. 830, 1953.

[2] J. J. Thomson, "Rays of Positive Electricity and Their Application to Chemical Analysis," Longmans, London, 1913; F. W. Aston, "Mass Spectra and Isotopes," Longmans, London, 1933.

sures, Wien was unable to make a precise determination, and indeed found a continuous spread of e/m values.

In a series of experiments initiated in 1906, J. J. Thomson made a careful study of the formation and properties of the canal rays. His apparatus is shown diagrammatically in Fig. 175. The large discharge tube B is provided with an anode (not shown) and a cathode K, perforated with an extremely fine hole. (In some of his later experiments, Thomson made this canal by ruling a scratch in a piece of flat steel and laying another piece on top of it.) The canal rays, or, as Thomson came to call them, the positive rays, stream out of the canal into the space C, where they strike a screen covered with a scintillating material or a photographic plate P. A magnet M_1M_2 with electrically insulated pole

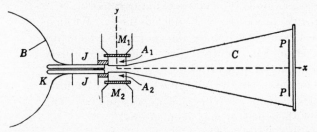

FIG. 175. Thomson's positive-ray spectrograph. Positive ions produced in the discharge tube B pass through the cathode K. After deflection in the magnetic and electric fields at A_1A_2, the positive-ion beam produces a parabolic trace on the photographic plate P.

pieces A_1A_2 provides a strong magnetic field, and by electrical connection to A_1 and A_2, an electrostatic field parallel to the magnetic field can be applied. Cooling of the cathode is accomplished by a water jacket J, and a large, soft iron shield (not shown) reduces the effect of the stray field from the magnet on the discharge in B. It is advantageous to operate the tube at as low a pressure as possible in order to minimize scattering and capture and loss of electrons. Thomson used pressures of the order of 10^{-3} mm Hg and discharge voltages from 1,000 to 20,000 volts.

In passing through the magnetic and electrostatic fields at A_1A_2, the particle suffers simultaneous deflections along the z axis (perpendicular to the plane of the drawing) and along the y axis. The displacement at the end of the gap due to the magnetic deflection is

$$z' = \frac{1}{2}\frac{Bev}{m}\left(\frac{l}{v}\right)^2 \tag{250}$$

and the displacement due to the electrostatic deflection is

$$y' = \frac{1}{2}\frac{Ee}{m}\left(\frac{l}{v}\right)^2 \tag{251}$$

where l is the length of the gap. Since the rays travel in straight lines after leaving the gap, the displacement on the plate PP is proportional to these quantities. To obtain the shape of the trace on the plate, we eliminate the velocity, obtaining

$$z^2 = C \frac{B^2}{E} \frac{e}{m} y \tag{252}$$

where C is a constant depending on l and other geometrical features. This equation represents a parabola, with vertex at the origin: ions of

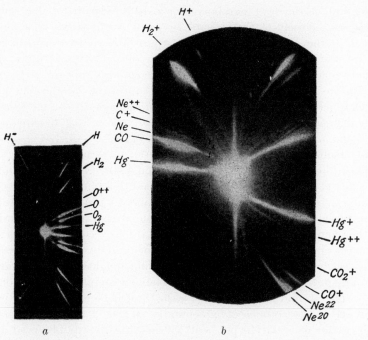

FIG. 176. Parabolic traces of ions deflected in the positive-ray spectrograph. (*From E. W. Aston, "Mass Spectra and Isotopes," 1933, by permission of E. Arnold, Ltd., publishers.*)

various velocities but with the same value of m/e lie at various points on the parabola, the highest velocities nearest the vertex. If we consider ions of only a single charge, the highest velocity will be given by

$$\tfrac{1}{2}mv_{max}^2 = Ve$$

where V is the potential across the discharge tube; inserting this in the expression for y' above, we see that

$$y'_{min} = \frac{1}{4} \frac{E}{V} l^2$$

Thus all parabolas, regardless of the value of m/e which they represent, cut off at the same value of y.

Photographs showing the traces obtained with various gases are reproduced in Fig. 176. These photographs, published by J. J. Thomson in 1911, show clearly the parabolic form and the abrupt termination at a constant value of y (the electric deflection is horizontal in the figure, and the magnetic field has been reversed for half of the exposure time to produce both legs of the parabolas). The value of e/m obtained for the extreme outside parabola, marked H in Fig. 176a, is 10^4 emu per gram, while that of the next parabola is 5×10^3. The first value obtained corresponds closely to the electrolytic value for hydrogen ions, and the second to the expected value for a singly ionized hydrogen molecule. Traces attributable to singly and doubly ionized oxygen, singly ionized oxygen molecule, and singly ionized mercury also appear on the photograph as do some negative ions formed by capture of electrons in the cathode channel. *The fact that these traces are sharp constitutes the first experimental proof that atoms have discrete masses—or at least discrete values of e/m—and are not spread over a continuous range.*

181. Isotopes of Stable Elements. In an investigation (1913) of the composition of liquid-air residues, Thomson discovered, in addition to the neon line at the position expected for mass 20, a faint, just-resolved line at mass 22 (see Fig. 176b). After a number of tests to eliminate other possible sources of such a line, he concluded that this line was due to another component of neon, with mass 22. This was the first observation of the isotopic constitution of a stable element, and verified the prediction made by Soddy that elements with atomic weights differing markedly from integral values would be found to have a complex isotopic constitution. The atomic weight of neon is 20.18; if it be assumed that neon is composed of two isotopes, of mass number 20 and 22, a relative abundance of the latter of about 10 per cent will account for the observed atomic weight, and this estimate is not in disagreement with the relative intensities of the lines in Fig. 176b. Actually, there is a third isotope, of mass number 21, with about 0.3 per cent abundance, but Thomson's apparatus was incapable of revealing this line.

The subsequent development of mass-measuring techniques[1] in the hands of Aston, and later Dempster, Bainbridge, Mattauch, Nier, and others, has enormously improved the sensitivity and precision of the method. Fundamental to all these improvements has been the use of focusing principles which greatly increase the intensity available at the detector. The development of more efficient ion sources has also been

---

[1] E. Segrè, "Experimental Nuclear Physics," vol. I, article by K. T. Bainbridge Wiley, New York, 1953.

a matter of great importance in increasing the usable ion currents and extending the techniques to materials which are not available in gaseous form.   The applications of the mass spectrometer can be generally divided into three categories: the identification of isotopes, the determination of the relative abundances, and the precise measurement of their masses.

a. Identification of Isotopes.   Between 1919, when Aston's first spectrograph was completed, and 1922, the isotopic constitution of 27 elements was investigated, and in the following two years 26 more were reported. A table published by Bainbridge[1] in 1953 lists over 280 naturally occurring isotopes, most of which have been discovered by the mass-spectrographic techniques.   In every case in which the chemically determined atomic weight differs greatly from a whole number, the element is found to consist of more than one isotope.   We may anticipate our later discussion of the exact masses by saying that the isotopic masses observed are not quite integral multiples of the atomic mass unit, but all stable isotopes have masses which lie within less than 0.07 amu of an integer: it is this integer that we call the mass number A.

A table exhibiting the number of stable isotopes of the elements occurring in nature and their masses and relative abundances is given in Appendix II.   Figure 177, in which the stable nuclides are plotted as a function of A and Z, shows how the number of isotopes observed varies from element to element.   A number of interesting regularities appear in these data.   Most striking is the fact that the nuclides which exist in nature cluster rather closely about a given ratio of A to Z, a ratio which varies smoothly from 2.0 for light elements to about 2.5 at the upper end of the curve.   No stable isotope has a mass which differs by more than a few mass numbers from the average value appropriate to its charge.   This fact we shall see later to be intimately connected with the greater stability of such nuclides as compared with other imaginable species which lie far away from the optimum ratio.   With four exceptions, namely the light nuclei $_1H^2$, $_3Li^6$, $_5B^{10}$, and $_7N^{14}$, no stable nucleus exists with odd Z and even A.   Among the 280 stable nuclides, about 160, or more than half, have even Z and even A.   With the above-mentioned four exceptions, the remainder are about evenly divided between the two classes with odd Z and odd A and those with even Z and odd A.

b. Abundances.[2]   The relative abundances of the various isotopes of a given element are, in the main, independent of the source of the element or the chemical combination in which it is examined.   This observa-

[1] *Op. cit.*

[2] "Annual Review of Nuclear Science," vol. 1, article by A. O. Nier, Annual Reviews, Inc., 1952.

tion merely reflects the fact that most chemical processes, including those which led to the separation of the elements in the earth's crust, are rather independent of the mass of the atoms and are largely determined by the charge.   In some of the light elements the mass difference is sufficiently great that some differences do appear between various terrestrial sources: thus the content of $_1H^2$ (deuterium) in water depends somewhat on the

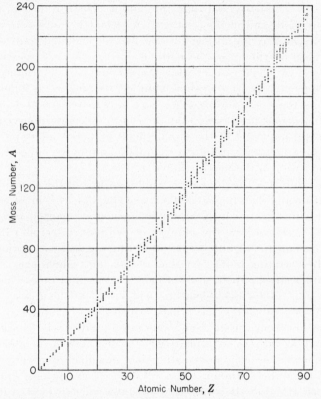

FIG. 177. Mass and charge numbers of the naturally occurring nuclides.

source, as do the isotopic ratios C^{12}/C^{13} and O^{16}/O^{18} observed in compounds of various origins.   The isotopic constitution of lead varies greatly with the source, since different radioactive chains lead to different lead isotopes as final products.   Argon^{40} is more abundant in potassium-containing minerals than in the atmosphere because it is produced in the β-decay of K^{40}: in fact measurements of the A^{40}/A^{36} ratio are used to determine the ages of minerals in much the same way as is the helium content of radioactive minerals mentioned earlier.

Despite the comparative intractibility of isotopes to separation by purely chemical means, considerable success has been achieved in producing separated isotopes in weighable amounts by physical processes. The most versatile device for this purpose is the electromagnetic separator, in which a generously proportioned magnetic spectrograph is used to separate ions according to their e/m values. One important application is in the separation of the two principal isotopes of uranium, U^{235} and U^{238}, where kilogram quantities of pure U^{235} have been produced (Sec. 203). The same technique has been used to separate other isotopes for research use, and more than 150 pure isotopes are now available in quantities ranging from a few milligrams to tens or hundreds of grams.

Another separation technique depends on the fact that the diffusion coefficient of a molecule depends upon the mass, and, by passing a gaseous compound containing a mixture of isotopes through a porous septum, one can achieve a minute separation. With a large number of such separators in series, and arrangements whereby the heavy fraction is recycled to earlier stages while the light fraction progresses forward, a practical quantity can be separated. Thus, using the gas uranium hexafluoride, hundred-kilogram quantities of U^{235} have been produced in the large diffusion plants constructed during World War II. Isotopes of carbon and those of nitrogen are separated by a chemical exchange method, in which many successive fractionations separate substances with the most minute differences in chemical properties.

Isotopes can also be produced in practical quantities in nuclear reactions: thus plutonium, which does not occur in nature, has been produced in hundred-kilogram amounts in nuclear reactors (Sec. 203), and several other elements have been produced in sufficient quantity to permit chemical and physical analysis.

c. Isotopic Masses. Coupled with the increase in sensitivity gained in the course of something over 30 years' development of the mass spectrograph has also come an enormous increase in resolution and accuracy. Some present-day instruments have resolving powers as high as 50,000: i.e., the width of the image measured in m/e units is 1/50,000 of the nominal value in the same units. Like chemical atomic weights, the masses of isotopes are seldom expressed in absolute units, but are given in terms of an adopted standard. The standard for the physical atomic mass unit is based on the most abundant isotope of oxygen, $O^{16} = 16$ exactly. The absolute value of the mass unit in grams can be obtained from the Avogadro number (which is, in turn derived from several other basic physical constants).[1] Thus:

$$1 \text{ amu (phys)} = \frac{1}{6.024\ 72 \times 10^{23}} = (1.659\ 83 \pm 0.000\ 10) \times 10^{-24} \text{ gram}$$

[1] J. W. M. DuMond and E. R. Cohen, *Revs. Mod. Phys.*, vol. 25, p. 691, 1953.

The most precise direct mass measurements are now made by the so-called doublet method, in which two ions of the same nominal mass are compared. Figure 178 shows the (He^4 $^+$-H_2^2 $^+$) doublet: the left-hand line is due to singly ionized helium atoms—4 amu and one charge—and the right-hand line is from singly ionized deuterium molecules—also 4 amu and one charge. The separation of the two lines is only 0.026 amu, and, from a microphotometer tracing of the two lines, the center-to-center spacing can be determined to an accuracy of about 1 part in 3,000. If the dispersion of the spectrometer is known to the same accuracy, the value of the He^4 mass relative to that of the deuteron can be deduced with an accuracy of 0.000 008 amu. By use of such other doublets as H_2^1 $^+$-H^2 $^+$, $C^{12}H_4^1$ $^+$-O^{16} $^+$, and H_3^2 $^+$-C^{12} $^{++}$ the mass can be linked to the standard O^{16}, using only mass-difference measurements. A few of the values for the masses of the light elements obtained in this way are given in Table 10-3. A complete mass table, containing values derived in part from mass-spectrograph doublets and in part by nuclear-reaction methods, which we shall discuss presently, is given in Appendix II.

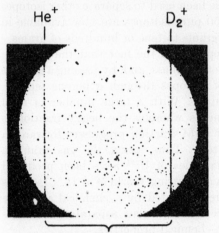

He$^+$ D$_2$$^+$

0.025604 amu
±0.000008

FIG. 178. Mass-spectrograph record of (He^{4+} − H_2^{2+}) doublet. (*H. Ewald, Z. Naturforsch.*, vol. 5a, p. 1, 1950.)

Not infrequently mass-spectrograph results are quoted in terms of the "packing fraction," $(M - A)/A$, where M is the exact mass and A the mass number. The packing fraction varies from a few times 10^{-3} for the light elements, through zero at O^{16}, reaches a minimum of about -8.5×10^{-4} at $Z = 28$, and becomes positive again for $Z > 72$.

TABLE 10-3. ATOMIC MASSES OF SOME NUCLIDES, OBTAINED
BY MASS-SPECTROGRAPH TECHNIQUES*

H^1	1.008 141 ± 0.000 002
H^2	2.014 732 ± 0.000 003
He^4	4.003 860 ± 0.000 012
C^{12}	12.003 807 ± 0.000 011

* H. Ewald, Z. *Naturforsch.*, vol. 6a, p. 293, 1951.

Because of the presence of O^{17} and O^{18} in oxygen as found in nature, the chemical and physical atomic mass units differ slightly. The relation can be obtained by calculating the average atomic weight of oxygen on the physical scale and comparing it with the chemical value, 16 exactly. Using the masses and relative abundances (for atmospheric oxygen) given in Appendix II, we have

$$16.000\ 000\ \text{amu (chem)} = 16.000\ 000 \times (1 - 0.000\ 373 - 0.002\ 039)$$
$$+ 17.0045 \times 0.000\ 373 + 18.0049 \times 0.002\ 039$$
$$= 16.004\ 463\ \text{amu (phys)}$$

Thus the ratio of the chemical to the physical scale is:[1]

$$\frac{1\ \text{amu (chem)}}{1\ \text{amu (phys)}} = 1.000\ 279$$

ARTIFICIAL TRANSMUTATIONS BY ALPHA-PARTICLES

It occurred to a number of workers, after the high energy of the radiations from radioactive substances was discovered, that these radiations might be capable of inducing transmutations in other elements. Several experiments were tried in which radioactive materials were mixed with stable substances and the products of transmutation searched for by chemical analysis. Production in this way of neon and argon from water was reported as early as 1907, but later experiments failed to substantiate this claim and the effect was generally attributed to contamination. Actually the number of atoms which one could hope to transmute by such procedures is so small as to preclude any possibility of detection by chemical means, and it was not until methods had been developed whereby individual events could be detected that artificial transmutation could be demonstrated.

182. Discovery of Artificial Transmutation. The first conclusive evidence for artificially induced transmutation was obtained by Rutherford in 1919, in connection with some experiments on the scattering of α-particles in various gases. The apparatus used in these studies is illustrated in Fig. 179. In a gas-tight chamber B is mounted a source D of RaC + C' which emits α-particles of about 7 cm range in standard air. A thin silver foil W covers a hole in the end of the chamber, and a zinc sulfide scintillation screen F, observed with a microscope M, permits counting of individual particles coming through the window. Provision is made for inserting absorbing foils between the window W and the screen F and for varying the distance x between the source and the window. The whole apparatus is placed in a transverse magnetic field to eliminate the β-rays. In the first experiments, carried out by Marsden in 1914, hydrogen gas was used in the chamber and scintillations due to the

---

[1] The value 1.000 272, derived by R. T. Birge in 1941, appears in a good deal of literature: *J. Am. Chem. Soc.*, vol. 74, p. 2699, 1952. Cf. also A. O. Nier, *Phys. Rev.*, vol. 77, p. 789, 1950.

hydrogen recoils were observed with absorbers having thicknesses up to
about 28 cm air equivalent.   This range was approximately in agreement
with expectations.   If we consider the conservation of momentum and
energy in an elastic collision between an incident particle of mass M_0
and the struck particle, of mass M_1, the energy transferred is

$$E = E_0 \frac{4M_0M_1}{(M_0 + M_1)^2} \sin^2 \frac{\theta}{2} \tag{253}$$

where θ is the angle of deflection of the incident particle and E_0 is the
initial energy.   For a RaC$'$ α-particle striking a proton head-on, the

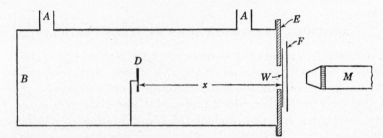

FIG. 179. Apparatus by which Rutherford observed production of protons in the disintegration of light elements under α-particle bombardment.   The source is at D;
particles produced by transmutations in the gas strike the screen F, giving rise to
scintillations which are observed by means of the microscope M.

maximum energy transfer is $\frac{16}{25} \times 7.680$ Mev.   The expected proton
energy is then 4.9 Mev, and the range of such a proton in air is 32.5 cm
(Fig. 170), in reasonable agreement with the value found by Marsden.[1]

In an investigation of certain peculiarities of the effects in hydrogen,
Rutherford[2] made some tests in 1919 with air in the chamber, with the
unexpected result that long-range particles appeared again.   Further
work showed that the effect was due to nitrogen, that neither oxygen nor
carbon dioxide produced similar particles, and that the particles were
much too numerous to be ascribed to hydrogen contamination.   Rough
magnetic analysis indicated that the particles probably were protons,
and Rutherford concluded that they must have been knocked out of the
nitrogen nucleus by the impact of the α-particles.   The number observed
was about 1 per million α-particles.   The work was extended by Rutherford and Chadwick in 1922, and protons with ranges as long as 40 cm were
observed from nitrogen.   Five other elements, boron, fluorine, sodium,
aluminum, and phosphorus, were also found to yield long-range par-

[1] The range-energy relation for protons had not been determined experimentally
at that time, but was derived from Bohr's theory of the stopping of charged particles
in matter.

[2] E. Rutherford, *Phil. Mag.*, vol. 37, p. 581, 1919.

ticles; with aluminum as the target, they observed protons with ranges up to 90 cm air equivalent.   In a later version of the experiment (1924), the protons were observed at 90° to the α-particles, where no elastically scattered protons from hydrogen impurities would be expected at all. With this apparatus, they could be sure that any particles they saw at ranges greater than 7 cm (the maximum range of the α-particles) were due to processes other than elastic scattering.   In testing a variety of target materials, they found that all the light elements up to and including potassium could be disintegrated, with the exception of hydrogen, helium, lithium, beryllium, carbon, and oxygen.

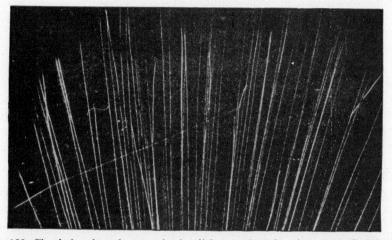

FIG. 180. Cloud-chamber photograph of a disintegration of a nitrogen nucleus by an α-particle.   Alpha-particles from a ThB-C source travel upward in the figure.   To the right of center an α-particle makes a collision with a nitrogen nucleus, producing a long proton track extending across the picture to the left, and a short track extending upwards and slightly to the right, due to the recoiling O^{17} nucleus.   (*P. M. S. Blackett and D. S. Lees, Proc. Roy. Soc. (London), vol.* 136, *p.* 325, 1932.)

Rutherford's original surmise that the α-particle knocked out a proton from the target nucleus turned out to be only partially correct.   In a series of cloud-chamber pictures of α-particles traversing a nitrogen atmosphere, Blackett photographed eight disintegrations (in 415,000 α-tracks).   In all eight cases, the α-track terminated in a fork, with a lightly ionizing particle, identifiable as a proton, as one branch and a heavy recoil, similar in behavior to the nitrogen recoils observed in elastic scattering, as the other (see Fig. 180).   In no case was a third track corresponding to the α-particle itself visible after the collision.   From this it was concluded that the α-particle had been absorbed into the nucleus, releasing a proton and forming a residual nucleus 3 amu heavier than nitrogen and with one more unit of charge.   In the terminology of nuclear reactions, the events observed by Rutherford, Chadwick, and Blackett may be written

$$_7N^{14} + {_2}He^4 \rightarrow {_8}O^{17} + {_1}H^1$$

where the conservation of charge and mass number are explicitly exhibited. The existence of O^{17} in ordinary oxygen was unknown in 1925, but the conclusion that it was formed in the reaction was inescapable.

From the range of the protons observed, the energy release could be calculated. In the case of nitrogen, this turned out to be negative: i.e., part of the kinetic energy of the α-particle was used up in forming the two products, but, in several other instances, a positive energy release was observed. In aluminum, for example, a 90-cm proton was produced, corresponding to a kinetic energy of 8.6 Mev. Even ignoring the kinetic energy of the residual nucleus, this represents a gain of nearly 1 Mev over the initial kinetic energy of the α-particle.

At the time of these experiments, the question arose whether the new nuclides produced were stable, and a systematic investigation was undertaken to detect radioactive effects, with negative results. Unfortunately the detection methods used were insensitive to β-rays: otherwise the discovery of the activity induced in aluminum, among others, might have been anticipated by more than a decade.

183. Discovery of the Neutron. For nearly 12 years after Rutherford's discovery of the production of protons from α-particle bombardment of light elements, this was the only type of artificial disintegration known. By 1930 several other laboratories had entered the field and several important new facts had been brought to light. Bothe and Fränz had shown, in 1927, that the less-energetic α-particles of polonium (5.3 Mev) were also capable of producing transmutations, and Pose in 1929 was able to show that α-particle bombardment of aluminum (a single isotope) produced three distinct groups of protons. A particularly significant observation was made by Pose in 1930 when he found that the yield of protons exhibited maxima for certain α-particle energies: this is the phenomenon of "resonance" which had been predicted by Gurney in 1929, and about which we shall have more to say in a later section.

The first observation of nuclear radiations other than protons from the transmutation of the light elements was made by Bothe and Becker in 1930. Using a Geiger counter, they observed penetrating radiation from α-bombardment of several elements, among them Be and B. The radiation was so weak—only a few millicuries of polonium were available—that they could only make the roughest estimate of the absorption coefficient; they could establish, however, that the radiation they observed was more penetrating than any known γ-ray (the hardest radiation then known was the ThC″-ThD, 2.62-Mev γ-ray).

In 1932, Mme. Joliot-Curie and F. Joliot[1] discovered a remarkable property of these radiations. In an attempt to compare the absorption coefficients in various materials, they set up the arrangement shown schematically in Fig. 181. Alpha-particles from the polonium source P bombarded a piece of beryllium B, and the radiation was detected in the ionization chamber I. A 1.5-cm-thick Pb filter F reduced the effect on the ionization chamber of the soft γ-radiation from the Po source. Inserting absorbers of such materials as Al, Cu, Ag, and Pb in front of

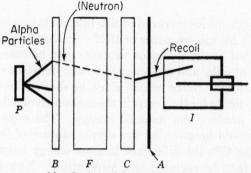

FIG. 181. Arrangement used by Curie and Joliot to study the recoils ejected from various materials by the radiation produced in beryllium and boron under α-particle bombardment. Alpha-particles from the source P strike the target B, producing neutrons. In the layer C, some of the neutrons may produce recoils which are detected in the ionization chamber I. The penetrating power of the recoils may be determined by interposing screens at A.

the ionization chamber, at C in the figure, they found only a slight diminution in intensity, but with paraffin, water, and cellophane, they actually observed an *increase* in the ionization-chamber reading. The greatest effect was observed with paraffin, which produced an increase by a factor of 2. Acting on the conjecture that the effect was due to protons ejected from the paraffin by the radiation, Curie and Joliot placed aluminum absorbers between the paraffin and the ionization chamber (at A in the figure) and found that 0.2 mm of Al was sufficient to destroy the effect. The increase in ion-chamber current was therefore not attributable to fast electrons, and tests with a magnetic field showed that no easily deflectable particles, like slow electrons, were responsible. This evidence and the association of the effect with hydrogenous substances made the identification with protons reasonably certain. Knowing the range-energy relation for protons in aluminum, they concluded that the protons had an energy of about 4.5 Mev, and concluded that they were recoils from a high-energy γ-ray.

From the equations derived for the Compton process (Sec. 160), it

[1] I. Curie and F. Joliot, *Compt. rend.*, vol. 194, p. 273, 1932.

is easy to see that the maximum energy transferable to a proton by a γ-ray of energy $h\nu$ is

$$E_{max} = h\nu \frac{2\zeta}{1 + 2\zeta} \qquad \zeta = \frac{h\nu}{Mc^2} \qquad (254)$$

where M is the mass of the proton. Using their value of 4.5 Mev for the proton energy, Curie and Joliot arrived at a γ-ray energy of approximately 50 Mev. A similar examination of the radiation from boron bombarded with α-particles yielded a γ-ray energy for this reaction of 35 Mev.

Two serious difficulties involved in this interpretation were pointed out by Chadwick[1] in his famous paper of 1932. In the first place, the number of protons ejected in the Compton process could be calculated from the Klein-Nishina formula[2] and was many thousand times too small to account for the observations. In the second place, he showed that, even allowing rather generous limits for the errors in the masses involved, no conceivable reaction could produce the required energy. The most energetic possible reaction would be given by the simple capture of the α-particle by the Be^9, forming C^{13}; the difference in mass energy between $Be^9 + He^4$ and C^{13} could then be radiated as a γ-quantum. Now the mass of C^{13} and of the α-particle were known, and an upper limit for the mass of Be^9 could be obtained from the fact that Be^9 is stable.[3] The mass difference $Be^9 + He^4 - C^{13}$ added to the kinetic energy available from the α-particle gave an upper limit for the energy of the γ-ray of only 14 Mev— considerably less than the 50 Mev reported.

In extension of the work of Curie and Joliot, Chadwick redetermined the range of the recoil protons from hydrogen, obtaining a range of 40 cm, corresponding to a velocity of 3.3×10^9 cm per sec and an energy of 5.7 Mev. He also observed recoils from a number of other light substances, including nitrogen, and made rough measurements of the recoil energies. Now, from Eq. (254), the maximum energy transferred by a γ-ray should be roughly inversely proportional to the mass of the struck nucleus [note that $2\zeta \ll 1$ so that $E_{max} \sim 2(h\nu)^2/Mc^2$], so it would be expected that nitrogen recoils would have an energy of 5.7/14 Mev. The observed energy was more than three times this value.

It thus appeared that the assumption that the observed effects were produced by high-energy γ-rays was quite untenable. If, on the other hand, it was assumed that the radiation consisted of uncharged particles of about the same mass as the proton, all difficulties were resolved. Such

[1] J. Chadwick, *Proc. Roy. Soc. (London)*, vol. 136A, p. 692, 1932.

[2] Cf. W. Heitler, "Quantum Theory of Radiation," Oxford, London, 1944.

[3] If the mass of Be^9 were greater than the sum $2He^4 + n^1$, it would disintegrate spontaneously (see Sec. 186). Chadwick assumed, in his preliminary estimate, $Be^9 \leqq 2He^4 + p + e$.

particles, having no interaction with the atomic electrons, would be able to pass relatively freely through matter, losing their energy only through comparatively rare nuclear collisions. In such collisions they could transfer a large fraction of their energy and the observed recoils could be accounted for with only moderate primary energies. The existence of such particles, called "neutrons," had in fact been suggested by Rutherford some 12 years earlier, and many attempts to observe them had been made at the Cavendish Laboratory before Chadwick's discovery.

Comparison of the recoil energies from hydrogen and nitrogen permitted a quantitative determination of the mass of the neutron. From the ordinary laws of elastic collisions, the maximum velocity which can be imparted to a proton by a particle of velocity V_0 having a mass equal to M_0 times the proton mass is

$$V_H = V_0 \frac{2M_0}{M_0 + 1} \tag{255}$$

while the maximum velocity of a nitrogen recoil will be

$$V_N = V_0 \frac{2M_0}{M_0 + 14} \tag{255a}$$

Dividing these two relations to eliminate V_0, we obtain

$$\frac{V_H}{V_N} = \frac{M_0 + 14}{M_0 + 1} \tag{256}$$

For V_H, Chadwick used his value of 3.3×10^9 cm per sec; V_N was obtained from cloud-chamber measurements by Feather[1] as 4.7×10^8 cm per sec. Inserting these values in Eq. (256), Chadwick obtained $M_0 = 1.15$ with an estimated error of about 10 per cent. The velocity of the neutrons, calculated from Eq. (255) or (255a), is 3.2×10^9 cm per sec, corresponding to a kinetic energy of about 6 Mev.

Chadwick suggested that the reaction involved in the production of neutrons from α-particle bombardment of beryllium is

$$_4Be^9 + _2He^4 \rightarrow _6C^{12} + n^1$$

where n^1 refers to the neutron. From the known masses, again assuming an upper limit for Be^9, he concluded that a maximum of 8 Mev was available for the neutron when polonium α-particles (5.3 Mev) were used. In the case of boron he assumed the reaction

$$_5B^{11} + _2He^4 \rightarrow N^{14} + n^1$$

Here the masses were all known, and from the energy balance he was

[1] N. Feather, *Proc. Roy. Soc. (London)*, vol. 136A, p. 709, 1932.

able to obtain a mass for the neutron of 1.0067 amu, with a probable error of about 0.1 per cent. More recent determinations involving several nuclear reactions (Sec. 192e) yield a value

$$M_n = 1.008\ 982 \pm 0.000\ 003 \text{ amu (phys)}$$

NUCLEAR BINDING ENERGIES AND NUCLEAR FORCES

The discovery of the neutron revolutionized our ideas about the structure of nuclei: until that time it was generally believed that nuclei contained protons, electrons, and, possibly, α-particles. The theory of nuclear structure based on this assumption was fraught with perplexing difficulties, particularly with respect to the properties of electrons in the nucleus. The introduction of the neutron as a nuclear constituent eliminated some of these problems and provided a much more satisfactory picture of the composition of nuclei. The theory has still many difficulties, it must be confessed, but at least they are now of another kind.

184. Properties of Nuclei.[1] Before we embark on a discussion of the theory of nuclear structure, it will perhaps be appropriate to review some of the more important properties of nuclei as they were known in 1932. In the ensuing discussion we shall have the advantage of another 20-odd years of development, but most of the concepts we shall need for our preliminary discussion were at hand by 1932.

a. Charge. We begin with the nuclear charge: since atoms are normally neutral, the nuclear charge is equal in magnitude and opposite in sign to that of the atomic electrons. Since the latter all have the same charge e (Millikan, 1909, Sec. 48), the nuclear charge is Ze, where Z is an integer. The value of Z is known from x-ray scattering experiments (Barkla, 1909, Sec. 148), from the nuclear scattering of α-particles (Geiger and Marsden, 1913, Sec. 79), and from the x-ray spectrum (Moseley, 1913, Sec. 153).

b. Mass. The masses of nuclei, determined by measurement of the ratios of charge to mass in the mass spectrometer (Sec. 181), and by nuclear reaction energies (Sec. 192), are all very close to integers when expressed in terms of $O^{16} = 16$ exactly (see Appendix II). It is in some ways a fortunate accident that an element as heavy as oxygen was chosen as the standard. On a scale where $H^1 = 1$ exactly, many mass values would differ greatly from integers. The important point is that the masses are closely integral multiples of some single value. The mass number A is about $2Z$ for light elements and increases to about $2.5Z$ for heavy ones.

---

[1] H. A. Bethe and R. F. Bacher, *Revs. Mod. Phys.*, vol. 9, p. 83, 1936; H. A. Bethe, "Elementary Nuclear Theory," Wiley, New York, 1947; J. M. Blatt and V. F. Weisskopf, "Theoretical Nuclear Physics," Wiley, New York, 1952.

c. Size. The "size" of a nucleus, like that of an atom, is not a uniquely defined quantity, since the specification depends upon what property is under consideration. If two atoms approach one another, they may exhibit a weakly attractive force at large distances, which changes at short distances to a strongly repulsive force. The distance at which this change occurs may be used as a measure of the sum of the radii of the two atoms. On the other hand, the "radius" may also be defined in terms of the distribution of electronic charge in the atom. The two definitions may give quite different results, and both are subject to some arbitrariness because the functions involved change only slowly with distance. In the nuclear case, too, various definitions of the radius are used, but it happens that all agree fairly well, and in each case the measurements suggest a rather sharp boundary.

One useful measurement of the size of nuclei comes from α-particle scattering experiments of the kind described in Sec. 79. In these experiments, a beam of α-particles is directed onto a thin foil of the material under study and the number of α-particles scattered at various angles is determined. For moderate α-particle energies, the experimental results are consistent with the assumption of a simple inverse-square force acting between the nucleus and the α-particle. As the α-particle energy is increased, however, deviations from the Rutherford scattering law appear, particularly at large angles. These deviations are associated with the fact that the α-particle trajectory reaches closer to the nucleus at the higher energies, and can thus be interpreted as a failure of the inverse-square law at small distances. Analysis of the scattering experiments leads to the conclusion that the radius at which the force law changes varies from a few times 10^{-13} cm in light nuclei to about 10^{-12} cm in heavy nuclei.

Scattering of high-energy neutrons by nuclei (Sec. 197) also gives a measure of the extent of the force field around a nucleus. Since neutrons are unaffected by the electrostatic forces, their scattering must be interpreted in terms of some nonelectrical force. The experimental results indicate an attractive force which sets in rather abruptly at short distances. The radius at which the force begins to act strongly varies approximately as the cube root of the mass number and appears to be well represented by the expression

$$R = R_0 A^{\frac{1}{3}} \qquad R_0 = 1.1 \text{ to } 1.5 \times 10^{-13} \text{ cm} \qquad (257)$$

A frequently used value for R_0 is $e^2/2m_0c^2 = 1.41 \times 10^{-13}$ cm.

We shall discuss in later sections still other determinations of the nuclear radius as defined in various ways and shall find that all are reasonably consistent with Eq. (257).

d. Spin. The spin—better referred to as the total angular momentum—of the nucleus can be obtained from the hyperfine-structure pattern, from spectra of homonuclear molecules, or by atomic-beam methods (Secs. 136 and 144). The magnitude of the angular momentum is specified, in units of $h/2\pi$, by the number I,[1] where I is the maximum possible projection of the angular-momentum vector on any arbitrary axis in space. In nuclei with even A, I is found to be an integer or zero; it is always zero if both Z and A are even. In nuclei with odd A, I is a half-integer. Protons, electrons, and neutrons have spin $I = \frac{1}{2}$.

e. Magnetic Moment. A magnetic dipole moment is always associated with nuclear spin; the magnitudes of nuclear moments, obtained from the spacing in hyperfine structure and from atomic-beam experiments (Secs. 135 and 136), are of the order of the nuclear magneton $eh/4\pi Mc$, where M is the proton mass. They are thus about one-thousandth of the magnetic moment of the electron. Nuclei with zero spin have no magnetic moment.

f. Statistics. It is found that quantum-mechanical systems can be divided into two classes depending upon what kind of statistics are obeyed by the particles composing them (Sec. 168). Thus, the distribution of energy among electrons in a metal, for example, requires quite different assumptions about the wave function describing the particles than does the behavior of helium gas at low temperatures. In the first case, it is found that the properties of the system are accounted for by the assumption that the wave function describing two identical particles, for example two electrons with the same spin direction, changes its sign when the space coordinates of the two particles are interchanged; the wave function in this case is said to be antisymmetric with respect to the exchange (Sec. 107), and the particles are said to obey Fermi-Dirac statistics. For the other class of particles, the wave function is symmetric—does not change sign—and the particles obey Bose-Einstein statistics. It can be shown that Fermi-Dirac particles obey the Pauli exclusion principle, while Bose-Einstein particles do not. Experimentally it is found that all particles with half-integral spins (e.g., protons, neutrons, and electrons) obey Fermi-Dirac statistics, and all those with integral or zero spin obey Bose-Einstein statistics.

Which statistics will be obeyed by a complex structure like the nucleus can be determined in principle by studying the behavior of the wave function describing two identical nuclei when they are interchanged piece by piece. If a nucleus contains an odd number of Fermi-Dirac particles, it will itself obey Fermi-Dirac statistics; if the number is even, it will obey Bose-Einstein statistics. The statistics of nuclei may be determined experimentally from the rotational (Raman) spectra of homonuclear mol-

---

[1] The symbol J is sometimes used.

ecules (Sec. 144).   It is found that all nuclei with odd A obey Fermi-Dirac statistics, while those with even A obey Bose-Einstein statistics.

g. Parity.   The parity of a system refers to the behavior of the wave function under inversion of the coordinates through the origin, i.e., when x is replaced by $-x$, y by $-y$, and z by $-z$.   If the potential-energy function is unchanged by this process $[V(x,y,z) = V(-x,-y,-z)]$ then it can be shown that the wave function may either remain the same or it may change sign; it is said to have *even* parity if the sign remains the same, if the sign changes, the *parity* is *odd*.   The wave functions describing a particle in a box (Sec. 102) have alternately even and odd parities:[1] the parity of the wave functions of the one-electron atom (Sec. 104) are even or odd as l is even or odd.   Nuclear states are characterized by a definite parity (which may be different for different states of the same nucleus), and the conservation of parity has an important bearing on nuclear reactions.

h. Electric Quadrupole Moment.   A system of charges with nonzero spatial extension may produce, in addition to the ordinary radial electrostatic field of force, fields of higher complexity, characterized as dipole, quadrupole, and higher-multipole fields.   There is good evidence that nuclei do not have electric dipole moments, but electric quadrupole moments have been observed in many nuclei (Sec. 145).

185. Constituents of Nuclei.[2]   The fact of the transmutability of nuclei argues that they are complex systems, composed of some common constituents.   The integral values of Z and the near-integral values of M suggest the proton as one candidate, while the occurrence of α-particles and β-particles as decay products early suggested electrons as fundamental constituents and helium nuclei either as constituents or as particularly stable "subassemblies."   Thus, in the early theories, a nucleus of charge number Z and mass number A was thought of as comprising A protons and $A - Z$ electrons, grouped as far as possible in units of four protons and two electrons.   The hypothesis that electrons exist in the nucleus encounters a number of difficulties, however, several of which were already apparent long before the neutron was discovered.[3]   For one thing, there was the problem of the magnetic moment: a single odd electron in a nucleus would be expected to contribute, from its spin alone, a moment of 1 Bohr magneton.   Since nuclear moments are very much smaller than this value, it had to be supposed that, somehow, the electron's magnetic moment was suppressed in the nucleus.   More perplexing still

[1] To exhibit this property it is necessary to use a potential symmetric in x: thus, in Sec. 102, the edges of the box are set at $x = \pm L/2$, and the solutions alternate between sine and cosine functions as n is increased.

[2] Bethe and Bacher, *loc cit.*

[3] G. Gamow, "Constitution of Atomic Nuclei and Radioactivity," Oxford, London, 1931.

was a problem arising in the light nuclides with even A and odd Z. N^{14}, for example, would have 14 protons and 7 electrons—all Fermi-Dirac particles with spin $\frac{1}{2}$. With an odd number of such particles, N^{14} should evidently obey Fermi-Dirac statistics and have a half-integral spin, but study of the band spectrum of nitrogen gas showed in fact that N^{14} obeys Bose-Einstein statistics and has a spin of 1 (cf. Sec. 144). Finally, it could be shown that, according to the uncertainty principle, a particle with so small a mass as the electron would have an implausibly large kinetic energy if it were confined to nuclear dimensions. If there were to be electrons in the nucleus, then they must differ from ordinary electrons in practically all the features which identify them in their normal environment.

With neutrons and protons as the building blocks of nuclei, on the other hand, these problems find a natural solution. On this picture a nucleus with charge number Z and mass number A would contain Z protons and $A - Z$ neutrons, or A particles in all. Thus N^{14} has seven protons and seven neutrons; if neutrons are assumed to be Fermi particles and to have half-integral spin (as has been confirmed by experiment) the spin and statistics of N^{14} are accounted for. The magnetic moments present less difficulty than before, since only heavy particles are involved. The problem of β-decay is taken care of—or at least put in another category—by assuming that a neutron in the nucleus changes to a proton, *creating* the β-particle (and a neutrino) in the process. Two other types of decay, which were discovered later, also fit into this picture: a nuclear proton may be converted into a neutron, creating a positive electron (positron decay) or capturing an atomic electron (electron capture). The quantum-mechanical treatment of β-decay bears a close resemblance to that describing the creation of light quanta in atomic transitions, and the formal similarity of the two processes emphasizes the point that the appearance of an electron coming out of a nucleus does not imply that it ever was in the nucleus. The assumption that neutrons and protons are constituents of nuclei, and electrons are not, is consistent with all known facts and may be regarded as a basic tenet of nuclear theory. The term "nucleon" is often used in referring to either protons or neutrons.

186. Masses and Binding Energies. Under the assumption that nuclei are composed of neutrons and protons, we can now discuss the various factors which enter into the masses of nuclei and gain some insight into their binding. The mass of any permanently stable nucleus is found to be less than the sum of the masses of the neutrons and protons which it contains. This fact is accounted for by the conversion of part of the mass energy of the particles into energy of binding, the relation between the change in mass and the binding energy being given by Einstein's equation, $E_{\text{binding}} = \Delta M c^2$. The significance of the binding energy can perhaps be seen most easily in the more familiar atomic case. In the capture of a free electron by a proton to form a hydrogen atom, a certain amount of energy, 13.6 ev, is released (in the form of one or more light quanta): the mass of the hydrogen atom is therefore slightly less than the sum of the masses of a free electron and free proton.   To ionize the hydrogen atom, an amount of energy at least equal to the binding energy of 13.6 ev must be added.   In an atom containing more than one electron, the binding energy is the total energy required to remove all the electrons: it is thus to be distinguished from the "ionization potential," which is the energy required to remove one electron.   In atoms, the ionization potential of the most loosely bound electron is a few electron-volts; the total binding energy for all but the lightest atoms is given approximately by the empirical expression $E_B = 15.6Z^{7/3}$ ev.   The change in mass corresponding to the binding energy in atoms is rather small—in the uranium atom it amounts to about 1 electron mass, or about 3×10^{-6} of the total —and is just at the limit of direct measurability; in the nucleus, on the other hand, the binding energy may represent an appreciable fraction of the total mass.

The mass of the nucleus with charge number Z and mass number A may be written

$$M_N(A, Z) = ZM_p + (A - Z)M_n - \frac{E_B}{c^2} \tag{258}$$

where M_p is the mass of the proton and M_n is the mass of the neutron. The term E_B/c^2 represents the mass equivalent of the total binding energy, the energy which must be added to the nucleus in order to break it up into Z protons and $(A - Z)$ neutrons.   Because it is more nearly the atomic than the nuclear mass which is measured in the mass spectrograph, the values given in mass tables usually refer to the mass of the neutral atom, including the electrons.   Expressed in terms of *atomic* rather than nuclear masses, Eq. (258) becomes

$$M(A, Z) = M_N(A, Z) + ZM_e = ZM_H + (A - Z)M_n - \frac{E_B}{c^2} \tag{259}$$

where now M_H is the mass of the hydrogen atom.   Actually a very small correction for the binding energy of the atomic electrons should be made if the quantity E_B is to refer to the nuclear binding energy only, but the correction is negligible for our purposes, except perhaps in the heaviest nuclei.

With the help of expression (259) and the known masses of the neutron and hydrogen atom, we can now compute the binding energy of any nuclide for which the mass has been measured.   As a simple example, we take the deuterium atom (hydrogen isotope of mass number 2):

$$M(H^2) = M_H + M_n - \frac{E_B}{c^2}$$

From the mass table

$$2.014\ 735 = 1.008\ 142 + 1.008\ 982 - \frac{E_B}{c^2}$$

$$\frac{E_B}{c^2} = 0.002\ 389 \text{ amu}$$

Inserting the value in grams of the physical mass unit (Sec. 181) we obtain[1]

$$E_B = \frac{0.002\ 389 \times 1.660 \times 10^{-24}c^2}{1.602 \times 10^{-6}} = 2.225 \text{ Mev}$$

We conclude that it requires 2.225 Mev of energy to dissociate a deuteron, and that the capture of a free neutron by a proton releases 2.225 Mev of energy (in the form of a γ-ray). In the same way, we find for the binding energy of the U^{238} nucleus

$$\frac{E_B}{c^2} = 92 \times 1.008\ 142 + 146 \times 1.008\ 982 - 238.12493$$

$$= 1.9355 \text{ amu}$$
$$E_B = 1{,}802 \text{ Mev}$$

Thus the binding energy in this nucleus amounts to nearly 1 per cent of its mass.

One interesting result of the computation of nuclear binding energies is the observation that, except for the lightest nuclides, the binding energy varies practically linearly with A, or to put it another way, the binding energy per particle is very nearly constant over a large range of A. In Fig. 182 is shown a plot of the binding energy per particle as a function of A for the stable nuclides listed in Appendix II. Aside from certain irregularities among the light elements, the general course of the curve shows a gradual increase to a value of about 8.8 Mev per particle near the middle of the table with a falling off to about 7.6 Mev per particle in the region of the heavy elements. It is worth observing that the near constancy of the binding energy per particle is in striking contrast to the behavior of atoms, where the average binding energy per electron is a steadily increasing function of the number of electrons (proportional to $Z^{\frac{2}{3}}$).

a. Stability against Heavy-particle Emission. That the total binding energy of a nucleus is positive is not a sufficient condition for its stability: in order that a nucleus be stable, it is necessary that its mass be less than the sum of the masses of any other combinations of its constituent protons and neutrons, whether free or bound in smaller groups. The α-radioactive nuclei are unstable because the α-particle itself is a tightly

---

[1] An often-used relation is the energy equivalent of the mass unit:

$$1 \text{ amu (phys)} \times c^2 = 931.16 \text{ Mev}$$

bound structure and, at the upper end of the periodic table, the binding
energy per particle increases as the number of particles decreases. The
energy required to remove any given particle from the nucleus is called

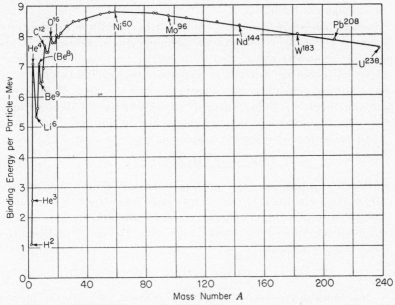

FIG. 182. Average binding energy per particle for the naturally occurring nuclides
(Be^8 has been included because of its high binding energy; it is actually just unstable
with respect to two α-particles).

the *separation energy*,[1] E_s. The separation energy for an α-particle in
the nucleus (Z, A) is

$$\frac{E_s(\alpha)}{c^2} = M(\text{He}^4) + M(Z - 2, A - 4) - M(Z, A) \qquad (260)$$

If the α-particle separation energy is negative, the nucleus (Z, A) is
unstable to α-emission. For the light elements, the separation energy
of an α-particle is positive: for example, it requires 0.007 677 amu, or
7.149 Mev, to remove an α-particle from Ne^{20}. On the other hand, the
α-separation energy of Po^{210} is -5.4 Mev. There exists a large class of
heavy elements where the masses are insufficiently well known to determine whether they are stable or unstable with respect to α-particle emission. Because of the extremely long lifetimes expected for low-energy
α-emitters, it is almost certain that some of the elements that we regard
as stable actually do emit a few α-particles. A still larger class are, in
principle, unstable with respect to fission into two or even three roughly

Sometimes also called the "binding" energy of the particle in the nucleus (Z, A).

equal parts, but again the lifetimes are so long that the effect is generally unobservable. Stability against neutron or proton emission is no problem: the separation energy for these particles is generally around 7 to 8 Mev, or about the same as the average binding energy per particle, for all but the lightest nuclides.

b. *Stability against Beta-decay.* Still a further condition for the stability of nuclei comes as a result of the phenomenon of β-decay. It may occur, and frequently does, that although a nucleus has insufficient energy to emit a nuclear particle, a system of lower energy can be formed by transforming a neutron into a proton, or vice versa. Most often it is the requirement of stability against β-decay which is the most stringent condition for the existence of a given nuclide in nature. The nuclide (Z, A) is stable against negative β-decay if

$$M(Z, A) \leqq M(Z + 1, A) \tag{261}$$

where the M's are atomic (not nuclear) masses. To see this, we note that $M(Z, A)$ is the mass of the nucleus plus Z electrons: if the nucleus is to decay, it must supply sufficient mass for the new nucleus plus the created β-particle (the neutrino has no mass[1]). The mass condition then is

$$M(Z, A) = M_N(Z, A) + ZM(e) \leqq M_N(Z + 1, A) + ZM(e) + M(\beta)$$

where M_N refers to the mass of the nucleus alone, $M(e)$ to the mass of an atomic electron, and $M(\beta)$ to the β-particle. Since the negative β-particle is an electron, the right-hand side adds up to $M(Z + 1, A)$, the atomic mass.

In the decay by *positron* emission, the initial nucleus must furnish mass for the new nucleus and a β^+-particle; the condition for positron stability of the nuclide $(A, Z + 1)$ is then

$$M_N(Z + 1, A) \leqq M_N(Z, A) + M(\beta^+)$$

Adding $(Z + 1)$ electron masses to both sides and noting that the positron and electron masses are the same, we obtain the expression in terms of atomic masses:

$$M(Z + 1, A) \leqq M(Z, A) + 2M(e) \tag{262}$$

A third type of β-process which is of particular importance for stability considerations is decay by electron capture, in which an orbital electron—usually from the K shell—is absorbed into the nucleus. In this case, no new particle is created, and the condition for stability becomes more

---

[1] The mass of the neutrino is known to be less than 0.05 per cent of the electron mass. Cf. L. M. Langer and R. J. D. Moffat, *Phys. Rev.*, vol. 88, p. 689, 1952.

restrictive than Eq. (262), namely

$$M_N(Z + 1, A) + M(e) \leqq M_N(Z, A)$$

or, in terms of atomic masses,

$$M(Z + 1, A) \leqq M(Z, A) \tag{263}$$

We have in all three of these expressions for β-stability ignored the change in the binding energy of the atomic electrons: this quantity is in almost all cases quite negligible.

The two conditions (261) and (263), for stability against negative β-decay and electron capture, guarantee that of any two neighboring isobars one must be unstable, for the heavier will always[1] be able to transform into the lighter by one process or the other. Thus if the masses of isobars (nuclides with fixed A) increase uniformly as Z is varied away from some optimum value, only one will be stable. It is just this fact that gives the study of the naturally occurring nuclides its great importance in connection with the understanding of nuclear structure, for of any combination of A neutrons and protons, just the one which we find in nature will represent the configuration of minimum energy. There do occur cases among species with even A where the mass is not a uniform function of Z; we have then the situation where a nuclide may be unstable with respect to both its neighbors, and, for these values of A, two isobars and sometimes three, differing in charge by 2 units, may occur. The isobars Ca^{40}–A^{40} and Zn^{64}–Ni^{64} are examples.[2]

187. Nuclear Forces. We wish now to see what can be inferred from the material at hand about the character of the forces which hold nuclei together. It is in the first place clear that they are not ordinary electrostatic forces, if for no other reason than that all the particles involved either have positive charge or are neutral, and such a system could not be bound by classical forces. Even aside from the sign of the force, electrostatic forces are much too weak to account for the main effects; gravitational forces are weaker still and offer no assistance in the problem. It is therefore necessary to postulate an entirely new type of interaction, a type which never manifests itself in large-scale phenomena and which has no evident relation to either gravitational or electric forces. Since we have no previous experience with such forces, the best we can do is to make the simplest possible postulates about them consistent with the

[1] Still ignoring the electron-binding-energy correction: no case is known where this prevents a decay which would otherwise be possible. There exist some cases where K-electron capture is not possible and capture from L or higher shells occurs instead.

[2] There do occur a few apparent exceptions to the rule prohibiting neighboring stable isobars: for example, Cr^{50}, V^{50}, and Ti^{50} all exist in nature. Direct mass measurements show, however, that V^{50} is in fact unstable. Its long life is attributed to the very high angular-momentum change of 6 units, which inhibits the decay.

available data. With a finite number of facts available, we cannot be sure of a unique solution; it can only be hoped that the solution will contain sufficient elements of truth to permit further progress as experimental knowledge expands.

One characteristic feature of nuclear forces is their short range. Although little is known about the exact dependence on the distance, there

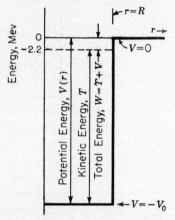

FIG. 183. Simplified "square-well" potential representing the interaction of a neutron and proton.

is good evidence that the force vanishes for all practical purposes at distances greater than a few times 10^{-13} cm (Sec. 184). There are many experiments which suggest that the force between two nucleons[1] sets in quite abruptly at a separation of 1 or 2×10^{-13} cm. In the interest of simplicity, the force is usually regarded as derivable as the gradient of a potential (in the hope, among other things, that the force between nucleons is independent of their velocity), and a shape of the potential is chosen which is mathematically not too intractable. It will be sufficient for our purposes to use as a convenient approximation the so-called "square well"— a potential with a constant negative value out to a certain radius and vanishing thereafter. Conceptual difficulties with the infinite force at the boundary can be resolved by allowing the transition to take place over a small range in radius.

a. *Theory of the Deuteron.*[2] In order to exhibit some of the concepts involved in discussing nuclear potentials and the quantum states of nuclei, we consider the deuteron. Although the deuteron is the only nucleus which admits of a reasonably exact solution, many features of the deuteron problem occur in more complicated nuclei and an understanding of this relatively simple case is useful in these applications. Our discussion will be based on the square-well potential illustrated in Fig. 183, where the heavy line indicates the potential energy of the neutron in the nuclear field of the proton (or vice versa). The potential energy has the value $V = -V_0$ out to the radius R, and is zero for larger values. We write the wave function for the neutron, in coordinates relative to the proton, as $\psi(r,\theta,\phi)$, and look for a spherically symmetric[3] solution to the wave equation, of the form $\psi = u(r)/r$; the absolute square

---

[1] Aside from the electrostatic force, which acts only between protons.

[2] H. A. Bethe, *op. cit.*; Blatt and Weisskopf, *op. cit.*

[3] With the assumed potential, the spherically symmetric solution will have the lowest energy.

of $u(r)$ represents the probability of finding the neutron at distance r (cf. Sec. 104).   The Schrödinger equation (112b) may then be written

$$\frac{d^2u(r)}{dr^2} + \frac{4\pi^2M}{h^2}\,(W + V_0)u(r) = 0 \qquad r < R \qquad (264a)$$

$$\frac{d^2u(r)}{dr^2} + \frac{4\pi^2M}{h^2}\,Wu(r) = 0 \qquad r > R \qquad (264b)$$

Because the neutron and proton have practically equal mass M, the "reduced mass" $M/2$ [Eq. (82), Sec. 81] is used in these equations.   We must now ascertain whether there exist any solutions to Eqs. (264) which correspond to stationary, bound states: evidently we require solutions for which W, the total energy, is negative (see Fig. 183).   Since the deuteron is known to be a bound system, with $W = -2.225$ Mev, the question really amounts to choosing values of V_0 and R which will reproduce this fact.   For $r < R$, the solution of (264a) is of the form

$$u(r) = A \sin Kr \qquad K = \sqrt{\frac{4\pi^2M(W + V_0)}{h^2}} \qquad r < R \quad (265a)$$

The cosine solution is inadmissible because it is finite at $r = 0$ and $\psi = u(r)/r$ would be infinite.   The outside solution is

$$u(r) = Be^{-kr} \qquad k = \sqrt{\frac{4\pi^2M(-W)}{h^2}} \qquad r > R \qquad (265b)$$

where the positive-exponential solution is rejected because it produces an infinite ψ as r approaches infinity.   The condition that these two solutions join smoothly at $r = R$ then determines whether a real eigenvalue for the energy exists.   Equating the values and first derivatives of u at $r = R$, we obtain

$$A \sin KR = Be^{-kR} \qquad\qquad (266a)$$
$$AK \cos KR = -Bke^{-kR} \qquad\qquad (266b)$$

Dividing (266b) by (266a),

$$K \operatorname{ctn} KR = -k \qquad \text{or} \qquad \operatorname{ctn} KR = -\frac{k}{K} \qquad (267)$$

This transcendental equation can be solved numerically or graphically to produce the required condition on V_0 and R for any (negative) value of W.   For the present purpose, it is sufficient to observe that if we choose $V_0 \gg W$, then k/K is small and the cotangent of KR is small and negative; KR is then slightly greater than $\pi/2$.   The situation is illustrated in

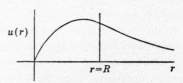

Fig. 184. Radial variation of the wave function describing the deuteron in its ground state;

$$u(r) = r\psi(r).$$

Fig. 184, where $u(r)$ is indicated as a function of r.   The inside (sine)

function has reached a maximum and just started to decrease where it joins the outside exponential. This condition represents the first possible eigenvalue, since, if the interior function had not yet passed its first maximum, it could not be made to fit a decreasing exponential outside. The condition $KR \cong \pi/2$ gives

$$\frac{\pi}{2} \cong KR \cong \frac{2\pi R}{h} \sqrt{MV_0}$$

or $$V_0 R^2 \cong \frac{h^2}{16M} = 1.02 \times 10^{-24} \text{ Mev cm}^2 \qquad (268)$$

using the definition of K in (265a) and ignoring the small quantity W. If we choose for R the reasonable value of 2×10^{-13} cm, we obtain $V_0 \cong 25$ Mev for the potential energy of the neutron-proton bond in the ground state of the deuteron. Taking $KR = n\pi/2$, with $n = 3, 5, \ldots$, would yield excited states of the system, corresponding to the excited levels of an atom. It can be shown, however, that no bound excited states exist in the deuteron.[1]

b. *Scattering of Free Nucleons.*[2] We have seen, from the fact that the deuteron is a bound system, that attractive forces exist between neutrons and protons. Further information on the forces can be obtained from a study of the scattering of free neutrons by protons. In such experiments a parallel beam of neutrons is allowed to impinge upon a target containing hydrogen atoms—paraffin, for example—and the number of neutrons deflected through various angles in elastic encounters is determined as a function of neutron energy (Sec. 197c). Since they have no charge, neutrons are unaffected by the electrostatic field and their scattering will directly reflect the operation of the nuclear forces.

The wave-mechanical theory of neutron-proton scattering is constructed along much the same lines as is the theory of the deuteron, with the difference that the total energy W is positive for a free neutron, and hence all energy values are allowed. The wave function outside the radius R is no longer an exponential function but is a superposition of a plane wave, representing the stream of incoming particles, and expanding spherical waves, representing the scattered particles. The calculated scattering turns out to be relatively independent of the assumed shape of the potential in the case of low-energy neutrons, and the result is essentially fixed by the binding energy of the deuteron.

The amount of scattering observed for low-energy neutrons by protons turns out to be more than twice the maximum possible value predicted by this simple theory. So great a discrepancy clearly indicates that some factor enters the scattering problem which is not present in the deuteron.

[1] Bethe, *op. cit.*
[2] Blatt and Weisskopf, *op. cit.*

The missing factor was pointed out by E. P. Wigner in 1936, who observed that while in the ground state of the deuteron the neutron and proton necessarily have parallel spin orientations (to produce the observed spin of 1 for the deuteron), no such restriction applies in the scattering of free neutrons, where both parallel and antiparallel spins occur. It is then possible to adjust the assumed interaction between neutrons and protons with *antiparallel* spins in such a way as to fit the scattering data. The results of this adjustment show that the forces depend rather strongly on the relative spins, the potential well in the antiparallel case being considerably less deep and having a larger effective radius than that in the parallel case. The situation is sometimes described in terms of an excited (singlet) state of the deuteron, with $I = 0$ and a negative binding energy of about 0.1 Mev.

c. Charge Independence of Forces. It was for some time generally believed that nuclear forces operated only between neutrons and protons, and a number of theories of nuclear structure were based on this assumption. In 1935, however, experiments[1] on the scattering of high-velocity protons in hydrogen gas showed that nuclear forces also play a role in the interaction of protons with protons.[2] Further work on the same line has led to the conclusion that the nuclear part of the force between two protons (p-p) is the *same* as that between a proton and a neutron (p-n), at least when the relative energy is less than some tens of millions of electron-volts.[3] In addition, a comparison of energies of certain isobars in which neutrons are replaced by protons and protons by neutrons yields evidence for the equality of (n-n), (p-p), and (p-n) forces, at least in the light nuclei (Sec. 193). The now generally accepted view that these three forces are essentially the same is often referred to as the assumption of "charge independence" of nuclear forces. This close similarity between neutrons and protons in their behavior in the nucleus suggests that these two particles are fundamentally very closely related, that they may in fact simply represent two different "states"—differing as to charge—of the same particle.[4]

[1] M. A. Tuve, N. P. Heydenburg, and L. R. Hafstad, *Phys. Rev.*, vol. 50, p. 806, 1936.

[2] G. Breit, E. U. Condon, and R. D. Present, *Phys. Rev.*, vol. 50, p. 825, 1936.

[3] This statement applies only to interactions which are allowed in both cases: The Pauli principle excludes certain interactions of two protons; for example, two protons with otherwise identical quantum numbers must have antiparallel spins.

[4] It would seem logical to assume, then, that all the observed differences between neutrons and protons are due to purely electromagnetic effects. On this view, it might be expected that the proton would be heavier than the neutron, because of the energy associated with the electrostatic charge. That the opposite is the case does not appear to admit of a straightforward explanation, although there are indications that the solution may be found in the theory of quantum electrodynamics. See R. P. Feynman and G. Speisman, *Phys. Rev.*, vol. 94, p. 500, 1954.

d. Interaction of Nucleons in Nuclei: Exchange Forces.[1]   Thus far, we have discussed mainly the character of the forces acting between pairs of nucleons, as observed in simple two-body systems.   We have found that an adequate account of these interactions can be given under the assumption that the forces are derivable from a potential which depends somewhat upon the relative spin orientations of the particles, but apparently not upon whether they are protons or neutrons.   When we come to consider systems comprising more than two particles, we must expect some complications to enter.   Even if the forces between pairs of nucleons were known in detail, the mathematical complexity of the many-body problem would be formidable, but we do not even know whether the relatively simple two-body forces apply at all in nuclei.   Again we are obliged, in order to obtain some insight into the binding of nuclei, to assume the simplest possible forces and to test the consequences of these assumptions by experiment.

The most natural assumption about internucleon forces in nuclei is that they are simply additive; that each nucleon is attracted by every other one in the nucleus with a force like that acting between two isolated nucleons.   That this is not the case can be shown from the fact that the observed binding energy per particle is essentially constant in all but the lightest nuclei.   In a nucleus containing A particles, $A(A - 1)/2$ pairs can be formed; if attractive forces existed between all such pairs, the total binding energy would be roughly proportional to A^2 rather than to A (the spin dependence does not affect this argument since both types of force are attractive).   By a more detailed discussion, in which the change in kinetic energy is also taken into account, it can be shown that the nucleus would collapse to a radius of the order of the range of nuclear forces.   The observed radii of nuclei actually increase as if each nucleon occupies a constant volume, irrespective of how many others are present in the nucleus.   It is evident then that the forces between nucleons must "saturate" in some way, that once a nucleon has formed a few bonds, so to speak, it ignores any further nucleons which may be added to the system.

It is possible, of course, that the law of force between two nucleons within a nucleus is radically modified by the presence of other nucleons, or that the forces are dependent on the relative velocities.   Theories based on both of these hypotheses have in fact been proposed, but are necessarily subject to considerable arbitrariness, and have not thus far been sufficiently explored to establish their usefulness.   It could also be assumed that at some small distance, less than the range of the normal attractive force, the two-body force suddenly becomes strongly repulsive, so that the nucleons act like hard spheres in close packing, and each inter-

[1] Blatt and Weisskopf, *op. cit.*

acts only with those in its immediate neighborhood. The van der Waals forces which bind the atoms in solids and liquids have just this property. If such forces exist in the nucleus, they must operate over a range much shorter than that of the attractive force, since otherwise their effects would appear in the two-body scattering experiments. In this event, the nucleus would collapse to a size determined by the smaller range, in contradiction to observation. Because of these and other difficulties of a more complicated character, it seems unlikely that such forces, taken alone, offer an acceptable solution to the problem.

A common hypothesis about internucleon forces in the nucleus is that they have at least in part an "exchange" character, i.e., that the law of force between two particles depends in a direct way upon the symmetry of the wave function with respect to their interchange. The binding of homonuclear molecules (Sec. 113) has something of this character, in that the effectiveness of the electrostatic force is determined by the spatial distribution of the charges, which in turn is governed by the symmetry requirements. In molecular binding, however—and, in fact, in all atomic phenomena—the forces are purely electrostatic or electromagnetic in origin and do not themselves contain any explicit dependence on symmetry properties. The energy difference between states of different symmetry character is then given by the "exchange integral" [Eq. (141), Sec. 106], which takes account of the tendency of particles to cluster together in some states and to avoid one another in other states. Such effects presumably operate within the nucleus, and a force depending only on distance, called an "ordinary" force, will have some saturation effects. Quantitative calculations show,[1] however, that the effects so produced are insufficient, and it is necessary to introduce a force which depends *explicitly* on the symmetry of the wave function: such a force is called an "exchange" force. Several types of exchange forces have been proposed; perhaps the simplest of these is the so-called "Majorana" interaction, in which it is assumed that two particles attract one another if the wave function describing the entire system does not change sign (i.e., is symmetric) when the spatial coordinates of the two particles are interchanged, and that they repel if the wave function changes sign (is antisymmetric). It can be shown by quite general arguments that this assumption can be made to account for the observed constancy of the binding energy per particle independently of the details of the structure of the nucleus. We shall not attempt to discuss these arguments here, but only try to make them plausible from a very simple model.

We assume that the wave function describing a nucleus can be written as a combination of one-particle wave functions, each characterized by a set of quantum numbers n, l, λ, analogous to those used in constructing

[1] L. Rosenfeld, "Nuclear Forces," chap. XI, North-Holland, 1949.

atomic wave functions. Because of the Pauli principle, there can be at most four nucleons in any state with a given value of n, l, and λ: two protons with opposite spins and two neutrons with opposite spins. The wave function is automatically symmetric with respect to the exchange of the spatial coordinates of any pairs among these four particles, and hence there are attractive forces between all pairs. Thus an α-particle, comprising four nucleons in the lowest state, will be a tightly bound structure. If now a fifth nucleon is added, it must necessarily go into another state, and the wave function will be antisymmetric with respect to exchange of this particle with an identical particle in the first level. Exchanges with any of the other three lead to wave functions which are partly symmetric and partly antisymmetric. Since the antisymmetric pairs are assumed to lead to repulsive forces, the net effect is to make the five-nucleon system less strongly bound than the α-particle (Li^5 and He^5 are in fact not bound, and do not occur in nature). As further nucleons are added, the number of both symmetric and antisymmetric pairs increases, and, by a suitable adjustment of the assumed magnitudes of the resulting attractive and repulsive forces, the observed linear dependence on A of the binding energy and volume per nucleon can be accounted for. Detailed studies of the scattering of very high energy—up to 350 Mev—neutrons and protons in hydrogen give strong evidence for the existence of exchange forces; however, the amount of repulsion observed in the antisymmetric interactions seems too small to account for the saturation.

e. Nuclear Potential. Although the details of the interactions between nucleons within an actual nucleus are undoubtedly very complicated, it is possible and useful to make a representation in terms of a relatively simple potential well for the interaction between an "average" nucleon and the rest of the nucleus. The crude square well used in the deuteron problem (Fig. 183) can be used in this way to indicate the situation of an average neutron: for a moderately heavy nucleus, the binding energy is about 8 Mev and the kinetic energy is 10 to 15 Mev. The nuclear potential acting on the *most loosely* bound neutron fluctuates from one nucleus to the next: the binding energy (or "separation energy") of the last neutron varies between 6 and 8 Mev in the stable nuclides.

The potential acting on a *proton* must include the electrostatic effect due to the repulsion of the other protons in the nucleus. Outside the nuclear surface, the electrostatic potential has the form Ze/r [more accurately $(Z - 1)e/r$ as far as the effect on the last bound proton is concerned]. Inside, the electrostatic potential is modified because of the volume distribution of the charge, and there it is usually taken simply as a constant added (algebraically) to the nuclear potential.

The *total* electrostatic energy of a nucleus may be estimated from the work necessary to assemble a charge Ze uniformly distributed in a sphere of radius R, or

$$E_E = \frac{3}{5}\frac{(Ze)^2}{R} \qquad (269)$$

An alternative calculation, in which only the mutual electrostatic energy of the Z protons is included, leads to

$$E_E = \frac{3}{5}\frac{Z(Z-1)e^2}{R} \cong 0.61\frac{Z(Z-1)}{A^{1/3}} \qquad \text{Mev} \qquad (270)$$

The situation of the last proton in a medium or heavy nucleus is shown in Fig. 185, where W is again about 7 or 8 Mev. It may be mentioned that even that part of the potential which is due to purely nuclear forces (V_N on the diagram) is not quite the same for protons and neutrons in a heavy nucleus which contains more neutrons than protons. The protons, being in the minority, will be able to form more symmetric bonds per particle and hence will be subject to a deeper potential, as far as nuclear forces are concerned, with the result that the net binding energy is about the same for protons and neutrons.

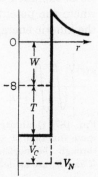

FIG. 185. Potential-energy function applying to the most loosely bound proton in a medium or heavy nucleus.

f. *Nuclear Barrier.* A diagram of the type shown in Fig. 185 can also be used to represent the binding of a combination of particles, such as an

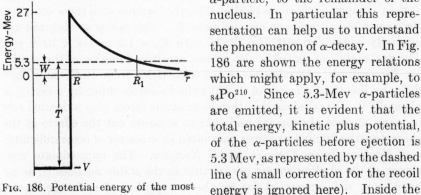

FIG. 186. Potential energy of the most loosely bound α-particle in $_{84}Po^{210}$.

α-particle, to the remainder of the nucleus. In particular this representation can help us to understand the phenomenon of α-decay. In Fig. 186 are shown the energy relations which might apply, for example, to $_{84}Po^{210}$. Since 5.3-Mev α-particles are emitted, it is evident that the total energy, kinetic plus potential, of the α-particles before ejection is 5.3 Mev, as represented by the dashed line (a small correction for the recoil energy is ignored here). Inside the nucleus, the potential energy is negative, so we may presume that the kinetic energy is quite high—several times the value which it will ultimately have when the α-particle escapes outside to the region of zero potential. In the intermediate region, however, the electrostatic potential is given by

$$V_c = \frac{Z_1 Z_2 e^2}{}$$

where $Z_1 = 2$ and $Z_2 = 82$.   If we use the value of the nuclear radius R given by Eq. (257), we find a potential of some 27 Mev at this point, just outside the range of the nuclear potential.   Classically, then, the α-particle is excluded from the whole region from R to some larger value R_1 where the potential energy has dropped to 5.3 Mev, since in this region the kinetic energy would be negative.   Quantum-mechanically, however, there is a finite probability of penetrating this region. The wave function will have qualitatively the appearance of Fig. 187, with a rapidly oscillating character inside the nucleus, joining on to an exponentially falling function in the barrier region, and, for $r > R_1$, a sinusoidal function of small amplitude.

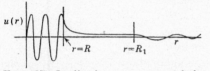

FIG. 187. Qualitative appearance of the wave function of an α-particle escaping through the nuclear barrier. The radii R and R_1 are as defined in Fig. 186.

The ratio of the flux outside to that inside is a measure of the probability of escape of the α-particle and hence of the disintegration constant.   An approximate calculation, first made by Gamow, and independently by Gurney and Condon, in 1929, yields for the probability of escape

$$P \cong \exp\left[-\frac{4\pi \sqrt{2M}}{h} \int_R^{R_1} \sqrt{V(r) - W}\, dr \right] \qquad (271)$$

This expression for the probability is a sensitive function of the radius R, and, by comparing lifetimes predicted by the formula with those observed for known α-emitters, one can estimate R.   The values so obtained are generally consistent with Eq. (257), with $R_0 = 1.2$ to 1.4×10^{-13} cm. The probability of escape is also a most sensitive function of the energy W: for example, the energies of the α-particles from RaC′ and Th[232] differ by less than a factor of 2, while the half-lives differ by a factor of about 10^{20}!   It is evident that the electrostatic forces play a decided role in many nuclear phenomena and that to separate out the effects of the characteristically nuclear forces may often be a matter of some difficulty.

g. Neutron-proton Ratio in Stable Nuclides.   The approximate constancy of the binding energy per particle in the stable nuclides is, as we have seen, well accounted for by the assumption of exchange forces. Certain other features of the distribution of such nuclides also find a natural explanation under this hypothesis.   Thus, the observed preference for near equality of N and Z follows immediately from the strong dependence of the nuclear force on the spatial symmetry of the wave function.   Referring to our previous argument, we remember that four *different* nucleons (differing as to charge or spin orientation) can be placed in one n, l, λ, level (Fig. 188a), where they will attract one another strongly. If we wish to construct a nucleus from four protons, on the other hand, two would have to be placed in another level (Fig. 188b) and the total number of attractive bonds would be smaller and the system less stable. The same argument can be extended to larger numbers of nucleons and shows that, in general, nuclei with $N = Z$ or $N = Z \pm 2$ are the most stable as far as the purely nuclear forces are concerned. As the number of particles increases, however, the mutual electrostatic repulsion of the protons will begin to make itself felt, effectively reducing the potential to which the protons are subject (Fig. 185). In consequence of this effect, the proton levels will be displaced from the neutron levels, as indicated schematically in Fig. 189, and it will become advantageous to add a few extra neutrons. Thus $_{28}\mathrm{Ni}^{60}$, with 28 protons and 32 neutrons, is more stable than $_{30}\mathrm{Zn}^{60}$. Since the electrostatic energy increases roughly as Z^2, this effect becomes more pronounced as Z increases, and for high Z there are not only many more neutrons than protons, but the average binding energy per particle is effectively decreased.

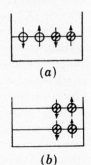

FIG. 188. Occupancy of nuclear quantum states by (a) two neutrons and two protons, and (b) four protons.

A word of warning is perhaps in order at this point concerning such diagrams as Fig. 189. Since the potential is contributed by the nucleons themselves, the shape of the potential function will change as nucleons

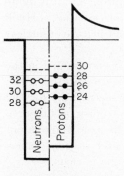

FIG. 189. Neutron and proton levels in $_{28}\mathrm{Ni}^{60}$. Only the uppermost levels are shown.

are added or removed, and the location of levels representing other than the most loosely bound nucleons has very little significance. The diagram can be used to indicate qualitatively the effect of adding or removing one or two nucleons, or of moving one nucleon from one state to another, but even so the magnitude of the total energy change may be quite different from the value the diagram would suggest.

We observed earlier (Sec. 181a) a strong preference among the stable nuclides for even N ($N = A - Z$, the number of neutrons) and even Z, as opposed to odd N and odd Z, while nuclides with odd Z and even N and those with even Z and odd N occur in roughly equal numbers. These facts we can now understand in terms of the displacement of proton levels with respect to neutron levels. In $_{28}\mathrm{Ni}^{60}$ (Fig. 189), for example, there are 14 filled proton levels, each with two protons (with spins opposed), and 16 occupied neutron levels. If another particle is to be added, it must go into an unoccupied level, and the chances are about even that the next available level will be a neutron level. Thus among the stable isotopes with an odd total number of particles A, it is to be expected that about half will have odd N and about half odd Z. In Ni^{60}, it happens that the next available level is a neutron level, corresponding to Ni^{61}; if now another particle is to be added, it is evident that adding a second neutron will be more favorable than adding a proton, simply because the neutron level is lower and there is room for two particles in it. Thus $_{28}Ni^{62}$ is more stable than $_{29}Cu^{62}$: in fact Cu^{62} is observed to be radioactive and decays to Ni^{62}. Had the proton level been the more stable, i.e., if Cu^{61} were more stable than Ni^{61}, the preferred second particle would have been a proton, forming $_{30}Zn^{62}$. In either case, the result is a preference for the even-N, even-Z combination over the odd N, odd Z and the latter, in medium and heavy nuclei, is always unstable with respect to the former. Among the light elements there are a few cases of stable odd-N, odd-Z nuclei: in these instances, the electrostatic effect is relatively unimportant and the small spin dependence of the force gives rise to a preference for equal N and Z.

We have thus accounted for the main properties, the mass, charge, and size of the nuclides which are found in nature, making only rather general assumptions about the nature of nuclear forces. We have assumed that the forces act only over a short range, that they act approximately equally strongly on neutrons and protons, and that they have a strong dependence on the symmetry of the wave function. On the other hand, we have seen that there exist several alternatives to the last assumption, and it is by no means clear that this assumption is either adequate or essential. Much work remains to be done before any clear and consistent picture of nuclear forces can be formulated.

About the *structure* of the nucleus, very little has been assumed in the foregoing. Whether the "quantum states" which we have used really represent the independent motions of individual nucleons, or whether the motions are so strongly perturbed that the "states" must be taken to refer to some sort of collective motion of the nucleons as a whole is not essential to these arguments. We shall discuss in later sections experiments which have a bearing on a specific model for the nucleus.

POSITRONS, ARTIFICIAL RADIOACTIVITY, ARTIFICIALLY ACCELERATED PARTICLES

188. The Positron. In the same year that Chadwick established the existence of the neutron, still another fundamental particle, the positive electron, was discovered. Interestingly enough, the positron manifested itself in three quite independent experiments, carried on in three different laboratories, and its existence was predicted by a theory developed for another purpose.

a. Anomalous Absorption of Gamma-rays.   Shortly after the development of the Klein-Nishina formula for the Compton scattering of x-rays, a number of investigators (Chao, Meitner, Hupfield, Tarrant, Gray[1]) found that the experimental cross sections for absorption of the ThC'' (2.62 Mev) γ-radiation in heavy materials were 20 to 25 per cent higher than the predicted values.   With the excess absorption was associated a "scattered" secondary radiation which appeared to consist of two components with energies of about 0.5 and 1.0 Mev.   The same secondary radiation was observed from Sn, Fe, and Pb, with a cross section roughly proportional to Z^2, but only primaries with energies above 1.5 Mev were capable of producing the effect.   Since no process involving extranuclear electrons was known which could result in such radiation, it was supposed that excitation of the nucleus must be involved.

The second, seemingly unassociated, observation came in connection with a study by Curie and Joliot of the secondary electrons produced in lead by the radiation from Be bombarded by α-particles.   Becker and Bothe had reported a spectrum of electrons extending up to 4.5 Mev, which they attributed to a γ-ray of about this energy accompanying some of the neutrons.   To study the matter further, Curie and Joliot placed a lead foil and a polonium-beryllium source in a cloud chamber, and with a magnetic field of about 1,000 gauss, proceeded to study the electrons ejected from the lead by the beryllium radiation.   In the course of this work, reported in November, 1932, they observed a number of electrons which seemed to be moving *toward* the lead foil, since their tracks were curved in the wrong sense.   (The sense of deflection depends, of course, both on the sign of the charge and the direction of motion.) At the time they believed that these tracks were probably due either to scattered electrons or to some interaction of the neutrons with the walls of the cloud chamber, but the experimental data were insufficient to admit any definite conclusion.

b. Positrons in the Cosmic Radiation.   The decisive proof of the existence of a positive electron came in a cloud-chamber study of cosmic radiation, published by Anderson[2] in September, 1932, and March, 1933. We shall discuss the cosmic radiation more extensively in the next chapter; suffice it here to say that it consists of high-energy particles and γ-radiation traveling generally downward through the atmosphere.   To investigate the composition of this radiation, Anderson set up a cloud chamber in a vertical plane, in a magnetic field of 15,000 gauss.   In the center of the cloud chamber was a horizontal lead plate 6 mm thick. Among some 13,000 exposures taken with this apparatus, several pictures appeared which suggested the presence of a light, positively charged particle; the most convincing of these is reproduced in Fig. 190.   Here

[1] L. H. Gray and G. T. P. Tarrant, *Proc. Roy. Soc. (London)*, vol. 136A, p. 662, 1932.
[2] C. D. Anderson, *Phys. Rev.*, vol. 43, p. 491, 1933.

one sees a lightly ionizing track with a relatively large radius of curvature in the lower half of the cloud chamber, apparently passing through the lead plate, and emerging on the upper side with a considerably smaller radius of curvature.   The sense of the magnetic field is such that negative particles curve to the left if traveling downward, to the right if traveling upward.   The magnetic rigidities deduced from the curvature of the

track below and above the plate are $B\rho = 2.1 \times 10^5$ and 0.5×10^5 gauss cm, respectively. If the particle were a proton, the energy of the upper portion would be 0.3 Mev.   The range of such a proton would be about 5 mm in air, while the actual track shows no change in curvature over a distance ten times as great.   Interpreted as a particle of electronic mass and charge, the energies are 63 Mev below and 23 Mev above the plate.   If the particle were negative, it would be traveling downward, and must have *gained* about 40 Mev in traversing the plate. The only reasonable hypothesis, then, is that the track was produced by a positive particle of considerably less than protonic mass, traveling upward.   From the energy loss in the plate it could be determined that the charge

FIG. 190. Reproduction of the first cloud-chamber photograph showing a track recognized as that of a positron. From the curvature of the track, produced by a magnetic field perpendicular to the plane of the figure, it may be seen that the particle has lower energy in the upper part of the chamber, above the lead plate, indicating that it came from below. In this case, the sense of deflection indicates a positive charge. (*Photograph kindly lent by Professor C. D. Anderson.*)

was less than twice that of the electron and the mass less than twenty times the electron mass.   (It was quite accidental that this particle should be traveling upward: most cosmic ray particles travel downward.)

c. Theory of the Positron.   Anderson's result was confirmed almost immediately by Blackett and Occhialini,[1] who had been engaged in a similar study of the cosmic radiation.   The appearance of the positive particles was interpreted by them as a consequence of the creation of a positive and negative pair by a γ-ray interacting with a nucleus.   They pointed out that this process was to be expected on the basis of the Dirac relativistic theory of the electron.[2]   The principal feature of Dirac's

[1] P. M. S. Blackett and G. P. S. Occhialini, *Proc. Roy. Soc.* (*London*), vol. 139A, p. 699, 1933.

[2] Cf. W. Heitler, "Quantum Theory of Radiation," Oxford, London, 1936.

theory, which was published in 1930, was the requirement that the equations describing the electron be invariant under Lorentz (relativistic) transformations (as are Maxwell's equations, but not the Schrödinger equation). This requirement has as a direct consequence the effects on atomic energy levels which were ascribed in the classical theory to spin and relativistic mass changes (see Sec. 120), but, in addition, the "unfortunate" property that there should be a symmetry between electronic states of positive and negative kinetic energy. According to this picture, a free electron would have available to it not only a continuum of states of total energy W from $+m_0c^2$ to plus infinity, but also a continuum extending downward from $-m_0c^2$. A free electron could then make a transition to a negative-energy state with the emission of energy in the form of γ-quanta, and eventually all electrons would find themselves in states with negative kinetic energy. In order to avoid this catastrophe, Dirac assumed that all the negative-energy states were occupied beforehand, so that no transitions could occur. There remained, however, the problem that under certain circumstances a γ-ray of energy greater than $2m_0c^2$ could interact with an electron in a negative-energy state, lifting it to one of the positive-energy states and leaving a vacancy, or "hole." The "hole" would then behave in every respect like a positively charged electron and would constitute an available state into which a "normal" electron could jump, resulting in its annihilation.

These ideas can perhaps be made a little clearer by reference to the diagrams of Fig. 191. Here we represent the possible energy states of a free electron by a continuum, extending from $W = +m_0c^2$ upward and from $W = -m_0c^2$ downward. The lower levels are all filled, and their effect merely adds a constant (infinite) charge which is undetectable. In Fig. 191(b) a γ-ray of energy $E_\gamma(>2m_0c^2)$ raises an electron in a state of energy $-W_1$ to a state of positive energy $+W_2$: the electron now has a positive kinetic energy $T_2 = E_\gamma - W_1 - m_0c^2$, and the "hole" behaves like a positron of (positive) kinetic energy $W_1 - m_0c^2$. Since momentum cannot be conserved in the interaction of a γ-quantum and two electrons,[1] the event must take place near a nucleus which, because of its great mass, can take up the excess momentum without noticeably affecting the energy balance. The interaction with the nucleus takes place through the Coulomb field, and calculation gives a roughly Z^2 dependence for the cross section for pair formation. The positron so created can interact with atomic electrons through its electrostatic field, gradually losing its kinetic energy until it finally undergoes an annihilation process

[1] This can be seen most easily by making a Lorentz transformation of the coordinates to a system in which the center of mass of the electron and positron is at rest: since the momentum of a photon $(h\nu/c)$ cannot be transformed away entirely, there will be an unbalanced momentum in this system.

with a (negative) electron at rest (Fig. 191c).   Momentum can be conserved in this process if two quanta, each of energy m_0c^2, are emitted. One-quantum annihilation, resulting in a single γ-ray of energy $2m_0c^2$, is also possible if the electron is strongly bound to a nucleus.   Positrons can be annihilated in flight through collisions with electrons, but the probability falls off rapidly as the velocity increases.   The lifetime of a very slow positron in Pb is about 10^{-10} sec.

   d. Pair Formation.   According to Blackett and Occhialini, what was happening in the cosmic-ray observations was the "materialization" of high-energy γ-rays in the walls of the cloud chamber or in the material

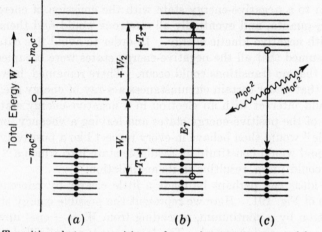

FIG. 191. Transitions between positive and negative energy states of free electrons.

nearby, producing positron-electron pairs.   The appearance of positrons in Curie and Joliot's experiment was accounted for as a similar process involving a γ-ray from the Be^9 plus α-particle reaction, converted in the foil.   Finally, the "excess scattering" of Gray and Tarrant was attributed to pair production by the hard γ-rays of ThC"-ThD and subsequent annihilation of the positrons, producing mainly 0.5-Mev (m_0c^2) radiation from two-quantum annihilation with free electrons, but also some 1.0-Mev ($2m_0c^2$) radiation from single-quantum annihilation.   (It was later shown that part of the "1-Mev" radiation is a continuous x-ray spectrum from the slowing down of secondary electrons.)

   The process of pair-formation turns out to be a major effect in the attenuation of high-energy γ-rays.   Its importance can be seen from the curves of Fig. 227 (Sec. 213), where the effects of photoelectric absorption, Compton scattering, and pair formation in Pb are individually exhibited as a function of γ-ray energy.   In lighter elements, the pair formation is relatively less important for energies around 5 to 10 Mev.   In all cases, the threshold for pair formation is $E_\gamma = 2m_0 c^2 = 1.022$ Mev. According to the theory, the positron and electron masses should be exactly equal: this has been checked by direct comparison of m/e for the two particles.[1] The values are found to agree to within less than 1 part in 10^4.

189. Induced Radioactivity. After the announcement of the discovery of the positron, Curie and Joliot conducted further experiments on the radiation produced in Be by α-particle bombardment. With some improvements in the arrangement used in their earlier experiments they were able to confirm that positive particles were produced when the hard γ-radiation was converted in lead, and that they were also produced in other materials. Relative to the number of negative electrons, more positrons were observed from converters of high atomic number than from converters of low atomic number. In a similar experiment in which aluminum, instead of beryllium, was bombarded by α-particles, they found positrons again, but this time no corresponding electrons. Further study showed that the positrons were not produced in the converter, but came from the aluminum source itself. Finally, in the course of an investigation of the effect of varying the α-particle energy, they noticed that the positrons did not appear immediately when the polonium source was put in place, but built up gradually over a period of minutes. When the α-particles were removed, the effect died down gradually, again with a period of some minutes. As a result of these experiments, announced in February, 1934, Curie and Joliot[2] concluded that the effect must be ascribed to a radioactive material produced by the α-particle bombardment. The reaction they suggested was

$$_{13}Al^{27} + {}_2He^4 \rightarrow {}_{15}P^{30} + {}_0n^1$$

The isotope P^{30} does not exist in nature, and they assumed that it decays spontaneously with emission of positrons, to a known stable isotope of silicon by the reaction

$$_{15}P^{30} \rightarrow {}_{14}Si^{30} + \beta^+$$

The half-life they observed to be 3.25 min. That the radioactive substance was an isotope of phosphorus they subsequently confirmed by showing that the active material had the same behavior under chemical analysis as does elemental phosphorus.

In the same experiments, Curie and Joliot found that boron bombarded by α-particles also produced a positron activity, with a half-life of about 14 min. This activity they attributed to another new isotope, N^{13}, formed in the reaction

$$_5B^{10} + {}_2He^4 \rightarrow {}_7N^{13} + {}_0n^1$$

[1] L. A. Page, P. Stehle, and S. B. Gunst, *Phys. Rev.*, vol. 89, p. 1273, 1953.

[2] I. Curie and F. Joliot, *Compt. rend.*, vol. 198, p. 254, 1934.

and decaying to C^{13}:

$$_7N^{1r} \rightarrow \,_6C^{13} + \beta^+$$

They suggested that the same radioisotope might be produced by artificially accelerated deuterons bombarding carbon, through the reaction

$$_6C^{12} + \,_1H^2 \rightarrow \,_7N^{13} + \,_0n^1$$

This reaction was reported by Crane and Lauritsen[1] in March, 1934.

Since the time of these early experiments, a great many radioactive isotopes have been produced artificially, with protons, deuterons, α-particles, and neutrons as bombarding agents, and, as of 1954, more than 900 species are known. In addition to the fact that the study of these radioisotopes has yielded an enormous amount of information about the nucleus, they have had a considerable practical importance, particularly as tracers in chemical and biological investigations.[2] In work of this kind, certain compounds are "tagged" by incorporating into them a radioactive isotope of one of their normal constituents, and the subsequent progress of this constituent through various chemical changes is traced by means of its easily detectable radioactivity. This technique permits many operations not amenable to chemical analysis, such as study of the rate of exchange of an element from one ionic form to another, or the rate at which a given element is exhausted and replaced in a living organism. Radioisotopes of almost all the elements of biological interest are available: some of the most used are C^{14} (with a half-life of 5,400 years), P^{32} (30 days), Na^{24} (14 hr), and S^{35} (87 days).

190. Nuclear Transformations with Artificially Accelerated Particles. From the time of the earliest observations of transmutations induced by α-particles from radioactive sources, there was speculation as to whether it might not be possible to use artificially accelerated positive ions for the purpose. One obvious advantage would lie in the much greater number of particles available, for even a current as small as 1 microampere represents some 6×10^{12} (singly charged) particles per second, or about the number of α-particles emitted by the polonium derived from 160 grams of radium. The prospect of inducing nuclear reactions with particles of practically attainable energies seemed rather hopeless, however, in view of the Coulomb barrier. The barrier height of a nucleus of charge Z and mass number A for a singly charged particle is

$$V = \frac{Ze^2}{R} \qquad \text{or} \qquad V \cong \frac{Z}{A^{1/3}} \text{ in Mev}$$

[1] H. R. Crane and C. C. Lauritsen, *Phys. Rev.*, vol. 45, p. 497, 1934.

[2] W. E. Siri, "Isotopic Tracers and Nuclear Radiations," McGraw-Hill, New York, 1949.

so something of the order of 1 or 2 million volts would seem to be required even for the lightest elements.

With the development of the theory of barrier penetration (Sec. 187), however, it appeared that nuclear processes might be observable even at energies considerably less than the barrier height, particularly in light nuclei. Accordingly, Cockroft and Walton,[1] at the Cavendish Laboratory, set out to construct an accelerating system to operate at 300,000 volts. Their first system, described in 1930, comprised a transformer-rectifier voltage source and a glass discharge tube into which ions were injected from a Wien-type canal-ray tube. With this installation they obtained a beam of 300-kev (thousand electron-volt) protons and looked briefly for reactions leading to γ-ray emission, with no definitive results. By 1932, they had extended and improved the apparatus, obtaining proton beams up to 10 microamperes at energies up to 700 kev. The accelerating tube was provided with an extension into which various targets could be inserted. Thin mica windows in the side of the extension permitted the escape of disintegration products to the outside, where they could be detected by means of a zinc sulfide scintillation screen. The mica window was thick enough to stop elastically scattered protons. The first successful experiment was with lithium. With protons of 125-kev energy bombarding a target of lithium metal, they observed bright scintillations—about five per minute with a beam of 1 microampere. As the proton energy was increased, many more scintillations were observed, and, at 500 kev, they estimated the efficiency to be about 10^{-8} disintegrations per incident proton. Absorption measurements gave a value of 8.4 cm for the maximum range of the particles producing the scintillations, and measurements of the ionization showed that they were α-particles. It was concluded by Cockroft and Walton that the reaction involved was

$$_3\text{Li}^7 + {}_1\text{H}^1 \rightarrow {}_2\text{He}^4 + {}_2\text{He}^4$$

From the (poorly known) masses, they estimated that 14.3 ± 2.7 Mev should be available for kinetic energy of the α-particles; from the observed range they calculated 17.2 Mev, in reasonable agreement. That two α-particles were in fact produced simultaneously, in opposite directions, they checked with the arrangement shown in Fig. 192. The target consisted of a thin layer of lithium deposited on a thin sheet of mica, mounted at 45° to the incident proton beam. Two mica windows in opposite sides of the target tube allowed α-particles produced in the target to escape and to be observed on the two scintillation screens S_1 and S_2. Two observers recorded the scintillations independently on a single mov-

[1] J. D. Cockroft and E. T. S. Walton, *Proc. Roy. Soc. (London)*, vol. 129A, p. 477, 1930; vol. 136A, p. 619, 1932; vol. 137A, p. 229, 1932; vol. 144A, p. 704, 1934.

ing tape: the existence of a large proportion of coincidences on the record was evidence that the process assumed was taking place. This conclusion was later confirmed by Dee and Walton[1] with cloud-chamber photographs.

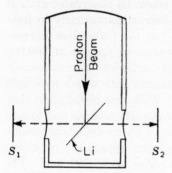

A number of other elements were investigated by Cockroft and Walton in the years 1932–1933. Both boron and fluorine were found to give comparatively large α-particle yields under proton bombardment, and many other elements, including Be, Na, and K, produced detectable numbers. The disintegration of Li, B, and F by 1.2-Mev protons from the cyclotron was reported by Lawrence, Livingston, and White in September, 1932, only a few months after Cockroft and Walton's first report. Oliphant, Kinsey, and Rutherford observed the disintegration of Li and B by deuteron bombardment in 1933, and Crane, Lauritsen, and Soltan announced the artificial production of neutrons by helium-ion bombardment of beryllium in September, 1933.

FIG. 192. Arrangement for detecting coincident α-particles produced in proton bombardment of Li[7].

It is of interest that the experiments on the disintegration of lithium with protons provided the first direct quantitative check of Einstein's equation, $E = mc^2$, relating mass and energy. The fact that all the masses involved were known from mass-spectrometer measurements and that the energy release was large compared to the errors of observation made it possible to check the agreement between the loss in mass and the observed kinetic energy within about 20 per cent. We shall see later (Sec. 192) that modern determinations from other nuclear reactions check this relation to considerably higher accuracy.

191. Accelerators.[2] The years that have passed since the experiments of Cockroft and Walton have seen a considerable development in techniques and equipment for production of high-energy charged particles. We shall enumerate here some of the principal types which have found application in problems of nuclear physics.

a. High-tension Set. Voltages up to 1 or 2 million have been produced by straightforward cascade connection of transformer-rectifier sets. Because of the difficulty of building rectifiers capable of withstanding high voltage, such sets are ordinarily built in units of about 200 kilovolts, either with individual transformers, each excited by a special winding on the previous one, or with a single transformer and some form of voltage-

[1] P. I. Dee and E. T. S. Walton, *Proc. Roy. Soc. (London)*, vol. 141A, p. 733, 1933.

[2] D. Halliday, "Introductory Nuclear Physics," Wiley, New York, 1950; E. L. Chu and L. I. Schiff, "Annual Reviews of Nuclear Science," vol. II, 1953.

multiplying circuit.   The principal load on such a set is often corona loss (local ionization of the air near sharp points), which may amount to several milliamperes, and, unless large condensers are used, an undesirable ripple in voltage results.   For example, if the capacitance is of the order of 10^{-2} microfarad, a drain of 1 milliampere produces a voltage change of 1.6 kilovolts in $\frac{1}{60}$ of a second.   For many purposes, a ripple of this magnitude is quite acceptable, but situations do occur where a steadier voltage is desirable.   For this reason, such installations are often designed to work at frequencies of 500 cycles per sec or more.

A sketch of a typical accelerating tube is shown in Fig. 193.   The tube is broken up into many sections, preferably with a controlled voltage for each section, partly to aid in focusing the ion beam and partly to distribute the voltage gradient as uniformly as possible along the insulating surfaces.   The positive ions to be accelerated are generated in an auxiliary "ion source," located on the top of the tube.   Gas—hydrogen, if protons are desired—is admitted into a discharge tube, in which the atoms are ionized by electron bombardment.   An electrode at the bottom of the ion source, provided with a fine hole and held at a negative potential with respect to the discharge tube, extracts the ions and injects them into the main accelerating tube. By means of a series of electrostatic lenses, the ions are collected into a narrow bundle as they are accelerated down the tube.   Since a certain amount of gas also escapes into the tube, it is necessary to evacuate the tube continuously with large diffusion pumps.

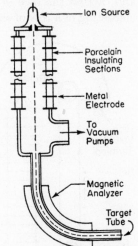

FIG. 193. Schematic diagram of a high-voltage accelerating tube and magnetic analyzer. Ions produced in the top of the tube are accelerated and focused by a series of electrostatic lenses. At the bottom of the tube they are deflected through 90° by a magnet.

The ion source produces, besides protons (H^+), also singly charged hydrogen molecules of mass both 2 and 3 (H_2^+ and H_3^+).   In addition, incidental ions formed in the residual gas in the main tube are also collected in the beam and accelerated.   It is necessary, therefore, to provide a magnetic deflection or combined magnetic and electrostatic deflection at the lower end of the tube to reject the undesired components.   With a properly designed magnetic or electrostatic analyzer, the measured field can be used to determine the particle energy with much higher accuracy than a direct voltage measurement can give.

b. Electrostatic Accelerator.   A convenient way to produce a steady high voltage without the difficulties of ripple associated with transformer-rectifier sets is to use a continuously charged moving belt, as devised by Van de Graaff[1] in 1931. The principle is shown by the schematic diagram of Fig. 194. Two rollers are provided, the lower driven by a motor, the upper located in the high-voltage terminal, well insulated from ground. Over the rollers passes an endless belt of insulating material, and, across the face of the belt, opposite the lower roller, is a "comb" consisting of a row of sharp pins with their points just clear of the moving

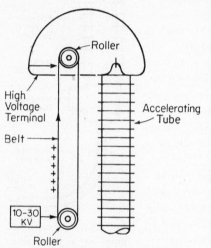

belt. A supply of 10 to 30 kilovolts between the comb and the belt produces a corona discharge, causing positive ions to flow from the comb to the belt and negative ions and electrons from the belt to the comb. The positive charges are then carried by the belt to the high-voltage terminal (the motor supplying the necessary energy) where a second comb connected to the terminal picks them off. The voltage to which the terminal can rise is determined by the balance between the current supplied by the belt and that lost by corona or drained down the accelerating tube. In a variation designed by Herb, Parkinson, and Kerst[2] and now universally used for high-voltage applications, the machine, together with the accelerating tube, is mounted in a pressure tank so that it can be oper-

FIG. 194. Diagram of an electrostatic accelerator. Charges are sprayed on a moving endless belt and carried up to an insulated terminal, producing a high voltage which is applied to an accelerating tube.

ated under several atmospheres' pressure of air or other insulating gas. Since the electrical breakdown strength of a gas is roughly proportional to pressure, it is possible to construct a machine with much smaller dimensions when high pressure is used. For example, clearances of the order of 10 to 15 ft are required around a 1-million-volt installation at atmospheric pressure, while 5- to 8-million-volt electrostatic accelerators can be housed in 8- or 10-ft-diameter pressure tanks.

c. *Cyclotron.* High particle energies can be obtained without the use of high voltages by means of the "magnetic-resonance accelerator" or "cyclotron," devised by Lawrence and Livingston[3] in 1932. In the cyclotron, charged particles are given repeated accelerations in a radio-

[1] R. J. Van de Graaff, *Phys. Rev.*, vol. 38, p. 1919, 1931; vol. 43, p. 149, 1933.
[2] R. G. Herb, D. B. Parkinson, and D. W. Kerst, *Phys. Rev.*, vol. 51, p. 75, 1937.
[3] E. O. Lawrence and M. S. Livingston, *Phys. Rev.*, vol. 40, p. 19, 1932.

frequency field. Under the influence of a strong magnet, the particles move alternately through field-free regions and regions of high field, in phase with the changing electric field. A diagram illustrating the principle is shown in Fig. 195. Within a flat, cylindrical vacuum chamber B, placed between the poles of a magnet (not shown) are two D-shaped electrodes D_1, D_2 (called dees) consisting of hollow, flat half-cylinders. The dees are coupled to or made part of a resonating electric circuit driven by a high-power radio-frequency oscillator, so that an alternating voltage appears across the gap separating the dees. An ion source C,

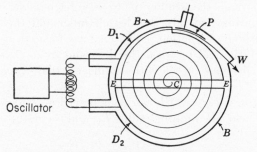

Fig. 195. Diagram of the essentials of a cyclotron, except for the magnet, whose pole pieces would be situated just above and just below the box B. Ions originating at C are accelerated in a radio-frequency field in the gap E; under the influence of the magnetic field they execute semicircular paths, returning to the gap in time to be accelerated again.

located at the center of the chamber, supplies positive ions with a relatively low initial velocity.

We consider now a positive ion which finds itself in the gap between the dees, moving upward during the part of the cycle when the upper dee in the diagram is negative. The ion is accelerated in the electric field into the field-free region within the dee. Under the influence of the magnetic field, which we take to be directed out of the paper, the particle traverses a semicircle, returning to the gap (but now moving downward) after a time[1] $t = \pi/\omega_B$, where ω_B is its angular frequency in the magnetic field:

$$\omega_B = \frac{v}{r} = B \frac{e}{M} \qquad (272)$$

If the angular frequency of the radio-frequency field ω_E is so adjusted that the potential difference of the dees has reversed during the time that the particle was inside the dee, i.e., if $\omega_E = \omega_B$, the ion will again be accelerated. The crucial point is that the angular frequency ω_B is constant,

[1] We have here ignored the motion during the electric acceleration, i.e., we assume that the distance over which the electric field operates is small compared to the path in the field-free space. This is not a good assumption near the beginning of the motion, and the trajectories during the first few turns are rather complicated.

independent of the velocity of the particle (in so far as the relativistic variation of mass can be neglected); as the velocity increases, the radius of curvature also increases and the time per half-turn remains constant. This process of acceleration every half-period continues, with the particle moving in a series of connected semicircular arcs, until a limiting radius R_0, determined by the dimensions of the magnetic field, is reached. At this point, the ion can be extracted by means of a radial electrostatic field supplied by the deflector P, which provides enough deviation in the trajectory to allow the particle to escape through the fringing field of the magnet and through the window W to a target outside. Alternatively, targets may be inserted into the dee chamber and the circulating ion beam used without extraction. The ions are focused in the inhomogeneous electrostatic field between the dees and by a (deliberately introduced) slight decrease of B with radius so that a parallel beam is produced.

The maximum energy which can be achieved depends upon the available magnetic field, the limiting radius R_0, and the nature of the particle:

$$T_{max} = \frac{p^2}{2M} = \frac{B^2 e^2 R_0^2}{2M} \tag{273}$$

For example, a 60-in.-diameter cyclotron, operating at a magnetic field of 16,000 gauss, can produce 26-Mev deuterons with a radio frequency of 12 Mc per sec. In principle, protons of twice this energy can be produced by doubling the frequency, but changing the frequency usually involves a major operation, so cyclotrons are sometimes operated at reduced B for protons and produce only half the possible energy.

d. Synchrocyclotron. The constancy of the frequency ω_B in Eq. (272) breaks down when the particles have relativistic velocity ($v \cong c$), so that M deviates appreciably from the rest mass. This change could, in principle, be allowed for by shaping the magnetic field in such a way as to increase B slightly as the radius increases, but such a variation would introduce serious defocusing of the beam. The alternative, suggested independently by McMillan[1] and Veksler[2] in 1945, is to allow the magnetic field or the radio frequency to vary with time as the particles are accelerated in such a way as just to compensate for the changing mass. It can be shown that in either case there exist stable orbits in which the particles tend to keep in step with the changing fields. A cyclotron making use of this principle is called a synchrocyclotron. Ordinarily, a synchrocyclotron is used to accelerate heavy particles—protons, deuterons, or α-particles—and the radio frequency is varied while the magnetic field is held fixed. In the Berkeley 184-in. frequency-modulated

[1] E. M. McMillan, *Phys. Rev.*, vol. 68, p. 143, 1945.
[2] V. Veksler, *J. Phys. (U.S.S.R.)*, vol. 9, p. 153, 1945.

synchrocyclotron, which produces 340-Mev protons, the required frequency change is about 35 per cent. For electron acceleration, or for acceleration of heavy particles to energies exceeding a few hundred Mev, the "synchrotron" is generally preferred.

e. Synchrotron. The synchrotron operates on essentially the same principle as the synchrocyclotron except that the particles are injected at near-relativistic speeds, and the magnetic field is varied in time, with the radio frequency held constant. The particles are injected at a relatively low value of the magnetic field and pick up energy from the radio-frequency accelerating gap as the magnetic field increases. With constant radio frequency ω_0 and essentially constant velocity (near c) the particles remain at nearly the same radius, $R = c/\omega_0$, throughout the acceleration, and only at this radius is a magnetic field needed. This feature means a great saving, since the entire center portion of the magnet is eliminated. A number of electron synchrotrons yielding energies up to 500 Mev or more have been built.

For heavy particles, it is not so easy to inject with $v \cong c$. For this reason, one ordinarily varies both the radio frequency and the magnetic field in such a way as to keep the orbital radius approximately constant. Machines of this type are in operation with 2.3- and 6.1-Bev (billion electron-volt) protons at Brookhaven[1] and Berkeley,[2] respectively.

f. Betatron. The betatron or "induction accelerator," invented by Kerst[3] in 1940, is a device for accelerating electrons. Its operation depends simply on the fact that a changing magnetic flux induces an electromotive force in any enclosing circuit. From the law of Ampère, we have, for any closed path,

$$\oint \mathbf{E} \cdot \mathbf{dl} = \frac{d}{dt} \int \mathbf{B} \cdot \mathbf{dS}$$

An electron describing a circular path of radius R in a changing magnetic field is then subject to a force $f = eE$. The rate of change of momentum p is then

$$\frac{dp}{dt} = f = \frac{e}{2\pi R} \frac{d\phi}{dt}$$

where $\phi = \int \mathbf{B} \cdot \mathbf{dS}$ is the flux enclosed by the path. The momentum gained if the electron starts from rest when $\phi = 0$ is

$$p = \frac{e\phi}{2\pi R}$$

[1] *Rev. Sci. Instr.*, vol. 24, p. 723, 1953.
[2] W. M. Brobeck, *Rev. Sci. Instr.* vol. 19, p. 545, 1948.
[3] D. W. Kerst, *Phys. Rev.* vol. 60, p. 47, 1941.

On the other hand, the value of the magnetic field at the orbit required to keep the electron at the constant radius R is

$$B_R = \frac{p}{eR}$$

Thus we have an equilibrium situation at all times if

$$B_R = \frac{\phi}{2\pi R^2} \tag{274}$$

that is, if the value of B_R at the orbit is one-half the average of B over the area bounded by the orbit. The required variation of B can be obtained by choosing a suitable shape for the pole pieces of the magnet. The fact that the so-called "betatron condition" [Eq. (274)] can be satisfied independently of relativistic considerations means that the device can be used to accelerate electrons to very high energy. The maximum energy is determined by the available magnetic field and the radius:

$$W \cong pc = B_R eRc \cong 300B_R R \qquad \text{ev}$$

with B_R in gauss, R in centimeters. For a betatron with $R = 80$ cm and a maximum field of 4,000 gauss, $W \cong 100$ Mev.

g. Linear Accelerator. The linear accelerator[1] also uses the principle of repeated accelerations, but the particles are allowed to travel in straight lines instead of being deflected in a magnetic field. The accelerator consists essentially of a long pipe, with coaxial cylindrical accelerating electrodes mounted inside, separated by short gaps. The whole chamber constitutes a resonant cavity, excited by external oscillators in such a mode that the time-varying electric field is directed along the axis. The lengths of the electrodes are so adjusted that the ion is "coasting" in the field-free interior during the time that the radio-frequency voltage has the wrong sign and traverses the gaps only when the field is so directed as to accelerate the ion. Linear accelerators can be designed either for electrons or for heavy particles.

NUCLEAR REACTIONS AND NUCLEAR MODELS[2]

With the availability of artificially accelerated particles, the number of nuclear reactions amenable to study has increased enormously. Some thousands of different reactions have been studied, many in considerable detail. In the following sections we shall consider some of the kinds of

[1] L. W. Alvarez, *Phys. Rev.*, vol. 70, p. 799, 1946.
[2] H. A. Bethe and R. F. Bacher, *Revs. Mod. Phys., loc. cit.;* H. A. Bethe, *op. cit.;* J. M. Blatt and V. F. Weisskopf, *op. cit.;* E. Segrè, "Experimental Nuclear Physics," vol. II, article by P. Morrison, Wiley, New York, 1953; R. G. Sachs "Nuclear Theory," Addison-Wesley, Cambridge, Mass., 1953.

reactions which occur, the techniques which are used in studying them, and what can be said about nuclear models as a result of such studies.

192. General Features of Nuclear Reactions. *a. Types.* The most commonly used bombarding particles are protons, deuterons, and neutrons, the latter themselves produced in a nuclear reaction. Artificially accelerated α-particles are also frequently used, as well as H^3 ions (tritons) and He^3 ions, and even heavier ions have been used in a few special cases. Gamma-rays and x-rays can also be used as disintegrating agents, and some reactions induced by electron bombardment have been observed. In general, at moderate bombarding energies—less than 10 Mev—two products appear as a result of a nuclear reaction: a light particle, usually one of the above mentioned, and a heavier one, referred to as the residual nucleus. Three-body production does sometimes occur, however, and at high energies even more products may be observed. As a convenient classification of the simpler types of nuclear reactions, we enumerate the following categories.

(I) ELASTIC SCATTERING. The incident particle strikes the target nucleus and leaves without energy loss but, in general, with altered direction of motion. When this process is viewed in a coordinate system in which the target nucleus is initially at rest (the "laboratory system"), the scattered particle does lose energy because the target nucleus recoils. In the center-of-mass system, in which the two particles approach one another in such a way as to keep the center of mass at rest, there is no energy transfer. An example of an elastic process is the scattering of α-particles in gold, first studied by Rutherford:

$$He^4 + Au^{197} \rightarrow He^4 + Au^{197}$$

(II) INELASTIC SCATTERING. The incident particle reappears after the interaction with a lower energy: some of its energy has been taken up by the target nucleus, which is thus excited to a higher quantum state. An example is

$$Li^7 + H^1 \rightarrow Li^{7*} + H^1$$

The asterisk is used to indicate that the residual nucleus is in an excited state. In the present example the excess energy is later radiated away in the form of a γ-quantum.

(III) SIMPLE CAPTURE. The incident particle is captured by the target nucleus, and a new nucleus is formed. Nearly always the residual nucleus will have a considerable excess of energy and will radiate one or more γ-quanta. An example is

$$C^{12} + H^1 \rightarrow (N^{13}) \rightarrow N^{13} + \gamma$$

Here the parentheses are used to indicate that the nucleus in question is not necessarily in one of its quantum levels, but has an energy which is determined by the initial conditions of the reaction.

(IV) DISINTEGRATION. On striking the target nucleus, the incident particle is absorbed and a different particle ejected. An example is the disintegration of beryllium by α-particles, producing neutrons:

$$Be^9 + He^4 \rightarrow C^{12} + n^1$$

(V) PHOTOEXCITATION AND PHOTODISINTEGRATION. A γ-ray is absorbed by the target nucleus, exciting it to a higher quantum state; if the energy is sufficient, a particle may be ejected. The photodisintegration of the deuteron, requiring 2.225 Mev, is an example:

$$H^2 + \gamma \rightarrow H^1 + n^1$$

A special case of photoexcitation of some interest is the so-called "Coulomb" excitation, in which the varying electric field of a charged particle passing by a nucleus may induce transitions to higher states.

(VI) SPONTANEOUS DECAY. Beta- and α-decay processes may be regarded as nuclear reactions; they differ from those discussed above in that the total energy of the system is not under the experimenter's control.

b. Notation. It is convenient to have a shorthand notation for nuclear reactions; a commonly used form is the following:

$$X^A(a,b)Y^{A'}$$

where X^A and $Y^{A'}$ indicate the chemical symbol and mass number of the initial target and residual nuclei, respectively, and a and b the incoming (bombarding) and outgoing particles. Thus, the reaction first studied by Rutherford (Sec. 182) would be written

$$N^{14}(\alpha,p)O^{17}$$

A radioactive disintegration is sometimes represented as

$$X^A(\beta^{\pm})Y^A$$

for example; $$P^{30}(\beta^+)Si^{30}$$

The concomitant emission of the neutrino is usually not indicated. A reaction leading to an excited state of the residual nucleus which subsequently decays by γ-emission may be written in two stages;

$$N^{14}(\alpha,p)O^{17*}   O^{17*}(\gamma)O^{17}$$

or abbreviated,

$$N^{14}(\alpha,p\gamma)O^{17}$$

c. Conservation Laws. In any nuclear reaction, certain quantities must be conserved:

1. The *total energy* of the products, including both mass energy and kinetic energy of the particles, plus the energy of any γ-rays or neutrinos which may be involved, must equal the mass energy of the initial ingredients plus the kinetic energy brought in by the bombarding particle (the target nucleus is ordinarily taken to be at rest).

2. The total *linear momentum* of the products must be equal to the momentum brought in by the bombarding particle.

3. The total *electric charge* is conserved.

4. The total *number of nucleons* is constant: unlike the light particles, β^-, β^+, and ν (neutrino), which can be produced and annihilated, nucleons have never been observed to disappear in a nuclear reaction.

5. The total *angular momentum J*, comprising the vector sum of the intrinsic angular momenta I (spins) and relative orbital momentum l of the particles, is conserved. If two particles collide "head-on" they have no relative orbital angular momentum and the value of J will be given by vector addition of the two intrinsic spins. In a "glancing" collision, orbital angular momentum is present, and must be added (again vectorially) to the two I's to produce the total angular momentum J. In the general case, the beam of incident particles is represented as a plane wave which may be resolved into components representing various quantized values of the orbital angular momentum.

6. The *parity* (Sec. 184) of the system determined by the target nucleus and bombarding particle must be preserved throughout the reaction. The initial system comprises the target nucleus and the incident particle, approaching with a certain fixed orbital angular momentum. If the wave function describing this situation remains unchanged under inversion of the coordinates, the parity is even; if the wave function changes sign, the parity is odd. The parity for such a system is the product ($+1$ for even parity, -1 for odd) of the intrinsic parities of the target nucleus and bombarding particle and the contribution from the orbital angular momentum l: for even l, the contribution is $+1$, for odd l, it is -1.

d. Nuclear-reaction Kinetics. The energy balance in a typical nuclear reaction may be written

$$M_0 c^2 + M_1 c^2 + E_1 = M_2 c^2 + M_3 c^2 + E_2 + E_3 \qquad (275)$$

where M_0 represents the exact mass of the target particle, M_1 and M_2 the masses of the bombarding and ejected particles, and M_3 the residual nucleus. E_1, E_2, and E_3 are the kinetic energies of the corresponding particles. The "energy change" or "Q" of the reaction is defined by the mass difference:

$$M_0 + M_1 = M_2 + M_3 + \frac{Q}{c^2} \qquad (276)$$

Evidently
$$Q = E_2 + E_3 - E_1 \qquad (277)$$

Q can be thought of as the energy which would be released in the reaction if the bombarding energy were just zero.   If Q is positive, the reaction is exoergic, i.e., energy is released in the process; if it is negative, the reaction is endoergic, and energy is absorbed.   The determination of Q is of interest both from the standpoint of measuring masses—as a check on mass-spectrometer values for stable isotopes, and as the only method of obtaining masses for unstable ones (e.g., the neutron)—and also, where excited levels of the residual nucleus occur, for determining the energies of these levels.

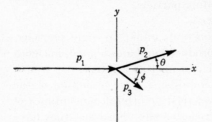

FIG. 196. Momentum diagram for a nuclear reaction. The momentum of the incident particle is p_1; p_2 and p_3 refer to the ejected particle and the residual nucleus respectively.

In an experiment to measure a Q value, the bombarding energy E_1 and the energy of the ejected particles E_2 at some specified angle θ are measured. The Q value can then be obtained by applying the laws of conservation of momentum.   The momentum diagram for a typical reaction is illustrated in Fig. 196.   We have, in an obvious notation,

$$p_{1x} = p_{2x} + p_{3x} \qquad 0 = p_{2y} + p_{3y} \qquad E_1 = E_2 + E_3 - Q$$

or, since $p = \sqrt{2ME}$,

$$\sqrt{2M_1E_1} = \sqrt{2M_2E_2}\cos\theta + \sqrt{2M_3E_3}\cos\phi$$
$$0 = \sqrt{2M_2E_2}\sin\theta + \sqrt{2M_3E_3}\sin\phi$$

We eliminate ϕ and E_3 to obtain Q in terms of E_1, E_2, and the masses:

$$Q = E_1 \frac{M_1 - M_3}{M_3} + E_2 \frac{M_2 + M_3}{M_3} - \frac{2}{M_3}(M_1M_2E_1E_2)^{\frac{1}{2}}\cos\theta \quad (278)$$

Since the masses M rarely differ from the mass numbers A by more than a fraction of 1 per cent, it is usually sufficiently accurate to use mass numbers in Eq. (278).   Relativistic corrections are only rarely necessary in work at moderate energies.

A typical experimental arrangement for measurements of this kind is illustrated schematically in Fig. 197.   A beam of particles, produced in some type of accelerator, enters the magnetic analyzer A_1, where it suffers a 90° deflection before striking the target T.   The path of the beam is defined by the set of slits S_1, and the energy of the particles is then determined by a measurement of the magnetic field in A_1.   Of the particles produced in the target T, some of those which emerge at $\theta = 90°$ enter the magnetic spectrometer A_2.   A measurement of the magnetic field in A_2 which is required to pass these particles through the slit system S_2 to the detector D then permits determination of $E_2(90°)$, the energy of the particles emitted at $\theta = 90°$. In principle, once the geometry is established, the Q-value determination requires only the measurement of the two magnetic fields.

With modern techniques, it is possible to measure Q values, for nuclear reactions producing charged particles, to an accuracy of 1 part in a thousand or better, and a great many Q values are now known to this precision.

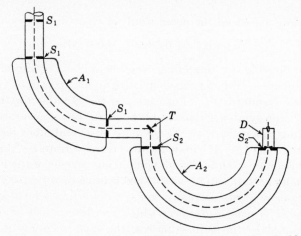

FIG. 197. Arrangement for a precise Q-value measurement. The incident particles entering from above are analyzed by the magnet A_1; particles produced in the target T are analyzed by A_2.

As an example of the close agreement obtained in different laboratories, the Q values of the reaction $Li^7(p\alpha)He^4$, are shown in Table 10-4. The mean deviation of these four values is less than 3 parts in ten thousand.

TABLE 10-4. Q VALUES FOR $Li^7(p\alpha)He^4$

Q, Mev	Source
17.338 ± 0.011	California Institute of Technology
17.340 ± 0.014	Massachusetts Institute of Technology
17.352 ± 0.009	University of Birmingham (England)
17.344 ± 0.013	Rice Institute

e. Mass Determinations.[1] As one result of the growing collection of such precise Q values as the one just discussed, it has become possible to establish the masses of a large number of nuclides which do not exist in nature. The mass of the neutron, for example, can be determined relative to that of the hydrogen atom in the following set of reactions:

$$H^2 + H^2 \rightarrow H^3 + H^1 \qquad Q_1 = 4.031 \pm 0.005 \qquad (279a)$$
$$H^2 + H^2 \rightarrow He^3 + n \qquad Q_2 = 3.265 \pm 0.009 \qquad (279b)$$
$$H^3 \rightarrow He^3 + \beta^- \qquad Q_3 = 0.0185 \pm 0.0002 \qquad (279c)$$

[1] C. W. Li, W. Whaling, W. A. Fowler, and C. C. Lauritsen, *Phys. Rev.*, vol. 83, p. 512, 1951; C. W. Li, *Phys. Rev.*, vol. 88, p. 1038, 1952.

If the second of these relations is subtracted from the sum of the first and third, there results

$$[M(n) - M(H^1)]c^2 = Q_1 + Q_3 - Q_2$$

and we obtain, for the neutron–hydrogen atom mass difference,

$$(n - H^1) = 0.785 \text{ Mev}$$

A better value, based on the mean result of eight sets of reactions, is

$$(n - H^1) = 0.7823 \pm 0.001 \text{ Mev}$$

It is also possible, by combining reactions involving various nuclides, to derive independently of mass-spectrographic data a set of masses based on the standard O^{16}. For example, the Q value for the reaction $O^{16}(d,\alpha)N^{14}$ (the symbol d represents the deuteron) is accurately known. By combining this value with the Q values of several other reactions, the mass difference $O^{16} - N^{14}$ may be directly determined. In a similar way, other reactions can be found, connecting various of the light nuclei, and eventually a chain can be established leading directly to O^{16}. Such a chain necessarily contains many links, with errors which accumulate, but because it is mass *differences* which are determined, and these are small compared to the actual masses, the final accuracy is still quite good. A few of the masses thus derived are listed in Table 10-5 and there compared with mass-spectrograph determinations, made by the doublet method (see Sec. 181). The close agreement of these two sets of values provides our most precise test of the relation $E = mc^2$.

TABLE 10-5. COMPARISON OF MASS VALUES FROM NUCLEAR REACTIONS
WITH MASS-SPECTROGRAPHIC DETERMINATIONS

Nuclide	Reactions,* amu	Mass spect.,† amu
H^1	1.008 142 ± 3	1.008 1459 ± 0.5
D^2	2.014 735 ± 6	2.014 7444 ± 0.9
He^4	4.003 873 ± 15	4.003 8797 ± 1.6
C^{12}	12.003 804 ± 17	12.003 8231 ± 3.3
N^{14}	14.007 515 ± 11	14.007 5150 ± 4.9

* Li, Whaling, Fowler, and Lauritsen, *loc. cit:* probable errors are given in 10^{-6} amu.
† J. Mattauch and R. Bieri, *Z. Naturforsch.*, vol. 9a, p. 303, 1954: errors in 10^{-6} amu.

193. Masses of Mirror Nuclides. Among the many unstable nuclides whose masses are known from nuclear-reaction Q values, a set of particular importance are the so-called "mirror nuclides." Two nuclei are said to be mirrors if one can be derived from the other by replacing all protons with neutrons and vice versa. Thus the mirror of $_5B^{11}$, with five protons and six neutrons, is $_6C^{11}$. Evidently it is not possible for both to exist in nature permanently, because one can be converted into the other by β-decay: in the present instance, C^{11} is unstable to positron emission and has a half-life of 20.4 min. The mass difference $(C^{11} - B^{11})$ can be found either from the observed end point of the positron spectrum,

$$M(C^{11}) - M(B^{11}) = E_{max}(\beta^+) + 1.022 \text{ Mev}$$

(Sec. 186b), or from the reaction $B^{11}(p,n)C^{11}$. The Q value of the (p,n) reaction has been determined with great precision, and is

$$Q = -2.762 \pm 0.003 \text{ Mev}[1]$$

Taking into account the 0.782-Mev $(n - H^1)$ difference, we obtain

$$M(C^{11}) - M(B^{11}) = 1.980 \text{ Mev}$$

The observed mass differences of mirror nuclides provide a sensitive comparison of the energies associated with $(p\text{-}p)$ and $(n\text{-}n)$ binding forces, for the only difference between two mirrors, as far as nuclear forces are concerned, is that some $(n\text{-}n)$ interactions in the one are replaced by $(p\text{-}p)$ interactions in the other.[2] This fact is most easily seen if we consider (for counting purposes only) a core, comprising equal numbers of protons and neutrons, which is the same for both nuclei, plus an odd neutron in the one case or an odd proton in the other. The extra neutron in B^{11}, for example, interacts with the protons and neutrons in the "core" and has a certain number, say a, of $(n\text{-}n)$ bonds and another number, b, of $(n\text{-}p)$ bonds. In C^{11} the a bonds will be of the $(p\text{-}p)$ character while the b will remain of the $(n\text{-}p)$ type. If now the $(p\text{-}p)$ bonds formed in C^{11} differ in strength from the $(n\text{-}n)$ bonds of B^{11}, there will be a difference in the masses of B^{11} and C^{11} from this effect. It is important to note that this result, though here derived with an admittedly crude model, is actually quite general and is independent of such considerations as whether, for example, all the various $(n\text{-}p)$ bonds are equally effective.

In order to compare the contribution of the purely nuclear forces to the binding energies of B^{11} and C^{11} we write the masses in the following form:

$$M(B^{11}) = 5M(H^1) + 6M(n) - \frac{E_N}{c^2} + \frac{E_E}{c^2} \tag{280a}$$

$$M(C^{11}) = 6M(H^1) + 5M(n) - \frac{E_N'}{c^2} + \frac{E_E'}{c^2} \tag{280b}$$

where the terms E_N, E_N' represent the binding energy due to nuclear forces, and the terms E_E and E_E' represent the electrostatic energy of the protons. An approximate expression for the latter was given in

[1] H. T. Richards, R. V. Smith, and C. P. Browne, *Phys. Rev.*, vol. 80, p. 524, 1950.
[2] W. A. Fowler, L. A. Delsasso, and C. C. Lauritsen, *Phys. Rev.*, vol. 49, p. 561, 1936.

Eq. (270) (Sec. 187); we find, from this expression, $E_E(B^{11}) = 5.50$ Mev, $E'_E(C^{11}) = 8.25$ Mev. Subtracting the second of the relations above from the first and solving for the difference of the nuclear binding energies, we obtain

$$\frac{E_N}{c^2} - \frac{E'_N}{c^2} = M(C^{11}) - M(B^{11}) + M(n) - M(H^1) + \frac{E_E}{c^2} - \frac{E'_E}{c^2} \quad (281)$$

Inserting the measured values of the mass differences times c^2, measured in Mev,

$$E_N - E'_N = 1.980 + 0.782 + 5.50 - 8.25 = 0.01 \text{ Mev}$$

Since the average binding energy per particle is some 5 or 10 Mev, it would appear that the assumption that $(p\text{-}p)$ and $(n\text{-}n)$ forces are equal is quite well supported by the observations. Of course the result depends to some extent on the validity of the electrostatic correction, but since this quantity occurs as a difference, even rather major changes in the assumed model could hardly alter the conclusion. Among the 20 or so mirror pairs for which the masses are known, the apparent differences in the nuclear contribution to the binding energies range from a few tens of kev up to a few hundred. The largest discrepancies occur among the lightest nuclei where the assumption of a uniform charge distribution might be expected to be least accurate. We shall have more to say about the comparison of mirror nuclei in a later section.

194. Particle Groups. It is frequently found in the study of the products of nuclear reactions that particles of more than one energy (or Q value) are present. This multiplicity of groups was early observed in the natural α-radioactive elements (Sec. 179) and was there interpreted as indicating the existence of excited quantum states in the residual nucleus. In Fig. 198 is shown a part of the spectrum of proton groups observed in the bombardment of B^{10} by deuterons.[1] The energy of the protons was measured in a semicircular magnetic spectrograph (cf. Fig. 197) placed at 90° to the incident beam, which in these observations had an energy of 1.510 Mev. The group labeled 1 on the figure corresponds to the transition to the ground state of B^{11}. From the figure, one can estimate the magnetic rigidity of these particles as (roughly) 448×10^3 gauss cm. The energy is then

$$E_p = \frac{p^2}{2M} = (Br)^2 \frac{e^2}{2M} = 0.15 \times 10^{-4} \text{ erg or } 9.6 \text{ Mev}$$

From Eq. (278), we obtain

$$Q = -\frac{9}{11}E_d + \frac{12}{11}E_p = -1.23 + 10.5 = 9.3 \text{ Mev} \quad (282)$$

[1] D. Van Patter, W. Buechner, and A. Sperduto, *Phys. Rev.*, vol. 82, p. 248, 1951.

The actual value reported, obtained from a more careful analysis, was 9.235 ± 0.011 Mev. That the group is properly identified can be tested by measuring E_p at some other value of the incident deuteron energy: if the Q value is the same, the mass numbers appearing in Eq. (282) have been correctly assigned. By this test, it was ascertained that groups 1, 3, 6, and 7 pertain to the present reaction, while the remaining

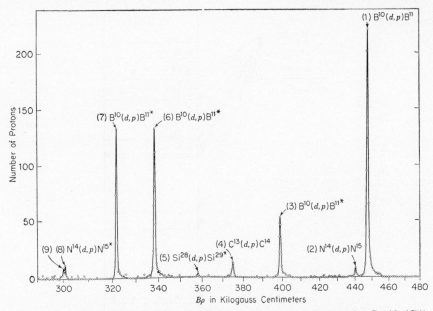

FIG. 198. Part of the spectrum of proton groups resulting from the reaction $B^{10}(d,p)B^{11}$. (*Van Patter, Buechner, and Sperduto, Phys. Rev., vol. 82, p. 248, 1951.*)

groups are associated with some contaminants in the target. The latter point was checked by separate bombardment of targets composed of the suspected contaminant materials.

The Q values for the $B^{10}(d,p)B^{11}$ groups of Fig. 198 are listed in Table 10-6. In the right-hand column are indicated the differences between

TABLE 10-6. PROTON GROUPS* OBSERVED IN THE REACTION $B^{10}(d,p)B^{11}$

Proton group	Q, Mev	Excitation energy in B^{11}
(1)	9.235 ± 0.011	0
(3)	7.079 ± 0.009	2.138 ± 0.014
(6)	4.776 ± 0.008	4.459 ± 0.014
(7)	4.201 ± 0.008	5.034 ± 0.014

* See Van Patter, Buechner, and Sperduto, *loc. cit.* Only a few of the groups observed are listed here.

each Q value and that corresponding to the ground state.   These differences give directly the energies of excited states of B^{11}.   In Fig. 199 is shown an energy-level diagram which illustrates the energetics involved. The difference in mass between the initial ingredients, $B^{10} + H^2$, and the final products, $B^{11} + H^1$, is Q/c^2, equivalent to 9.235 Mev.   If the total energy is plotted on a vertical scale, the initial state (ignoring for a

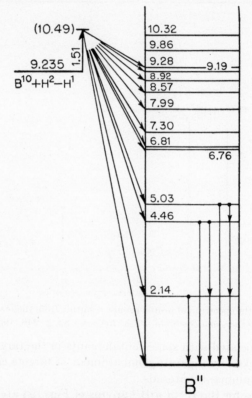

FIG. 199. Energy-level diagram for B^{11}.   The slanted arrows represent proton groups; the vertical arrows represent γ-ray transitions.

moment the bombarding energy) lies this amount higher than the final state: since the zero of energy is arbitrary, we may for convenience subtract the mass of the proton ($\times c^2$) from both energies, and represent the difference $M(B^{10} + H^2 - H^1) \times c^2 - M(B^{11}) \times c^2$ by a 9.235-Mev vertical displacement.   All energies on the diagram are then referred to the ground state of B^{11}.   Considering now the 1.510-Mev bombarding energy, we can see that a part of this energy goes into kinetic energy of the center of mass and is hence not available for internal rearrangements of the nuclei.   A straightforward computation shows that a fraction

$M_0/(M_1 + M_0)$, or $^{10}\!/_{12}$ in the present instance, of the bombarding energy is available in the system in which the center of mass is at rest. The total energy available in the center of mass system, relative to the ground state of B^{11}, is then $9.235 + {}^{10}\!/_{12} \times 1.510$, or 10.49 Mev.   In the transition to the ground state, represented by the longest slant arrow on the diagram, the proton and B^{11} recoil share this energy in such a way as to conserve momentum.   (Their velocities in the laboratory system are then obtained by adding vectorially the velocity of the center of mass.)   If the B^{11} is left excited in the 2.1-Mev or higher levels, the kinetic energies will be correspondingly less, as indicated by the shorter arrows.   Many other proton groups are known in addition to those in Table 10-6; the corresponding levels are shown in the diagram.   The subsequent decay of most of the levels shown proceeds by γ-radiation, either directly to the ground state, or by cascades through lower states; some of the possible combinations are indicated by vertical arrows on the diagram.   In many cases, it has been possible to check the level energies obtained from particle groups by direct measurements of the γ-ray energies.

It should be emphasized that the energy levels represented in Fig. 199 do not necessarily represent the energy states of any single nucleon. Just as in the similar atomic diagrams, a given level represents the energy of the system as a whole and need not refer to any specific model; thus the line at 2.14 Mev, for example, means only that at this energy above the ground state there exists a particularly long-lived configuration or mode of excitation, which may involve one or many particles.   For this reason also, it is convenient to plot energies from the ground state (as is done in x-ray diagrams) rather than from the "ionization potential," which, in the nucleus, has various values for different particles.

195. Nuclear Resonances.   The "yield" of a nuclear reaction, i.e., the number of processes observed per incident particle, usually depends strongly on the bombarding energy.   A curve showing the yield as a function of energy is called an "excitation function."   With charged particles of low energy, the penetrability of the Coulomb barrier increases rapidly with energy, and the yield will reflect this variation.   In addition, sharp peaks, called "resonances," may also be observed in the excitation function, and the properties of these resonances are of considerable interest to the nuclear physicist.

A striking example of a resonance effect occurs in the reaction $Li^7(p,\gamma)Be^8$. When Li^7 is bombarded by protons, there is produced, in addition to the α-particles which were discussed earlier, a γ-radiation of more than 17-Mev energy.   The process responsible for this γ-ray is the simple capture of the proton by the Li^7 nucleus, forming Be^8, which then radiates the excess energy in one quantum.   From the known masses, the Q of the

reaction is

$$\frac{Q}{c^2} = M(\text{Li}^7) + M(\text{H}^1) - M(\text{Be}^8) = 0.018\ 515\ \text{amu} \qquad Q = 17.242\ \text{Mev}$$

The energy available for the γ-radiation is the Q value plus that part of the proton's kinetic energy which is available in the center-of-mass system:

$$E_\gamma = 17.242 + \tfrac{7}{8}E_p \qquad (283)$$

where E_p is the bombarding energy measured in the laboratory coordinate system, i.e., the system in which the target nucleus is at rest.

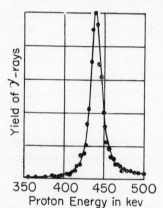

If the yield of γ-radiation from a very thin layer of lithium is measured as a function of bombarding energy, the curve shown in Fig. 200 results. The principal feature of this curve is a sharp maximum in the yield at a proton energy of 441 kev; the yield is reduced to one-half the maximum value by a change in either direction of only 6 kev. The observed variation of the yield is well approximated by the resonance formula[1] familiar from the theory of resonant electric circuits,

FIG. 200. Resonance in the yield of γ-rays from the reaction $\text{Li}^7(p,\gamma)\text{Be}^8$. (*T. W. Bonner and J. E. Evans, Phys. Rev., vol. 73, p. 666, 1948.*)

$$Y(E) = A(E)\ \frac{\Gamma^2/4}{(E - E_r)^2 + \Gamma^2/4} \qquad (284)$$

where $Y(E)$ is the yield of γ-rays at the proton energy E, and E_r is the value of the proton energy at the peak of the curve. The quantity Γ is the width of the curve in energy units, measured between the two points where the yield is one-half the maximum. The factor $A(E)$ is a function of energy which varies sufficiently slowly that it may be disregarded for our purpose.

The form of Eq. (284) suggests that, at the energy corresponding to E_r, the system formed by $\text{Li}^7 + \text{H}^1$ has an approximately stationary quantum level: the remarkable feature of this level is that it lies in the region which the atomic spectroscopist would refer to as the "continuum." Let us consider for a moment the analogous situation in the spectrum of the hydrogen atom. There the solutions of Schrödinger's equation are of two kinds, depending on the sign of the total energy measured with respect to the energy of the system comprising an ion with the electron at rest at infinity. If the total energy is negative, corresponding to a bound electron, the solution yields a set of discrete,

[1] G. Breit and E. P. Wigner, *Phys. Rev.*, vol. 49, p. 519, 1936.

nearly stationary[1] quantum states. If, on the other hand, the energy is positive, i.e., if the electron has kinetic energy at infinity, a continuum of states is allowed (cf. Sec. 81). When a hydrogen ion captures an electron in one of these positive-energy states, the energy available is equal to the ionization potential of 13.6 ev plus the kinetic energy of the electron, measured in the system in which the center of mass is at

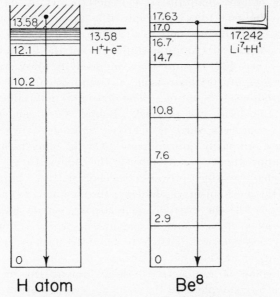

FIG. 201. Energy states of the hydrogen atom: the energies are measured in electron-volts from the ground state.

FIG. 202. Energy states of the Be[8] nucleus: the energies are measured in Mev from the ground state.

rest. If this energy is radiated in one quantum, the resultant radiation forms part of the continuum beyond the limit of the Lyman series: Fig. 33 shows this effect in the case of the Balmer series. In Fig. 201 is shown a level diagram for the hydrogen atom illustrating the bound, discrete states below the ionization potential and the continuum above: a transition corresponding to capture of a positive-energy electron is indicated by the vertical arrow. Because there exist no discrete states of positive energy, the probability of capture of a free electron is a monotonic function of energy.

The nuclear case is illustrated in Fig. 202. The "ionization potential" is now the separation energy of the proton, 17.242 Mev, measured

---

[1] "Nearly stationary" in the sense that if the interaction with the radiation field is included, the quantum state decays in time, corresponding to a radiative transition to a lower level.

with respect to the ground state of Be[8]. Indicated on the right side of the diagram is the yield curve of Fig. 200, with the yield now plotted horizontally, to the left, against energy on a vertical scale. The state formed by 441-kev protons lies at 17.63 Mev (Eq. 283) and the transition to the ground state results in a γ-ray of this energy. Several other excited levels of Be[8] are also indicated.

The *width* of any quantum state is determined by its lifetime, for, according to the uncertainty principle, if a system exists only for a time Δt, its energy can be defined only to an accuracy $\Delta E \cong h/2\pi \, \Delta t$. Actually all atomic and nuclear quantum states, except the ground states, have finite widths (Sec. 137) because they can decay to lower states by radiation: they represent, for this reason, only approximately stationary solutions of Schrödinger's equation. The lifetime is determined by the ease with which the decay can proceed. Bound states can only decay by γ-radiation,[1] a process which is relatively slow on a nuclear time scale, and hence are ordinarily quite narrow. On the other hand, if a state is to be even approximately stationary in the unbound region, there must be some mechanism which prevents or delays particle emission.

A part of the mechanism which delays the emission of charged particles and makes possible the existence of relatively narrow levels above the binding energy is to be found in the nuclear barrier. For, even if it is energetically possible for a particle to leave the nucleus, it may have to strike the barrier at the nuclear surface many times before it escapes. The phenomenon of radioactive α-decay among the heavy elements (Sec. 187f) is an example. In the light nuclei, the barrier is less important, but it may still play a significant role when the available energy is low. In the case of the Li[7](p,γ)Be[8] resonance, once the state is formed it is mainly the Coulomb barrier which delays the reemission of the proton and the combination lives sufficiently long that γ-emission is possible. Calculation of the barrier effect gives the result that, once the proton is inside the Be[8] nucleus, the probability of escape per appearance at the nuclear surface is about 10^{-2}. The velocity of the proton (corresponding to its roughly 10-Mev kinetic energy inside the barrier) is about 5×10^9 cm per sec. If the proton simply oscillated back and forth across the nucleus, without interacting with the other nucleons, it would make 100 traversals in a time of the order of $100 \times 6 \times 10^{-13}/5 \times 10^9$, or 10^{-20} sec. The observed mean life of the level is $\Delta t = h/2\pi\Gamma = 6 \times 10^{-20}$ sec. In view of the uncertainties in the calculations we may regard this fair agreement as evidence that the long life of this level is mainly ascribable to the barrier effect.

The time required to radiate a γ-quantum is estimated to be about

---

[1] In some cases internal conversion, nuclear pair formation, or β-decay occur instead of, or in addition to, γ-radiation, but these are also slow processes.

10^{-16} sec, so about one interaction in a thousand will result in γ-radiation: in the remainder of the cases the proton will reemerge and will seem only to have been elastically scattered. This process, called "resonance scattering," results in a characteristic interference with the normal Rutherford scattering.

When several types of decay are possible for a given quantum state, the total decay rate is the sum of the decay rates for the individual processes, and the reciprocal of the mean life is the sum of the reciprocals of the individual mean lives:

$$\frac{1}{t} = \frac{1}{t_a} + \frac{1}{t_b} + \cdots$$

where t_a may represent the mean time required for a proton to escape, t_b the mean life for γ-radiation, and $t_c + \cdots$, other conceivable processes. It follows then that the observed width of a level Γ may be regarded as made up of "partial widths" $\Gamma_a = h/2\pi t_a$ characteristic of the individual modes of decay.

In the present instance, it is energetically possible for the level to decay by α-particle emission; in fact the reaction $Li^7(p,\alpha)He^4$ has a Q value of 17.339 Mev. With this amount of energy available, the α-particles might be expected to leave very rapidly, contributing thereby an extremely large width to the level. That this does not occur here is attributed to the operation of a rigid selection rule. The character, as to total angular momentum and parity, of the compound system formed by proton bombardment of Li^7 depends upon the orbital angular momentum brought in by the protons—different l values corresponding in the classical sense to different impact parameters—and at any given bombarding energy, several different kinds of compound systems may be formed. Thus protons with $l = 0$ ("head-on" collisions) will produce states with $I(Be)^8 = I(Li^7) + I(H^1) = \frac{3}{2} + \frac{1}{2} = 2$ or 1, by vector addition. With ($l = 1$) protons, states of $I(Be^8) = 3, 2, 1,$ or 0 may be formed. Now states with odd total angular momentum cannot possibly decay into two identical particles with zero spin,[1] so, if the Be^8 state in question has $I = 1$ or 3, it cannot produce α-particles and its width will be determined entirely by the partial widths for proton- or γ-emission. It has been confirmed that the state actually has $I = 1$ and is formed by $l = 1$ (p-wave) protons.

196. Liquid-drop Model. There occur many cases of resonances much too narrow, i.e. much too long-lived, to be accounted for by barrier effects. Conspicuous among these are the extremely sharp resonances

---

[1] The relative orbital angular momenta of two identical Bose-Einstein particles are restricted to even integral values by the requirement that the wave function be symmetric.

observed in capture of slow neutrons (Sec. 197). It was in an attempt
to explain these cases that N. Bohr,[1] in 1936, proposed the "liquid-drop"
model of the nucleus. Prior to this time, most theories of the nucleus
were based on analogy with the atom, in the sense that the nuclear particles were thought of as moving more or less independently of one
another in a potential well of the character described in Sec. 187, a potential which simply represented the *average* effect of the other nucleons
and which took no other account of their existence. Under these circumstances the resonances were thought to arise mainly from the motion
of a single nucleon, and interactions with other particles were treated
by perturbation methods, just as is done in atomic theory.

In the liquid-drop model, on the other hand, the interaction of nucleons
is treated as a major effect, and any incoming particle is regarded as
almost immediately losing its identity once it enters the nucleus. The
course of a nuclear reaction is thus divided into two distinct stages. In
the first stage, the incoming particle enters the target nucleus, forming
a "compound" nucleus, and quickly shares its energy with several of the
nucleons already present, so that no single particle has sufficient energy to
escape. The second stage, the decay or disintegration of the compound
system, occurs some time later, when the energy is again accidentally
concentrated on some one particle, or when the energy is lost by radiation.
In this view, the compound nucleus embodies much more than a purely
formal description of a transitory interaction between the incident particle and the target nucleus: it is a system which may have an independent
existence for a time many orders of magnitude longer than the time
required for its formation, and its intrinsic properties have a decisive
influence on the outcome of the reaction. There may be several ways of
forming a given compound nucleus with a given energy, by various combinations of bombarding particles and target nuclei. Subject to certain
conservation laws relating to the angular momentum and parity, the
character of the subsequent disintegration of the compound nucleus is
considered to be independent of the details of its formation, the outcome
in a particular instance being determined entirely by competition between
the various possible modes.

As a simple analog for this picture of the course of nuclear reactions,
Bohr suggested the liquid drop. In such a drop, the binding forces
between molecules hold the system together and prevent evaporation,
unless heat is added from outside. We suppose now that an additional
molecule is introduced; since it was initially free, it must gain kinetic
energy in going through the surface of the drop. In principle, it gains
sufficient kinetic energy to permit its immediate reevaporation the next
time it appears at the surface; it is very likely, however, to collide with

---

[1] N. Bohr, *Nature*, vol. 137, p. 344, 1936.

another molecule and lose some of its energy in the meantime. In the course of further collisions, the energy will be divided among all the molecules present and no one will have sufficient energy to evaporate. From the point of view of the drop as a whole, the temperature has been raised slightly. The condition of the drop is thus defined completely by the number of particles and the total energy available, and its future behavior —for example, the eventual evaporation of some molecule through an accidental concentration of energy—will be quite the same as if the extra energy had been supplied to it in the form of heat.

Because of the many ways in which the extra energy made available by the capture of a particle can be shared among the other particles in the nucleus, a rather long time may elapse before the compound nucleus decays. Consequently the energy of the compound nucleus may be defined with relatively sharp limits. It is observed, for example in the capture of low-energy neutrons, that resonances only a fraction of an electron-volt wide may occur. From the relation $\Delta E \, \Delta t \cong h/2\pi$, we find for the mean life of a level 1 ev wide, $\Delta t = 0.7 \times 10^{-15}$ sec. Comparing this number with the characteristic time, of the order of 10^{-22} sec, for a single traversal of the nucleus by an incoming neutron,[1] we find that the neutron travels some 10^6 or 10^7 nuclear diameters during the mean life of the compound nucleus.

If sufficient energy is available, there may be several ways for a given compound nucleus to decay. For example, bombardment of C^{12} with deuterons is observed to lead to the following reactions:

$$C^{12} + H^2 \rightarrow (N^{14}) \rightarrow \begin{cases} C^{13} + H^1 \\ N^{13} + n^1 \\ B^{10} + He^4 \\ C^{12} + H^2 \end{cases}$$

The compound nucleus here (N^{14}) has an excitation energy of more than 10 Mev; with the extra energy brought in by deuterons of 2 Mev or more, it can eject a proton, a neutron, or an α-particle, or it can reemit a deuteron. Resonances have been observed in the first two reactions, and presumably occur for the others also. The same compound nucleus can be formed by bombarding C^{13} with protons. At a proton energy of more than 3 Mev, all the following reactions are energetically possible:

$$C^{13} + H^1 \rightarrow (N^{14}) \rightarrow \begin{cases} N^{13} + n^1 \\ C^{12} + H^2 \\ C^{13} + H^1 \\ N^{14} + \gamma \end{cases}$$

[1] Inside the nucleus, the kinetic energy is about 10 to 15 Mev, corresponding to a velocity of about 5×10^9 cm per sec. The diameter of a medium-weight nucleus is about 1 to 1.5×10^{-12} cm.

The first of these has been shown to exhibit the same resonances as the $C^{12}(d,n)N^{13}$ and $C^{12}(d,p)C^{13}$ reactions (the others have not yet been studied in this energy region). This observation supports in a very direct way the prediction that the disintegration of a compound nucleus of given energy is independent (subject to conservation of spin and parity) of the mode of formation, and emphasizes the dominant role which the properties of the compound nucleus play in determining the course of nuclear reactions.

197. Neutron Reactions. Already at the time of the discovery of the neutron, it was realized that such a particle might provide a powerful tool in inducing nuclear reactions, and, in fact, the first cloud-chamber studies of neutron recoils in nitrogen[1] gave evidence for a number of transmutations produced by neutrons. The great efficacy of the neutron is attributable to the fact that it has no charge, and hence has little or no interaction with the atomic electrons or with the Coulomb field of the nucleus. When a beam of protons passes through matter, by far the greatest number are brought to rest through electronic interactions, losing their energy by ionizing the atoms through which they pass, and only a very few ever produce a nuclear reaction. Neutrons, on the other hand, travel through matter sublimely indifferent to the electric fields, and practically all of them end up by producing a nuclear reaction of one sort or another. Just the fact that they do not produce ions directly makes them somewhat more difficult to detect, but they can be counted with acceptable efficiency through their nuclear encounters.

At low bombarding energies, less than a few Mev, positively charged particles find it difficult to enter the target nucleus because of the Coulomb barrier. In the classical theory, they could of course not enter at all, unless they had sufficient energy to surmount the barrier, but wave mechanics admits, as we have seen for the case of α-particles leaving the nucleus (Sec. 187), a certain small penetrability. From a calculation along similar lines it can be shown that for a 200-kev proton striking an O^{16} nucleus, for example, the probability of penetrating is only of the order of 10^{-3} as great as for a neutron of the same energy. At lower energies and for higher atomic numbers the disparity is even greater.

a. Production of Neutrons. The bombardment of beryllium with α-particles from a radioactive substance provides a convenient source of neutrons for experiments where high intensity is not required. The radioactive material is simply mixed with beryllium powder and sealed in a small container. With polonium α-particles (5.3 Mev), about one α-particle in 10^4 produces a neutron, so the number of neutrons from a source of, say, 10 millicuries strength is $3.7 \times 10^8 \times 10^{-4} \cong 3 \times 10^4$ neutrons per second. Much stronger sources can be made with artificially

[1] N. Feather, *Proc. Roy. Soc. (London)*, vol. 136A, p. 709, 1932.

accelerated particles.   For example, in the reaction $Be^9(d,n)B^{10}$ with 10 microamperes of 10-Mev deuterons from a cyclotron, some 4×10^{11} neutrons per second are produced.   For many purposes, it is desirable that the neutrons be homogeneous in energy.   Monoenergetic neutrons can be produced in several reactions: a commonly used one is $Li^7(p,n)Be^7$, which has a negative Q value of 1.677 Mev.   Neutrons first appear at a proton energy of 1.881 Mev, and can be produced with any desired energy by varying the bombarding voltage.[1]

The most powerful source of low-energy neutrons is the nuclear reactor or "pile" (Sec. 202).   Inside the Canadian experimental reactor at Chalk River, for example, neutron fluxes as high as 5.7×10^{13} neutrons per second per square centimeter can be obtained, and neutron beams can be brought outside with as many as 5×10^7 neutrons per second per square centimeter.

  b. *Neutron Total Cross Section.*   Because neutrons are essentially unaffected by the atomic electrons, a measurement of the attenuation of a neutron beam in passing through matter provides direct and useful information on the properties of nuclei.   As a quantitative measure of the probability of an interaction between a moving particle and a nucleus, the term "cross section" is used (cf. Sec. 148).   To define this quantity in the present connection, we consider a parallel beam of I particles per second crossing an area of A cm² in which there is located a single target nucleus: we assume that of the I particles a certain number i suffer some kind of interaction with the target nucleus, for example an elastic scattering.   The "cross section" for this process is then defined as

$$\sigma = \frac{\text{number of interactions per target nucleus}}{\text{number of incident particles per unit area}} = \frac{i}{I/A}$$

or, equivalently,

$$\sigma = \frac{\text{number of interactions per (target nucleus per unit area)}}{\text{number of incident particles}} = \frac{iA}{I}$$

Thus, if a target contains n nuclei per unit area perpendicular to an incident beam of I particles per second, the number of interactions per second is $I\sigma n$.   In a layer of material of thickness dx containing N nuclei per unit volume, the probability of an interaction is

$$dP = \sigma N \, dx \tag{285}$$

The cross section has the dimensions of an area, and is, in the classical sense, simply equal to that portion of the projected area of the target nucleus which is effective for the process in question.

  [1] For proton energies greater than 2.37 Mev, an excited state of Be^7 may be formed, and a second group of neutrons appears.

The total cross section σ_t for interaction of neutrons with nuclei is made up of several terms, including the cross sections for elastic scattering, inelastic scattering, disintegration, and simple capture. For reasonably fast neutrons, the total cross section can be crudely estimated as equal to the projected area of the nucleus πR^2, where R is the radius of action of the nuclear force field. Actually, because even with high-energy neutrons wave-diffraction effects are important, an effective area of $2\pi R^2$ is a better estimate. Experimental values of σ_t can be obtained by measurement of the attenuation of a narrow beam of neutrons in a known thickness of material. If such a beam, of intensity I_0 neutrons per second, is incident on a slab of material of thickness x, the number of neutrons emerging unchanged in direction is

$$I = I_0 e^{-\sigma_t N x} \qquad (286)$$

From a measurement of I/I_0, the cross section and hence the nuclear radius can be found. The values obtained[1] generally agree with Eq. (257), with values of R_0 lying in the neighborhood of 1.4×10^{-13} cm. For a medium-weight nucleus, πR^2 is an area of the order of 10^{-24} cm², and this magnitude thus provides a natural unit in which to express cross sections for nuclear processes. The unit is called a "barn"; by definition, 1 $barn = 10^{-24}$ cm^2.

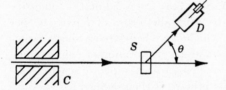

FIG. 203. Arrangement for a neutron scattering experiment. Neutrons passing through the collimator C may be scattered in a block of material at S. Scattered neutrons are counted by some form of detector D.

c. *Neutron-proton Scattering.* Generally speaking, the most probable result of a collision between a neutron of moderate energy—of the order of 1 to 5 Mev—and a light nucleus is a simple elastic scattering. This was the process observed by Curie and Joliot and by Chadwick in their experiments on the recoils produced in hydrogen and in nitrogen (Sec. 183). One of the most used neutron detectors consists essentially of an ionization chamber lined with some hydrogenous material: the neutrons eject protons from the wall by elastic collision and the protons are counted through their ionizing ability. Measurements of the elastic scattering of neutrons in hydrogen are of considerable interest in that they lead to direct information on the character of nuclear forces (Sec. 187b).

A typical arrangement for a scattering experiment is shown in Fig. 203. A monoenergetic beam, collimated at C, falls on the scatterer S. Those neutrons which are scattered through the (variable) angle θ are counted by the detector D. If it is the scattering in hydrogen which is under

[1] R. B. Day and R. L. Henkel, *Phys. Rev.*, vol. 92, p. 358, 1953.

study, the scatterer may be made of some compound of carbon and hydrogen, like paraffin or polyethylene. The observed scattering is then the
sum of the effects from the hydrogen and carbon nuclei, and the necessary correction is determined by an auxiliary experiment with a carbon
scatterer. The result of the experiment is expressed in terms of the number of neutrons scattered into the detector as a function of the angle θ
and of the energy of the incident neutrons. If the solid angle subtended
by the detector and the number of scattering nuclei are known, the
"differential" cross section $d\sigma/d\Omega$—i.e., the cross section for scattering

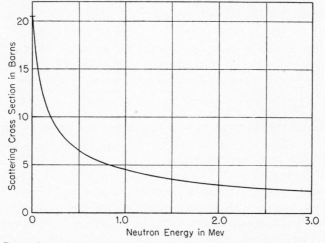

FIG. 204. Scattering cross section for neutrons in hydrogen. *One barn* = 10^{-24} cm².

into unit solid angle—may be calculated. For neutron energies above
1 ev and less than 10 Mev, the scattering in hydrogen turns out to be
spherically symmetric when the results are expressed in the center-of-
mass system. The total cross section for elastic scattering, obtained by
integrating the differential cross section over all values of θ, exhibits a
smooth variation in energy, decreasing monotonically from the value
20.36 ± 0.10 barns at a few electron-volts to about 2 barns at 4 Mev
(Fig. 204).

d. *Neutron-induced Reactions.* In addition to undergoing elastic scattering, neutrons can also produce nuclear reactions, and a great many
of these reactions result in the appearance of radioactive nuclides. An
extensive study of these effects made by Fermi and his collaborators[1] in
the years 1934 to 1936 led to the identification of a number of reactions
of this character. The experimental arrangement in these early investigations was quite simple. A source of neutrons, consisting of several

[1] E. Fermi, E. Amaldi, F. Rasetti, and E. Segrè, *Proc. Roy. Soc. (London)*, vol. 146A,
p. 483, 1934.

hundred millicuries of radon mixed with beryllium powder, was used to irradiate a sample of some element for a short time, after which the sample was transferred to the neighborhood of a Geiger counter and examined for radioactivity. Generally, the samples were in the form of cylinders which could be slipped over the source and then over the cylindrical Geiger counter in order to obtain the most favorable geometry. The counter had walls of aluminum, 0.1 to 0.2 mm thick, and so was sensitive to even rather low-energy β-rays. In each case where an activity was produced, the half-life was determined, and, wherever possible, a chemical identification of the radioisotope was made. Of some 60 elements investigated, about 40 showed radioactivity. Among the lighter elements—F, Mg, Al, Si, and several others—it was established that the activity resulted from (n,p) or (n,α) reactions. For example, bombardment of silicon produced a radioactive material with a half-life of about 3 min, chemically identified as aluminum; the process is

$$\text{Si}^{28} + n^1 \rightarrow \text{Al}^{28} + \text{H}^1$$

Reactions of the character $\text{X}(n,p)\text{Y}$, where X is a stable nuclide, invariably lead to radioactive products, for Y is an isobar of X, differing in charge by one unit, and according to the rules developed in Sec. 186 [Eqs. (261) and (263)], it is not possible for both X and Y to be stable. For the same reason (p,n) reactions also lead to unstable products when the target is stable. Most (n,p) reactions are endoergic, because the product nucleus is usually unstable by more than the 0.78 Mev which the $(n - \text{H}^1)$ mass difference makes available. A few cases exist in which (n,p) reactions have positive Q values: $\text{He}^3(n,p)\text{H}^3$ and $\text{N}^{14}(n,p)\text{C}^{14}$ are examples. The (p,n) reactions are all endoergic by more than 0.78 Mev.

The (n,α) reactions are generally endoergic in light- and medium-weight nuclei and are relatively weak because the Coulomb barrier discourages the escape of low-energy α-particles from the compound nucleus. Two important exoergic reactions are

$$\text{Li}^6(n,\alpha)\text{H}^3 \qquad Q = 2.780$$
$$\text{B}^{10}(n,\alpha)\text{Li}^7 \qquad Q = 2.792$$

Both have high cross sections for low-energy neutrons, and, because they produce charged particles, are much used for neutron detectors. If a proportional counter is filled with boron trifluoride gas—preferably enriched in B^{10}—neutrons entering the counter produce α-particles which, because of their dense ionization, give rise to large, easily detectable pulses. The associated amplifier can then be set to reject small pulses due to γ-ray background, and the counter responds only to neutrons.

In nuclei with high Z, the Coulomb barrier becomes so high that neutron reactions leading to charged-particle emission are quite improbable except with very high (greater than 10 Mev) bombarding energies. The important processes in heavy nuclei with moderate energies are elastic scattering, inelastic scattering, and simple capture followed by γ-radiation (Sec. 192). Of these, only capture produces radioactive nuclides. Among the reactions of this type which were identified by Fermi's group are $Au^{197}(n,\gamma)Au^{198}$, in which a strong activity of 2.7-day half-life is produced, and $I^{127}(n,\gamma)I^{128}$, resulting in a radioisotope of iodine with a half-life of 25 min. As a rule, the cross section for radiative capture is small compared with that for elastic and inelastic scattering when the neutron energy exceeds a few kev.

e. Slow Neutrons. In the course of their investigations of radioactivity induced in silver by neutrons, Fermi and his collaborators[1] observed that the amount of activation produced appeared to depend in some obscure way on the geometrical arrangement of the experiment. In a more careful study of this question, they found that the activation was affected by the presence of hydrogen-containing substances near the neutron source and silver sample, and, finally, that surrounding the whole arrangement with a large quantity of water or paraffin enormously increased the yield of radioactivity. Further tests showed that the enhancement of the yield in the presence of hydrogen was exhibited by a number of elements in addition to silver and that several of them had cross sections which were more than a hundred times greater than the geometric cross section.

When neutrons pass through a substance containing hydrogen, they are strongly scattered and rapidly lose energy in elastic collisions. A neutron striking a proton will transfer an amount of energy [see Eq. (253), Sec. 182]

$$\Delta E = E_0 \sin^2 \tfrac{1}{2}\theta$$

where θ is the angle of scattering in laboratory coordinates. For neutrons in the energy region of interest here, the scattering is isotropic (in center-of-mass coordinates) and all possible values of the energy loss are equally probable. It follows then that the average energy of the neutron is reduced by $\tfrac{1}{2}$ in each collision with a proton, and the average energy of a group of neutrons which had initially the same energy E_0 will after n collisions be

$$E_{av} = \frac{E_0}{2^n}$$

However, in determining the average energy, the relatively few neutrons with high energy are given a disproportionate weight; a better index of the energy distribution for our purposes is the *median* energy. The

[1] E. Amaldi, O. D'Agostino, E. Fermi, B. Pontecorvo, F. Rasetti, and E. Segrè, *Proc. Roy. Soc. (London)*, vol. 149, p. 522, 1935.

median energy can be shown[1] to be approximately, again for collisions in hydrogen,

$$E_{med} = \frac{E_0}{e^n}$$

(where e is the base of the natural logarithm). From this we can compute, for example, that of a group of 1-Mev neutrons, half will have energies less than 1 ev after about 14 collisions. The mean free path per collision, defined as the average distance traveled between collisions, is given by $\Lambda = 1/\sigma N$, where σ is the scattering cross section and N the number of protons per unit volume. Inserting the measured values of σ (Fig. 204) we find for 1-Mev neutrons a mean free path of about 3.3 cm in water, and for 1-kev neutrons, about 0.7 cm (we ignore the collisions with oxygen nuclei since they have relatively little effect on the energy). Thus a layer of water 10 cm thick around the neutron source will reduce most of the neutrons to an energy where they are in equilibrium with the thermal motion of the water molecules (about $\frac{1}{40}$ ev at normal temperature). Because of the large number of collisions which they undergo, the neutrons reaching thermal energies are moving in random directions and their motion is not unlike the diffusion of a gas.

The fact that slowing down the neutrons so greatly increases their effectiveness in producing nuclear reactions is easily explained when the problem is examined from the point of view of wave mechanics. In our earlier discussion, we estimated the maximum cross section for interaction of fast neutrons with nuclei by appealing to a simple geometrical picture of the projected area presented by a nucleus to an incoming particle. A usual measure of the applicability of such geometrical pictures is the ratio of the wavelength λ—or, better, the "reduced" wavelength $\lambda/2\pi$—to the nuclear dimensions. For a fast, say 5-Mev, neutron, the "reduced" wavelength is

$$\frac{\lambda}{2\pi} = \frac{h}{2\pi \sqrt{2EM}} = 2 \times 10^{-13} \text{ cm}$$

which is sufficiently smaller than the nuclear radius that the visualization of the neutron's trajectory presents no difficulty in principle. For neutrons of 1-ev energy, on the other hand, $\lambda/2\pi \cong 0.5 \times 10^{-9}$ cm, which is many times larger than the nucleus. In this situation it becomes more appropriate to think of the nucleus as a small diffracting center in a very long wave. Instead of trying to trace individual trajectories we now regard the incident neutrons as a beam, with a certain average probability of having a neutron in a unit volume. In such a beam, containing I_0

---

[1] E. Fermi, with J. Orear, A. H. Rosenfeld, and R. A. Schluter, "Nuclear Physics," p. 183, University of Chicago Press, Chicago, 1950.

neutrons of velocity v crossing 1 cm^2 per second, the number of neutrons per cubic centimeter is $\rho = I_0/v$. We now assume that the probability per unit time that a neutron be captured is simply proportional to the density of neutrons

$$N_{capt} \propto \rho = \frac{I_0}{v}$$

But the number of captures per unit time is, by definition, proportional to σI_0. Thus

$$\sigma_{capt} \propto \frac{N_{capt}}{I_0} \propto \frac{1}{v} \tag{287}$$

Equation (287), often referred to as the "$1/v$" law, is accurately confirmed in many neutron processes. The cross section for the reaction $B^{10}(n,\alpha)Li^7$, for example, shows no appreciable deviation from the $1/v$ dependence over the energy range from 10^{-2} to nearly 10^3 ev, and the activation of silver follows the law from 10^{-2} to about 1 ev. In some nuclides, the observed cross sections for thermal neutrons ($E \cong kT = \frac{1}{40}$ ev) are many thousand times greater than those for fast neutrons. One isotope of xenon has a thermal cross section of 3.5×10^6 barns!

f. Resonance Absorption. It would be expected that if the cross section for activation of, say, silver is very large for slow neutrons, the absorption coefficient in silver of such neutrons would also be high. That this is indeed the case was shown by Amaldi et al.[1] by measuring the activation produced in a silver sample with various thicknesses of silver absorbers wrapped around it. For silver, the thickness required to reduce the activation to half-value was about 1 mm, indicating an average cross section [Eq. (286)] of some hundreds of barns. It would thus appear that a relatively thin layer of silver should absorb many of the slow neutrons and greatly reduce the effect of the hydrogen "thermalizer" on all activations. Tests made with iodine[2] as the detector showed, however, that this was not so: the activation of iodine was only moderately affected by the silver absorber, and, although an iodine absorber would reduce the iodine activity greatly, it had little effect on silver samples. The obvious implication is that neither silver nor iodine follows strictly the $1/v$ law, but that both have extraordinarily high absorptions for certain, different neutron energies. The activation of silver must then be mainly due to a narrow band of neutron energies—for which its absorption is correspondingly high—and that of iodine is due to another band of a different energy. It was shown by Amaldi and Fermi[3] that these so-called "resonance-absorption" bands were in some cases only a frac-

[1] *Loc. cit.*
[2] P. B. Moon and J. R. Tillman, *Proc. Roy. Soc. (London)*, vol. 153, p. 476, 1936.
[3] E. Amaldi and E. Fermi, *Phys. Rev.*, vol. 50, p. 899, 1936.

tion of an electron-volt wide.   These were the resonances whose discovery led to the formulation of the liquid-drop model of the nucleus (Sec. 196).

Our information on these low-energy-neutron resonances has enormously increased with the development of more refined techniques.   One of the most useful of these has been the neutron "velocity selector,"[1] schematically illustrated in Fig. 205.   The neutrons are produced in the reaction $Be^9(d,n)B^{10}$, using deuterons accelerated by a cyclotron.   Next to the beryllium target is a "thermalizer" consisting of a few centimeters of paraffin.   Slow neutrons emerging in the forward direction pass

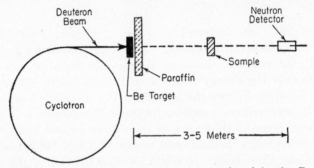

FIG. 205. Neutron "velocity selector."   Neutrons produced in the Be target are slowed down in the paraffin block and selected according to the time required to traverse the distance to the detector.   The various collimators and shields are not shown.

through the material whose absorption is to be studied and to the detector some distance away.   The velocity selection is accomplished by operating the cyclotron in such a way as to produce short "bursts" of neutrons, and synchronizing the detector so that it counts only those neutrons whose time of flight lies in a selected narrow range.   In a typical arrangement, the distance to the detector is 6.4 meters: the time of flight for a 1-ev neutron is then 470 microsec.   With a time resolution of 5 microsec, energies as high as 10,000 ev can be selected.

Another instrument, with particular applicability to the low-energy region, is the crystal spectrometer.[2]   The de Broglie wavelengths of thermal neutrons are of the order of magnitude of the lattice spacings of crystals, and they are scattered by such a lattice according to the Bragg law (Sec. 150).   With the large neutron fluxes available from nuclear reactors, it is possible to obtain scattered neutron beams of quite acceptable intensity and high homogeneity in energy.   The sample under study is placed in the beam, and its attenuation is measured as a function of the crystal angle.   A curve for silver, showing two strong resonances, is

[1] J. Rainwater and W. W. Havens, *Phys. Rev.*, vol. 70, p. 136, 1946.
[2] L. B. Borst and V. L. Sailor, *Rev. Sci. Instr.*, vol. 24, p. 141, 1953.

reproduced in Fig. 206. The close agreement obtained in the location of resonance energies by the crystal and direct time-of-flight measurements provides an accurate check of the validity of the de Broglie relation for neutrons.

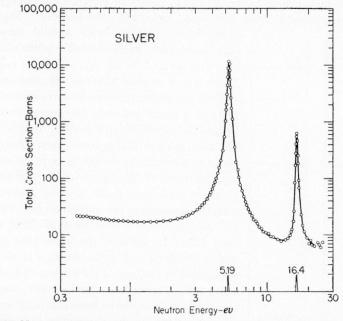

FIG. 206. Neutron capture resonances observed in silver with a crystal spectrometer. Because of the large range of cross sections and energies, the data are presented on a log-log scale. [*L. B. Borst and V. L. Sailor, Rev. Sci. Instr., vol. 24, p. 141, 1953; and R. E. Wood, Phys. Rev., vol. 95, p. 644, 1954.*]

198. Energy Levels of Nuclei.[1] One of the important results of the study of nuclear reactions is the location and identification of the excited states of nuclei. In the atomic case, it was of course just the study of the excited levels, as derived from the spectra, which guided the entire theoretical development of our present model of the structure of the atom. Unfortunately, the pronounced regularities which typify atomic term diagrams seem to have no counterpart in the nuclear case, and the situation is complicated by many effects which either have no analog in the atom or play only a minor role there. It is not possible, at the present writing, to give any systematic account of the origin of nuclear energy levels in general, so only one or two observations which appear to have a particularly straightforward interpretation will be related here.

[1] S. Devons, "Excited States of Nuclei," Cambridge, London, 1949; O. R. Frisch, "Progress in Nuclear Physics," vol. 2, article by W. E. Burcham, Pergamon, 1952. "Annual Review of Nuclear Science," vol. I, article by T. Lauritsen, 1952.

a. Energy Levels of Mirror Nuclei. In Sec. 193, evidence that the nuclear parts of $(p\text{-}p)$ and $(n\text{-}n)$ forces are equal was adduced from comparison of the masses of mirror nuclei. It follows from the arguments presented there that not only the ground states but also the excited states of mirror nuclei should agree in energy, once the electrostatic energy and the neutron-proton mass difference are taken into account. Furthermore, corresponding levels should agree in other properties, such as total angular momentum and parity, if the hypothesis is correct. There is now considerable evidence that excited levels of the mirror nuclides do agree remarkably well: as a single example, the energy levels of Li^7 and Be^7 are shown in Fig. 207. In this figure the two ground states have been arbitrarily made to coincide in energy in order to exhibit the alignment of the higher levels. (If the adjustment had been made in strict accordance with the elementary calculations of Sec. 193, the Be^7 ground state would lie 0.27 Mev lower than Li^7.) In general, the agreement of the higher levels is not quite exact, a small shift downward in the case of the nucleus of higher Z being often observed. Such small displacements, where they have been carefully investigated, appear to be explicable in terms of electrostatic or electromagnetic effects and do not affect the conclusion regarding the equality of the nuclear forces.

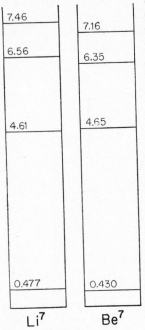

FIG. 207. Energy levels of Li^7 and Be^7: the ground states are arbitrarily adjusted to coincide.

b. Even Isobars. Something more can be learned about nuclear forces from a study of the even isobars. If we consider $_4Be^{10}$ and $_5B^{10}$, for example, as composed of a common "core" of four protons and four neutrons (again, only for the purpose of counting the number of interactions of various types) plus two neutrons or a neutron-proton pair, respectively, we find that some of the $(n\text{-}n)$ bonds in Be^{10} are replaced in B^{10} not by $(p\text{-}p)$ bonds, but by $(p\text{-}n)$ bonds. Thus, if the nuclear binding energies of these two nuclides are found to be equal, we have evidence for the far-reaching assertion that, at least in light nuclei, the interaction between unlike nucleons is the same as that between like nucleons, i.e., that the forces are not only *symmetric* in the "charge state" (cf. Sec. 187c) of nucleons, but are *charge-independent*.

A complication arises, however, in the comparison of Be^{10} and B^{10}, because certain $(p\text{-}n)$ interactions in the latter are not permitted in the former when the proton is replaced by a neutron. A proton and neutron in the same quantum level may have either parallel or antiparallel spins; two neutrons, on the other hand, can only have antiparallel spins. If the nuclear force is greater when the spins are parallel—as would appear to be the case from the neutron-proton scattering experiments (Sec. 187b)—the ground state of B^{10} may have a character which is forbidden in Be^{10}. On the other hand, there should exist an *excited* state

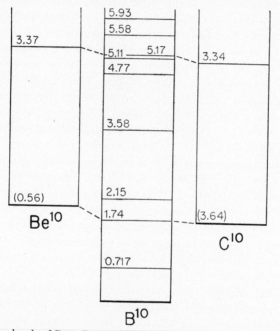

FIG. 208. Energy levels of Be^{10}, B^{10}, and C^{10}. The ground states of Be^{10} and C^{10} have been shifted by the electrostatic energy and $(n - H^1)$ mass difference with respect to B^{10}. Corresponding levels are connected by dashed lines.

of B^{10} in which the spins of the extra proton-neutron pair are antiparallel, and this state should have the same energy as the ground state of Be^{10}. The same argument applies to the mirror of Be^{10}, namely $_6C^{10}$, which has two extra protons. All the levels of these two nuclides should have counterparts in B^{10}, but B^{10} may have levels which are not possible in either C^{10} or Be^{10}.

The known energy levels of Be^{10}, B^{10}, and C^{10} are shown in Fig. 208, in which a correction for the electrostatic energies and $(n - H^1)$ mass difference has been applied, in the same manner as was done in Eqs. (280) and (281) (Sec. 193), so that the nuclear parts of the binding energies are shown relative to the ground state of B^{10}: Be^{10} has thus been shifted upward by 1.50 Mev, and C^{10} downward by 2.06 Mev. The levels of

B^{10}, C^{10}, and Be^{10}, which are connected by dashed lines, are found not only to agree well in energy but also to exhibit other properties which confirm their close genetic relation.

In general, the greater the difference between the numbers of protons and neutrons in a nucleus with a given total number of particles, the more restrictions will be placed by the Pauli principle on the number of possible interactions, and the smaller will be the number of levels as compared with configurations comprising equal numbers of neutrons and protons. In a formal way, this property of a nuclear configuration may be expressed[1] by the so-called "isotopic-spin projection" $T_\zeta = \frac{1}{2}(N - Z)$. The greater the value of T_ζ, the fewer the permitted levels, and any level which is possible for a nuclide with a given T_ζ will also appear in all nuclides with lower absolute values of T_ζ. The various common levels are said to represent components of an "isotopic-spin multiplet" characterized by a quantum number T equal to the maximum value of T_ζ. Thus all the states of B^{10} have $T_\zeta = 0$; the ground state and first excited state do not occur in Be^{10} or C^{10} (for which $T_\zeta = 1$ and -1), and are therefore isotopic-spin singlets: $T = 0$, $T_\zeta = 0$. The ground states of Be^{10} and C^{10} and the 1.74-Mev state of B^{10} comprise an isotopic-spin triplet: $T = 1$, $T_\zeta = 1$, 0, -1. In a sense, then, the various isobars comprise a kind of "fine structure" in nuclear spectroscopy much as the different components of ordinary spin comprise a fine structure in atomic energy levels. It is thus again emphasized that it is the total number of particles, and not the somewhat incidental nuclear charge, which principally determines the behavior of a nucleus.

199. The Shell Model.[2] We have discussed in some detail in previous sections the experiments which led to the development of the liquid-drop nucleus model for nuclear reactions. It is, as we have seen, an essential feature of this model that the nucleons must be regarded as strongly interacting within the nucleus, and any picture envisaging separate particles moving independently of one another in an average central field of force would give results at variance with many of the facts of nuclear reactions. There has, however, been a simultaneous development in the opposite direction, in which it has been made increasingly clear that for some properties of nuclei the "independent-particle" model gives surprisingly good results. This development is closely connected with the

---

[1] E. P. Wigner, *Phys. Rev.*, vol. 51, p. 106, 1937. In the wave-mechanical treatment, the isotopic spin plays a role quite analogous to the ordinary spin. Just as the two spin states of a nucleon can be represented by components of a spin vector, the two "charge states" of a nucleon, i.e., neutron and proton, may be represented by components of the isotopic-spin vector.

[2] O. R. Frisch, "Progress in Nuclear Physics," vol. 2, article by B. H. Flowers, Pergamon, 1952; H. A. Bethe and R. F. Bacher, *Revs. Mod. Phys.*, vol. 8, p. 168, 1936.

discovery of the so-called "magic" numbers, configurations of neutrons and protons which exhibit certain rather special properties.

a. Periodicities in Nuclear Species. A conspicuous feature of atomic structure is the marked periodicity in chemical properties, as reflected, for example, in Mendeleev's Table. We saw earlier (Sec. 110 *et seq.*) how this phenomenon found a straightforward explanation in terms of the "electronic shells," and how the closing of a shell or subshell made itself evident in a strong increase in the ionization potential (Fig. 69). It was natural enough, then, to search for analogous effects in nuclei in terms of specially stable nuclear species, in the hope of revealing a similar shell structure. Among the lightest nuclei, the peculiar stability of nuclei of the type $A = 2Z = 4n$, where n is an integer, was recognized at an early stage. This stability is exhibited in the pronounced peaks of the binding-energy curve of Fig. 182. In fact, this observation, and the fact that α-particles are emitted by many of the naturally radioactive substances, led for a time to the belief that the α-particle is a fundamental building unit of nuclei. That this is not so in any literal sense is evident among the heavier nuclei from the fact that these contain more neutrons than protons and the extra neutrons are just as tightly bound as are the protons. Among the light nuclei, the preference for equal, even numbers of protons and neutrons is accounted for by the high symmetry of such configurations (Sec. 187).

The suggestion that there are other shell-structure effects in addition to the "four structure" was first made by Bartlett,[1] in 1932, who observed that the pattern of composition of the naturally occurring isotopes underwent a change at O^{16} and again at A^{36}. Between He^4 and O^{16}, all the stable nuclides belong to the sequence $He^4 + n + p + n + p + \cdots$. From O^{16} to A^{36}, the sequence becomes $O^{16} + n + n + p + p + n + n + \cdots$. It was suggested that these changes might be associated with the filling of shells of neutrons and protons of given orbital angular momentum. In the first s shell (orbital angular momentum = 0) there could be just two neutrons and two protons without violating the Pauli exclusion principle. The next, the "p" shell, with orbital angular momentum 1, has room for six neutrons and six protons and would be complete at O^{16}. The "d" shell, with 10 neutrons and 10 protons, would be filled at A^{36} ($Z = 18$). In general, as in atoms, the number of particles of each kind in a shell is $2(2l + 1)$. Evidence for the existence of other shells was brought forward in 1933 and 1934 by Elsasser,[2] and by Guggenheimer[3] who found indications of particular stability for several values of neutron and proton numbers, among them $Z = 20$, N or $Z = 50, 82$,

[1] J. H. Bartlett, *Nature*, vol. 130, p. 165, 1932.

[2] W. M. Elsasser, *J. phys. radium*, vol. 4, p. 549, 1933; vol. 5, pp. 389, 635, 1934.

[3] K. Guggenheimer, *J. phys. radium*, vol. 5, pp. 253, 475, 1935.

and $N = 126$. Unfortunately the data available were insufficiently accurate, and the argument was weakened to some extent by the inclusion of several numbers which turned out not to be magic at all.

b. Central-field Approximation. Attempts were made to account for the existence of shells by calculations based on the Hartree central-field

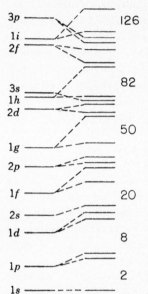

model, in which the mutual interactions of the nucleons are represented by an average central field. The solution then takes essentially the same form as that for the atomic case, where, as a first approximation, the wave function for the system is written as a linear combination of single-particle wave functions and the main effect of the electrostatic repulsion is included in the potential function. Other interactions, such as the residual electrostatic repulsion or the spin-orbit effect, are taken into account by perturbation methods.

As a first approximation to the central field in the nucleus, a simple square-well potential is assumed. Since the potential is solely a function of radius, the Schrödinger equation may be separated into radial and angular parts, and the angular-dependent solutions are identical with those of the hydrogen atom, discussed in Sec. 104. There will exist a number of stationary solutions, depending upon the depth and width chosen for the potential, and these are characterized by the quantum numbers ν, l, λ, where l and λ refer to the orbital angular momentum and its projection on any chosen axis, and ν is the radial quantum number, so defined that the number of nodes in the radial solution is given

FIG. 209. Spacing and order of levels in an infinitely deep, square potential well (left) and in the Mayer-Jensen potential (right). The total number of particles at each shell closing is indicated at the right.

by[1] $\nu - 1$ (excluding the node at the origin in $l = 0$ solutions). The energy of a given stationary state depends explicitly upon both ν and l, and the level order is $1s, 1p, 1d, 2s, 1f, 2p, \ldots$, as shown in the left-hand side of Fig. 209. The actual energies may be different for neutrons and protons, particularly in heavier nuclei where the electrostatic effect is important. In any case, with $2(2l + 1)$ particles in a "shell," closed shells should occur for 2, 8, 18, 20, 34, 40, 58, . . . neutrons, and similarly

[1] This ν is not the same as the total quantum number n used in atomic spectroscopy. In another commonly used notation, however, the solutions are designated by the total quantum number n (our $\nu + l$), and l; in this notation, the level order is $1s, 2p, 3d, 2s, \ldots$.   See for example H. A. Bethe and R. F. Bacher, *loc. cit.*

for protons.   The numbers 50, 82, and 126 do not appear to occur in any natural way, although they can be produced by arbitrarily omitting certain terms, for example 2s and 2p.

c. *Spin-orbit Coupling.*   At about this stage of development, the independent-particle model fell into disfavor, partly because the experimental evidence for "shells" among the heavier elements was something less than clear and partly because the conspicuous success of the liquid-drop model made it seem that any picture based on a fixed central potential

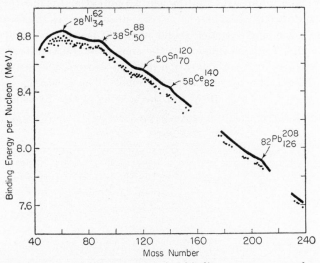

FIG. 210. Magnified portion of curve showing binding energy per nucleon.   (*H. E. Duckworth, Nature, vol.* 170, *p.* 158, 1952.)

was doomed to failure.   Evidence for periodicities in nuclear structure continued to accumulate, however, and the question was reopened by M. G. Mayer[1] in 1948.   In a survey of existing information on the naturally occurring nuclides, she noted that species with neutron or proton numbers 50, 82, or 126 are distinctly more abundant in the earth's crust than are their immediate neighbors, that there occur particularly large numbers of "isotones"—nuclides with the same neutron number N—for $N = 50$ and 82, and particularly large numbers of isotopes for $Z = 20$ and 50.   With these data, and certain others which we shall not enumerate here, she established the "magic" character of the numbers 50, 82, and 126 in addition to the well-recognized ones 2, 8, and 20.   Supporting evidence for the special stability of magic-number nuclides, obtained in direct mass-spectrograph measurements,[2] is shown in Fig. 210, in which the binding energy per nucleon (cf. Fig. 182) is exhibited on a magnified

[1] M. G. Mayer, *Phys. Rev.,* vol. 74, p. 235, 1948.
[2] H. E. Duckworth, *Nature,* vol. 170, p. 158, 1952.

scale for mass numbers 40 to 240. Changes in slope occur at Ni^{62} (28 protons), Sr^{88} (50 neutrons), Sn^{120} (50 protons), Ce^{140} (82 neutrons), and Pb^{208} (82 protons, 126 neutrons).

In 1950, Mayer,[1] and independently Haxel, Jensen, and Suess,[2] in Germany, proposed a simple independent-particle model which led to the observed magic numbers in straightforward fashion. Starting with a potential differing only slightly from a square well, they postulated a strong spin-orbit coupling, proportional to $\mathbf{l} \cdot \mathbf{s}$, which would split the zero-order states obtained from the central potential. Thus the $1p$ state would be split into two: $1p_{3/2}$ and $1p_{1/2}$ (the subscript gives the total angular momentum for a single particle); and $1d$ would become $1d_{5/2}$ and $1d_{3/2}$; the s state of course remains single. If the spin-orbit splitting is of the same order of magnitude as the separation between various l terms, the grouping of states may be considerably modified. The grouping which they derived is shown in Table 10-7, and the spacing of the levels is shown on

TABLE 10-7. GROUPING OF NEUTRON OR PROTON STATES IN THE SHELL MODEL
WITH SPIN-ORBIT COUPLING

State designation	$1s$	$1p_{3/2}$	$1d_{5/2}$	$1f_{7/2}$	$1g_{7/2}$	$1h_{9/2}$
		$1p_{1/2}$	$1d_{3/2}$	$1f_{5/2}$	$2d_{5/2}$	$2f_{7/2}$
			$2s_{1/2}$	$2p_{3/2}$	$2d_{3/2}$	$2f_{5/2}$
				$2p_{1/2}$	$3s_{1/2}$	$3p_{1/2}$
				$1g_{9/2}$	$1h_{11/2}$	$3p_{3/2}$
						$1i_{13/2}$
Total neutrons or protons	2	8	20	50	82	126

the right-hand side of Fig. 209. On the basis of strong spin-orbit splitting for large l values, the numbers 50, 82, and 126 become magic in a straightforward manner. Among the light elements where the l values are low, in the $1s$ and $1p$ shells, it is assumed that the spin-orbit splitting is not so great, and the level order and magic numbers (2, 8) are those of the square well. In the next shell, the close proximity of the $1d$ and $2s$ states is a consequence of the assumed potential, and the spin-orbit effect again plays a minor role. It is possible, however, that the spin-orbit effect may lower the $1f_{7/2}$ state in the next group sufficiently to make 28 a magic number; there is some indication for this in the relative stability of $_{28}Ni^{62}$. The next shell contains $1f$ and $2p$ states closely grouped, and the spin-orbit effect depresses the $1g_{9/2}$ state, so that this term, too, appears in the shell which closes at 50 nucleons. By the same procedure, then, shells at 82 and 126 nucleons are accounted for.

d. Single-particle Model. To make more specific comparisons between the predictions of the independent-particle model and experiment, it is

[1] M. G. Mayer, *Phys. Rev.*, vol. 75, p. 1969, 1949; vol. 78, pp. 16, 22, 1950.
[2] O. Haxel, J. H. D. Jensen, and H. E. Suess, *Z. Physik*, vol. 128, p. 295, 1950.

necessary to make some further assumptions. The most obvious of these, which is common to all models and which follows directly from the Pauli principle, is that the nucleons of a closed shell combine their spins and magnetic moments to give a resultant of zero. In the light nuclei He^4 and O^{16}, where $N = Z$, and in the "doubly magic" nucleus $_{82}Pb^{208}$, where both N and Z are magic, the ground-state angular momentum is in fact zero, but, since this is apparently a general characteristic of nuclei with even N and even Z, the point is not very strong. As regards the next assumption, two extremes are possible: in the so-called "single-particle" model, it is assumed that all like particles, including those outside closed shells, couple together in pairs to give angular momentum zero. The angular momentum and magnetic moment of all even-even nuclei would then be zero—as observed—and that of even-odd (Z even, N odd) or odd-even nuclei would always be that of the odd nucleon. The single-particle model works surprisingly well in accounting for the observed angular momenta. According to this model, in the $1p$ shell (He^4 to O^{16}), the total angular momenta expected are $\frac{3}{2}$, $\frac{3}{2}$, $\frac{3}{2}$, $\frac{3}{2}$, $\frac{1}{2}$, $\frac{1}{2}$ for A = 5, 7, 9, 11, 13, and 15, just as observed. Just above O^{16} there is some uncertainty as to whether the $s_{\frac{1}{2}}$ or $d_{\frac{5}{2}}$ "orbits" should fill first: for O^{17} and F^{19} the observed values of I are $\frac{5}{2}$ and $\frac{1}{2}$. For Ne^{21} and Na^{23}, on the other hand, $I = \frac{3}{2}$, which is a little difficult to account for. The remainder of the shell fills regularly to $_{19}K^{39}$ (odd protons) or $_{16}S^{35}$ (odd neutrons). In the next shell, the observed and predicted spins agree very well in the main, but again a few troublesome exceptions occur.

The single-particle model has also had some measure of success in accounting for the magnetic moments of odd-Z, even-N and even-Z, odd-N nuclei.[1] It was in fact suggested as early as 1937, by Schmidt, that the magnetic moments of nuclei might be attributable to the motion of a single nucleon, with the contribution from its intrinsic spin moment and that from its orbital motion coupled in the same way as are the corresponding electronic moments in an atom. Thus the total angular momentum I is considered to be the vector sum of the intrinsic spin of the nucleon s and an orbital angular momentum l. The magnetic moment so produced depends upon the value of l for the odd nucleon, and this value is so chosen as to give the closest possible agreement with the observed moment. Although the numerical agreement between predicted and observed moments is not very close, it is usually sufficiently good that a unique l value can be determined, and this value turns out in most cases to be just that predicted by the shell model.

  e. *Modifications of the Single-particle Model.* Despite its many virtues, the single-particle model leaves a good deal to be desired. The

[1] J. M. Blatt and V. F. Weisskopf, "Theoretical Nuclear Physics," p. 30, Wiley, New York, 1952.

exceptions to its predictions of total angular momentum are troublesome, and the quantitative agreement of calculated and observed magnetic moments is far from good. It is evidently necessary to consider in making calculations of this kind, not just the odd nucleon, but the configuration as a whole, or at least that part which lies outside a closed shell. Just as in the atomic case, the terms involving several interacting particles are both complex and numerous, and the calculations are beset with considerable difficulties, not least because the form of the interactions is unknown. Nevertheless some striking success has been achieved with this modified independent-particle model, and it seems clear that any faithful picture of the nucleus, at least in the ground state, must include something approximating single-particle motions. The curious dichotomy of the behavior of the nucleus as a liquid drop in some experiments and as an open structure with well-defined shells in others has occasioned no little perplexity, and the problem stands today (1954) as one for which no completely satisfactory solution has been found. In one current development,[1] which appears to hold a good deal of promise, it is assumed that the "core" of the nucleus, comprising the particles in closed shells, is not completely inert, but can be more or less strongly distorted by the extra nucleons. Thus, if many nucleons exist outside closed shells, the interaction may be relatively strong, and the motion of the core so produced may influence even the ground-state features. Among other things, the model predicts the existence in these cases of a set of low-lying rotational levels, with the regular spacing exhibited by rotational states in molecules; recent experiments appear to indicate the existence of such states in certain medium and heavy nuclei, with just the predicted properties.[2] It also seems to be possible, by choosing a suitably small interaction between the motion of a single particle and collective motions of the nucleus as a whole, to obtain a description of nuclear reactions which combines the essential features of both the independent-particle and the liquid-drop model. This approach has enjoyed a striking success in accounting for observed regularities in neutron-scattering cross sections at intermediate energies in medium and heavy nuclei.[3]

NUCLEAR FISSION AND NUCLEAR ENERGY

200. Discovery of Fission.[4] *a. "Transuranic" Elements.* The experiments which led to the discovery of fission began in 1934, in connection

---

[1] A. Bohr and B. R. Mottleson, *Kgl. Danske Videnskab. Selskab Mat.-fys. Medd.*, vol. 27, No. 16, 1953.

[2] T. Huus and C. Zupancic, *Kgl. Danske Videnskab. Selskab Mat.-fys. Medd.*, vol. 28, No. 1, 1953.

[3] H. Feshbach, C. E. Porter, and V. F. Weisskopf, *Phys. Rev.*, vol. 90, p. 166, 1953

[4] L. A. Turner, *Revs. Mod. Phys.*, vol. 12, p. 1, 1940.

with investigations by Fermi and his collaborators of neutron-induced radioactivity. The striking ability of neutrons to produce β^--unstable isotopes from many naturally occurring elements suggested to Fermi that it might be possible by this means to extend the periodic table to higher atomic numbers by neutron-induced processes in uranium. It was very soon shown by experiments in Rome that uranium samples can in fact be made radioactive by neutron bombardment, and, furthermore, several different materials are produced. Attempts at chemical identification soon revealed an embarrassing wealth of activities, which could be accounted for by known types of nuclear reactions only with considerable difficulty. Thus, it was concluded by Hahn, Meitner, and Strassman in 1937 that at least three separate chains of transitions must be assumed, all starting with neutron capture in the most abundant isotope of uranium, $_{92}U^{238}$, and involving several long-lived excited states of elements 93, 94, and perhaps 95. More problems arose with the discovery by I. Curie and Savitch in 1938 of active materials which coprecipitated with lanthanum ($Z = 57$) and appeared to be "almost" inseparable from this element by chemical means. In a series of very careful experiments, Hahn and Strassmann showed that there are in fact several activities which coprecipitate with barium and whose daughter products behave like lanthanum. Since radium and barium have almost identical chemical properties, and can be separated only with extreme difficulty, it was concluded that isotopes of radium ($Z = 88$) must be involved, formed by an ($n,2\alpha$) process from uranium. However it was difficult to understand how an ($n,2\alpha$) process could occur in such a heavy nuclide and especially in one so relatively stable as U^{238}. To establish the identification beyond doubt, Hahn and Strassmann set out to make the separation of the supposed radium isotopes from barium, using ThX and MsTh$_1$ (isotopes of radium) as carriers. To their surprise, they found that the activity followed the barium rather than the radium carriers and hence must be identified as barium itself! They soon found other activities which could be identified as isotopic with barium and lanthanum, and they were led to suggest that several of the supposed "transuranic" elements might actually be isotopes of other elements considerably lighter than uranium, possibly produced by an "explosion" of the uranium nucleus.[1]

b. *Physical Demonstration of Fission.* A physical picture of the mechanism by which a uranium nucleus could break up into two halves was first proposed by Meitner and Frisch,[2] within a few weeks after Hahn and Strassmann's publication of the chemical evidence. Basing their argument on the liquid-drop model of the nucleus, they pointed out that the

[1] O. Hahn and F. Strassmann, *Naturwiss.*, vol. 27, pp. 11, 99, 1939.
[2] L. Meitner and O. R. Frisch, *Nature*, vol. 143, p. 239, 1939.

binding forces acting on particles at the nuclear surface and producing an effective surface tension might be overcome by the electrostatic repulsion when the charge is sufficiently high. From a detailed model worked out by Bohr and Kalckar,[1] they estimated that at $Z \cong 100$, only a small amount of extra energy—such as that brought in by a single neutron—might suffice to overcome the surface tension and cause the nucleus to break up into two roughly equal fragments. An estimate of the change in energy indicated that 100 to 200 Mev might be released in the process, an amount which roughly corresponds to the difference in (total) binding energy of U and of two elements near the middle of the atomic table. The elements thus formed would be quite unstable, because of their great neutron excess, and would decay through several stages before reaching a stable product.

Confirmation of this hypothesis came almost immediately in the demonstration by Frisch in Copenhagen that ionizing fragments having energies of over 70 Mev were produced in a uranium-lined ionization chamber under neutron bombardment, and by Joliot in Paris that the active materials had sufficient kinetic energy to travel nearly 3 cm in air: the energy he estimated to be of the order of 250 Mev. The announcement of the results of Meitner and Frisch by Bohr at a conference on theoretical physics held in Washington, D.C., on January 26, 1939, led to an intense activity among experimentalists in this country. Within a matter of days, the existence of heavily ionizing particles with enormous kinetic energies was confirmed in several laboratories, and many new and important discoveries were made in the course of the next few months. By mid-1939 the following facts were well established:

1. Fission occurs in both uranium and thorium under fast-neutron bombardment; in uranium, thermal neutrons are also effective, the cross section following the "$1/v$ law."

2. U^{239}, with a half-life of 23 min, is formed in slow-neutron bombardment of uranium, the cross section exhibiting one or more strong resonances in the range 10 to 25 ev.

3. The fragments resulting from uranium fission occur in two broad groups, with energies around 60 Mev and 100 Mev. The one group comprises fragments with mass numbers near 140, the other, near 95; symmetrical disintegrations, producing nuclides with mass numbers 115 to 120, almost never occur.[2]

4. In about 1 per cent of the fissions, delayed neutrons, presumably associated with the decay of one of the fragments, are emitted.

5. A small number of neutrons—between one and three—is emitted simultaneously with the fission.

---

[1] N. Bohr and F. Kalckar, *Kgl. Danske Videnskab. Selskab Mat.-fys. Medd.*, vol. 14, no. 10, 1937.

[2] It was later found that symmetric fission does occur at high neutron energies.

201. Theory of Fission. *a. Mechanism of Fission.* The theory of the fission process was worked out in detail by Bohr and Wheeler.[1] In accordance with the common treatment of nuclear reactions (cf. Sec. 196), they assumed the process to occur in two distinct stages: the formation of an excited compound nucleus by capture of a neutron, and the subsequent decay of the system in one of several possible ways. In the compound nucleus, the excess energy is distributed among the many possible modes of motion of the particles, sometimes being concentrated on a single particle and sometimes exciting much more complicated motions, involving many particles. The final outcome of the reaction is determined by the competition between the various modes of motion which can lead to disintegration, and is independent of the way in which the compound nucleus was formed. In a heavy nucleus it may well occur that disintegrations resulting from these more general motions can compete favorably with single-particle emission or radiation.

In describing the complex motions of a system of many particles it is useful to deal with the changes in shape of the system as a whole, rather than attempting to visualize the behavior of individual particles. This treatment is particularly appropriate when the particles are closely packed, so the system is essentially incompressible. As a first approximation, then, the compound nucleus formed in the capture of a neutron by a heavy element is regarded as a drop of incompressible fluid. The simplest distortion of which a fluid drop is capable is that in which the drop elongates on some axis and assumes an ellipsoidal shape. The elongation results in an increase of surface area, and so the surface-tension forces tend to restore it to a spherical shape. Given a sufficient energy, however, it is possible to produce a distortion so extreme that the drop divides into two nearly equal spherical parts. The energy required for this can be shown to be 0.26 of the total surface energy. If now the effect of a uniformly distributed electric charge on the drop is considered, it is evident that the elongation decreases the electrostatic energy (since the charges are farther apart), so the electrostatic forces oppose the surface-tension forces and less energy is required to split the drop.

In the nuclear case, too, it is appropriate to think of a surface-tension effect, since particles near the surface will have fewer neighbors than those in the interior and hence will contribute less to the total binding. In fact, in the extreme liquid-drop model, it is just this effect which accounts for the general trend toward low binding energy per particle in the light nuclei (Fig. 182), where the surface-to-volume ratio is high. The surface area of a nucleus, and hence its surface energy, is proportional to $A^{2/3}$, where A is the mass number. The electrostatic energy, on the other hand, is proportional to $Z^2/A^{1/3}$ (Sec. 187), and the ratio Z^2/A is thus a measure of the relative importance of the electrostatic and sur-

[1] N. Bohr and J. A. Wheeler, *Phys. Rev.*, vol. 56, p. 428, 1939.

face effects.   Above a certain critical value for this ratio, a nucleus is unstable with respect to arbitrarily small distortions and will elongate more and more until it breaks into two roughly equal fragments.   The magnitude of the critical value can be estimated from known nuclear constants derived from the binding energies of stable nuclides and turns out to be $(Z^2/A)_{limit} = 45$, about 25 per cent higher than the value for $_{92}U^{238}$.   Thus it may be expected that elements of much higher atomic number than uranium are unstable to spontaneous fission, and hence cannot occur in nature.

   b. *Fission Threshold*.   For nuclei with less than the critical value of Z^2/A, a finite distortion is required to overcome the surface tension, and the amount of excess energy needed increases as the ratio Z^2/A decreases. The question whether fission can result from the capture of a neutron by a given nucleus then depends upon whether the energy brought in by the neutron (binding plus kinetic energy) is sufficient to produce the necessary distortion of the compound system.   This energy turns out to be about 6 Mev for the nucleus U^{239}, formed by capture of neutrons in the most abundant isotope of uranium, U^{238}, and about 5.3 Mev for U^{236}, formed from U^{235}.   The binding energy of a neutron in U^{239} is estimated to be 5.2 Mev, so neutrons of about 1 Mev kinetic energy are required to induce fission of U^{238}.   Because U^{236} has the favored even-Z, even-N character, the binding energy is nearly 1 Mev higher in this nucleus and exceeds the energy required for fission.   Thus fission by thermal neutrons is possible in U^{235}.   The observed thermal-neutron fission observed in natural uranium is due to this isotope, which has a relative abundance of about 1 part in 140.

   c. *Energy Release*.   The total energy released in fission of a uranium nucleus into two equal fragments can be estimated from the binding-energy curve of Fig. 182: near $A = 120$, the binding energy per particle is 8.5 Mev, while at $A = 240$ it is 7.6 Mev.   Thus there is available 0.9 Mev per nucleon, or 216 Mev.   In actual fact, it appears, for reasons that are not completely understood, that fission at low excitation energies is rarely symmetric: for the most common type of division, with mass ratio about 1:1.4, the energy release is about 200 Mev.   Most of this energy appears immediately as kinetic energy, but about 20 Mev is released later in β-decay of the fragments.   A considerable adjustment—the transformation of some six or eight neutrons into protons—is needed to bring the fission products to the curve of stable nuclides, and radioactive chains of considerable complexity are involved.   In a very few cases, less than 1 per cent, neutrons are emitted in the course of the decay process: these are the so-called "delayed neutrons," which follow the fission process with time delays varying from seconds to minutes.   Altogether, more than 160 different radioactive nuclides have been discovered among the fission products: small wonder that early workers had difficulty in unscrambling their chemical properties!

202. Prompt Neutrons—Chain Reactions.[1] Since the fission of uranium leaves the fragments with a considerable excess of neutrons as compared with the final, stable products, it might be expected that some neutrons would be set free even in the first separation. If each fission results in the production of one or more neutrons, it may be possible, with a suitable geometrical arrangement, to use these neutrons to produce fissions in other uranium atoms and, in this way, to bring about a self-sustaining, "chain" reaction. This possibility was recognized in the first discussions of fission and led to considerable speculation as to the practicability of producing nuclear energy on a large scale by this means. The magnitude of the energy available, about 200 Mev per event, is staggering compared with the few electron-volts available from a chemical reaction, and it was easy to see that the development had potentially a considerable importance as a source of power and, as events progressed, as a military weapon.

The crucial point in evaluating the feasibility of a self-sustaining reaction is the neutron economy: How many neutrons are emitted per fission, and how many of these can be expected to induce other fissions before being lost in some other reaction? The first estimates of these numbers, made in 1939, were sufficiently encouraging that committees were set up independently in Britain and the United States to study further the military potentialities. At the same time, the outbreak of the war and the general recognition among physicists of the implications of these developments led to a voluntary censorship of publication which resulted in the disappearance of the subject from the open literature for the next 5 years. The history of this period, which saw the growth of the work from the laboratory stage to a government-operated enterprise involving the expenditure of several billion dollars and resulting in the production of the "atomic" bomb, has been related in the admirable book "Atomic Energy for Military Purposes" by H. D. Smyth.[2] We have not space here even to summarize these important developments and shall be obliged to content ourselves with the barest outline of the physical principles involved.

a. Chain Reaction in Uranium. The number of "prompt" neutrons—i.e., neutrons emitted simultaneously with the fission—produced in the thermal-neutron-induced fission of U^{235} can be determined by bombard-

---

[1] C. Goodman, "Science and Engineering of Nuclear Power," Addison-Wesley, Cambridge, Mass., 1947; S. Glasstone and M. C. Edlund, "Elements of Nuclear Reactor Theory," Van Nostrand, New York, 1952; H. Soodack and E. C. Campbell, "Elementary Pile Theory," Wiley, New York, 1950.

[2] Princeton University Press, Princeton, N.J., 1946.

ing a thin sample of separated U^{235} with a beam of thermal neutrons and observing the number of fast neutrons produced.[1] The total number of fast neutrons is found to be 2.5 ± 0.1 per fission.[2] Their kinetic energies range up to 10 or 15 Mev (a few go still higher), with a most probable value near 1 Mev. If one of these 2.5 neutrons can be made to produce another fission, a chain reaction is possible; if more than 1.5 are lost or absorbed in other processes, the reaction will not be self-sustaining.

Let us consider the problem of producing a chain reaction in a block of ordinary uranium. For simplicity we take the block to be infinite in extent so no neutrons are lost through the surface. We assume that 2.5 neutrons have been produced in a fission process at some point in the block, and we endeavor to estimate whether one of these will produce another fission. Some of the pertinent cross sections are listed in Table 10-8.[3] For neutron energies about 1 Mev, fission of U^{238} is possible: the average effective cross section is about 0.3 barn. The cross section for U^{235} fission in this energy range is probably somewhat larger than

TABLE 10-8. NEUTRON CROSS SECTIONS FOR SOME FISSIONABLE MATERIALS (in barns)

	U^{235}	U^{238}	U^*	Pu^{239}
Average fission cross section, fast neutrons.....	(1)†	(0.29)	0.29	(1)
Fission cross section, thermal neutrons.........	549	0	3.92	664
Radiative-capture cross section, thermal neutrons	101	2.8	3.5	361
Inelastic-scattering cross section, fast neutrons..			2.47	
Elastic-scattering cross section, fast neutrons...			1.5	

* Natural uranium: $U^{238}/U^{235} = 140$.

† Numbers in parentheses are estimates.

that for U^{238} (cf. Sec. 203c), but, because of the small fraction ($\frac{1}{140}$) present, its effect here is negligible. Of the neutrons initially above the U^{238} threshold, however, rather few will have an opportunity to cause fission: most of them will lose energy quickly through inelastic scattering processes, in which a sizable fraction of the neutron energy is used up in exciting the U^{238} nucleus. The cross section for inelastic scattering is about 2.5 barns—nearly 10 times that for fission. In addition, neutrons may lose energy, albeit rather slowly, in elastic collisions ($\sigma = 1.5$ barns). Thus of the roughly 30 per cent of the initial neutrons which had energies above 1.5 Mev, about 10 per cent—3 per cent of the total—may produce fission in U^{238}, and the rest are slowed down to low energies.

As the neutrons approach thermal velocities, fission of the rare isotope

[1] *Phys. Rev.*, vol. 85, p. 600, 1952; vol. 87, pp. 1032, 1034, 1037, 1952.

[2] A. E. C. release, *Nucleonics*, vol. 10, p. 64, May, 1952.

[3] A. E. C. release, *loc. cit.*

U^{235} will assume importance: the fission cross section of U^{235} at thermal energy is 549 barns. In its natural dilution this represents an effective cross section of 3.9 barns. Not all the neutrons which reach thermal velocity produce fission, however, because the (n,γ) capture process occurs also, both in U^{235} and U^{238}, with an effective cross section of 3.5 barns in ordinary uranium. Thus only about half the neutrons which reach thermal energy will produce fission in U^{235}. A still more serious difficulty appears in the course of the slowing-down process; this is the resonant absorption of neutrons by U^{238}, in which U^{239} is formed. The (n,γ) cross section exhibits several peaks in the region from 5 ev up to a few kev neutron energy, of which the most important lies in the neighborhood of 11 ev, with an effective width of 0.2 ev and a cross section of 10,000 barns.[1] The scattering cross section at resonance is only about $\frac{1}{25}$ of the capture cross section, and, since at least one elastic collision is required to change the energy by the 2 per cent needed to carry a neutron across the resonance [cf. Eq. (253)], it would appear that most of the neutrons will be lost by capture before reaching thermal energies. The actual situation is somewhat more complicated, and it is not easy to make a precise calculation, but the conclusion that a sustained reaction is impossible in ordinary uranium is probably correct.[2]

b. Moderated Reactors. The problem of avoiding the resonant capture in U^{238} can be solved by the use of a "moderator," that is, a light material mixed with the uranium to slow the neutrons rapidly through the resonance region. In hydrogen, for example, the median energy is changed by a factor $1/e$ per collision and the scattering cross section for slow neutrons is 20 barns (Fig. 204). With an admixture of, say, 100 atoms of hydrogen (in the form of water or paraffin) to one of uranium, most of the neutrons would pass through the resonance region without loss by capture. Unfortunately hydrogen has a thermal-neutron absorption cross section of 0.33 barns, so it will swallow up the neutrons as soon as they reach thermal energy and prevent a self-sustaining reaction. Of the other light substances, lithium and boron present the same difficulty. Helium is not very suitable because it is a gas and forms no compounds. Deuterium, beryllium, and carbon, having very small thermal-absorption cross sections, remain as possibilities. Of these the most commonly used is carbon, in the form of graphite, although deuterium, as heavy water, is frequently used in experimental reactors. There is considerable advantage in a heterogeneous arrangement in which the uranium is in the form of lumps or bars imbedded in the moderater, and this arrangement is used in graphite-moderated reactors. It is possible, with careful design, to achieve a multiplication factor for an infinite lattice of about

[1] H. L. Anderson, *Phys. Rev.*, vol. 80, p. 499, 1950.
[2] Glasstone and Edlund, *loc. cit.*, chap. 9.

1.06 to 1.10 per generation: that is to say, of the 2.5 fast neutrons produced per fission, about 90 per cent survive to be thermalized, and of these about half produce further fissions.

  c. Critical Size.[1] In a reactor of finite size, escape of neutrons may be a problem. Since the escape is a surface effect and all other interactions are simply proportional to the volume, the smaller the reactor, the more serious the escape. The minimum size of reactor which can just maintain itself is called the "critical" size: its magnitude can be roughly estimated from the following argument. In the course of being thermalized in a graphite moderator, a neutron must make about 100 collisions with carbon nuclei. The cross section for collision is about 4 barns; the mean free path between collisions is then

$$\lambda = \frac{1}{\sigma N} = \frac{12}{4 \times 10^{-24} \times 6 \times 10^{23} \times 1.6} \cong 3 \text{ cm}$$

where σ is the elastic-scattering cross section and N the number of nuclei per cubic centimeter. Since the neutron changes direction in a random way at each collision, the radial distance it has traveled from its point of origin after n_1 collisions is, on the average, $\sqrt{n_1} \times 3$, or 30 cm. After it reaches thermal energy, the neutron makes further collisions before it is finally captured [producing either fission or an (n,γ) process]: the number of collisions before capture will be $n_2 = \Lambda/\lambda$, where Λ is the mean free path for absorption and λ the mean free path for scattering. The displacement is then $\sqrt{n_2}\,\lambda$ or $(\Lambda\lambda)^{\frac{1}{2}}$. In a pile containing 100 atoms of carbon to one of uranium, Λ will have roughly one hundred times its value in uranium:

$$\Lambda = \frac{100}{\sigma N} = \frac{100 \times 238}{7.4 \times 10^{-24} \times 6 \times 10^{23} \times 19} \cong 300 \text{ cm}$$

where σ is the combined cross section for fission and radiative capture. The scattering mean free path λ, determined by the graphite, is again about 3 cm. The combined distance for thermalizing and capture, $(30^2 + 300 \times 3)^{\frac{1}{2}} \cong 40$ cm, is then a rough measure of the average displacement of a neutron between production and capture. The actual paths of individual neutrons are of course subject to statistical fluctuations, and an appreciable fraction—roughly $1/e$—will suffer larger displacements than 40 cm. Also, since the displaced neutrons themselves constitute the sources for further neutrons through the fission processes they induce, it is clear that the dimensions of the system must be several times the average path if the loss is to be kept below the few per cent tolerance allowed. An actual calculation based on diffusion theory

[1] E. Fermi, *Science*, Jan. 10, 1947; "Nuclear Physics," University of Chicago Press, Chicago, 1950.

yields a value of about 300 cm for the critical radius of a spherical graphite-uranium reactor.

d. Reactor Control. In practice, a reactor is built of such dimensions as to make it slightly above critical size and the system is controlled by inserting rods or sheets of some material with a high neutron-absorption coefficient—cadmium is often used—into the reactor to reduce the multiplication factor to 1.00. The control of a reactor could be a rather ticklish problem: the lifetime of a neutron from production to ultimate absorption is only a few milliseconds, and even a small excess of the multiplication factor over 1.00 ("supercriticality") might lead to catastrophic results in a short time. Fortunately there are the delayed neutrons, with lifetimes ranging from fractions of a second to some minutes. These neutrons, comprising about 1 per cent of the total, provide an adequate time delay so that small changes in criticality are reflected in changes in neutron flux only after a time of the order of minutes or even hours.

e. Power Production.[1] As a practical matter, the most interesting characteristic of a pile is the number of fissions per unit time, or, what amounts to the same thing, the power level. Each fission releases about 200 Mev of energy, most of which appears eventually in the form of heat. A reaction rate of 3.1×10^{10} fissions per second corresponds to a power of 1 watt. The number of reactions which can be allowed to take place per second is limited by the rate at which this heat can be removed. The first successful pile had no special cooling and could be operated at only about 2 kilowatts. Some of the larger piles operate at power levels of the order of a thousand megawatts.[2] At a power level of 1 megawatt, the consumption of U^{235} is about 1.0 gram per day. The attractiveness of a nuclear reactor as a power source is obvious enough, but a number of problems remain to be solved before it can possibly compete in cost with more conventional sources. Nevertheless, an active program of development of power reactors is going on, and it is reasonable to expect that nuclear power will be of some considerable importance in the not-too-distant future. Known raw-material supplies appear to be adequate for many hundreds, perhaps thousands of years. Even ordinary granite contains sufficient uranium that it may someday be practicable to obtain energy from this source.[3]

203. Fast Fission—Explosive Reactors. The graphite-uranium pile is at best a bulky object, involving some tons of material, and that it works

[1] S. H. Schurr and J. Marschak, "Economic Aspects of Atomic Power," Princeton University Press, Princeton, N.J., 1950; R. L. Murray, "Introduction to Nuclear Engineering," Prentice-Hall, New York, 1954.

[2] H. S. Isbin, *Nucleonics*, p. 65, June, 1953.

[3] H. Brown, "Challenge of Man's Future," Viking Press, New York, 1954.

at all depends on the most skillful design and careful attention to the
precarious neutron economy.   If, on the other hand, a reactor could be
made with pure U^{235}—or some other thermal-fissioning material free
from undesirable (n,γ) resonances—the problem would be much simpler
and the dimensions and complexity of the reactor would be considerably
reduced.   Moreover, it was clear from the first stages of development
that the liberation of large amounts of energy in an *explosive* reaction
would require that the reactor have a satisfactory multiplication factor
with *fast* neutrons, demanding that it consist mainly of material with a
low fission threshold.   The separation of U^{235} and the production of
other fissionable materials has therefore been given a great deal of attention, and the solution of these problems represented a large fraction of the
effort of the war project.

a. *Separation of* U^{235}.   The two most practical means of separating
U^{235} have turned out to be the electromagnetic separator and the gaseous-
diffusion plant.   The former instrument is identical in principle to the
mass spectrometer (Sec. 181b) and depends for its action simply on the
fact that U^{235} and U^{238} ions have different ratios of charge to mass.   The
principal problem here is to obtain a sufficiently large ion current.   An
ordinary mass spectrometer operates on a fraction of a microampere
of ion current: a beam containing 1 microampere of U^+ ions will deposit
only about 1 microgram of U^{235} per day.   Since the quantity of U^{235}
needed was measured in kilograms, it was clear that a beam of many
amperes would be required.   Developments along these lines, conducted
at Berkeley by E. O. Lawrence and his collaborators, led to the design
of the "calutron," an enormous electromagnetic separator of which
several examples were built at Oak Ridge, Tennessee.   Details of the
plants and figures on their output capabilities are not available at the
present writing.

The gaseous-diffusion separator depends on the slight difference in
diffusion rate of gases of different molecular weight.   If a mixture of
$U^{238}F_6$ and $U^{235}F_6$ is pumped through a porous barrier, the fractional
enrichment in the light isotope will amount in a single stage to something
like 1.003; to produce 99 per cent pure $U^{235}F_6$, about 4,000 stages are
required.   A number of such diffusion plants have been constructed,
involving thousands of stages, thousands of vacuum pumps to circulate
the gas, and some acres of barrier area.   Again, production figures for
these plants have not been released, but one can guess that the output
must be of the order of grams to kilograms of U^{235} per day.

b. *Plutonium.*   Uranium is by no means the only element which
undergoes fission under neutron bombardment, nor is U^{235} the only
nuclide which has a threshold below the neutron binding energy.   The
behavior of thorium under neutron bombardment, studied by Fermi's

group, by Hahn and Strassmann, and others, was quite as complicated
as that of uranium and turned out to have the same explanation.   Thorium ($_{90}$Th^{232}) does not, however, undergo fission with thermal neutrons,
because the binding energy of a neutron in the nucleus $_{90}$Th^{233} (even Z,
odd A) is too low.   Protactinium ($_{91}$Pa^{231}) also is fissionable, but, again,
not with low-energy neutrons.   Clearly, a material with high Z is needed
(the critical energy for fission being a function of Z^2/A) and of the character: even Z, odd A.   Such a material is plutonium (Pu^{239}), discovered in
1940 by McMillan and Seaborg.   Plutonium is formed from U^{238} through
neutron capture followed by two successive β-decays:

$$_{92}U^{238} + n \rightarrow {}_{92}U^{239} + \gamma \qquad _{92}U^{239} \rightarrow {}_{93}Np^{239} + \beta^-$$
$$_{93}Np^{239} \rightarrow {}_{94}Pu^{239} + \beta^-$$

Plutonium^{239} is stable to further β-decay and has a half-life for α-decay
of 24,000 years.   The fission properties of Pu^{239} have not been published,
but it is known that it undergoes fission with thermal neutrons, and it
presumably behaves like U^{235}.   The important advantage of plutonium
is that it can be produced in a reactor and the separation from the parent
uranium can be carried out by chemical means.   In addition, the production of Pu from U^{238} converts what is otherwise a most undesirable
constituent of a reactor into a further source of nuclear power, increasing
the available source material by a factor of 140 at the cost of one neutron
per atom.   The major function of the enormous reactors at Hanford and
other sites has been the production of plutonium: the amount produced
can be estimated from the power level, 1,000 megawatts, as some kilograms per day.

   c. *Fission Bomb.*   A primary consideration in an explosive reactor is
the speed with which the chain multiplies, compared with the speed of
separation of the components as the heat and pressure begin to develop
from the reaction.   For a reactor depending on thermal neutrons, the
time constant is determined by the time required to slow down and capture the neutrons, a time of the order of milliseconds.   The rate of
expansion in a well-developed explosion, on the other hand, is measured
in microseconds.   Thus it is clear that reliance must be placed on fast-
neutron-induced fission in a bomb, and the critical size will depend on the
competition between the fast fission cross section and the combined losses
due to (n,γ) processes and loss through the surface.   Without precise
data on the cross sections for U^{235} and Pu^{239} we cannot estimate the critical size, but a crude guess can be made from elementary considerations.
The critical radius will be of the order of magnitude of the mean displacement of a neutron before it produces fission, as in the case discussed
above.   This displacement is given by $(\Lambda_f \lambda_s)^{1/2}$, where Λ_f is now the mean
free path for fission by fast neutrons and λ_s the corresponding mean free

path for scattering (elastic plus inelastic) in U^{235} or Pu^{239}. Since the neutron energy is well above threshold in these substances, we can guess that the cross section for fission may be an appreciable fraction of the projected area of the nucleus, which is about 2.4×10^{-24} cm^2; we take 1.0 barn as a reasonable estimate (the fission cross section somewhat above threshold is about 0.5 barn for U^{238}, 1.0 barn for U^{234}, and 1.5 barn for Np^{237}).[1] The scattering cross section is presumably not very different from that of U^{238}, 4 barns. With these figures, $(\Lambda_f \lambda_s)^{1/2}$ turns out to be of the order of 10 cm. The critical size will presumably not be much larger than this number and may even be smaller, since one can afford to be more prodigal with the neutrons in the present case and since (n,γ) processes are probably unimportant. The use of a neutron-reflecting layer around the core will reduce the critical size somewhat. In practice, the reactor is held below critical size before use, for example by dividing it into two parts which are held separated; the assembly might be made by firing one part against the other in a gun. Both U^{235} and Pu^{239} have been used in "atomic" bombs. The first bombs detonated produced an energy equivalent of about 20,000 tons of TNT.

204. Fusion: Energy from the Light Elements. Although the phenomenon of fission is a most spectacular example of the conversion of mass energy into other, less passive forms, considerably more energy can be released by fusion of the lightest elements into elements lying near the middle of the atomic table. From the observed variation of the average binding energy per nucleon, Fig. 182, it can be seen that the combination of free protons and neutrons to make $_{28}Ni^{60}$, for example, would release 8.8 Mev per nucleon—more than 10 times the energy released per nucleon in fission. About 7 Mev per nucleon of this energy is already released in the combination of two neutrons and two protons into an α-particle: because the α-particle is so tightly bound, further combinations of α-particles release comparatively little energy.

a. Stellar Energy Sources.[2] The conversion of hydrogen into helium is generally believed to be the principal source of energy in the sun and the stars. Hydrogen appears to constitute more than 90 per cent by mass of the total material in the universe, so there is a comparatively large amount of energy available. Two possible mechanisms of conversion have been given serious consideration: the so-called carbon-nitrogen cycle, and the direct proton-proton chain. Both processes depend for their operation upon extremely high temperatures: the reactions are

---

[1] The fast fission cross section for U^{235} and Pu^{239} is estimated as 3 barns in W. E. Stephens, "Nuclear Fission and Atomic Energy," p. 114, Science Press, 1948; this value would result in a critical radius of the order of 6 cm.

[2] E. E. Salpeter, *Ann. Revs. Nuclear Sci.*, vol. 2, 1953; W. A. Fowler, *Memoires, Soc. Roy des Sciences de Liége*, vol. 13, p. 88, 1954.

brought about by the bombardment of one particle by another in the course of thermal agitation. Because the particles are charged, the probability of approach within the range of nuclear forces is very small indeed, even at the high temperatures and densities which obtain in stellar interiors, and, in fact, the reactions proceed mainly with particles whose energies lie high upon the tail of the Maxwell energy distribution. The carbon-nitrogen cycle requires the previous existence (formed in another process) of a small amount of carbon: the carbon is not depleted in the cycle but acts only as a kind of catalyst for conversion of four protons into an α-particle. The reactions involved are

$$C^{12}(p,\gamma)N^{13}: N^{13}(\beta^+)C^{13}$$
$$C^{13}(p,\gamma)N^{14}$$
$$N^{14}(p,\gamma)O^{15}: O^{15}(\beta^+)N^{15}$$
$$N^{15}(p,\alpha)C^{12}$$

The net result is

$$4H^1 \rightarrow He^4 + 2\beta^+ + 2\nu + 25 \text{ Mev}$$

Most of this energy will be absorbed locally and converted into thermal energy which maintains the reaction: the temperature will remain fixed at such a value that the rate of production just equals the rate of loss by thermal radiation.

The probability of any of these (p,γ) processes at low energies is governed by the Gamow penetration factor [Eq. (271), Sec. 187], which is a very steep exponential function of the kinetic energy. At the estimated temperature of the sun's center, $13 \times 10^{6}°$K, the most probable energy kT of the protons is 1 kilovolt, but the rise of the cross section is so steep that the main contribution comes from the few protons with thermal-agitation energies some 10 times this value. The rate of reaction increases about as the 20th power of the temperature.

The direct combination of protons may take place through the reaction

$$H^1(p,\beta^+)H^2$$

followed by

$$H^2(p,\gamma)He^3$$
$$He^3(He^3,2p)He^4$$

The formation of a β-particle (and a neutrino) in a nuclear encounter is an exceedingly rare event, as can be seen from the fact that the characteristic time for β-decay is of the order of seconds. On the other hand, the Coulomb barrier is relatively less important here than in the reactions involving carbon and nitrogen, and the rate is less temperature-dependent. In the sun the (pp) reaction appears to contribute about 90 per cent of the energy: in hotter stars, the C-N reactions will dominate.

b. Thermonuclear Bomb. A considerable development has been carried out to make use of fusion reactions in a nuclear weapon. In such a device a large number of reactions are started in an assembly of suitable light elements, possibly with the aid of the enormous temperatures developed by a fission bomb. The energy release in these reactions then maintains the local temperature, and the chain proceeds until the supply of material is exhausted, or until sufficient expansion has taken place that the system cools below the point of further reaction. One reaction which might possibly be used in such a "thermonuclear" bomb is $H^2(t,n)He^4$, in which 14-Mev neutrons are produced.[1] These neutrons can give a large part of their energy to any deuterons or tritons they strike, and since the reaction has a high cross section even at low energy, it is conceivable that a self-sustaining reaction could be established. Whether this reaction is actually used is not at the present writing (1954) a matter of public information: it is not unlikely that several reactions may actually be involved. Thermonuclear bombs yielding an energy release equivalent to 10^7 tons of TNT have been successfully detonated.

[1] The symbol t represents a triton, nucleus of H^3.

CHAPTER 11

COSMIC RAYS AND FUNDAMENTAL PARTICLES

The study of the phenomena associated with the cosmic radiation commands the interest of the physicist not only because of his natural curiosity about the character and origin of the cosmic rays themselves but also because their interactions with terrestrial materials furnish information on the most fundamental constituents of matter. Nature has in fact provided us in the atmosphere with a gigantic laboratory in which atoms are bombarded with projectiles, not of a few million electron-volts energy, but with energies of many billions of electron volts. As a result of this bombardment, many extraordinary processes occur, including the production of a variety of particles which seem in some way, not yet entirely clear, to be intimately connected with the basic composition and structure of atomic nuclei.

205. Early Work on Cosmic Rays.[1] *a. Discovery of the Radiation.* It has been known for more than 100 years that the air possesses a slight electrical conductivity. In 1899–1900 a careful study of the phenomenon was made by Elster and Geitel[2] and by C. T. R. Wilson.[3] The method used was to mount an electroscope on an insulating support inside a closed vessel, and to observe the rate at which electric charge was lost by the electroscope. Wilson took the precaution of connecting the other end of the insulating support to a source of potential equal to the initial potential of the electroscope, so that leakage along the support would tend to maintain the charge; thus the observed loss of charge could only be due to its neutralization by ions collected out of the air. The conductivity of the air enclosed in the electroscope was found to be permanent, in spite of the continual removal of ions from it by the electric field. From this fact it may be inferred that the ions are continually being regenerated in the air by some agency.

---

[1] R. A. Millikan, "Electrons + and −," University of Chicago Press, Chicago, 1947; L. Jánossy, "Cosmic Radiation," Oxford, London, 1950; D. J. X. Montgomery, "Cosmic Ray Physics," Princeton University Press, Princeton, N.J., 1949; A. Corlin, "Cosmic Ultra Radiation in Northern Sweden," dissertation, Lund, 1934.

[2] J. Elster and H. Geitel, *Physik. Z.*, vol. 1, p. 11, 1899; H. Geitel, *Physik. Z.*, vol. 2, p. 116, 1900.

[3] C. T. R. Wilson, *Proc. Cambridge Phil. Soc.*, vol. 11, p. 32, 1900.

For a time, the cause of this natural ionization of air was supposed to lie in traces of radioactive material residing in the apparatus or in its surroundings, or perhaps in the earth or the atmosphere. Other experimenters found that the ionization varied with the material of which the electroscope or ionization chamber was constructed, and that it could be partially screened off by surrounding the apparatus with a heavy layer of lead. In the expectation that the ionization should be much less at a considerable height above the earth, Gockel ascended in a balloon and made observations at various heights. He found that the ionization did decrease with increasing height, but only slightly.[1] In 1911-1914 Hess and Kolhörster extended balloon observations[2] to much higher altitudes and found that above a few hundred meters the conductivity *begins to increase again.* Kolhörster showed that the increase was continuous up to 9,000 meters, at which 93 ions per cubic centimeter per second were produced in the ionization chamber attached to his electroscope, as against 13 at the earth's surface.

To explain the greatly increased ionization at these high altitudes, Hess proposed the novel hypothesis that it was caused by a penetrating radiation falling upon the earth from the outside. He remarked that this radiation could not be coming in large part from the sun, since the ionization was found to be sensibly the same by night as by day. Its penetrating power must be much greater than that of the hardest γ-rays known. For the very hard (2.6-Mev) γ-rays from ThC'', the value of the mass absorption coefficient μ/ρ, or absorption coefficient divided by density (Sec. 157), is 0.036 cm^2 per gm in Al or 0.041 in Pb, hence perhaps 0.035 in air. Thus a beam of these γ-rays would be reduced to half-intensity in a thickness x of air at standard density, given by $e^{-\mu x} = \frac{1}{2}$, where $\mu/\rho = 0.035$ and $\rho = 0.001293$, or in a thickness $x = 153$ meters. In his balloon observations, Kolhörster found that the ionization decreased to half-value in a descent of roughly 2,200 meters at an average height where the density of the atmosphere is $\frac{5}{12}$ of its density at the surface. At normal density this would mean a decrease to half in about 1,000 meters, or $6\frac{1}{2}$ times the distance required for the γ-rays.

The observations of Hess and of Kolhörster may be regarded as constituting the discovery of cosmic rays. They became known in Germany as "Höhenstrahlung" or "Ultrastrahlung"; the name "cosmic rays" is due to Millikan and Cameron (1925).

b. First Observations of Cosmic Rays under Water. Even after it was shown that the ionization increased with altitude, many physicists, among

---

[1] A. Gockel, *Physik. Z.*, vol. 11, p. 280, 1910; vol. 12, p. 595, 1911.

[2] V. F. Hess, *Physik. Z.*, vol. 12, p. 998, 1911; vol. 13, p. 1084, 1912; vol. 14, p. 610, 1913; W. Kolhörster, *Verhandl. deut. physik. Ges.*, vol. 15, p. 1111, 1913; vol. 16, p. 719, 1914.

them Rutherford himself, remained unconvinced of the extraterrestrial origin of the rays.   It was argued that the source of the radiation might lie in the atmosphere itself, perhaps emitting rays of quite ordinary penetrating power, but so distributed as to produce a fictitiously low absorption coefficient in the air.   An important step forward was taken by Millikan and Cameron[1] when, in 1928, improving upon earlier observations by Kolhörster,[2] they lowered sealed electroscopes to various depths below the surfaces of snow-fed mountain lakes, which should be especially free from radioactive contamination.   The type of instrument used is described in the next section.   Even above the water, the ionization was observed to be less than over the land, presumably because γ-rays from the earth were screened off by the water.   As the electroscope was lowered into the lake, the ionization fell off rapidly in the first meter or so; thereafter it decreased more slowly with increasing depth, and less rapidly as the depth grew greater.

Observations were made in two lakes in California, Arrowhead Lake, at an elevation of 5,100 ft (latitude 34°), and Gem Lake at 9,080 ft (latitude 38°).   In Gem Lake, the ionization was still decreasing at 50 meters below the surface.   When the ionization found in the two lakes was compared at the same depth below the surface in both lakes, it was seen to be less in the lake at the lower elevation.   When, however, the comparison was made in a different manner, viz., between points in the lower lake at a given depth below the surface and points in the upper lake so chosen as to be situated farther below the surface, the increase in the depth of water in the upper lake being equivalent in mass to the column of air between the elevations of the two lakes, then the observed values of the ionization were found to be in close agreement.   Hence, by plotting cosmic-ray intensities, as measured by the ionization, against the total depth below the top of the atmosphere, expressed in equivalent meters of water, the observations in the two lakes could be represented by a single curve.   On the assumption that the initial intensity of the rays entering the earth's atmosphere is the same at the two localities, this result showed that the intervening layer of air between the two lake levels acted only as an absorber and did not contain sources to any appreciable extent.   It was therefore concluded that the apparent great penetrating power of the rays is real and that their source is extraterrestrial.[3]

---

[1] R. A. Millikan and G. H. Cameron, *Phys. Rev.*, vol. 28, p. 851, 1926; vol. 31, p. 921, 1928.

[2] W. Kolhörster, *Verhandl. Preuss. Akad.*, p. 366, 1923.

[3] Actually, the effective absorption of the air layer should have been somewhat *larger* than that of the same mass of water, because of the μ-meson decay (Sec. 215), but this does not affect the present argument.   Cf. H. V. Neher and G. Stever, *Phys. Rev.*, vol. 58, p. 766, 1941.

From this time on, the number of workers in the field rapidly increased. Until about 1932, the main object of investigation was the magnitude of the ionization due to cosmic rays as a function of elevation, position on the earth, time of day, and so on.   During this period the radiation itself was generally believed to consist of photons resembling γ-rays but of much shorter wavelength, and speculation was common as to the possible place of origin of such photons.   Apparently they could not be coming from the sun or even from the stars, for the cosmic-ray ionization has always been found to be almost, or quite, uninfluenced by changes in the position of the sun or of the star masses composing the galaxy.   Yet it has been estimated that the total amount of energy brought to the earth by cosmic rays is comparable with that brought in by starlight[1] (see Sec. 207).

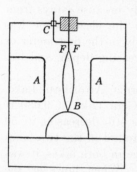

FIG. 211. The electroscope of Millikan and Otis.   The two fibers F repel one another when charged, and their separation is measured by means of a microscope.

206. Measurement of Cosmic-ray Ionization.[2] To measure the ionization, a string electrometer of very small capacity was usually used. Millikan and Cameron, in the work discussed in the last section, used an instrument of the Wulf type, the essentials of which are shown diagrammatically in Fig. 211.[3]   The two fibers FF, of platinized quartz, hung from an insulating quartz rod, are charged by means of the charging wire C and tend to spread apart because of their mutual repulsion. The spreading is resisted by the downward pull of the quartz bow B.   The positions of the fibers are read by means of a microscope; they are kept in a plane perpendicular to the axis of the microscope by the attraction of induced charges on the metal wires AA.

Sometimes only one fiber is employed, opposite a grounded plate.   In any case, the position of the fiber is either observed visually from time to time, or it may be projected upon a slowly moving photographic film driven by clockwork, so that the instrument is self-recording.   In the latter case, the fiber may either be illuminated intermittently by an attachment connected to the clockwork, or it may be made to produce a continuous trace on the film.   The clock can also be made to charge the electroscope from time to time.   Carefully made self-recording apparatus of this kind has been mounted on ships by Millikan, Compton, and others, and sent on long voyages over the ocean in order to compare the ioniza-

[1] E. Regener, *Z. Physik*, vol. 80, p. 666, 1933.
[2] J. Strong et al., "Procedures in Experimental Physics," chap. VI, Prentice-Hall, New York, 1938.
[3] R. A. Millikan and R. M. Otis, *Phys. Rev.*, vol. 27, p. 645, 1926.

tion at different geographical locations.   The apparatus required no other attention than the periodic winding of the clock.

In any instrument for measuring ionization there is a zero effect due to residual radioactive contamination of the instrument itself.   This zero effect has usually been determined by shielding the instrument with lead and sinking it deep under water or taking it down a coal mine, the residual ionization there observed being assumed to be due to radiation from the walls or the instrument.   In later instruments, the residual effect was rendered less important by using large ionization chambers attached to the electroscope, so as to increase the volume of the enclosed gas in comparison with the area of the walls, and also by raising the pressure of the gas (e.g., to 30 atmospheres).   Often other gases than air are used, in which the ionization is greater or in which ion collection is more efficient.   Reduction of the readings to correspond to air at standard density is then made by means of comparison tests using γ-rays from radium; it is assumed that the observed ionization varies in the same way with the density of the gas whether it is produced by cosmic rays or by γ-rays.   In making measurements near the surface of the earth, the apparatus is commonly shielded with 10 cm or more of lead, in order to cut off radioactive rays from the surroundings.

The *absolute magnitude* of the ionization, or the number of ions formed per cubic centimeter per second, may be determined by an elementary calculation from the known capacity of the electroscope system and the observed rate of decrease in its potential.   The value recorded by any particular instrument depends on a number of factors, including the latitude, longitude, barometric pressure, and shielding.   In an unshielded instrument, at latitude 41°N, the ionization due to cosmic rays[1] is 2.74 ions per cubic centimeter per second at sea level.

207. The Altitude-depth Curve.   A great deal has been learned about the properties of cosmic rays from measurements of the variation of their intensity both as a function of height in the atmosphere and of depth under the earth's surface.

a. Observations below the Surface of the Earth.   The measurements of Millikan and Cameron mentioned above were extended to a depth of 260 meters under water by Regener,[2] who found an appreciable intensity persisting even at this depth, equivalent to 25 atmospheres.   Later work, both under water and in mines, has been summarized by E. P. George,[3]

---

[1] J. G. Wilson, "Progress in Cosmic Ray Physics," vol. I, article by H. V. Neher, p. 245, Interscience, New York, 1952.

[2] E. Regener, Z. *Physik*, vol. 74, p. 433, 1932; cf. also *Physik. Z.*, vol. 34, p. 306, 1933.

[3] J. G. Wilson, "Progress in Cosmic Ray Physics," vol. I, p. 395, Interscience, New York, 1952.

and by P. H. Barrett et al.,[1] who cite observations at depths as great as 3,000 meters water equivalent (about 1,100 meters actual depth), where the intensity is only 3×10^{-6} of the sea-level value. A curve of the observed intensity as a function of depth, adapted from the paper by George, is presented as a log-log plot in Fig. 212. The intensity does not vary as a simple exponential function of the depth, but shows an absorption coefficient which decreases rapidly with increasing depth. At a depth of 10 meters water equivalent, the mass absorption coefficient is about 1.5×10^{-3} cm² per gram; at 1,000 meters, it is about 50 times smaller. Most of the effects observed below the earth's surface are due to the μ-meson component, of which we shall speak later (Sec. 214).

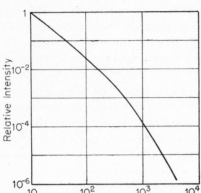

FIG. 212. Variation of cosmic-ray intensity with depth, in meters of water equivalent, below the surface of the earth (both scales are logarithmic).

b. *Cosmic-ray Intensity at Various Altitudes above the Earth.* As a typical example illustrating the variation of the ionization with altitude may be cited the results obtained by Millikan, Neher, and Haynes[2] near Fort Sam Houston in Texas (latitude 39°). Instruments were carried up into the stratosphere by sounding balloons, each instrument containing a recording electroscope and a recording barometer and thermometer, all operated by clockwork. The electroscope was recharged every 4 min from a charged condenser, which was so well constructed that it lost by leakage only ½ per cent of its charge per hour. The instrument weighed 2.5 lb and was carried aloft by five 1-meter balloons. As the intended top of the flight was approached, the rate of ascent was diminished by the bursting of two or three balloons; and after 3½ hr the instrument, automatically detached from the balloons, floated back to earth supported by a parachute. The parachute was of silk colored red, so as to attract attention, and an envelope offering a reward for the return of the instrument was attached. Four out of five instruments were eventually recovered, two within 12 hr, one from a distance of 80 miles.

The average results from two of these flights are shown by curve C in Fig. 214 (Sec. 208). The ordinate represents the number of ions per

[1] P. H. Barrett, L. M. Bollinger, G. Cocconi, Y. Eisenberg, and K. Greisen, *Revs. Mod. Phys.*, vol. 24, p. 133, 1952.
[2] R. A. Millikan, H. V. Neher, and S. K. Haynes, *Phys. Rev.*, vol. 50, p. 992, 1936

cubic centimeter per second that would be produced by the cosmic rays in air at standard density, which serves as a measure of their intensity. The actual ionization at high altitudes is much less because of the lower density of the air.   The abscissa in the figure represents the depth below the top of the atmosphere in equivalent meters of water (calculated as pressure in centimeters Hg times 10.33/76, sea level being, therefore, at 10.33 on the axis of abscissas).   The altitude itself can also be calculated from the recorded pressure,[1] being about 92,000 ft for the last point shown on the curve ($p = 1.29$ cm Hg, 98 per cent of the way to the top of the atmosphere).   Actually the absolute altitude is ordinarily of only minor interest; the important parameter in such experiments is the mass of air above the instrument, and this is directly measured by the pressure. A convenient and much-used unit is the mass of air in a column of unit cross section above the point in question, expressed in grams per square centimeter.   At an altitude where the pressure is p cm of Hg, the residual atmosphere amounts to $13.6p$ grams per cm^2; thus, sea level corresponds to $13.6 \times 76 = 1,033$ grams per cm^2.

Curve C in Fig. 214 reveals a maximum ionization of nearly 240 ions per cubic centimeter per second (in standard air), as against about 3 at the earth's surface.   The most interesting feature, however, is the *decrease* of the ionization in the uppermost 5 per cent of the atmosphere.   This decrease is explained in the following way.   As the primary cosmic rays approach the earth, they interact with the atoms in the upper atmosphere, producing a large number of secondary particles.   Most of this interaction occurs within the top 1-meter water equivalent, or about 100 grams per cm^2 of the atmosphere.   Because each primary produces many secondaries, the number of particles and the total ionization are increased during this process.   In the course of their passage down through the atmosphere, the secondaries are gradually absorbed, and comparatively few survive to sea level.   The details of the complex processes involved will be discussed in later sections.

The *area* under such an ionization-altitude curve as C, Fig. 214, is a measure of the total amount of energy brought to the earth in the form of cosmic rays, assuming that all the energy eventually appears in the form of ionization.   From the form of the curve, it is evident that almost all the ionization has occurred by the time sea level is reached, and we make very little error in ignoring the further energy loss below the surface; similarly we make very little error in extrapolating the curve to zero at the top of the atmosphere.   The total ionization in a 1 cm^2 column

---

[1] Very roughly, the altitude in kilometers is given by $Z = 8 \ln (p_0/p)$, where p_0 is the pressure at sea level and p the pressure at altitude Z.   An empirical curve relating altitude and pressure for the "standard" atmosphere is given in B. Rossi, "High Energy Particles," appendix VI, Prentice-Hall, New York, 1952.

extending from sea level to the top of the atmosphere (at San Antonio) is then the integral under curve C. By counting the squares under the curve we find an area of about 700 ions per cubic centimeter per second (per atmosphere) $\times$ (meters of water equivalent). To convert meters of water to the equivalent height of the air column at 1 atmosphere, we multiply by 100 $\times$ the density ratio (water/air) obtaining $(7.0 \times 10^4/ 0.0013) = 5.5 \times 10^7$ ions per square centimeter per sec (per atmosphere). Assuming an average value of 33 ev per ion (Sec. 178) we obtain for the total power incident (from all directions in the upper hemisphere) on 1 cm^2 at the top of the atmosphere at latitude 38°N, 1.8 Bev per sec or 3×10^{-10} watts.[1]   *This is a flux of the same order as the total energy received by the earth in the form of starlight.*

208. Discovery of the Latitude Effect.   A number of workers realized by 1925 that a study of the variation of the cosmic-ray intensity with latitude could provide useful information on the nature of the primaries because of the influence of the earth's magnetic field.   If the primaries are charged particles, the field will affect their trajectories at great distances and might result in a strong dependence of the intensity upon the latitude of observation; uncharged particles or γ-rays, on the other hand, will be unaffected.

Millikan and Cameron[2] looked for such an effect in 1926, making measurements on a sea voyage from geomagnetic latitude 32°N to the equator, but failed to find any systematic change outside their instrumental error of about 6 per cent.   However, in voyages made in 1927 and 1928, covering a larger range of latitudes, Clay[3] found an effect which he reported as a decrease of about 25 per cent at the equator. Millikan then made careful measurements from 41°N to 69°N finding again no effect, this time within 1 per cent.   The resulting controversy was finally resolved by the discovery that Clay's estimate of the magnitude of the decrease was too large and that a large part of the effect occurs between 40° and 30°N, just the region Millikan had missed.

In 1930, a group headed by A. H. Compton[4] initiated an extensive survey of cosmic-ray intensity at various locations on the earth.   Observations were made at 69 stations by a number of cooperating observers, all using similar instruments calibrated on the spot by means of the ionization produced by a standard radium capsule.   These observations confirmed the existence of the equatorial drop in intensity, as reported by Clay.

---

[1] This is a minimum estimate, since neutrinos present either as primaries or secondaries would produce no ionization.

[2] R. A. Millikan, "Electrons, + and −," *loc. cit.*

[3] J. Clay, *Proc. Roy. Acad. Amsterdam,* vol. 30, p. 1115, **1927.**

[4] Cf. A. H. Compton, *Phys. Rev.,* vol. 43, p. 387, 1933.

Compton pointed out that his results correlated much better with *geomagnetic* latitude than with *geographic* latitude, and this has been confirmed by later work, especially by the extensive sea-level observations of Millikan and Neher.[1] The latter observers, and Clay independently, discovered in 1934 that even the slight variation in the strength of the earth's magnetic field along the equator is reflected in the cosmic-ray intensity, which is some 4 per cent lower in the East Indies and the Indian Ocean, where the magnetic field is strongest, than it is on the opposite side of the earth, in equatorial South America, near which the field is weakest.

All observations indicate, on the other hand, that the cosmic-ray intensity at sea level does not vary much from one location to another above geomagnetic latitude 40°, N or S, which means in the United States above, roughly, 30° in geographic latitude. From a geomagnetic latitude of 40°N or 40°S to the equator, the drop in intensity amounts to about 10 per cent on the average, rising to 12 per cent in eastern Asia and falling to 8 per cent in the longitude of equatorial South America. The drop in intensity begins rather suddenly as the limiting latitude is passed.

The most accurate study of the equatorial drop is probably that made by Compton and Turner.[2] They mounted a recording electroscope on a steamship plying regularly between Vancouver (Canada), Auckland (New Zealand), and Sydney (Australia), the route crossing the geomagnetic equator almost where the latter crosses the geographic equator. The observations were extended over 10 months.

A decided *seasonal effect* was noted in these observations, especially at the extreme north and south ends of the range, where the cosmic-ray intensity during the warm months averaged less than during the cold months. In Fig. 213 are shown the curves obtained by Compton and Turner for the four seasons, ordinates representing average cosmic-ray intensity and abscissas the geomagnetic latitude. The seasonal variation, which has also been recorded by others, is believed to be correlated with atmospheric temperature; such an interpretation is supported by observations in Europe showing a variation of the same order of magnitude with temperature at a given station. (Temperature effects on the apparatus itself were shown not to occur.) From their data, Compton and Turner inferred a decrease of about 0.18 per cent per degree C of rise of temperature.

The temperature effect was believed by Compton and Turner to account for perhaps 3 per cent of the observed decrease of 10 per cent from high latitudes to the equator. Correcting for it, they found as the

---

[1] R. A. Millikan and H. V. Neher, *Phys. Rev.*, vol. 50, p. 15, 1936.

[2] A. H. Compton and R. N. Turner, *Phys. Rev.*, vol. 52, p. 799, 1937. Other references are given by T. H. Johnson, *Revs. Mod. Phys.*, vol. 10, p. 193, 1938.

true geomagnetic effect the curve labeled *NS* in Fig. 213, representing
ionization corrected to a temperature of 21°C.   In drawing this curve,
the southern half, *SS*, has been folded back over the northern half, *NNN*,
in order to show how nearly they agree.

The close correspondence thus revealed between variations in cosmic-
ray intensity and the features of the magnetic field at the surface of the
earth constitutes convincing evidence that at least part of the primary
cosmic rays must consist, not of photons, but of charged particles of some

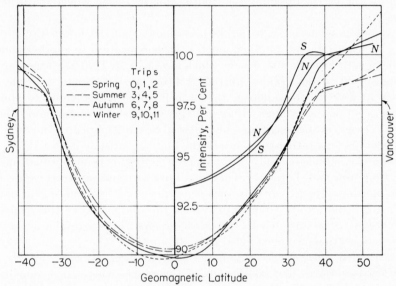

FIG. 213. Variation of cosmic-ray ionization with latitude over the Pacific Ocean.   The
value called "100 per cent" is chosen arbitrarily (and differently for the curves *NN*,
SS).   (See text.)

sort.   The effect of the magnetic field upon the particles must be produced before they enter the earth's atmosphere; for the atmosphere is
so thin relative to the earth's dimensions that any effect produced within
it could have little influence on the large-scale distribution of cosmic-ray
intensity over the earth.

The latitude effect is much more pronounced at high altitude, as was
shown in an airplane survey by Bowen, Millikan, and Neher[1] in 1932 and
by observations at mountain stations by Compton in 1933.   Since that
time, there have been made a great many measurements on the latitude
effect at altitudes extending all the way from sea level to over 100,000 ft
(about 10 grams per cm²).   For the observations at high altitudes,
balloon-carried electroscopes or Geiger counters are used.   In later

[1] I. S. Bowen, R. A. Millikan, and H. V. Neher, *Phys. Rev.*, vol. 43, p. 661, 1933.

experiments, these instruments have been fitted with radio transmitters to relay information on discharge rate, barometric pressure, and temperature to the ground station. A typical set of observations reported by Bowen, Millikan, and Neher[1] in 1938 is shown in Fig. 214. Here it may be seen that the maximum ionization, observed at high altitude, changes by nearly a factor of 4 between the equator and latitude 60°N. As is the

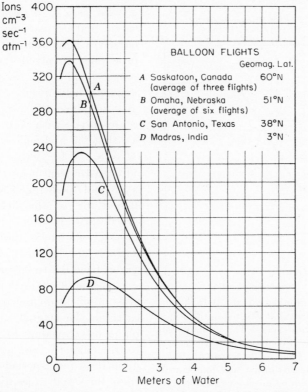

FIG. 214. Cosmic-ray ionization as a function of altitude at four different latitudes. (*Bowen, Millikan, and Neher.*)

case for the sea-level ionization, the rate of increase in ionization with latitude is considerably smaller at the higher latitudes, although some increase is still evident between 51 and 60°N (curves *B* and *A*). More recent experiments by Neher, Peterson, and Stern,[2] in which balloon flights were made at latitudes as great as 88°N, indicate no further increase beyond 58°N. Their results for the total energy dissipated in the atmosphere, obtained by integrating the altitude-ionization curves

[1] I. S. Bowen, R. A. Millikan, H. V. Neher, *Phys. Rev.*, vol. 53, p. 855, 1938.
[2] H. V. Neher, V. Z. Peterson, and E. A. Stern, *Phys. Rev.*, vol. 90, p. 655, 1953.

as described at the end of Sec. 207, are shown in Fig. 215. We shall discuss this curve further after considering briefly the theory of geomagnetic effects.

209. Theory of Geomagnetic Effects.[1] The mathematical theory of the effect of the earth's magnetic field on incoming charged particles has been worked out in considerable detail by Störmer, Epstein, Vallarta, LeMaitre, and others. Since the analysis of the trajectories in the general case is a rather complicated matter, we shall content ourselves here with outlining the principles involved and citing some of the main results. The magnetic field of the earth at some distance above the surface may be represented with fair accuracy as that of a dipole of moment $M = 8.1 \times 10^{25}$ gauss cm³, tilted 11.5° with respect to the earth's axis and pointing south. The magnitude of the field at any given latitude drops off as the inverse cube of the radius; at the surface of the earth the value varies from 0.3 to 0.6 gauss.

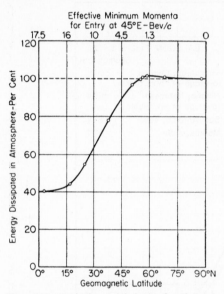

FIG. 215. Variation with latitude of total cosmic-ray energy dissipated in the atmosphere, per unit area. The ordinates are expressed as percentages of the value at the North Pole. The apparent excess near 60°N is attributed to a temperature effect on the fraction of energy converted into neutrinos. (*Adapted from Neher, Peterson, and Stern, Phys. Rev., vol. 90, p. 655, 1953.*)

Consider a charged particle of given momentum approaching the earth in the magnetic equatorial plane: it is traveling at right angles to the magnetic lines and is acted upon by a force perpendicular to these lines and to its direction of motion. The trajectory will then be curved more or less, depending upon the momentum of the particle (the magnitude of the momentum is of course unaffected) and upon its initial impact parameter, i.e., the perpendicular distance from the dipole axis to the projected line of the initial motion.

A few typical trajectories for particles of the same momentum but with different impact parameters are illustrated schematically in Fig. 216. Of these, one, labeled *B*, has the interesting property that it approaches a circle concentric with the magnetic-dipole axis: in principle, particles

[1] D. J. X. Montgomery, "Cosmic Ray Physics," Princeton University Press, Princeton, N.J., 1949; F. K. Richtmyer and E. H. Kennard, "Introduction to Modern Physics," 4th ed., McGraw-Hill, New York, 1947.

with an impact parameter slightly less than this one can traverse the circle many times before flying off in an orbit of type B or plunging inward on such a path as C. The radius r_1 of the critical circle is evidently given by $p = Ber_1$, where p is the momentum of the particle, e its charge (in electromagnetic units), and B the value of the magnetic field at the radius r_1. For the equatorial plane, $B = M/r_1^3$ and $p = Me/r_1^2$. It can be shown by solving the equations of motion explicitly that, for impact parameters less than that corresponding to trajectory B, the particles execute loops inside the critical circle (C and D are examples); the one of these which reaches closest to the center—an orbit lying close to B—gets in to a radius $r_2 = (\sqrt{2} - 1)r_1$, or $0.414r_1$. It can be seen from the figure that trajectories cross the circle r_1 at all angles, but at r_2 only tangential intersections occur.

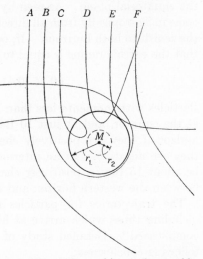

Fig. 216. A few orbits (only roughly correct) for a charged particle in the equatorial plane of a magnetic dipole M. All the orbits shown refer to the same momentum; they differ only in the impact parameter. The circle drawn with a solid line is the "critical circle," $r_1 = p/Be$ (see text), and the dashed circle, $r_2 = 0.414r_1$, represents the limit inside which no trajectory can penetrate.

The trajectories shown in Fig. 216 apply to particles of any momentum; only the scale of the figure, as fixed for example by the radius of the critical circle r_1, need be changed as the momentum of the particles under consideration is varied. Conversely, to represent the trajectories of particles of a specified momentum in their relation to the surface of the earth, we need only superimpose on the figure a circle representing this surface, drawn to appropriate scale. For example, if we choose such a scale that the earth's radius $r_e = r_1$, the trajectories correspond to the momentum $p = Me/r_e^2$. Inserting numerical values, we find for this case $p = 60$ Bev/c,[1] corresponding to a kinetic energy for an electron

---

[1] The dimensions of momentum may be expressed as (energy/velocity); a momentum of 1 ev/c corresponds to $1.6 \times 10^{-12}/3 \times 10^{10} = 0.53 \times 10^{-22}$ gram cm per sec. The kinetic energy of a particle with momentum p is

$$T = (p^2c^2 + M_0^2c^4)^{1/2} - M_0c^2$$

where M_0 is the rest mass. If $W_0 = M_0c^2$ in Mev and $p_c = p$ in units of Mev/c, $T = (p_c^2 + W_0^2)^{1/2} - W_0$, in Mev. If $T \gg M_0c^2$ (0.5 Mev for electrons, 0.93 Bev for protons), $T \cong p_c$, that is, the kinetic energy in Mev is numerically equal to the momentum in Mev/c.

of 60 Bev, for a proton 59 Bev. From the argument of the preceding paragraph it may be seen that particles traveling in the equatorial plane with momenta greater than 60 Bev/c have critical radii smaller than the earth's radius and can enter the atmosphere from any direction in the equatorial plane. As seen by an observer on the equator, they will come in isotropically from all directions in a vertical, east-west plane from the zenith to both horizons. If, on the other hand, the scale is so chosen that the earth's radius is equal to r_2, the particle momentum is

$$60 \times (0.414)^2 = 10 \text{ Bev}/c$$

Particles with momenta less than 10 Bev/c will not reach the earth at all at the equator, and at just 10 Bev/c they will arrive from the western horizon if they are positively charged and from the eastern horizon if they are negative. At an intermediate momentum, which turns out to be about 15 Bev/c, positively charged particles can arrive at any angle between the western horizon and the zenith.

The trajectories for particles not moving in the equatorial plane, including those which arrive at higher latitudes, are considerably more complicated.[1] Detailed study of the equations of motion leads to the following conclusions:

1. At any given geomagnetic latitude, there is a minimum momentum below which no particles can reach the earth. At the equator the minimum is about 10 Bev/c; at the poles, particles of any momentum can enter.

2. As the momentum of the particles is increased above the minimum appropriate to the latitude in question, particles begin to arrive above the atmosphere within a certain cone of directions near the horizon; this cone opens from the west if the particles carry a positive charge, from the east if they are negative. As the momentum rises, the cone enlarges. It consists of a principal part and a number of narrow bands. By an application of Liouville's theorem,[2] it can be shown that everywhere within the allowed cone the flux of particles arriving per unit solid angle is the same as the flux at great distances, assuming that the latter is isotropic.

3. When the momentum reaches a second critical value, the cone fills the whole sky; particles now arrive with equal intensity from all directions, and with the same intensity as they would if the magnetic field were absent. Both the upper and lower critical momenta decrease with increasing latitude.

[1] Some interesting photographs of electron paths are given by Brüche, *Physik. Z.*, vol. 31, p. 1011, 1930.

[2] Cf. L. Jánossy, *op. cit.*

The fraction of the sky from which particles of various given momenta can arrive is plotted as a function of geomagnetic latitude in Fig. 217. Because of Liouville's theorem this fraction also represents the total intensity of the radiation of the given momentum, expressed as per cent of the maximum possible intensity which would be observed in absence of the field. The curves drawn in the figure refer to particles having given values of $\rho = r_e/r_1$, where r_1 is the radius of the critical circle and r_e the radius of the earth: the corresponding momenta, for singly charged particles,

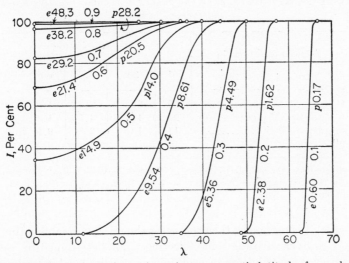

FIG. 217. Dependence of cosmic-ray intensity on magnetic latitude: for explanation, see text. (*Adapted from G. LeMaitre and M. S. Vallarta, Phys. Rev., vol. 43, p. 87, 1933.*)

are given by $p = 60\rho^2$ in Bev/c. Energies in Bev, calculated for electrons (e) and for protons (p), are indicated on the curves. In these calculations any possible deflection of incoming particles due to interference by the earth's atmosphere has, of course, been ignored.

It is sometimes useful to know the minimum momenta for certain specified directions of entry, at various latitudes. For particles entering at the zenith, the minimum momentum is given approximately by

$$p = 15 \cos^4 \lambda \qquad (288)$$

where λ is the geomagnetic latitude and p is in Bev/c. More precise values are given for several angles in Table 11-1.

210. Primary Momentum Spectrum. We return now to the interpretation of Fig. 215, which shows the variation of the total energy dissipated in the earth's atmosphere as a function of latitude. From the considerations of the preceding section it is clear that this curve must be closely related to the integral momentum spectrum of the primaries, since at each latitude there is a definite lower limit to the momentum of particles reaching the earth.   The relation between minimum momentum and latitude would be given directly by Eq. (288) above, if only particles arriving in the vertical direction were counted, but since the electroscopes used in these studies respond equally well to particles coming from any direction, particles entering at angles away from the zenith are also

TABLE 11-1. CRITICAL MOMENTA FOR SINGLY CHARGED, POSITIVE COSMIC-RAY PRIMARIES,* in Bev/c.

Allowed directions in east-west plane	Magnetic latitude				
	0°	30°	45°	60°	90°
(1) all	60	38	8.4	1.8	0
(2) west to 45° east	24	11	4.5	1.3	0
(3) west to zenith............	14	10	3.5	0.9	0
(4) west only	10	6.4	3.1	0.9	0

* Montgomery, *op. cit.*; J. G. Wilson "Progress in Cosmic Ray Physics," vol. I, article by H. V. Neher, Interscience, New York, 1952.   Entries (2) and (3) apply to longitude 80°.

effective.   It is necessary then to use for the minimum momentum appropriate to a given latitude some effective value determined by weighting the fractional contribution of each momentum interval according to the curves of Fig. 217, using a crudely estimated incident spectrum.   To a sufficiently accurate approximation, we may use for the minimum momentum that value for which one-half of the sky is effective ($I = 50$ per cent in Fig. 217).   For simplicity in the following discussion, we shall assume that *all* of the sky is effective for these or greater momenta, and that *no* particles of smaller momenta can enter.   The values so derived are indicated at the top of Fig. 215.

Two interesting features may be seen at once from examination of the figure.   One of these is the fact that the total energy incident upon unit area at the top of the atmosphere at the equator is 40 per cent of the value at the pole.   Since (effectively) no particles of less than 17.5 Bev/c momentum are counted at the equator,[1] this observation indicates that of the total flux of particles crossing unit area in free space, those with momenta greater than 17.5 Bev/c account for 40 per cent of the energy. The second feature, which has been the subject of some controversy, is

[1] We are here consistently ignoring the possibility of primaries of charge other than 1 elementary unit (cf. Sec. 220).

the apparent existence of "cutoff" in the spectrum, at about 1.5 Bev/c, corresponding to 0.8-Bev protons; no particles of lower momentum appear to reach the earth.[1]   It has been suggested that this effect is due to a solar magnetic field, but direct evidence for such a field appears to be lacking.

If the curve of Fig. 215 is plotted with the minimum momentum as abscissa instead of the geomagnetic latitude, there results a curve showing, for each momentum value, the total amount of energy brought in by particles of momentum greater than this value.   If the primaries are assumed to be protons, this curve may be converted into an energy spectrum, exhibiting the integral

$$\int_E^\infty EN(E)\, dE$$

where $N(E)\, dE$ is the number of particles of energy E in the range dE, as a function of the lower limit.   Differentiation of the curve and division by E then yields $N(E)$ as a function of E: this is the *differential* energy spectrum of the cosmic-ray primaries.

A somewhat more direct measurement of the energy spectrum of the primaries can be obtained by counting the *number* of particles above the atmosphere arriving from a specified direction.   Such determinations may be made by means of "counter telescopes" (Sec. 211) flown in balloons or rockets.   Balloon observations have been made to altitudes over 90,000 ft, by Winckler[2] and others, and rocket flights extending more than 150 kilometers above the earth's surface have been used for such studies by Van Allen[3] and his collaborators.   The results obtained from such flights give directly the number of particles having momenta greater than a certain minimum value, fixed by the latitude and angle of observation.   Again, with the assumption of protonic mass, this number can be expressed as $\int_E^\infty N(E)\, dE$, the *integral* energy spectrum of the particles. A curve derived from data of this kind is shown in Fig. 218.   In general the data obtained with counter telescopes and that derived from the measurement of total ionization agree as to the shape of the spectrum.   In the absolute value of the energy flux there is apparently some disagreement, which is at least partially to be attributed to the production of neutrinos

---

[1] Experiments carried out in 1954, on the other hand, showed a considerable increase in the intensity of low-energy particles arriving at high latitudes, and no evidence for a "cutoff" above 0.15 Bev.   It would thus appear that the number of such low-energy particles fluctuates greatly, possibly reflecting changes in sunspot activity.   Cf. H. V. Neher and E. A. Stern, *Phys. Rev.*, vol. 98, p. 845, 1955.

[2] J. R. Winckler, T. Stix, K. Dwight, and R. Sabin, *Phys. Rev.*, vol. 79, p. 656, 1950.

[3] J. A. Van Allen, *Nuovo cimento*, vol. 10, p. 630, 1953.

in secondary processes.[1]   Since they produce no ionization, the neutrinos do not contribute to the electroscope readings and the energy recorded is lower than that calculated from the particle flux.   Neutrinos present in the primary radiation will not be observed in either method.

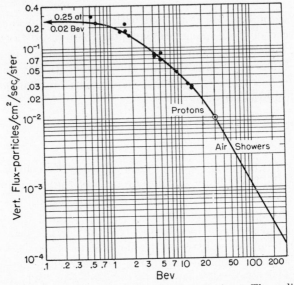

FIG. 218. Primary flux of protons in the cosmic radiation. The ordinate gives the number of particles per second with energy greater than E which are normally incident on unit area per unit solid angle. (*From Winckler et al., Phys. Rev., vol. 79, p. 656, 1950.*)

In the region above 1 Bev, the spectrum can be roughly approximated by a function of the type

$$\int_{E}^{\infty} N(E)\, dE = \frac{\text{const}}{(1 + E)^{n}} \qquad (289)$$

with E in Bev. In the range 2 to 15 Bev, n is about 1.1; for higher energies, the exponent, as determined from a study of extensive air showers[2] (Sec. 219) and from underground measurements,[3] appears to be about 1.5.

An indication of the sign of the primaries' charge can be obtained from a study of the relative numbers arriving from east and west at a given

---

[1] The flux derived from the counter telescope experiments refers to particles arriving in a certain direction, while the measurement of total incident energy includes particles arriving in all directions. Because of Liouville's theorem and the assumed isotropy at large distances, the shape of the derived spectral distribution is the same in either case.

[2] N. Hilberry, *Phys. Rev.*, vol. 60, p. 1, 1941.

[3] P. H. Barrett et al., *Revs. Mod. Phys.*, vol. 24, p. 133, 1952.

latitude.   If the primaries are positive, lower momenta, and hence more particles, will be admitted from the western horizon than from the east. Measurements with directional-counter telescopes show that this is the case and are consistent with the assumption that *all* primaries are positive.[1]

211. Observations on Single Cosmic-ray Particles.   Thus far, the experiments which have been discussed have had mainly to do with the ionization produced in the atmosphere by the cosmic rays.   It has been established by these experiments that the primaries are positively charged particles, and something about their distribution in momentum has been learned.   For further information on their nature, or on the nature of the secondaries they produce in the atmosphere, we must appeal to observations of individual events.

The first *cloud-chamber* observations of cosmic-ray particles were made by Skobeltzyn in 1927.[2]   While studying the secondary electrons produced by γ-rays from radioactive materials he noticed occasional tracks which were hardly curved at all in his magnetic field of 1,500 gauss.   The ionization along these tracks was about as dense as along the tracks of the secondaries; therefore, he concluded that they also were made by electrons.   From the smallness of the curvature of the tracks he calculated that the energy of the particles must be above 15 Mev, which exceeds any energies encountered in naturally radioactive substances.   In direction the tracks were strongly concentrated toward the vertical.   Skobeltzyn concluded, therefore, that these tracks were those of the particles that are responsible for the ionization ascribed to cosmic rays.

From the frequency of the occurrence of such tracks in his cloud chamber, Skobeltzyn estimated that about 1.2 particles per minute crossed each square centimeter of a horizontal plane.   Assuming a specific ionization of 40 ion pairs per centimeter of track, he concluded that the particles would cause a total ionization of $1.2 \times 40/60 = 0.8$ pairs of ions per second in each cubic centimeter of air.   This is of the same order of magnitude as the observed cosmic-ray ionization, 1.5 to 2 ion pairs per cubic centimeter per second.   A better modern estimate would be an average of perhaps 110 ion pairs per centimeter of track[3] and 1.4 particles per square centimeter per minute;[4] these data give about 2.6 ion pairs per cubic centimeter per second.

Counter observations constitute a second method for the detection of individual charged particles and have been widely adopted in the study of cosmic rays.   Whenever a counter is used for any purpose, a slow back-

[1] J. G. Wilson, *op. cit.*, article by H. V. Neher.

[2] D. Skobeltzyn, *Z. Physik*, vol. 43, p. 354, 1927; vol. 54, p. 686, 1929.

[3] H. V. Neher, *op. cit.*, p. 261.

[4] K. Greisen, *Phys. Rev.*, vol. 61, p. 212, 1942.

ground rate is always observed.   Part of this is doubtless due to radio-active contamination in the walls of the counter, for the background count varies with the material of the wall; but part of it is caused by cosmic-ray particles.

In order to eliminate effects due to rays from the walls of the counters, Bothe and Kolhörster introduced the device of using *two counters* and recording only instances in which both counters discharged at the same moment, which they called *coincidences.*[1]   In their work the counter dis-charges were recorded on a moving photographic film, and a coincidence was considered to have occurred when two counts were recorded within 0.01 sec of each other.   It will occasionally happen, to be sure, that a coincidence occurs owing to the independent passage of two particles, one through each counter; but the number of such chance occurrences to be expected in a given time can be calculated from the total counting rates of the individual counters and the resolving time of the recording system.   The number of chance coincidences so determined is subtracted from the observed number as a correction.

The arrangement just described was used by Bothe and Kolhörster in

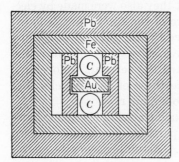

FIG. 219. Apparatus of Bothe and Kolhörster for measuring the absorption of cosmic-ray par-ticles in gold.

an attempt to measure directly the ab-sorbability of the cosmic-ray particles. Their apparatus is sketched in Fig. 219. The circles C represent in cross section two tubular counter chambers 5 cm in diameter and 10 cm long. Between these could be placed a (borrowed) block of gold 4.1 cm thick to act as an absorber. The whole arrangement was surrounded by iron 5 cm thick and also by lead 6 cm thick, in order to screen off all local radiations and thereby permit only the highly penetrat-ing cosmic-ray particles to actuate the counters.   Two blocks of lead were placed alongside the counters in an effort to stop particles that might pass through the upper one obliquely and then be scattered into the lower.

When observations were made with this apparatus near the roof of the building, about three coincidences per minute were observed, and this number decreased by 25 per cent when the gold absorber was put in place. From this result, Bothe and Kolhörster deduced the value

$$\mu/\rho = 3.5 \times 10^{-3} \text{ cm}^2 \text{ per gram}$$

for the mass absorption of the cosmic-ray particles.   A similar experi-

[1] W. Bothe and W. Kolhörster, *Z. Physik*, vol. 56, p. 751, 1929.

ment performed later by Rossi,[1] in which the cosmic rays were filtered through a layer of lead 5 cm thick placed above the counters, gave $\mu/\rho = 1.6 \times 10^{-3}$ cm^2 per gram in a lead absorber 9.7 cm thick.   For comparison, we may cite the value deduced from Millikan and Cameron's curve for the (apparent) mass absorption coefficient of the cosmic rays in air at sea level, $\mu/\rho = 2.5 \times 10^{-3}$ cm^2 per gram.

At the time Bothe and Kolhörster's experiment was carried out, it was generally supposed that the great penetration observed in ionization-chamber measurements was to be ascribed to a hard γ-radiation, which made its presence known by ejecting relatively easily absorbable electrons from the walls of the instrument.   With the evidence that the particles themselves had great penetrating power it became necessary to modify this view, and further study of individual particles took on an enhanced interest.

The counter method was improved later by Rossi in two respects. First, he replaced the photographic film by an electromechanical device for recording the discharges of the counters.[2]   This was accomplished by connecting each counter to the grid of a vacuum triode in such a way that the discharge of a counter momentarily lowers the potential of the grid and stops the current flow.   The tubes are connected in parallel and function as comparatively low resistances in a circuit that also contains a detector tube.   When the current through the triodes is completely stopped by their functioning simultaneously, the grid of the detector tube rises momentarily in potential and so causes a pulse of current in its anode circuit, which may be made to actuate a mechanical counter.   Such a counter circuit can be used to record coincidences between any number of counters.

The second improvement introduced by Rossi was the use of *three* counters in a row,[3] an observation being recorded only when all three counters respond simultaneously (or at least within a certain very small fraction of a second of each other).   In this way spurious coincidences due to secondary electrons ejected from surrounding materials are effectively eliminated, and the arrangement selects charged particles moving within a narrow solid angle of directions.   Such an arrangement of counters is sometimes called a *counter telescope*.

Using three counters (Fig. 220) in a vertical line, Rossi studied the absorption in lead of cosmic-ray particles which had already been filtered through 7 cm of lead (placed above the counters).   Moving one counter out of line was found to reduce the frequency of coincidences to that which

[1] B. Rossi, *Z. Physik*, vol. 68, p. 64, 1931.

[2] B. Rossi, *Nature*, vol. 125, p. 636, 1930.

[3] B. Rossi, *Z. Physik*, vol. 82, p. 151, 1933.   Cf. also M. A. Tuve, *Phys. Rev.*, vol. 35, p. 651, 1930.

was to be expected as a result of chance (one in 26 hr as against one to two per hr with the counters in line). He found that 46 ± 5 per cent of the coincidences remained when 101 cm of lead were placed between the counters, and concluded that nearly half the particles can penetrate such a thickness of lead. If we assume for the purpose of a rough estimate that the absorption is exponential through each successive layer of lead, the following values are found for the mean mass absorption coefficient: in the first 10 cm of lead $\mu/\rho = 1.8 \times 10^{-3}$ (total absorption, 19 per cent); in the next 15 cm, $\mu/\rho = 0.5 \times 10^{-3}$; and in the last 76 cm, $\mu/\rho = 0.55 \times 10^{-3}$. The relatively great change in the absorption coefficient observed in the first few centimeters of lead compared to that in the deeper layers suggested that the particles must be of two kinds: one, later called the "soft" component, able to penetrate only a few centimeters of lead, and the other, called the "hard" or "penetrating" component, able to penetrate a meter or more. As we shall see later, the soft component consists mainly of electrons, positrons, and γ-ray quanta, while the hard component, as observed at sea level and underground, consists mainly of μ mesons (Sec. 214).

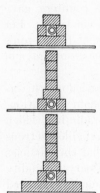

FIG. 220. A "counter telescope" used by Rossi in studying the absorbability of cosmic-ray particles.

The counter and cloud-chamber techniques for observing cosmic-ray particles were brought together in 1931 by Mott-Smith and Locher, who placed a cloud chamber between two counters and noted that tracks in the cloud chamber and coincident responses of the counters occurred together. In 1932, Blackett and Occhialini introduced the system, now generally employed, of allowing the coincident discharge of the counters to trigger the expansion of the cloud chamber. Such an arrangement is sketched in Fig. 221. The counters can be connected so that a particle passing through any chosen combination of them will release the mechanism that withdraws the piston and operates the cameras. In this way, much useless photographing is avoided (otherwise, it requires 10 to 20 random expansions to obtain a

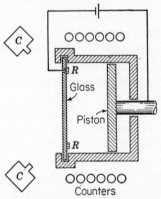

FIG. 221. A counter-controlled cloud chamber, with stereoscopic cameras CC. An electric field is momentarily applied between the ring R and the piston to sweep the space clear of ions. (*After Stearns and Froman, Am. Phys. Teacher, vol. 7, p. 79, 1939.*)

track), and only tracks having a suitable position and direction are photographed.

212. Showers and Bursts. *a. Showers.* When cosmic-ray tracks are observed in a cloud chamber, it frequently happens that two or more tracks are seen which appear to have been produced simultaneously; often they diverge from a common center lying in the walls or outside the chamber. The first observation of this sort was made by Skobeltzyn (1927), in the course of the work described above. If there is a solid obstacle in the chamber itself, such as a sheet of lead, groups of tracks may often be seen diverging from a point in this obstacle; frequently a single cosmic-ray track coming from above seems to end at the initial point of a group of tracks (cf. Fig. 222).

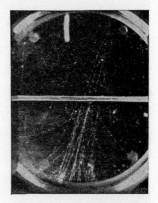

FIG. 222. Cloud-chamber photograph of an electron cascade shower exhibiting multiplication in a lead plate mounted across the center of the chamber. (*Courtesy of Professor C. D. Anderson: see Phys. Rev., vol. 50, p. 263, 1936.*)

Such groups of tracks are made by showers of (negative) electrons and positrons created as the result of the impact of a high-speed particle or photon upon matter. From a statistical study of the curvature of the tracks in a magnetic field, it is inferred that positive and negative particles occur about equally often, and with energies ranging from 1 Mev up to 500 Mev, 5 to 20 Mev being the most common energy[1] for showers produced in lead.

Interesting statistical data on the occurrence of showers of various sizes were obtained by Anderson and Neddermeyer.[2] They used a counter-controlled cloud chamber divided midway by a horizontal lead plate 3.5 mm thick, placed in a horizontal magnetic field of 7,900 gauss and viewed horizontally. At Pasadena, near sea level, out of 2,684 photographs of cosmic-ray tracks, 383, or 14 per cent, showed showers of two or more particles. On Pikes Peak (4,300 meters above sea level), out of 1,775 photographs, 42 per cent showed showers. Two-particle showers were the commonest; but showers containing many more particles also occurred. One photograph obtained on Pikes Peak showed more than 300 tracks of electrons and positrons, their total energy being estimated to exceed 15 Bev; four others showed showers of at least 100 particles. Often it was evident that the number of particles in a shower

[1] C. D. Anderson and S. H. Neddermeyer, "International Conference on Physics," p. 174, Cambridge University Press, Cambridge, 1935.

[2] C. D. Anderson and S. H. Neddermeyer, *Phys. Rev.*, vol. 50, p. 263, 1936.

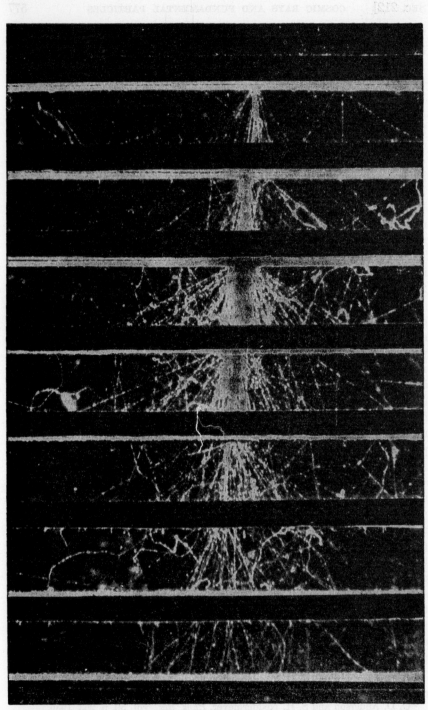

FIG. 223. Cloud-chamber photograph of a large cascade shower, developing in 1.27-cm lead plates. (*Photograph by C. Y. Chao, from B. Rossi, "High Energy Particles," Prentice-Hall*. 1952.)

increased as the shower passed downward through the lead sheet (cf. Fig. 223).

The *increased frequency of showers at higher elevations* is an important feature of these observations. An increase in the frequency of all tracks would be expected, since the cosmic-ray ionization itself increases with altitude; but *the showers increase much faster than the single particles*, especially the larger ones. Frequencies of occurrence were calculated by dividing the number of photographs showing showers by the total sensitive time of the counter control system, exclusive of the 15-sec intervals required after each expansion to reset the cloud chamber. The rate was thus found to be 34 photographs showing tracks per hour in Pasadena and 120 per hour on Pikes Peak. The ratio of the number of photographs per hour showing n tracks on Pikes Peak to the corresponding number at Pasadena, for various values of n, was found to be as follows:

n	1	2	3	4	5	6–10	11–20	21–100
Ratio	2.7	7.5	6.9	17	24	18	33	24

The increase in the frequency of large showers at the higher elevation is very striking.

b. Bursts of Ionization. In 1927, the German physicist Hoffmann, while studying the ionization caused by cosmic rays in an ionization chamber, noticed that occasionally a large deflection of his electrometer occurred.[1] He convinced himself that these deflections were not caused by a defect in the apparatus and indicated, therefore, the sudden production of a large "burst" of ionization. The phenomenon has been studied extensively, especially since 1932. Bursts are observed to vary greatly in size, their frequency decreasing with increasing size. Apparently no limit can be set as yet to the possible size of a burst. While using an ionization chamber 36 cm in diameter filled with argon at 50 atmospheres and shielded by 12 cm of lead, at Huancayo, Peru (altitude, 3,350 meters), Schein and Gill observed a burst of some 10^9 ion pairs, which they ascribed to about 10,000 cosmic-ray particles having a total energy of some 10^{12} ev; and they say that even larger bursts occurred.[2]

No further details concerning observations on bursts will be given here, however, chiefly because it seems to be well established that most bursts in ionization chambers shielded by several centimeters of lead are caused by the same showers of particles that are observed in cloud chambers. This conclusion has been supported by observations in which a cloud chamber and an ionization chamber were placed one above the other and

[1] Cf. "International Conference on Physics," p. 226.
[2] M. Schein and P. S. Gill, *Revs. Mod. Phys.*, vol. 11, p. 267, 1939.

coincidences between showers in the former and bursts in the latter were studied.   Burst observations thus constitute an alternative method of studying showers.[1]   In *unshielded*, thin-walled ionization chambers, most bursts result from nuclear disintegrations produced by cosmic-ray particles (cf. Sec. 219).

c. Observations on the Production of Showers.   Still a third method of observing showers of charged particles is by means of three or more coincidence counters *not* placed in a row (if placed in line, they count both showers and single particles).[2]   In 1932, Rossi used the arrangement shown in Fig. 224.   A coincident discharge of the three counters can be caused only by a shower which contains at least two particles, including the incident one (or, very rarely, by two independent particles passing through the apparatus almost simultaneously).

FIG. 224. Sketch of three noncollinear counters for detection of showers generated in the block A.

With the apparatus unshielded, Rossi observed 6.75 triple coincidences per hour.   The number of chance coincidences, calculated from the rates of the counters when counting separately, he estimated as three per hour. A lead plate 1 cm thick, placed above the upper counter at A, increased the coincidences to 14.1 per hour.   This increase is ascribed to the production of showers in the lead plate.

The number of showers as a function of the thickness of the shower-producing matter was studied, using a similar arrangement, by varying the thickness of the block A.   The result is shown in Fig. 225, where it may be seen that the coincidence rate rises sharply to a maximum, at about 20 grams per cm^2 (1.7 cm) of Pb.   Beyond the maximum, the curve drops rapidly at first, falling off more slowly as the depth increases.   The initial rise and fall is evidently due to the production of showers by a relatively easily absorbable radiation—presumably the "soft" component observed in the earlier absorption measurements (Sec. 211).   Increasing the thickness of the block A can be thought of as adding layers of lead to the top.   Each added layer will contribute a certain number of shower particles, and these will contribute to the coincidences as long as their range is sufficient to penetrate the layers of lead below.   Beyond 20 grams per cm^2, they are apparently not able to reach the counters, so additional layers do not increase the coincidence rate.   At the same time, however, the increased thickness of lead is attenuating the shower-producing particles, so the number of coincidences decreases on this account, and should

[1] For a summary of burst observations see D. K. Froman and J. C. Stearns, *Revs. Mod. Phys.*, vol. 10, p. 133, 1938, and B. Rossi, "High Energy Particles," *loc. cit.*
[2] B. Rossi, *Physik. Z.*, vol. 33, p. 304, 1932, *Z. Physik.* vol. 82, p. 151, 1933.

very soon vanish, judging from the steepness of the curve between 20 and 80 grams per cm². The almost flat part of the curve, extending to 600 grams per cm² (50 cm) or more, must then be attributed to a much more penetrating shower-producing radiation. The course of the shower curve thus supports the evidence obtained from the cruder absorption measurements, that the cosmic radiation contains at least two components, differing radically in their penetrating power. In the following section we shall discuss the properties of the softer component, returning in Sec. 214 to the identification of the penetrating particles.

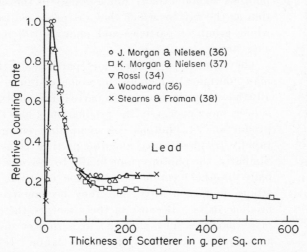

FIG. 225. Rossi transition curve, giving the relative number of showers observed under various thicknesses of lead. (*Froman and Stearns, Revs. Mod. Phys., vol. 10, p. 133, 1938.*)

213. Theory of the Shower Phenomenon.[1]   *a. The Shower Process.* Until 1934, the origin of showers of cosmic-ray particles was something of a mystery. The materials for a theoretical understanding of them had already been accumulated, however, and during the next 3 years a reasonably satisfactory theory for the common type of shower was developed.

Several physicists, noting that shower tracks usually do not all diverge from a common point, suggested that they may originate in cascade fashion.[2] In 1935, Auger pointed to the production of electron-positron pairs by photons, which was described in Sec. 188, as a possible step in the process. These ideas led to the following picture of the life history of a shower. A high-energy photon becomes converted, in the field of a nucleus, into an electron and a positron [cf. Fig. 226(a)]. These particles

[1] B. Rossi, "High Energy Particles," Prentice-Hall, New York, 1952.
[2] Cf. C. G. Montgomery, *Phys. Rev.*, vol. 45, p. 62, 1934.

constitute a shower of two rays; or, if the photon itself had been generated by a high-speed particle, we have at this stage a shower of three rays. The particles, accelerated in the fields of other nuclei, then radiate part of their energy in the form of further photons, this process constituting the extension to high energies of the process by which the continuous x-ray spectrum is produced [Fig. 226(b)]. These photons in turn disappear in giving rise to additional pairs of electrons and positrons; these produce fresh photons; and so on. At such high energies, it can be shown that the particles and photons should usually move almost in the same direction as the ray by which they are produced, so that the whole group of particles and photons will move on in close array.

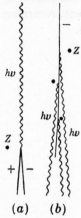

(a)   (b)

FIG. 226. Diagrams illustrating the processes by which showers are built up.

The number of photons and particles in the shower may continue to increase for some distance. Eventually, however, the energy of a particle becomes so low that it loses more energy in the production of ions than in the production of photons; its remaining energy is then rapidly frittered away and the particle comes to rest. Similarly, the photons come finally to lose energy principally by the ejection of Compton electrons from the atoms, and soon after that they become too weak to produce pairs. Because of these factors, the number of rays (particles and photons) in a shower increases to a maximum and then decreases again. In the end the positrons that have been produced all combine with atomic electrons, and the total number of charged particles in the world is thereby restored to its initial value. The entire history of the shower occupies, of course, only a very small fraction of a second, since the particles are moving almost with the speed of light.

To develop this hypothesis concerning the growth and decay of showers in quantitative form, it is necessary to know the probabilities for the various elementary processes that are involved. We shall consider these in turn.

b. Laws of Pair Production by Photons. The theory of the conversion of photons into pairs is given in Heitler's book on radiation.[1] The probability for the occurrence of such a conversion can conveniently be stated in terms of a cross section σ_p for pair production. If a beam of photons, each of energy $h\nu$, passes through a layer of matter of thickness dx containing n nuclei per cubic centimeter, the fraction converted into pairs will be $dI/I = n\sigma_p\, dx$. The mean distance L that a photon travels before being converted into a pair is $L = 1/n\sigma_p$. Theory indicates that

[1] W. Heitler, "Quantum Theory of Radiation," 2d ed., Oxford, London, 1944.

σ_p should vary rapidly with the atomic number Z of the nuclei, in fact almost as Z^2.

As the photon energy increases above the threshold value, $h\nu = 1.02$ Mev, the cross section σ_p increases slowly at first, and then more rapidly as the energy is increased, becoming the dominant factor in the total attenuation coefficient at 5 to 20 Mev (depending on the material) and

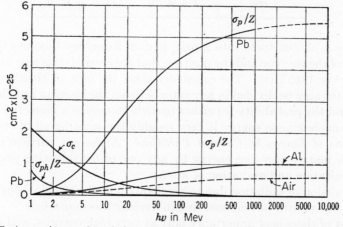

FIG. 227. Approximate plot of the theoretical cross sections for the action of high-energy photons upon atoms of lead, aluminum, or air: σ_p/Z is the cross section for absorption of the photon with production of an electron-positron pair, divided by the atomic number Z of the atom ($Z = 7.26$ for air); σ_c is the mean cross section for the Compton ejection of each electron from any atom (the cross section for the entire atom being $Z\sigma_c$); σ_{ph}/Z is the cross section for photoelectric absorption of the photon divided by Z (shown for lead only, inappreciable in aluminum or air for $h\nu > 1$ Mev). The photon energy $h\nu$ is plotted logarithmically. (*From data in Heitler, "Quantum Theory of Radiation," 1944.*)

finally reaching an essentially constant value at some hundreds of Mev. For $h\nu \gg 137 m_0 c^2/Z^{1/3}$, the cross section is given by[1]

$$\sigma_p = \frac{Z^2}{137} r_e^2 \left(\frac{28}{9} \ln \frac{183}{Z^{1/3}} - \frac{2}{27}\right) \qquad \text{cm}^2 \qquad (290)$$

where r_e is the "classical radius" of the electron $= e^2/m_0 c^2 = 2.8 \times 10^{-13}$ cm (e and m_0 are the charge, in esu, and rest mass, in gm, of the electron). Theoretical values of σ_p for three materials, divided by Z, are shown in Fig. 227. For comparison, curves are also shown for the cross section per electron for Compton scattering σ_c ($nZ\sigma_c$ being, therefore, the number of Compton electrons produced per photon per centimeter of path), and the cross section σ_{ph} for photoelectric absorption of photons in lead. Some

---

[1] Rossi, *op. cit.*, p. 81.

values of L, the mean distance for pair production, in centimeters are as follows:

Energy $h\nu$, Mev	In standard air	In Al	In Pb
25	9.8×10^4	27.4	1.25
100	5.9×10^4	17.0	0.86
1,000	4.5×10^4	13.2	0.70

When a photon turns into a pair, part of its energy becomes the rest energy of the electron and the positron that are created; this part amounts to $2m_0c^2$ or 1.02 Mev. The remainder takes the form of kinetic energy. The latter may be divided in any ratio between the electron and the positron; and the probability for either particle to receive a given fraction of the available kinetic energy is very roughly the same for all fractions.

c. *Loss of Energy by Charged Particles.*[1] A charged particle passing through matter may lose energy by any one of the following processes:

1. ionization and excitation of atoms
2. emission of radiation due to acceleration in the atomic fields[2]
3. collision with nuclei, resulting in nuclear transmutations

The last of these is of importance only at very high energies, and since it has no bearing on the electronic cascade showers, it will not be discussed here.

The loss of energy by a charged particle due to ionization and excitation can be calculated from considerations similar to those applied in deriving the Rutherford scattering formula (Sec. 79). If a high-speed charged particle approaches an atomic electron, the incident particle is deflected and gives up some of its energy to the electron, causing it to recoil. Because of its small mass, the electron receives a considerable energy even for a small momentum transfer. In the case of an encounter with a nucleus, the energy transfer associated with a given deflection is much smaller: at the same time the probability of deflection is greater, because of the greater charge. It thus comes about that while the change in direction of motion, or *scattering* of the incident particle, is mainly due to interactions with nuclei, the *energy loss* is almost entirely due to encounters with electrons. For a particle of charge Z_1e and velocity βc traversing a substance of atomic number Z_2, the calculated rate of energy loss is[3]

---

[1] B. Rossi, *op. cit.*, chap. 2. E. Segrè, "Experimental Nuclear Physics," vol. I, article by H. A. Bethe and J. Ashkin, Wiley, New York, 1953.

[2] Often referred to as "bremsstrahlung" in the literature.

[3] Bethe and Ashkin, *op. cit.*, pp. 167, 254.

$$-\frac{dE}{dx}\bigg]_{coll} = 4\pi n r_e^2 m_0 c^2 \frac{Z_1^2 Z_2}{\beta^2} f(\beta, Z_2) \qquad (291)$$

where n is the number of atoms per cubic centimeter. The function $f(\beta, Z_2)$ varies only slowly with the energy of the incident particle, rising gradually as the energy is increased; it depends somewhat on the nature of the stopping material and is different for incident electrons and heavier particles. At low energies ($\beta \ll 1$) the energy loss by collision and

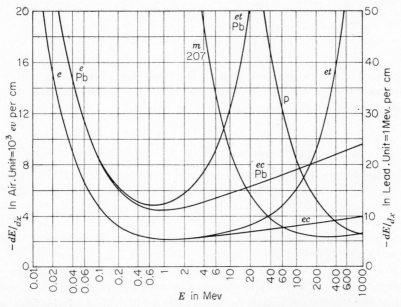

FIG. 228. Theoretical curves for energy loss by charged particles. Abscissa: kinetic energy E of the particle on a logarithmic scale. Ordinate: expectation $(-dE/dx)$ of loss of energy by the particle per centimeter. Curve ePb-ecPb: loss due to ionization and excitation of atoms by an electron in lead. ePb-etPb: total loss when radiative losses are included. Curve e-ec: collision loss by an electron in standard air. e-et: total energy loss, including radiation, in air. Curves $m207$ and p: total loss in air by a μ meson and by a proton.

excitation—generally called the "collision" or "ionization" loss—falls rapidly with increasing velocity, as $1/\beta^2$. As the kinetic energy becomes of the order of twice the rest energy $E \rightleftharpoons M_0 c^2$, where M_0 is the rest mass of the incident particle, the ionization loss reaches a minimum, after which it rises slowly at higher energy, because of the increase of the function f. Approximate values for the ionization loss of electrons, μ mesons ($M_0 = 207 \times$ electron mass, cf. Sec. 215), and protons are given in Fig. 228. The minimum ionization, observed when $E \cong 2M_0 c^2$, corresponds in air to about 2,100 ev per cm; dividing by the average energy required to form an ion pair, 33 to 35 ev, we obtain about 65 ion pairs per centimeter.[1]

The *energy lost in radiation*, owing to acceleration of the charged particle in the fields of the nuclei (partly screened by the atomic electrons), has been studied in a number of theoretical papers, culminating in the treatment given by Bethe and Heitler in 1934.[2] The average rate of energy loss due to radiation by a particle of mass M_0 carrying a charge Z_1e, moving with kinetic energy E through material composed of atoms of atomic number Z_2, is found to be represented by an expression of the type[3]

$$-\frac{dE}{dx}\bigg]_{rad} = n\,\frac{Z_1{}^4Z_2{}^2}{M_0{}^2}\,Ef\left(\frac{E}{M_0c^2}\right) \qquad (292)$$

where f denotes a function that is the same for all particles and, for moderate energy, the same for all materials. For radiative loss by high-energy electrons, the energy loss may be written

$$-\frac{dE}{dx}\bigg]_{rad} = n\,\frac{Z_2{}^2r_e{}^2}{137}\,E\left(4\ln\frac{183}{Z^{1/3}}+\frac{2}{9}\right) \qquad (293)$$

The rate of emission of radiant energy is then nearly proportional to the energy of the particle. The loss of energy by radiation decreases rapidly with increase in the mass M_0 of the particle; hence it is usually important only in the case of electrons and positrons. Because of the factor $Z_2{}^2$, the rate of loss by radiation is much larger in matter composed of heavy atoms, such as lead, than in matter composed of light atoms.

For our purpose it will be convenient to express the rate of loss of energy in terms of an equivalent mean free path for radiation ξ, commonly called the "radiation length." This quantity is defined by the relation

$$\xi = \left(\frac{4Z_2{}^2r_e{}^2}{137}\,n\ln\frac{183}{Z^{1/3}}\right)^{-1} \qquad (294)$$

where n is the number of nuclei per cubic centimeter. As may be seen from Eq. (293), the average radiation loss per centimeter, for high-energy electrons or positrons, is very nearly

$$-\frac{dE}{dx}\bigg]_{rad} \cong \frac{E}{\xi}$$

[1] This number includes losses due to close encounters, in which a considerable energy may be transferred to an atomic electron. In a cloud chamber or photographic emulsion, such electrons may produce visible tracks, called "δ-rays." Since they are rather rare, δ-rays are usually not included in estimates of the ionization density, and the observed ionization is therefore somewhat less than the values indicated in Fig. 228.

[2] H. A. Bethe and W. Heitler, *Proc. Roy. Soc. (London)*, vol. 146A, p. 83, 1934; Heitler, *op. cit.*

[3] Heitler, *op. cit.*, p. 172.

To a good approximation, the radiation length is the distance in which, on the average, the kinetic energy of an electron is reduced to $1/e$ of its initial value.

The radiation is actually emitted in quanta or photons; the statements just made have reference to the mean expectation of the emission of photons, not to a continuous emission of radiation as in classical theory. A photon may contain any fraction, from 0 to 1, of the kinetic energy possessed by the particle before emission of the photon. According to the theory, slightly more energy is radiated, on the average, in the form of photons containing less than half the kinetic energy than in photons containing more than half. If we *count* the photons emitted by a group of particles, we shall find many more of the low-energy ones than of the high-energy ones; the mean number of photons per unit energy varies a little faster than the reciprocal of $h\nu$.

Curves showing the combined effects of collision and radiation loss are exhibited in Fig. 228, for electrons in air (*et*) and in lead (*et* Pb). The curves illustrate strikingly the fact that the radiation loss predominates over all other losses for electrons at high energies (above 100 Mev in air or 10 Mev in lead). It may be added that, at energies exceeding the limits for the curves shown, an electron whose kinetic energy is $E \times 10^6$ ev radiates on the average about $30E$ ev per cm in standard air, or $1.95E \times 10^6$ ev per cm in lead.

d. Growth and Decay of Showers.[1] The application of the theoretical results just described to the growth and decay of showers is complicated by the great *straggling* of the elementary processes. A photon may travel a relatively short distance or a long distance before turning into a pair; and charged particles may generate photons early or late in their career. Furthermore, the energy of individual particles or photons may vary over a wide range. For this reason, to follow the course of a shower mathematically presents a difficult problem which has been solved only roughly. We can cite only the results of the approximate analysis. Before doing this, however, it may be instructive to describe a simplified model of the shower process which succeeds in predicting correctly many of its principal features.

For this purpose, let us assemble rough values of a few of the quantities that are important in shower production, as follows:

	Standard air	Al	Pb
L (for $h\nu = 1$ Bev).............	4.5×10^4	13	0.7 cm
ξ (for radiation)...............	3.3×10^4	10	0.5 cm
E_i (ionization = radiation)......	85	50	8 Mev
E_{cp}........................	25	16	5 Mev

[1] B. Rossi, "High Energy Particles," chap. 5.

Here L is the mean free path for pair production by photons, and ξ is the corresponding quantity for the emission of radiation by an electron or positron, as just defined. E_i is the critical kinetic energy of an electron or positron at which its mean loss of energy due to inelastic collisions (ionization and excitation) equals that due to the emission of radiation. E_{cp} is the photon energy at which the probability of loss of energy from the photon by production of a Compton electron equals the probability of loss due to pair production.

To develop a simplified theory, let us now assume, arbitrarily, that each charged particle produced as one member of a pair goes a distance ξ and then emits *all* its kinetic energy in one or more photons. Since the average frequency at which radiation is actually emitted, as stated above, is about $\nu/2$, where $h\nu = E$, the kinetic energy of the particle, we might expect about 2 photons from each particle. The number of photons increases rapidly, however, as the frequency is decreased; a given amount of energy at a frequency $\nu/4$, for example, would make 4 photons, as against $\frac{4}{3}$ at frequency $3\nu/4$. A better estimate of the number, therefore, should be 3 photons per particle. Each photon, we will assume, goes a distance exactly equal to L and then turns into two particles, whose energies we suppose to be equal, as they actually are on the average. The net result, on this simplified picture, will then be that in a distance $\xi + L$, one particle is replaced by $3 \times 2 = 6$ particles. This is equivalent to an average rate of multiplication in proportion to $e^{\gamma x}$, where x is the distance covered from the beginning of the shower and $e^{\gamma(\xi+L)} = 6$; since, as appears from the data given above, $L = 1.4\xi$ roughly, this makes $e^{2.4\gamma\xi} = 6$ and

$$\gamma = \frac{\ln 6}{2.4\xi} = \frac{1}{1.34\xi}$$

In an actual shower, of course, photons and particles will coexist. But photons are produced more rapidly than particles, and low-energy photons are produced especially rapidly; hence, we might expect to find about twice as many photons as particles in a shower.

To allow roughly for the effects of ionization, an attractive hypothesis is the simple assumption that the shower stops when the kinetic energy of each particle equals E_i, the value at which losses by ionization become equal to losses by radiation. Assuming that particles and photons have equal energies, we should thus obtain for the maximum number of particles in a shower $\frac{1}{3}E_0/E_i$, E_0 being the initial total energy. The distance covered up to this point would be x_1, where

$$e^{\gamma x_1} = e^{x_1/1.34\xi} = \frac{E_0}{E_i}$$

or $x_1 = 1.34\xi \log (E_0/E_i)$, E_0/E_i representing the total number of particles and photons. Actually, however, ionization losses interfere continually with the growth of the shower from the start, so that its maximum size should be reached somewhat before it has traveled a distance x_1. A further feature tending to decrease the number of particles is that, in the production of each pair, energy equal to $2mc^2$, or about 1 Mev, is lost in the rest energy of the pair particles. On the other hand, because of straggling (in time) in the individual processes, many particles will travel beyond the point x_1. We may try to make a first correction for straggling by assuming that at the point x_1 only half the particles have sunk below E_i in energy and have been stopped. We are thus led to put down as rough estimates of the maximum number N_m of charged particles in the shower and of the distance x_m from the starting point at which the maximum number occurs the simple expressions

$$N_m = \frac{1}{6}\frac{E_0}{E_i} \qquad x_m = \xi \ln \frac{E_0}{E_i} \qquad (295a,b)$$

The corresponding values derived from the mathematical analysis[1] are well represented, for high energies and low-atomic-number materials, by the expressions

$$N_m = 0.31 \frac{E_0}{E_i}\left(\ln \frac{E_0}{E_i} - 0.37\right)^{-\frac{1}{2}} \qquad (296a)$$

$$x_m = 1.01\xi\left(\ln \frac{E_0}{E_i} - 1\right) \qquad (296b)$$

A few values of N_m and x_m calculated from these equations, for selected values of E_0/E_i, are:

E_0/E_i	50	100	250	500	1,000	10,000
$\ln (E_0/E_i)$	3.91	4.61	5.52	6.21	6.91	9.21
N_m	10	15	34	64	120	1,040
x_m/ξ	2.9	3.7	4.6	5.3	6.0	8.3

These values are of the same order of magnitude as the rough estimates given by the more easily remembered Eqs. (295).

Additional features more or less predicted by the simplified theory and confirmed by the more exact analysis are the following:

1. The general course of the shower is the same whether it is started by a particle or by a photon.

---

[1] Cf. Rossi, *op. cit.*, p. 257. For low energies, see R. R. Wilson, *Phys. Rev.*, vol. 86, p. 261, 1952. It should be remarked that significant corrections are required when these results are applied to heavy elements (cf. Rossi, *op. cit.*, p. 285).

2. Showers occurring in different materials differ chiefly in the spatial scale of the phenomenon. A shower attains its maximum number of particles in lead after traveling from 1 to 3 cm, depending on the energy of the initiating ray, in iron after traveling four times as great a distance, and in standard air after $\frac{2}{3}$ to 2 kilometers. The whole range of the shower will be several times as great as the distance at which the maximum number of particles is observed.

3. The number of photons in a shower should be nearly double the number of particles.

4. The maximum number of particles should increase linearly with E_0 (actually a little more slowly); and it may attain any magnitude if the initial energy is sufficiently large.

5. The density of the shower at a given level should be greatest in the center and should decrease rapidly toward the sides. This feature results from the crisscrossing of the slightly diverging paths, which produces a distribution somewhat analogous to that of gaseous molecules diffusing from a common initial position.

Several of the features of the shower theory are well illustrated by the cloud-chamber photograph reproduced in Fig. 223. The shower is developed almost entirely in the lead plates mounted in the chamber, and its growth and decay are visible in the gaps between. Each lead plate is 1.27 cm, or about 2.3 radiation lengths, thick. Since no track is visible above the top plate, we may conclude that the shower must have been initiated by a photon. The shower reaches its maximum development in the third or fourth plate, or after about eight radiation lengths. This number corresponds, in lead, to an initial energy of the order of 7 Bev, and about 70 particles would be expected to appear at the level of maximum development, a number which is not inconsistent with the appearance of the picture. The main energy in the shower is carried in the relatively narrow central core of particles, which disappears in the fifth plate. The particles diverging at large angles are generally of low energy, as evidenced by the fact that they produce no cascades in the plates. In air, this shower would have had a longitudinal extension of about 1 kilometer and would have contained perhaps 15 particles. Much more energetic showers, representing energies up to 10^{17} ev, have been observed by counter methods. Such showers, called "Auger" showers or "extensive air showers," contain mesons and nucleons, in addition to large numbers of electrons and photons (see Sec. 219).

214. Discovery of the Mu Meson. After the discovery of the latitude effect on cosmic-ray ionization, and before the east-west effect had been established, the belief became general for a time that the primary cosmic rays consist, at least in large part, of (negative) electrons. It was also believed that the cosmic-ray tracks seen in cloud chambers are mostly made either by these primary electrons or by secondary electrons or positrons produced by them in atomic collisions. By the end of 1934, however, several difficulties with this hypothesis had emerged.

In the first place, it was difficult to see how any appreciable number of primary electrons could possibly penetrate the atmosphere. From the latitude effect, it was clear that a significant part of the sea-level ionization must be connected with primaries with energies of the order of 10 Bev, and it appeared that, in view of the large radiative loss predicted by the Bethe-Heitler theory, the probability of any individual electron's surviving to sea level (18 radiation lengths) was quite negligible.[1] Even more perplexing was the question of accounting for the penetration of such particles through hundreds of meters of water or through as much as a meter of lead. The difficulty became accentuated when direct measurements of the loss of energy by an electron in passing through a layer of matter were attempted. Such measurements can be made in a cloud chamber placed in a magnetic field; it is only necessary to measure the difference in the curvatures of the tracks above and below the layer of matter, from which the change in energy can be calculated (with a possible error of a few per cent in case the mass of the particle is uncertain —see footnote, Sec. 209). Extensive measurements of this sort were begun by Anderson in 1932, at Millikan's suggestion, and were continued by Anderson and Neddermeyer[2] and others.[3] In such observations it was found very difficult to secure consistent results. In some cases, energy losses were observed that agreed well with the Bethe-Heitler theory; in other cases, especially for high-energy particles, the loss was certainly much less.

For a few years, it was believed by some that all the known facts taken together pointed toward a breakdown of the wave-mechanical theory of radiation for electron energies above 10^8 ev. The development of the theory of showers was probably delayed for a time by this erroneous conclusion, since it seemed to render hopeless any attempt to construct a theory on the basis of accepted principles.

As the experimental work progressed, however, it gradually became more clear that not all cosmic-ray particles are of the same nature. In 1934, E. J. Williams suggested that the more penetrating rays might be protons. In 1936, Anderson and Neddermeyer reported observations on the amount of energy lost by cosmic-ray particles in passing through a lead plate 3.5 mm thick placed across a cloud chamber. They found that the average loss by particles forming part of showers was in approximate

---

[1] Cf. W. Heitler, "Quantum Theory of Radiation," 1st ed., 1936.

[2] C. D. Anderson, *Phys. Rev.*, vol. 41, p. 405, 1932.

[3] For references see *Revs. Mod. Phys.*, vol. 10, p. 174, 1938.

agreement with the theory,[1] although the individual variations were enormous (presumably due to straggling in the emission of photons). For a further test, Neddermeyer and Anderson replaced the lead plate by one of platinum 1 cm thick, equivalent to nearly 2 cm of lead.[2]   It was found, on the one hand, that even shower particles of energy below 500 Mev could get through such a thick plate in small numbers, but they emerged with almost a total loss of their energy.   This can be understood if these particles are electrons or positrons and are occasionally able to

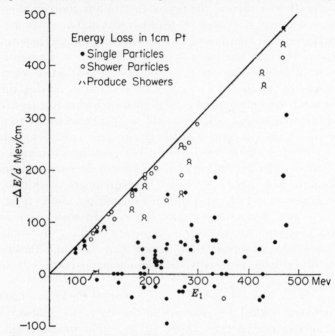

FIG. 229. Energy loss in 1 cm of platinum as function of incident energy.   (Energy calculated on assumption of electronic mass.)   (*Anderson and Neddermeyer.*)

traverse the plate only because their radiative energy losses happen to be abnormally low.   The particles occurring singly, on the other hand, lost, as a rule, less than half of their energy in traversing the platinum.

The data in question and some later ones are shown in Fig. 229.   The abscissa represents the energy with which a particle entered the cloud chamber, the ordinate, its loss of energy in passing through 1 cm of platinum.   Circles refer in the figure to particles forming part of a shower, solid dots to particles that occurred alone.   All points referring to particles that traverse the platinum must necessarily lie below the line drawn in the diagram, since this line represents total loss of energy in the plate.

[1] C. D. Anderson and S. H. Neddermeyer, *Phys. Rev.*, vol. 50, p. 263, 1936.
[2] S. H. Neddermeyer and C. D. Anderson, *Phys. Rev.*, vol. 51, p. 884, 1937

The plot furnishes clear evidence for the conclusion that at least two different kinds of cosmic-ray particles occur in cloud chambers, characterized by wide differences in penetrating power.   (The occurrence of cases of an *apparent gain* of energy, however, well illustrates the difficulty of making accurate measurements of this type.)

The great penetrating power of the single particles can most easily be accounted for by the assumption that their masses are greater than those of electrons, for the radiative energy loss decreases rapidly as the mass of the particle increases [Eq. (292)].   On the other hand, they can hardly be as heavy as protons, because a proton with the same magnetic rigidity as a 200-Mev electron would ionize about 10 times as heavily as a high-energy electron, and the tracks reported in this study all showed minimum ionization.

In view of these considerations, it was concluded that the penetrating cosmic-ray particles were of a new type, with a mass intermediate between the masses of the electron and the proton.   As we shall see shortly, there are several kinds of particles which have masses in this range: all are called *mesons*.[1]   The one referred to here, characterized by its great penetrating power, is called the *mu meson* (μ meson).[2]   Mu mesons constitute more than half the total cosmic radiation at sea level.   Almost all the remainder is accounted for by electrons, positrons, and photons from cascade showers.

The general acceptance of a new particle of intermediate mass was eased to some extent by the fact that there existed a theory which called for just such a particle.   In 1935, the Japanese physicist Yukawa[3] had published a theory of nuclear forces in which he suggested that the attractive field which holds the nucleons together in nuclei may well involve the existence of "quanta" of some sort, in analogy with the photons that appear in the electromagnetic field in association with the forces between electric charges (cf. Sec. 162).   Because of the short range of action of the nuclear field of force the "quanta" have a nonzero rest mass M_0, given by the relation

$$R = \frac{h}{2\pi M_0 c}$$

where R is the range of nuclear forces.   On the basis of what was then known about the range, M_0 was estimated to be 100 to 200 electron masses.   It follows from the theory that there should exist both charged and neutral quanta and that, when free, they should manifest themselves

[1] *Meson* is the neuter form of the Greek adjective *"Mesos"* meaning middle; it should be pronounced "meezon."

[2] Also called the "muon."

[3] H. Yukawa, *Proc. Math. Phys. Soc. Japan*, vol. 17, p. 48, 1935; *Revs. Mod. Phys.*, vol. 21, p. 474, 1949.

as particles with a limited lifetime.   The spin of the particles should be a whole integer or zero.   Curiously enough, although the mass fitted Yukawa's estimate as well as could be asked, the μ meson discovered by Anderson and Neddermeyer was later found not to be the particle predicted by Yukawa at all!

215. Properties of Mu Mesons.[1]   *a. Charge.*   Both positive and negative μ mesons are observed: at sea level there are about 20 per cent more positives than negatives.   The magnitude of the charge can be determined with fair accuracy by a comparison of the specific ionization of high-energy μ meson and electron tracks, since the minimum ionization produced by such a particle is proportional to the square of the charge [Eq. (291)].   Such comparisons have been carried out by Hazen[2] and by Frost,[3] with the result that the charge is found to be the same as that of the electron within 2 per cent.

b. Mass.   The mass of an energetic meson is not easy to determine with precision.   The curvature of the track of a meson in a magnetic field gives at once its momentum, since the charge is known.   To find the mass, either the speed or the energy must then also be known.   The speed can be inferred, if it is not too great, from the degree of ionization produced (Sec. 213); the energy can be inferred from the range, provided the end of the trajectory can be located.

One of the first good observations by the ionization method was made by Street and Stevenson,[4] who obtained a track in a cloud chamber under 11 cm of lead with $B\rho = 9.6 \times 10^4$ gauss cm and a specific ionization about six times as great as in normal, thin tracks.   If the particle entered from above, its sign was negative.   The heavy ionization would be explained if the particle had a mass 175 ± 40 times the electronic mass.[5] It certainly was not a proton, for, if it had been, its energy would have been only 4.5×10^5 ev and a proton of this energy would have a range of only 1 cm in standard air, whereas the track in question was clearly visible over a length of 7 cm.   A thousand counter-controlled expansions were necessary to obtain this single useful track.

In the years 1946–1950 an extensive study of the masses of the mesons observed at sea level was carried out by Brode, Fretter, and others[6] at

[1] A. M. Thorndike, "Mesons, A Summary of Experimental Facts," McGraw-Hill, New York, 1952; B. Rossi, *loc. cit.*

[2] W. E. Hazen, *Phys. Rev.*, vol. 67, p. 269, 1945.

[3] See R. B. Brode, *Revs. Mod. Phys.*, vol. 21, p. 37, 1949.

[4] J. C. Street and E. C. Stevenson, *Phys. Rev.*, vol. 52, p. 1003, 1937.

[5] The value originally quoted was 130 ± 30: the value 175 is based on a more accurate curve for the relation between specific ionization and velocity (cf. Rossi, *op. cit.*, p. 154).

[6] R. B. Brode, *Revs. Mod. Phys.*, vol. 21, p. 474, 1949; T. C. Merkle, E. L. Goldwasser, and R. B. Brode, *Phys. Rev.*, vol. 79; p. 926, 1950.

the University of California.   In these measurements, two cloud chambers, one above the other, were used.   The upper chamber was in a strong magnetic field and served to determine the momentum of the particles; the lower was provided with a series of horizontal lead or copper plates in which the range could be determined.   The result[1] of these measurements was a mass of $(206 \pm 2)m_e$ (m_e = rest mass of the electron).   More recent determinations of the mass of artificially produced positive μ mesons (Sec. 217) give the value $m_\mu = (207 \pm 1)m_e$.

c. Mean Life.   According to Yukawa's theory, a free meson should decay into an electron ($+$ or $-$) and a neutrino: a meson which is captured by a nucleus should interact strongly with the nucleus and give rise to a violent disintegration.   That the decay of the μ meson might be responsible for certain anomalies in the absorption of the hard component of cosmic rays was first suggested by Kulenkampff in 1938.   It had been observed by a number of workers that cosmic rays are more strongly attenuated in the atmosphere than in condensed materials of the same equivalent thickness, measured in grams per square centimeter.   This behavior could be accounted for if the mesons in the atmosphere decayed with a mean life of the same order as the time required to stop them by ionization loss; in condensed materials, the time required to traverse a given number of grams per square centimeter is much smaller and the decay is less important.

In a series of experiments undertaken to provide quantitative data on this point, Rossi, Hilberry, and Hoag[2] set up a counter telescope with 12.7 cm of lead between the counters, so that it would respond only to the hard component—i.e., the μ mesons.   With this instrument, they measured the meson intensity at several altitudes in the atmosphere, and compared the apparent absorption with that observed in 87 grams per cm² of carbon.   Since carbon has the same number of electrons per unit mass, and roughly the same atomic number as air, the true absorption due to ionization loss should be the same for layers of carbon and air having the same mass.   The result of these experiments was that, at all altitudes, the *apparent* absorption coefficient in air is about twice as great as in carbon, indicating that about half of the loss of mesons in air is to be attributed to decay.   The mean life they obtained for the μ mesons passing through their apparatus was $\tau = 3.2 \times 10^{-5}$ sec.   In a coordinate system at rest with respect to the meson, the "proper" mean life τ_0 (cf. Sec. 35) is given by

$$\tau_0 = \tau \sqrt{1 - \beta^2} = \tau \frac{W_0}{W}$$

---

[1] Quoted by Rossi, *op. cit.*, p. 177.
[2] B. Rossi, N. Hilberry, and J. B. Hoag, *Phys. Rev.*, vol. 57, p 461, 1940.

where W is the total energy and W_0 the rest energy, M_0c^2. The effective energy of the μ mesons could be estimated from the known energy spectrum as 1.3 Bev. Thus from this experiment, the mean life of the μ meson at rest was determined to be about 2.7×10^{-6} sec.

It was natural to assume that the decay of a μ meson produces an electron, since this would account for the large number of electrons and positrons observed at sea level. Direct evidence of the decay of μ mesons into electrons was obtained in cloud-chamber pictures in 1940. One such event is reproduced in Fig. 230: a negative μ meson comes to rest in the gas, producing a heavy track, strongly curved in the magnetic field. From the end of the heavy track there issues a light track identifiable as that of a negative electron. As the result of analysis of a large number of decay events, it has been found that the electrons and positrons from the decay of μ mesons at rest have a continuous distribution in energy,[1] from zero to a maximum of about 55

Fig. 230. Cloud-chamber photograph showing the decay of a μ meson (heavy track) into an electron (light curved track). There is a magnetic field perpendicular to the plane of the figure. (*Photograph courtesy of Professor R. B. Leighton.*)

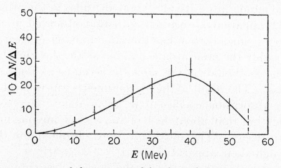

Fig. 231. Energy spectrum of electrons resulting from decay of μ mesons. Each point represents the number of electrons observed within an energy interval of 10 Mev. The vertical lines indicate the expected statistical spread. (*Leighton, Anderson, and Seriff, Phys. Rev., vol. 75, p. 1432, 1949.*)

Mev, as shown in Fig. 231. Such a distribution requires that at least two other particles besides the electron must result from the decay (in ordi-

[1] R. B. Leighton, C. D. Anderson, and A. J. Seriff, *Phys. Rev.*, vol. 75, p. 1432, 1949.

nary β-decay, the two are the neutrino and the daughter nucleus).   It is
generally believed that two neutrinos are involved in the process:

$$\mu^{\pm} \rightarrow e^{\pm} + \nu + \nu$$

The maximum energy available, calculated from the masses, is 52.4 Mev.
From the balance of angular momentum in this relation it follows that
the μ meson has half-integral spin, for the vector sum of the spins of the
three particles on the right is restricted to half-integral values (both the
electron and neutrino have spin $I = \frac{1}{2}h/2\pi$).   Other information suggests $I = \frac{1}{2}$ as the most likely value for the spin of the μ meson.

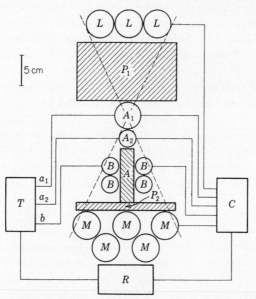

FIG. 232. Diagram of an experimental arrangement for the study of μ-meson decays.
(*Nereson and Rossi, Phys. Rev., vol. 64, p. 199, 1943.*)

A direct determination of the lifetime of the μ meson at rest was undertaken by Rasetti[1] in 1941 and by Nereson and Rossi[2] in 1943.   The
experimental arrangement used by the latter group is diagramed in Fig.
232. P_1 is a lead block thick enough to transmit only mesons.   Some
of the mesons are stopped in the brass block A, where they may decay;
the electrons or positrons emitted have a good chance of passing through
one of the counters B.   Counters L, connected in parallel, counters A_1 and
A_2, and counters B, connected in parallel, all feed in coincidence into circuit C.   Counters M, connected in parallel, also feed into C but in anti-
coincidence with the other counters, i.e., C responds only when counters

[1] F. Rasetti, *Phys. Rev.*, vol. 59, p. 706, 1941; vol. 60, p. 198, 1941.
[2] N. G. Nereson and B. Rossi, *Phys. Rev.*, vol. 64, p. 199, 1943.

LA_1A_2B all act within a millisecond or so of each other whereas all the counters M do *not* act. In such cases it is clear that no particle passed through M, hence it is practically certain that LA_1A_2B were not activated by a single meson passing through all of them, since such a meson would also have passed through one of the counters M. One of the B counters might be activated by a meson scattered widely in the absorber A, or by an electron ejected from A in a scattering process, but such occurrences will be very rare. It is thus practically certain that C responds only when a meson has stopped and decayed in A, with emission of an electron or positron that activated one of the counters B.

To measure the time spent by the meson in A before decaying, counters A_1A_2 and B are also connected to a time circuit T in such a way that, when a coincidence A_1A_2 is followed after a certain interval of time τ by a pulse from B, T emits a pulse whose amplitude is proportional to τ. Finally, the recorder R records with a pen the magnitude of the pulse received from T, but only in case a pulse is simultaneously received from circuit C, indicating that an event of the desired kind has occurred.

It was assumed that the meson decay followed the exponential law that is familiar in radioactive decay; thus, life periods of all possible magnitudes will be obtained from individual mesons, and their average will be the mean life, independently of the time already spent by the mesons before entering the absorber. The exponential law of decay was verified from the observations; and the mean life of a meson at rest was found from the decay curve to be $(2.15 \pm 0.07) \times 10^{-6}$ sec.[1]

   d. Interaction of Mu Mesons with Nuclei. It was pointed out in 1940 by Tomonaga and Araki[2] that slow positive and negative mesons should behave quite differently in matter because of the effect of the Coulomb field of the nucleus. A negative meson which finds its way into an atom will be attracted by the positively charged nucleus just as electrons are. In the field of the nucleus, its behavior is governed by a form of the Schrödinger equation similar to that applying to the one-electron atom, and it will have a set of stationary, bound states entirely analogous to those of such an atom.[3] Because of the greater mass of the μ meson ($207m_e$), the characteristic radii of the wave function in the "μ-mesonic" atom will be about 200 times smaller than the corresponding radii in normal atoms. Thus, in the lowest possible stationary state, the meson will have a high probability of being found *within* the nucleus, where it may

   [1] For a summary of more recent determinations, see H. A. Morewitz and M. H. Shamos, *Phys. Rev.*, vol. 92, p. 134, 1953.

   [2] S. Tomonaga and G. Araki, *Phys. Rev.*, vol. 58, p. 90, 1940.

   [3] Cf. V. L. Fitch and J. Rainwater, *Phys. Rev.*, vol. 92, p. 789, 1953; L. N. Cooper and E. N. Henley, *Phys. Rev.*, vol. 92, p. 801, 1953; J. A. Wheeler, *Phys. Rev.*, vol. 92, p. 812, 1953.

interact with the nucleons before undergoing spontaneous decay.   This probability depends upon the atomic number both because, as Z increases, the nucleus grows larger, and because the electronic distributions grow smaller.   A positive meson, on the other hand, is repelled by the Coulomb field and will remain a free particle until it decays. Thus the lifetimes of stopped positive and negative mesons could be expected to be quite different.

Experimental studies on the decay of positive and negative mesons in various materials were reported in 1945 and 1947 by Conversi, Pancini, and Piccioni.[1]   The apparatus they used, illustrated in Fig. 233, was similar in principle to that just described.   The counters L and A are connected in coincidence, and the counters M are connected in parallel into a delayed-coincidence circuit, in such a way that a count is registered when a meson passes through L and A, decays in the block C and emits an electron or positron with a delay between certain fixed limits.   The blocks P_1 and P_2 are of iron, and are so magnetized—one into the plane of the figure and the other in the opposite direction—as to act as a magnetic lens, focusing mesons of one sign on the counter A. Mesons of the opposite sign could be selected by interchanging the blocks $P_1 P_2$.

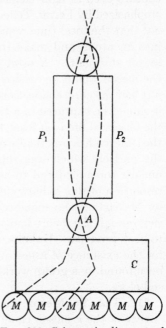

FIG. 233. Schematic diagram of an arrangement for studying separately the decay of positive and negative mesons. P_1 and P_2 are magnetized iron blocks. (*Adapted from Conversi, Pancini, and Piccioni, Phys. Rev., vol. 71, p. 209, 1947.*)

When the absorber C was iron, it was found, as expected, that only the positive mesons undergo spontaneous decay: no delay electrons were observed when the magnetic field was set to focus negative mesons.   In carbon, on the other hand, both kinds of mesons exhibited decay, and both with the same lifetime, indicating that in an element as light as carbon the *nuclear capture is small* compared to spontaneous decay.   Further experiments showed that a smooth transition from the one case to the other takes place as the atomic number of the absorber is increased: at $Z = 10$, nuclear capture and decay are about equally probable for negative μ mesons.

[1] M. Conversi, E. Pancini, and O. Piccioni, *Phys. Rev.*, vol. 71, p. 209, 1947.

The surprising feature of the result obtained by Conversi and his collaborators was that the spontaneous decay of negative μ mesons, requiring a time of the order of microseconds, could compete at all with nuclear capture even in light elements.   The magnitude of the discrepancy was emphasized by Fermi, Teller, and Weisskopf,[1] among others, who pointed out that the total time required for the meson to slow down, be captured into an atom, and make the necessary (x-ray) transitions to reach the lowest stationary "K orbit" is less than 10^{-12} sec.   Once in the K shell, the meson would be exposed to direct interaction with the nucleus, and, if it had the close connection with nuclear forces which had been assumed, it should be captured in a time of the order of 10^{-18} sec.[2]   The fact that the observed life is at least 10^6 times too large is then clear evidence that the μ meson has practically no interaction at all with nuclei.   Yet this was the particle which was supposed to represent the "quantum" of the nuclear force field and to be responsible for the binding of nuclei!   The resolution of this unhappy dilemma was proposed in the summer of 1947 by Marshak,[3] who suggested that the μ meson was *not* the Yukawa particle, and, if the theory had any validity, there must still be another meson to be discovered.   Unknown to physicists in this country, direct evidence for the existence of a new meson, heavier than the μ meson, had in fact been found by a group working under C. F. Powell in Bristol, a month or so before.

216. The Pi Meson.   *a. Nuclear Emulsion Technique.*[4]   The discovery of the π meson came as a result of a systematic effort, largely on the part of C. F. Powell and his collaborators, to increase the usefulness and adaptability of the photographic emulsion as a tool for nuclear research.   As was mentioned in Sec. 178, the ordinary photographic plate is much too insensitive to be useful in recording tracks of single particles, and only with the introduction of emulsions containing large percentages of sensitive silver halide grains did it become at all possible to record trajectories of individual high-energy particles.   Of equal

---

[1] E. Fermi, E. Teller, and V. F. Weisskopf, *Phys. Rev.*, vol. 71, p. 314, 1947.

[2] The probability of finding the meson within the nucleus of carbon can be estimated by integrating the wave function [Eq. (137), Sec. 104] over the nuclear volume, and is of the order of 10^{-3}.   The time for the meson, once inside, to traverse the nucleus is about 10^{-21} sec.   With the assumed strong interaction, it should be absorbed in less than one traversal.

[3] R. E. Marshak and H. A. Bethe, *Phys. Rev.*, vol. 72, p. 506, 1947.

[4] C. F. Powell and A. P. S. Occhialini, "Nuclear Physics in Photographs," Oxford, London, 1947; H. J. Yagoda, "Radioactive Measurements with Nuclear Emulsions," Wiley, New York, 1949; O. R. Frisch, "Progress in Nuclear Physics," vol. 1, article by J. Rotblat, Butterworth-Springer, 1950; J. G. Wilson, "Progress in Cosmic Ray Physics," vol. II, article by L. Voyvodic, Interscience, New York, 1954; Y. Goldschmidt-Clermont, *Ann. Revs. Nuclear Sci.*, vol. 3, 1953.

importance was the development of techniques for handling emulsions of great thicknesses—up to several millimeters, since otherwise tracks which did not lie accurately in the plane of the emulsion were lost.   With modern emulsions, it is possible to form a block of any desired dimensions, using strips a millimeter or so thick, separated by thin sheets of paper, and thus to obtain a continuously sensitive detector yielding a permanent record of any nuclear event occurring within the block.   Because of the high density of the material, the path of a particle which would travel many tens of meters in air is compressed into a few centimeters, and the entire life history of even very energetic particles can be examined in detail by microscopic study of the emulsion strips.   Such blocks of emulsion have been flown in free balloons to altitudes well over 100,000 ft and have been invaluable in furnishing information on the nature of cosmic-ray particles.

Many ingenious techniques have been developed for identifying particles from their trajectories in photographic plates.   These techniques have mainly been directed toward mass determinations, although methods for measuring charge have been developed as well.   The three most directly measurable characteristics of a track in a photographic emulsion are the *range*, the *grain density*, and the *mean scattering*.   For high-energy particles other than electrons, the range can be approximated by the expression[1]

$$R = A \frac{M_0}{Z^2} f_1(v) \tag{297}$$

where M_0 is the mass of the particle, Z_e its charge, and v its velocity. A is a constant and $f_1(v)$ a function which can be determined empirically or estimated from the theory of energy loss.   The grain density, or number of developed grains per unit length of the track, is proportional to the ionization loss, which in turn is given by

$$-\frac{dE}{dx}\bigg]_{\text{coll}} = BZ^2 f_2(v) \tag{298}$$

where B is a known constant [cf. Eq. (291)], and $f_2(v)$ again is a semi-empirically determined function.   Thus, if unit charge (in electronic units) is assumed, a measurement of the grain density at a known distance from the end of the track permits determination of the mass.

Particularly near the ends of their paths, moving charged particles are observed to undergo numerous small-angle scatterings which result in a general curvature of the trajectory.   Such scatterings are due almost entirely to interactions with nuclei and are governed by the Rutherford scattering formula.   The root-mean-square scattering angle $\sqrt{\langle\Theta^2\rangle}$ over

[1] Rossi, *op. cit.*, p. 135.

a given distance is given approximately by

$$\sqrt{\langle\Theta^2\rangle} = \frac{CZ}{pv} \qquad (299)$$

where p is the momentum, v the velocity, and C a constant. Measurement of the scattering, coupled with a determination of the grain density, permits an estimate of the mass even when the end of the track is not visible.

b. Discovery of the Pi Meson. In a group of nuclear emulsions which had been exposed at mountain altitudes for some weeks, Lattes, Muirhead, Occhialini, and Powell[1] found several instances in which a meson apparently stopped and decayed into another meson. One such track, a mosaic of a large number of microphotographs, is shown in Fig. 234. Here may be seen, coming in from the upper left, a track (marked π)

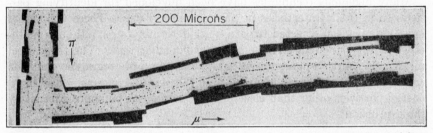

FIG. 234. Decay of a π meson into a μ meson, observed in a photographic emulsion. (*Lattes, Muirhead, Occhialini, and Powell, Nature, vol.* 159, *p.* 694, 1947.)

which becomes progressively more dense and in which the random curvature becomes progressively more marked as the particle travels downward. The particle is clearly not a proton, since a proton track would be almost perfectly straight except for the last few microns. In addition, other tracks in the same emulsion which could be clearly identified as protons showed much greater grain densities at corresponding range. The particle is also not an electron, because these emulsions were not sensitive to electrons. From the end of the π track proceeds another track (marked μ) about 600 microns long, showing the same features of increasing grain density and multiple scattering toward the end. It is evidently quite impossible that a single meson could have produced these two tracks, and the conclusion that the μ track represents the decay of the π is inescapable. It was natural to identify the μ track with the familiar μ meson found in the sea-level cosmic radiation, and later measurements on a number of such events confirmed that the mass of this

[1] C. M. G. Lattes, H. Muirhead, G. P. S. Occhialini, and C. F. Powell, *Nature,* vol. 159, p. 694, 1947; *Proc. Phys. Soc. (London),* vol. 61A, p. 173, 1948.

particle is very nearly $200m_e$; the mass of the π meson[1] turned out to be about $270m_e$.

In the same emulsions there occurred a number of instances where a meson track terminated in a "star" with several heavily ionizing tracks, evidently a disintegration of a nucleus in which the meson had been captured. The mesons producing stars were first called "σ mesons," to distinguish them from mesons which merely decayed. Measurements of the masses of the "σ mesons" showed they had the same mass as the π meson, and it was tentatively concluded that they were negative π mesons, which had been brought to rest in the emulsion and captured by a nucleus before they could decay. Such behavior would be consistent with the assumption of a strong nuclear interaction of π mesons and lent support to the assumption that *these* were the Yukawa particles.

217. Artificial Production of Pi Mesons. *a. Positive and Negative Pi Mesons.* If π mesons are the "quanta" of the nuclear field, it ought to be possible to produce them by a strong acceleration of a nucleon, in much the same way as x-rays (light quanta) are produced when electrons are accelerated. The required acceleration can be produced in a nuclear collision, provided sufficiently energetic particles are available. To provide the rest energy corresponding to the mass of $270m_e$, nucleons of at least 135 Mev are required. The first successful experiment of this kind was carried out with the Berkeley 184-in. synchrocyclotron with a beam of 380-Mev α-particles bombarding a carbon target.[2] The arrangement is shown in Fig. 235. The cyclotron beam, circulating inside the dee (this machine has only one), struck the edge of the target. Any negative mesons ejected from the target in the forward direction would be deflected through

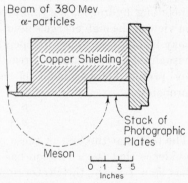

Fig. 235. Target and detector arrangement for observation of artificially produced mesons. There is a magnetic field perpendicular to the figure. (*Gardner and Lattes, Science, vol.* 107, *p.* 270, 1948.)

a semicircle by the magnetic field of the cyclotron and would strike the detector, which was shielded by a large copper block. The detector consisted of a stack of nuclear emulsions, set at an angle of 5° to the plane of the meson trajectory, so that mesons entering the surface would be stopped in the emulsion.

---

[1] Also called "pion."

[2] E. Gardner and C. M. G. Lattes, *Science*, vol. 107, p. 270, 1948.

A copious production of mesons was observed, as many as 50 useful tracks being obtained in each emulsion in a 10-min exposure. The masses could be determined from the curvature in the magnetic field and the range in the emulsion, and proved to be about $300m_e$, indicating that the particles were π mesons. As was expected, the great majority of the negative π mesons which stopped in the emulsion gave rise to stars: no π-μ decays were observed.

In later experiments, the Berkeley group[1] succeeded in detecting π^+ mesons also, coming from the target. These they found almost invariably ended up by decaying into μ mesons; in no case was star production by a positive meson observed. They were ultimately able to bring a "beam" of mesons, with a flux of about 5,000 π^+ mesons per second, out of the cyclotron vacuum chamber.[2] Compared with the few π mesons obtained in month-long exposures to the cosmic rays at mountain altitudes, this was a great advance indeed.

It has been found that mesons can be produced with a variety of bombarding agents and target nuclei. Pi mesons have been observed with α-particle, proton, neutron, and γ-ray bombardment of various elements, including hydrogen, beryllium, and carbon. As a first approximation, in view of the high energies involved, the individual nucleons in the target may be assumed to act independently of one another, and the process is visualized as a two-nucleon reaction. Thus, in the production of mesons by proton bombardment of carbon, the fundamental processes are probably

$$p + p \rightarrow p + n + \pi^+$$
$$p + n \rightarrow p + p + \pi^-$$

The fact that the first of these processes can be observed in hydrogen is evidence that the π^+ meson has integral or zero spin. Since the proton has spin $I = \frac{1}{2}$, the vector sum of the spins of two free protons plus their relative orbital angular momentum l (restricted to integral values) is a whole integer. The angular momenta on the right side of the equation must then add up to a whole integer, and, since the neutron has spin $\frac{1}{2}$, this is only possible if the spin of the π^+ meson is itself an integer (including zero).

b. Properties of Pi Mesons. (I) MASS. The masses of artificially produced mesons may be measured most conveniently by simultaneous determination of their magnetic rigidity and their range in a photographic emulsion. The values obtained by the Berkeley group[3] are

$$\pi^+ = (273.4 \pm 0.2)m_e$$
$$\pi^- = (272.5 \pm 0.3)m_e$$

[1] J. Burfening, E. Gardner, and C. M. G. Lattes, *Phys. Rev.*, vol. 75, p. 382, 1949.
[2] C. Richman, M. Skinner, J. Merritt, and B. Youtz, *Phys. Rev.*, vol. 80, p. 900, 1950.
[3] F. M. Smith, W. Birnbaum, and W. H. Barkas, *Phys. Rev.*, vol. 91, p. 765, 1953.

The two values differ by somewhat more than the combined probable errors; it is not known whether the difference is real or is to be ascribed to a difference in the range-energy relation for the two particles. In any case the close agreement with the masses determined for the cosmic ray π mesons leaves no doubt as to their identity. Similar measurements on μ^+ mesons produced in the decay of π^+ mesons gave the result

$$\mu^+ = (207.0 \pm 0.4)m_e$$

The mass of the μ^- meson, determined from the x-ray spectrum of the μ-mesonic atom[1] (cf. Sec. 215d) is

$$\mu^- = (207.9 \pm 1)m_e$$

(II) LIFETIME. The fact the π mesons are rare compared to μ mesons in the sea-level cosmic radiation suggests that they must be shorter-lived. A measurement of the lifetime of artificially produced π mesons was made by Richardson[2] and by Martinelli and Panofsky,[3] who determined the number of mesons in a beam as a function of the distance they had traveled. The mean life obtained by the latter group was $(2.0 \pm 0.15) \times 10^{-8}$ sec for π^+ mesons. The mean life of π^- mesons was determined by Lederman et al.,[4] by counting the number of decays in a beam of mesons passing through a cloud chamber; they obtained a mean life of $(2.9 \pm 0.3) \times 10^{-8}$ sec. In a later experiment, using mesons produced by the Nevis cyclotron (Columbia University), Durbin, Loar, and Havens[5] made a direct comparison of the lifetimes of π^- and π^+ mesons, again by measuring the attenuation of a beam of mesons of known energy as a function of distance. The resulting values of the mean lives,

$$\tau(\pi^+) = (2.55 \pm 0.19) \times 10^{-8} \text{ sec}$$
$$\tau(\pi^-) = (2.44 \pm 0.18) \times 10^{-8} \text{ sec}$$

agree within the experimental errors.

(III) DECAY PRODUCTS. When they decay in flight, both π^+ and π^- mesons decay into μ's (μ^+ and μ^-, respectively). Negative π mesons which come to rest in matter are first captured into atomic orbits and then quickly absorbed by the nucleus, where they cause a violent disintegration. The decay of a π^+ which has stopped is found practically always to produce a μ of definite range, about 600 microns in a nuclear emulsion, corresponding to a kinetic energy of 4.1 Mev. The constancy of this

[1] S. Koslov, V. Fitch, and J. Rainwater, *Phys. Rev.*, vol. 95, p. 291, 1954.

[2] J. R. Richardson, *Phys. Rev.*, vol. 74, p. 1720, 1948.

[3] E. A. Martinelli and W. K. H. Panofsky, *Phys. Rev.*, vol. 77, p. 465, 1950.

[4] L. M. Lederman, E. T. Booth, H. Byfield, and J. Kessler, *Phys. Rev.*, vol. 83, p. 685, 1951.

[5] R. P. Durbin, H. H. Loar, and W. W. Havens, *Phys. Rev.*, vol. 88, p. 179, 1952.

energy strongly argues for a single neutral particle: there is good evidence

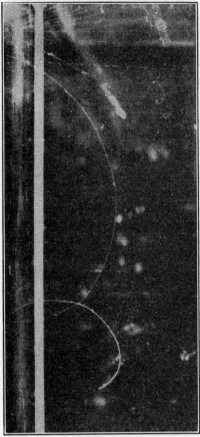

FIG. 236. Cloud-chamber photograph of the decay of a π^+ meson into a μ^+ meson and subsequent decay of the μ^+ meson. The π meson enters from the upper left, is deflected by the magnetic field into the wall of the chamber, where it decays. The μ meson emerges from the wall and stops in the gas, producing a positron, visible as a faint track traveling to the right. (*Courtesy of Professor R. B. Leighton.*)

that this is not a photon. The process is presumed to be

$$\pi^+ \rightarrow \mu^+ + \nu$$
$$\pi^- \rightarrow \mu^- + \nu \text{ (in flight only)}$$

where ν represents a single neutrino. From the mass difference (assuming the neutrino has zero rest mass) we can calculate the energy release $Q = (273 - 207) \times 0.511 = 33.7$ Mev. In a decay at rest, most of this energy goes to the neutrino because a given momentum implies a smaller energy for the heavier particle. A rare cloud-chamber photograph showing the decay of a π^+ into a μ^+ and the subsequent decay of the μ^+ into a positron is shown in Fig. 236.

c. *Neutral Pi Meson.* If the π mesons are to account for nuclear forces, there must also exist neutral π's, since forces exist not only between unlike particles (p-n) but also between like particles (n-n and p-p). It could be shown from the theory that free neutral mesons would most likely decay into two γ-quanta, and it was suggested in 1947 by Oppenheimer[1] that this process might provide a source for the cascade showers which form so prominent a part of the cosmic rays. Acting on the conjecture that neutral π mesons (π^0) might be produced in the cyclotron, Bjorklund, Crandall, Moyer, and York[2] looked for hard radiation from beryllium and carbon targets bombarded by protons of energy up to 340 Mev.

[1] Cf. H. W. Lewis, J. R. Oppenheimer, and S. A. Wouthuysen, *Phys. Rev.*, vol. 73, p. 127, 1948.

[2] R. Bjorklund, W. E. Crandall, B. J. Moyer, and H. F. York, *Phys. Rev.*, vol. 77, p. 213, 1950.

They found evidence for such radiation, beginning at a proton energy of about 175 Mev with an intensity which increased rapidly with bombarding energy.   At a proton energy of 340 Mev, photons emerging in the forward direction with respect to the beam were observed with energies ranging from 40 to 200 Mev, with a broad maximum at 120 Mev. In the backward direction, a broad distribution in energy was again observed, this time with a maximum at 60 Mev.   The difference of energy observed in the forward and backward direction is attributed to a Doppler shift, due to the motion of the source emitting the γ-ray; an elementary calculation gives the average velocity of the source as 0.3 times the velocity of light.

Several mechanisms for the production of such high-energy photons other than meson decay were considered.   The suggestion that they might result from a high excitation of the target nucleus was easily disposed of, since even a 340-Mev proton carries with it insufficient momentum to project a beryllium or carbon nucleus with a velocity of $0.3c$. Radiation of the required energy could be produced by the abrupt deceleration of protons, but such radiation would be expected to have a continuous distribution in energy with an intensity decreasing monotonically with increasing photon energy.   In addition, the observed intensity at 340-Mev bombarding energy was nearly 100 times greater than could be accounted for by such a process.

On the other hand, all observations were consistent with the hypothesis that a neutral meson, of mass about $300m_e$, was produced in a collision between the incoming proton and some nucleon in the target.   Within a very short time, less than 10^{-13} sec, the π^0 decays into two γ-quanta of about 70 Mev each.   The mesons would have initial velocities which would be distributed over a wide range, depending on the motion of the struck nucleon (due to its roughly 25-Mev kinetic energy in the nucleus), and this distribution of velocities would account for the breadth of the photon spectrum.   A crucial test of the π^0 hypothesis was made by Steinberger, Panofsky, and Steller,[1] who showed by means of a coincidence technique that the photons are in fact emitted in pairs.   It can be shown[2] quite generally that a particle which decays into two γ-quanta must have integral spin, different from unity.   The usual assumption that the π^0 has zero spin seems to be consistent with all experiments.

The mass of the π^0 can be determined relative to that of the π^- from a study of the γ-radiation emitted when π^- mesons are captured in hydrogen.   The reaction involved is

$$\pi^- + p \to n + \pi^0$$

[1] J. Steinberger, W. K. Panofsky, and J. Steller, *Phys. Rev.*, vol. 78, p. 802, 1950.

[2] C. N. Yang, *Phys. Rev.*, vol. 77, p. 242, 1950.

followed by

$$\pi^0 \rightarrow \gamma + \gamma$$

If the π^- is at rest when captured, the sum of the kinetic energies of the neutron and π^0 is equal to the mass difference (times c^2) between the initial and final components. The velocity with which the π^0 is emitted can be determined either from the Doppler shift in the γ-ray energies or from the angle between the directions of emission of the two γ-quanta. Panofsky, Aamodt, and Hadley[1] used the former method and obtained a mass difference $M(\pi^- - \pi^0) = (10.6 \pm 2.0)m_e$; Chinowsky and Steinberger,[2] using the latter method, obtained

$$M(\pi^- - \pi^0) = (8.8 \pm 0.6)m_e$$

The first measurements on the lifetime of the π^0 were made by producing them in a thin target, from which they could escape, and determining how far they moved before decaying: the result gave an upper limit of 10^{-11} sec. More recent measurements[3] in photographic-emulsion records of cosmic-ray stars, based on the same principle, yield a value of about 10^{-14} sec. Some of the properties of π and μ mesons are summarized in Table 11-2, Sec. 218.

d. Interaction of Charged Pi Mesons with Nuclei. From the fact that negative π mesons which come to rest in matter are almost never observed to decay,[4] despite their relatively short (10^{-8} sec) lifetime, it is evident that their interaction with nuclei is much greater than that of the μ meson (Sec. 215). How strong the interaction actually is can best be determined by studying the passage of high-energy (10 to 1,000 Mev) mesons through matter, for example, by examining their tracks in photographic emulsions or cloud chambers or by measuring the attenuation of a meson beam in various materials. Both μ and charged π mesons will be subject to the usual electrostatic forces, resulting in loss of energy by ionization and in scattering by the nuclear Coulomb fields, the latter manifesting itself mainly in the form of multiple small-angle deviations of the track. If the meson is also directly affected by the purely nuclear force, other effects may be expected, such as frequent large-angle elastic scatterings, inelastic scattering (with energy loss), and capture resulting in nuclear disintegrations.

For particles sufficiently energetic that the wavelength is of the order of nuclear dimensions or less, a simple geometric picture may be used to

[1] W. K. H. Panofsky, R. L. Aamodt, and J. Hadley, *Phys. Rev.*, vol. 81, p. 565, 1951.

[2] W. Chinowsky and J. Steinberger, *Phys. Rev.*, vol. 93, p. 586, 1954.

[3] A. G. Carlson, J. E. Hooper, and D. T. King, *Phil. Mag.*, vol. 41, p. 701, 1950; W. Heisenberg, "Kosmische Strahlung," Springer, Berlin, p. 148.

[4] A few cases—about one in one thousand—of π^- decay in nuclear emulsions are reported by W. F. Fry and G. R. White, *Phys. Rev.*, vol. 93, p, 1427, 1954.

describe a nuclear encounter and hence to provide a simple interpretation of the observed cross section for such events.   Thus, if the interaction between the incident particle and the nucleus is strong—i.e., if the nucleus is "opaque"—we may expect the cross section for an elastic scattering, or a reaction of some kind, to be of the order of the geometrical projected area of the nucleus.   If the interaction is weak, much smaller cross sections will be observed.   The "geometric" cross section is, approximately, (cf. Sec. 197)

$$\sigma_g \cong \pi R^2 = \pi A^{2/3} R_0{}^2 \cong 2\pi A^{2/3} \times 10^{-26} \qquad cm^2 \qquad (300)$$

For lead, this expression gives $\sigma_g \cong 2.2$ barns; for carbon, $\sigma_g \cong 0.32$ barns.

A great many measurements have been made on the cross sections for nuclear interactions of π mesons.   As one example, we cite the work of Chedester et al.,[1] who measured the attenuation of a beam of 85-Mev π^- mesons in various materials.   For eight elements, varying from Li to Pb, they found cross sections in good agreement with the values calculated from Eq. (300) above, indicating a strong interaction.   In an extensive cloud-chamber study of the scattering of 62-Mev π^+ and π^- mesons in carbon, Byfield, Kessler, and Lederman[2] were able to establish that the nuclear potential for π mesons is attractive and is described by parameters which are quite consistent with other information about nuclear forces.

218. Heavy Mesons and Hyperons.[3]   There is a considerable body of evidence for the existence of unstable particles called "heavy mesons" or "K-particles," with masses intermediate between the π meson and the proton, and for particles of nucleonic mass, intermediate between the neutron and the deuteron, for which the name "hyperon" or "Y-particle" has been suggested.   These particles occur mainly in penetrating showers or high-energy nuclear interactions produced by the cosmic rays (Sec. 219).   Some of the new particles have manifested themselves sufficiently often under conditions where reasonably precise measurements were possible that their existence may be regarded as well established, while others have appeared so far only in isolated instances and their nature is much less certain.   We shall mention here only those for which the evidence appears at the present writing (1954) to be fairly conclusive; the reader is referred to the current literature for more complete information in this rapidly developing field.

a. Heavy Mesons.   A considerable number of events have been observed in which a particle comes to rest and decays into three other

[1] C. Chedester, P. Isaacs, A. Sachs, and J. Steinberger, *Phys. Rev.*, vol. 82, p. 958, 1951.

[2] H. Byfield, J. Kessler, and L. M. Lederman, *Phys. Rev.*, vol. 86, p. 17, 1952.

[3] L. LePrince-Ringuet, *Ann. Rev. Nuclear Sci.*, vol. 3, p. 39, 1953; J. G. Wilson, "Progress in Cosmic Ray Physics." vol. II, p. 57, Interscience, New York, 1954.

particles.[1]   In several cases it has been possible to determine the masses
of all four particles, by combinations of measurements of ionization density, scattering, range, and magnetic rigidity, with sufficient accuracy to
identify the three products as π mesons and to set a value of about $950m_e$
for the mass of the incident particle.   A particularly good example[2] is
shown in Fig. 237.   The sequence of tracks shown was found in a block
of stripped nuclear emulsions (Sec. 216a) which had been flown at an
altitude of 80,000 ft.   At the left in the figure is a violent nuclear disintegration, produced by a cosmic-ray particle.   One of the resulting
particles, marked τ, was traced through 27 emulsion strips, aggregating

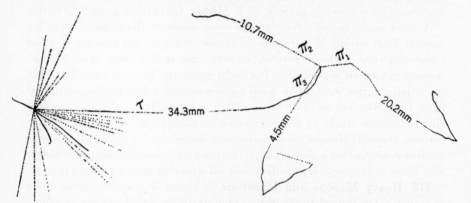

FIG. 237. Production and decay of a τ-meson observed in a stack of photographic emulsions.   The particle emerges from an energetic nuclear disintegration, traverses
several centimeters of material, and finally decays into three π mesons.   Two of the
π mesons show $\pi^+ \to \mu^+ \to e^+$ decays.   (*From Debenedetti et al., Nuovo cimento, vol. 11,
p. 420, 1954.*)

34.3 mm of material.   When it came to rest it produced three particles,
two of which (π_1 and π_3) eventually came to rest, producing μ mesons
which in turn decayed into electrons.   These two tracks are thus identified definitely as positive π mesons.   The third particle stops without
visible decay, having presumably been captured by a nucleus which then
ejected a neutron: such behavior is consistent with the decay of a negative π meson in matter.   The decay of the τ meson is represented as

$$\tau^\pm \dashrightarrow \pi^\pm + \pi^- + \pi^+$$

Tau-mesons of both signs have been observed.   The energy release, determined both from the observed energies of the decay products and from
momentum balance in individual events, is 75 Mev; the mass is then

[1] R. H. Brown et al., *Nature*, vol. 163, p. 82, 1949.
[2] A. Debenedetti, C. M. Garelli, G. Lovera, L. Tallone, and M. Vigone, *Nuovo
cimento*, vol. 11, p. 420, 1954.

$3 \times 273 + 75/0.511 = 966$ electron masses.   The mean lifetime is probably in the range 10^{-9} to 10^{-8} sec.

There is good evidence that at least one other charged particle exists with a mass comparable with that of the τ meson,[1] characterized by a decay into a single light meson instead of three.   Such particles, called κ mesons, have been observed to decay at rest ("S events") and in flight ("charged V events").   In a few cases it has been definitely established that a μ meson is produced, and it seems clear from momentum measurements that at least one and probably two neutral particles are also emitted.   Several instances have been observed in which cascade showers developed near the event, suggesting that one of the neutral particles is a photon.   The most probable mode of decay is believed to be

$$\kappa^{\pm} \to \mu^{\pm} + \gamma + \nu$$

(where γ represents a photon, ν the neutrino).   The mass of the κ meson appears to be about $1{,}000m_e$, and its mean life is 10^{-9} sec or greater.

Another heavy meson which seems to be well established[2] is a neutral particle, called the θ^0 meson, which decays into two light mesons, probably a π^+ and π^- pair, with an energy release of 214 Mev.   A typical example is shown in Fig. 238, where an inverted V track appears, presumably as a result of the decay of a nonionizing particle coming from above, associated with several penetrating particles.   There is good evidence that only two products occur, and, on the assumption that they are π mesons, the mass is determined as $(966 \pm 10)m_e$.   The lifetime is estimated as about 10^{-10} sec.

b. Hyperons.   Among the unstable particles observed to have masses greater than that of the proton $(1{,}836m_e)$ is one whose decay products, like those of the θ^0, form an inverted V in cloud-chamber photographs.[3]   This particle, called the Λ^0, has a mean life of about 3×10^{-10} sec and evidently decays into a proton and a π^- meson.   All observers agree that an energy release of about 35 Mev occurs; whether another type of Λ^0 exists which decays with an energy release of about 75 Mev is not established.   Under the assumption of the decay scheme

$$\Lambda^0 \to p + \pi^-$$

[1] C. O'Ceallaigh, *Phil. Mag.*, vol. 42, p. 1032, 1951; L. LePrince-Ringuet and B. Rossi, *Phys. Rev.*, vol. 92, p. 722, 1953; D. M. Ritson, *Phys. Rev.*, vol. 91, p. 1572, 1953.

[2] G. D. Rochester and C. C. Butler, *Nature*, vol. 160, p. 855, 1947; A. J. Seriff et al., *Phys. Rev.*, vol. 78, p. 290, 1950; Armenteros et al., *Phil. Mag.*, vol. 42, p. 1113, 1951; R. W. Thompson et al., *Phys. Rev.*, vol. 90, p. 1122, 1953.   This particle was earlier called the V_2^0.

[3] R. B. Leighton, S. D. Wanlass, and C. D. Anderson, *Phys. Rev.*, vol. 89, p. 148, 1953; H. S. Bridge, C. Peyrou, B. Rossi, and R. Safford, *Phys. Rev.*, vol. 91, p. 362, 1953; Armenteros et al., *loc. cit.*   This particle was earlier called the V_1^0.

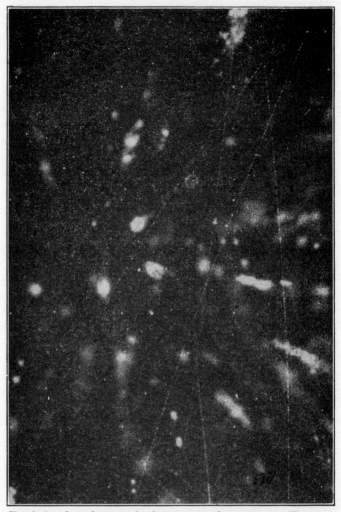

FIG. 238. Cloud-chamber photograph of a θ^0-meson decay event.   The two products, presumably π mesons, start from a point in the gas (upper right) and form an inverted V.   There is a magnetic field perpendicular to the plane of the figure.   (*Photograph courtesy of Prof. R. B. Leighton.*)

and a Q value of 35 Mev, the mass is $2{,}180m_e$.   An interesting case of the simultaneous production of a Λ^0 and a θ^0 by a high-energy π^- meson produced in the Brookhaven Cosmotron[1] is shown in Fig. 239.

Possibly related to the Λ^0, but less well established, is the Λ^+, which appears as a single track with a sharp bend,[2] interpreted as the decay of

[1] W. B. Fowler, R. P. Shutt, A. M. Thorndike, and W. L. Whittemore, *Phys. Rev.*, vol. 93, p. 861, 1954.

[2] C. M. York, R. B. Leighton, and E. K. Bjornerud, *Phys. Rev.*, vol. 90, p. 167, 1952; M. W. Friedlander, *Phil. Mag.*, vol. 45, p. 418, 1954.

FIG. 239. Cloud-chamber photograph of production of a θ^0 and a Λ^0 particle from the interaction of a 1.5-Bev π^- meson with a hydrogen nucleus. The π^- meson, produced in the Brookhaven Cosmotron, enters from the top of the figure, stopping about halfway down. Presumably two neutral particles are produced, one decaying into a π^+ and a π^- (tracks 1b and 2b), the other into a proton (1a) and a π^- (2a). (*From Fowler, Shutt, Thorndike, and Whittemore, Phys. Rev., vol. 93, p. 861, 1954; figure has been slightly retouched.*)

a charged particle into a charged and a neutral secondary. These particles are distinguished from the κ mesons both by the fact that their mass exceeds that of a proton and that they appear to have a half-life of the order of 10^{-10} sec. Possible modes of decay are

$$\Lambda^+ \rightarrow n + \pi^+$$
$$\Lambda^+ \rightarrow p + \pi^0$$

The mass is believed to be about $2,200 m_e$. One or two possible negatively charged Λ^--particles have been reported produced by 1.5-Bev π mesons in the Brookhaven Cosmotron.

That there may exist even heavier hyperons (Y-particles) is suggested by observation of cascade decays[1] in which a charged hyperon produces among its decay products a Λ^0-particle, possibly according to the scheme

$$Y^- \rightarrow \Lambda^0 + \pi^- \qquad \Lambda^0 \rightarrow p + \pi^-$$

c. Antinucleons. It is inherent in current theory that antinucleons—corresponding to unoccupied negative-energy states of normal nucleons—should also exist.[2] The antiproton, for example, bears a relation to the proton quite analogous to that of the positron to the electron in the Dirac theory. When free, an antiproton should behave like a negatively charged proton and should annihilate with ordinary protons, with an energy release of $2M_0 c^2$, or 1.8 Bev, in a manner analogous to the annihilation of positrons and electrons (Sec. 188). A few negative particles apparently of protonic mass have been observed in the cosmic radiation but their identity is not yet clearly established. In Fig. 240 is shown an example[3] which is presumed to represent the decay of a neutral hyperon, producing an inverted V track. From the sense of deflection in the magnetic field, it can be determined that the right-hand leg is due to a positive particle and its behavior is consistent with the assumption that it is a π^+ meson. The left-hand leg is due to a negative particle whose mass, determined from the magnetic rigidity (momentum) and ionization density, is $(1,850 \pm 250) m_e$. In the light of the errors of measurement, the mass of this particle is near or equal to that of a proton and is not consistent with the mass of any negative particle that has thus far been identified. There is no clear evidence that the particle is actually an antiparticle to the proton. No annihilation phenomenon is observed, and the energy release is definitely below the accepted range of values for the Q of the Λ^0 decay.

[1] Armenteros et al., *Phil. Mag.*, vol. 43, p. 597, 1952; E. W. Cowan, *Phys. Rev.*, vol. 94, p. 161, 1954.

[2] R. E. Marshak, "Meson Physics," McGraw-Hill, New York, 1952.

[3] E. W. Cowan, *Phys. Rev.*, vol. 94, p. 161, 1954.

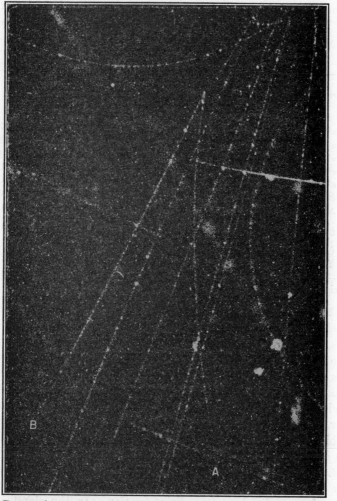

Fig. 240. Decay of a neutral hyperon into a π^+ meson (A), and a possible negative proton (B). The mass of particle B, as determined from the magnetic rigidity and ionization density, is 1850 ± 250 electron masses. (*From E. W. Cowan, Phys. Rev., vol. 94, p. 161, 1954.*)

It should be possible, according to theory, to produce antiprotons in violent nucleon-nucleon impacts, with a threshold energy of about 5.6 Bev. It may be hoped that experiments with the Berkeley Bevatron will yield some information on this matter.

Table 11-2 summarizes the principal properties of the more certain kinds of mesons and hyperons. As has been remarked, fragmentary evidence exists for several more, and it is not at all impossible that a whole spectrum of unstable particles of varying masses and modes of decay exists. To what extent these particles are interrelated and whether they have any connection with atomic nuclei remain to be seen.[1]

TABLE 11-2. MESONS AND HYPERONS*

Symbol	Character of decay	Mean life, sec	Energy release, Mev	Mass ($\times m_e$)
$\mu^\pm$	$e^\pm + \nu + \nu$	2.1×10^{-6}	105	207
$\pi^\pm$	$\mu^\pm + \nu$	2.6×10^{-8}	34	273
π^0	$\gamma + \gamma$	$\sim 10^{-14}$	135	264
$\tau^\pm$	$\pi^\pm + \pi^- + \pi^+$	$\sim 10^{-9}$	75	966
$\kappa^\pm$	$\mu^\pm + (\nu + \gamma)$	$\sim 10^{-9}$		$\sim 1,000$
θ^0	$\pi^+ + \pi^-$	1×10^{-10}	214	966
Λ^0	$p + \pi^-$	3×10^{-10}	35	2,180
(Λ^+)	$\begin{pmatrix} n + \pi^+ \\ p + \pi^0 \end{pmatrix}$	$\sim 10^{-10}$	~ 100	2,200
(Λ^-)	$(n + \pi^-)$			
Y^-	$\pi^- + \Lambda^0$	$\sim 3 \times 10^{-10}$	~ 65	

* Entries in parentheses are uncertain.

219. Nuclear Interactions of Cosmic Rays.[2] In addition to the normal, steady bombardment of single μ mesons and electrons from cascade showers, which together comprise the bulk of the cosmic radiation at sea level and mountain altitudes, there are occasionally observed events in which a great deal of ionization is produced in a single act. Such events may take many different forms, depending upon the nature of the detecting device, the surrounding material, and the depth in the atmosphere. In view of this complexity, we shall content ourselves here with a phenomenological description of a few of these events, reserving until a later section an attempt to combine them into a consistent picture.

a. Stars Observed in the Cloud Chamber. A star consists of a number of heavily ionizing particles radiating from a common center, evidently resulting from a local nuclear disintegration. In the cloud chamber, stars are sometimes formed in the solid materials of the walls or in screens placed across the chamber; more rarely, they may be formed in the gas itself. An example is shown in Fig. 241. In photographs taken at random (i.e., without counter control) such events are relatively infrequent. In a study made with an argon-filled cloud chamber at an altitude of 4,300 meters above sea level W. M. Powell[3] obtained only 13 stars with two or more "prongs" formed in the gas in 20,000 photographs.

[1] Cf. M. Goldhaber, *Phys. Rev.*, vol. 92, p. 1279, 1953; M. Gell-Mann, *Phys. Rev.*, vol. 92, p. 833, 1953; G. Cocconi, *Phys. Rev.*, vol. 94, p. 741, 1954.
[2] Cf. Rossi, "High Energy Particles."
[3] W. M. Powell, *Phys. Rev.*, vol. 69, p. 385, 1946.

The efficiency of star detection can be much improved by placing within the cloud chamber a proportional counter which triggers the chamber whenever a heavily ionizing event occurs.   Such an arrangement was used by Brown[1] in an extensive study of star production in various gases at sea level and at a mountain station at 3,240 meters.   In 9,210 expansions,

FIG. 241. Cloud-chamber photograph of a star produced in an argon atmosphere, probably by one of the two minimum-ionization particles entering from above.   One of the heavy fragments undergoes a beta decay, yielding a low-energy electron which executes a helical trajectory in the magnetic field. (*Courtesy of Professor R. B. Leighton.*)

about 2,800 stars, each having a number of "prongs" from one[2] to more than ten were observed when the chamber was filled with argon gas; three-pronged stars were the most common at the higher altitude, one or two prongs being more common at sea level.   For small stars, the average energy per prong, determined by Powell,[3] is about 12 Mev.   Adding the average nuclear binding energy of about 8 Mev, and assuming that one neutron is emitted for each proton, one finds an average energy per visible prong of about 40 Mev.

[1] W. W. Brown, *Phys. Rev.*, vol. 93, D 528, 1953.
[2] A one-pronged star is a single track whose origin can be identified.
[3] *Loc. cit.*

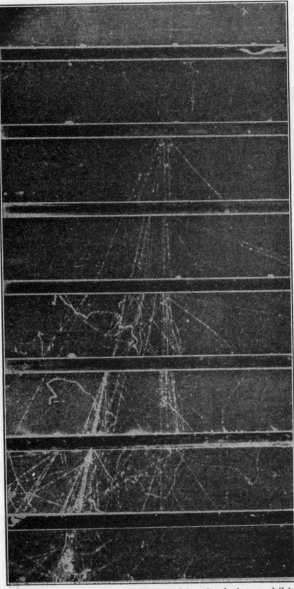

FIG. 242.   A local penetrating shower is produced in a lead plate, exhibiting a number of secondaries of minimum ionization.   From the fact that most of them penetrate a series of lead plates without giving rise to cascades, it can be concluded that they are not electrons.   The decay products of a neutral heavy meson or hyperon appear below the fourth plate as an inverted V.   (*Courtesy of Professor W. B. Fretter.*)

In some of the events observed by Brown, there occurred one or more tracks of minimum-ionization particles: those which appeared to come nearly vertically from above he assumed to represent the initiating particles. By comparing the number of such events with the number in which there was no visible primary, he concluded that only about $\frac{1}{5}$ of the stars observed at 3,240 meters elevation are produced by charged particles: at sea level the fraction was even less, about $\frac{1}{7}$.

The attenuation in the atmosphere of the star-producing radiation—called the N component—can be estimated by comparing the rate of star formation at sea level and high altitude. Brown found 12.5 times as many at 3,240 meters as at sea level and obtained a mean free path for the N component of 132 grams per cm^2 (cf. Sec. 221). The number of stars observed at the higher altitude was, in argon, about 9 per gram-atom per hour, or 1.1×10^{-7} per cubic centimeter per second: in nitrogen the number was about 0.7×10^{-7} per cubic centimeter per second.

b. Local Penetrating Showers. In the cloud chamber, a local penetrating shower is characterized by the appearance of a large number of minimum-ionization particles able to penetrate several lead plates without producing electron cascades. An example is shown in Fig. 242. The secondaries produced are mainly π mesons and protons, although heavier fragments sometimes occur; heavy mesons are also seen occasionally. The total energy release may be more than 10^{10} ev. A typical counter arrangement[1] for detection of local penetrating showers is shown in Fig. 243. Three layers of Geiger counters, A, B, and C, are imbedded in a large block of lead, in such a way that a particle passing through all three layers must penetrate at least 20 cm of lead. The electronic circuit is arranged to respond to simultaneous discharges of two or more counters in each of the three layers. Often an arrangement of this kind is used to trigger a cloud chamber, thereby favoring the detection of these rare events.

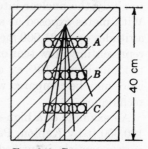

FIG. 243. Counter arrangement for detection of penetrating showers. Simultaneous discharge of at least two counters in each layer is required.

Local penetrating showers are found to be produced about equally often by charged and uncharged particles. They are evidently related to the stars just discussed, presumably representing particularly energetic nuclear disintegrations produced in the immediate neighborhood of the detector. It is probable that the main effects are due to energetic protons and neutrons, with π mesons causing a few of the highest-energy events.

[1] J. Tinlot, *Phys. Rev.*, vol. 74, p. 1197, 1948.

   c. *Extensive Air (Auger) Showers.*[1]   The most energetic events of the
cosmic radiation manifest themselves in the extensive air showers.   Such
showers may be observed, for example, in the simultaneous discharge of
counter arrays separated by as much as a hundred meters and make their
appearance in a cloud chamber as a series of closely spaced "cores" of
cascade showers of high density.   Showers containing as many as 10^8
particles, representing a total energy of more than 10^{17} ev, have been
observed at mountain altitudes.

   About 98 per cent of the particles occurring in extensive air showers are
electrons: the development, from their initiation near the top of the
atmosphere, is therefore largely governed by the cascade theory (Sec.
213).   Penetrating particles, both μ mesons and nucleons, comprise
about 2 per cent of the shower particles observed at mountain altitudes.

   d. *Nuclear Disintegrations Observed in Photographic Emulsions.*   With
the development of photographic emulsions capable of revealing tracks of
minimum ionization, i.e., tracks of singly charged particles having kinetic
energies of the order of their rest mass or greater, it has become possible
to study the nuclear interactions of cosmic-ray particles in great detail.
With plates exposed at sea level, deep underground, and at free-balloon
altitudes up to 21,000 meters, events ranging from the lower-energy stars,
representing a few tens or hundreds of Mev, to large, complex disintegrations involving 10^{13} ev or more may be observed, and their characteristics may be compared with those observed by cloud-chamber or counter
techniques.

   An example of a high-energy disintegration, recorded at an altitude of
100,000 ft by Kaplon, Peters, and Bradt,[2] is shown in Fig. 244.   A high-
energy particle, identified as an α-particle by its ionization density, strikes
a heavy nucleus, presumably Ag or Br, in the emulsion, and produces a
major disruption.   Eighteen heavily ionizing tracks, 33 minimum-
ionization particles in a wide cone, and 23 minimum-ionization particles
in a very narrow "core" are produced.   The total energy represented is
about 10^{13} ev.   In the core, which is believed to consist primarily of π
mesons, there are found at varying distances from the origin a number of
paired tracks (not visible in the figure), almost certainly representing
electron-positron pairs arising from the conversion of high-energy γ-rays
accompanying the core.   These γ-rays presumably result from the decay
of neutral mesons, which because of their short lifetime could only travel
a fraction of a micron before decaying into pairs of γ-quanta.   Such an
event as this may be typical of those giving rise to the extensive air

[1] G. Cocconi, V. Cocconi Tongiorgi, and K. Greisen, *Phys. Rev.*, vol. 76, p. 1020,
1949; K. Sitte, *Phys. Rev.*, vol. 87, p. 351, 1952; W. E. Hazen, R. W. Williams, and
C. A. Randall, *Phys. Rev.*, vol. 93, p. 578, 1954.
   [2] M. F. Kaplon, B. Peters, and H. L. Bradt, *Phys. Rev.*, vol. 76, p. 1735, 1949.

showers, for, as the energetic mesons and γ-rays proceed downward through the atmosphere, further interactions will take place, resulting in a large number of cascade showers and individual penetrating particles.

Detailed study of a great many nuclear interactions observed in photographic emulsions lead to the following picture of the course of such

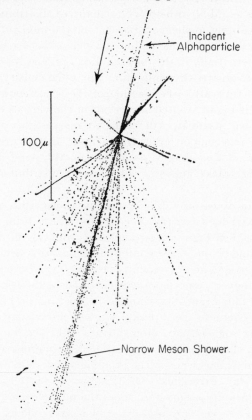

Incident
Alphaparticle

100μ

Narrow Meson Shower

FIG. 244. The "R" star, a nuclear disintegration produced by a 10^{13}-ev α-particle. Fifty-six tracks of minimum ionization and eighteen heavily ionized tracks appear. (*From Kaplon, Peters, and Bradt, Phys. Rev., vol. 76, p. 1735, 1949.*)

reactions.[1] The incident primary particle entering a nucleus strikes one of the nucleons present: because its kinetic energy is large compared with the average binding energy (about 8 Mev) it does not greatly disturb the rest of the nucleus at this stage.[2] If the primary energy is less than about 1 Bev, no mesons are produced and the result is an "elastic" collision in

[1] J. G. Wilson, "Progress in Cosmic Ray Physics," vol. I, article by U. Camerini, W. O. Lock, and D. H. Perkins, Interscience, New York, 1952.

[2] Note that the de Broglie wavelength of the incident particle is sufficiently smaller than nuclear dimensions that a semiclassical picture is appropriate.

which some of the primary's energy is transferred to the struck nucleon. As the two particles travel through the nucleus, further encounters may take place and a kind of "cascade" develops, in which many nucleons may be involved. Some of these will escape from the nucleus after only a few collisions, carrying with them a considerable energy, of the order of some hundreds of Mev; others will remain to distribute their energy among the remaining nucleons. Because of the momentum brought in by the incident particle, the secondaries which escape early in the process are ejected preferentially in the forward direction and will be observed as tracks of slightly greater than minimum ionization density (called "grey" tracks). Some time after the ejection of these particles, the remaining nucleus, which is highly excited as a result of the various collisions which have taken place inside it, will begin to release its excess energy by "evaporating" nucleons or larger fragments. In this process, the average energy per nucleon is only some tens of Mev, and a star of short, heavily ionizing tracks appears, with prongs distributed more or less isotropically.

At energies in excess of 1 Bev, π mesons (both charged and neutral) may be produced in the initial encounters of the primary, and these, together with a few high-energy nucleons, will emerge in the forward direction, forming a "shower" of minimum-ionization tracks. The number of shower particles increases relative to the "grey" tracks as the energy increases and they become more concentrated in the forward direction. There is some indication, for example in the star of Fig. 244, that at extremely high energies, two separate cones of shower particles occur, one with an opening angle of only a few degrees and the other opening 30° or more, possibly corresponding, respectively, to mesons emitted preferentially forward or backward in the center-of-mass system.

220. Cosmic-ray Primaries. Of the known particles which might constitute the primary cosmic radiation, the possible candidates are electrons (+ and −), photons, protons, and heavier nuclei. None of the known mesons can be considered, because of their short lives, and, unless the source lies within our own solar system, the neutron is excluded for the same reason (the free neutron has a half-life of about 15 min). It can be concluded from the observation of the geomagnetic variation of cosmic-ray intensity that most, if not all, of the primaries are charged, and the east-west asymmetry, as well as the observed excess of positive over negative μ mesons, indicates that positively charged primaries predominate (Sec. 210).

Evidence that neither electrons nor positrons can constitute any important fraction of the primaries was obtained by Schein, Jesse, and Wollan,[1]

---

[1] M. Schein, W. P. Jesse, and E. O. Wollan, *Phys. Rev.*, vol. 59, p. 615, 1941.

who found, by means of a balloon-carried counter telescope, that no more than a few per cent of those particles near the top of the atmosphere which can penetrate a few centimeters of lead exhibit the multiplication typical of electronic radiation.   In another experiment for the same purpose, Critchfield, Ney, and Oleksa[1] fitted a small automatic cloud chamber with two $\frac{1}{4}$-in. lead plates and sent it up with a balloon to an altitude of more than 25 kilometers, where the mass of the residual atmosphere amounts to 20 grams per cm^2. From the number of cascade showers observed in the cloud chamber, they concluded that energetic electrons (more than 1 Bev) comprise less than 0.2 per cent of the primary flux. Photons are presumably also eliminated by these experiments since they would produce similar effects.

It seems evident, then, that if the primaries are to be identified with known particles they must be atomic nuclei, and it is generally believed that they are mainly protons.   In favor of this assumption is the observation that the average ionizing power of the particles observed in rocket-borne counters is only slightly higher than the minimum value expected for high-energy particles of unit charge.[2]   The rocket flights in question were made at the equator and reached an altitude of more than 100 kilometers.   The interpretation of the results is considerably complicated, even at this altitude, by the "albedo," a relatively large contribution of particles either reflected from the atmosphere or caught in stationary orbits about the earth, but it is nevertheless possible to conclude that the bulk of the ionizing radiation above the atmosphere carries a single charge.[3]   The hypothesis of primary protons is further supported by observations in photographic emulsions, where it is found that most of the high-energy nuclear disintegrations—i.e., those with many prongs or those exhibiting "showers" of minimum-ionization particles—observed at 29 kilometers altitude (15 grams per cm^2 residual atmosphere) are produced by singly charged particles of minimum ionization.[4]   Farther down in the atmosphere a good many stars are observed to be produced by neutrons, presumably arising as secondaries from the initial interactions of the primaries.

Atomic nuclei heavier than protons also occur among the cosmic-ray primaries, in not inconsiderable numbers.   Direct evidence for the existence of such particles was first obtained in balloon-borne cloud chamber

[1] C. L. Critchfield, E. P. Ney, and S. Oleksa, *Phys. Rev.*, vol. 79, p. 402, 1950.

[2] S. F. Singer, *Phys. Rev.*, vol. 76, p. 701, 1949.

[3] Because the ionization is proportional to Z^2, high-energy α-particles would contribute four times the normal ionization density.   The observed effects do not exclude an admixture of α-particles as high as 20 per cent.

[4] J. J. Lord and M. Schein, *Phys. Rev.*, vol. 77, p. 19, 1950; J. J. Lord, *Phys. Rev.*, vol. 81, p. 901, 1951.

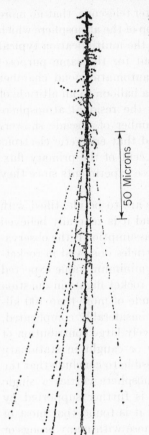

50 Microns

FIG. 245. An argon nucleus strikes a hydrogen nucleus in a photographic emulsion, breaking up into seven fragments, one of which (central heavy track) is a sodium nucleus. Many δ-rays are visible on the two heavy tracks. (*Courtesy of Professor M. F. Kaplon.*)

and nuclear-emulsion observations by Freier et al.,[1] who found very dense tracks at altitudes above 28 kilometers (14 grams per cm²). From the observed ionization and range, they estimated that particles with charge as high as 40 and kinetic energies up to 60 Bev are present among the primaries. A microphotograph of a track due to an argon nucleus is shown in Fig. 245. The charge is in this example determined from the number of δ-rays (electrons which have received sufficient energy in close encounters to produce visible tracks). Subsequent work with photographic emulsions has resulted in the positive identification among the primaries of nuclei of values of Z as high as 26 (Fe). The number of nuclei heavier than protons appears to represent about 11 per cent of the total primary flux and to carry about 30 per cent of the incident cosmic-ray energy.[2] The distribution in Z corresponds approximately to the abundance of elements in the universe,[3] with helium about 10 per cent of the total and all other elements aggregating about 1 per cent. There is some suggestion that the heavy elements are relatively more abundant in the cosmic rays.

The total flux of particles incident upon the atmosphere[4] can be measured by counter telescopes carried to altitudes sufficiently great that no important contribution is made by secondary processes. Winckler, Stix, Dwight, and Sabin[5] made such determinations at various latitudes with balloon flights extending to a residual atmosphere of 15 grams per cm². From these experiments they found that the number of primary particles traveling near the vertical direction at northern latitudes is 0.25 particles

[1] P. Freier, E. J. Lofgren, E. P. Ney, F. Oppenheimer, H. L. Bradt, and B. Peters, *Phys. Rev.*, vol. 74, p. 213, 1948.

[2] J. G. Wilson, "Progress in Cosmic Ray Physics," article by B. Peters, Interscience, New York, 1952.

[3] As derived from analysis of the composition of the earth and of meteorites, and from stellar spectra. Cf. H. Brown, *Revs. Mod. Phys.*, vol. 21, p. 625, 1949.

[4] J. G. Wilson, *op. cit.*, article by G. Puppi and N. Dallaporta.

[5] J. R. Winckler, T. Stix, K. Dwight, and R. Sabin, *Phys. Rev.*, vol. 79, p. 656, 1950.

per square centimeter per second per steradian. At the equator, the number is about one-tenth as large. From a rocket flight well above the atmosphere, Van Allen and Singer[1] obtained a vertical flux of 0.29 per cm² per sec per sterad at latitude 58°N. To the extent that the directions of motion are isotropically distributed (this will be true above the atmosphere for energies higher than the geomagnetic cutoff), the total flux of particles incident upon 1 cm² is π times the perpendicular flux, or about 0.8 particles per second per square centimeter.

221. Development of the Cosmic Radiation in the Atmosphere.[2]   We are now in a position to discuss in a coherent fashion the interrelations of the various components of the cosmic radiation which have been the subjects of the preceding sections. It should be emphasized that some of the details of the description which follows are rather speculative and may require revision as the subject develops with further investigation. The main outlines of the picture, however, seem to be fairly well established. We shall begin with the interactions of the primaries at the top of the atmosphere and then trace the propagation of the various secondary components as they proceed downward.

a. Primaries. The primary radiation consists, as has been said, of protons and heavier nuclei, with energies ranging from 10^9 to more than 10^{16} ev per nucleon. As these particles enter the atmosphere, they lose a small amount of energy by ionization processes, but the main loss will be by nuclear collisions. From experiments with artificially accelerated protons in the 100- to 300-Mev range it is found that the cross section for nuclear collision is somewhat less than the "projected area" of the target nucleus: for nitrogen and oxygen nuclei, a cross section of $\sigma = 2 \times 10^{-25}$ cm² seems to be a reasonable estimate. The mean free path of primary protons between nuclear collisions in the atmosphere, in terms of the mass of material traversed, is given by $L = A/N_0\sigma$, where A is the mass number—14 or 16 for nitrogen or oxygen—and N_0 the Avogadro number; in the present instance L = 120 grams per cm². (In this distance a 10-Bev proton would lose only about 250 Mev by ionization: cf. Fig. 228.) This number is in reasonable agreement with observations on the altitude dependence of the production of energetic stars. The fraction of primary protons vertically incident on the top of the atmosphere which survive to the depth x is then $e^{-x/L}$ where x is the mass of air in grams per square centimeter above the altitude in question. The curve marked p in Fig. 246 shows in approximate absolute scale the number of high-energy protons (above 400 Mev) as a function of depth in the atmosphere.

[1] J. A. Van Allen and S. F. Singer, *Phys. Rev.*, vol. 78, p. 819, 1950.
[2] W. Heisenberg, "Kosmische Strahlung," Springer, Berlin, 1953; Rossi, "High Energy Particles."

The heavy primaries interact with the atmosphere much more quickly than do the protons,[1] those with $Z \geqq 10$, for example, having a mean free path of only 19 grams per cm^2. In their first encounters, they are broken up into smaller fragments—mainly protons and neutrons, so that already at a depth below the top of the atmosphere of 20 grams per cm^2,

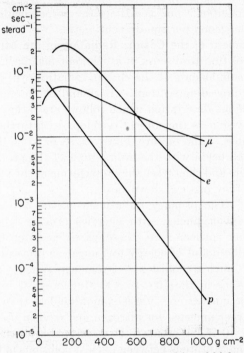

FIG. 246. Approximate values of the vertical intensities of high-energy protons (p), μ mesons (μ), and electrons or positrons (e) as a function of atmospheric depth. The ordinate gives the number of particles per steradian per second traveling vertically downward across 1 cm^2. (*From B. Rossi, "High Energy Particles," Prentice-Hall, 1952.*)

corresponding to an altitude of 27 kilometers, there will be many such secondary particles.

b. Secondary Nucleonic Component. In the first collision of a high-energy primary proton with a nucleus of the atmosphere, a number of high-energy charged fragments—mainly protons—and neutrons are produced, in addition to the spray of mesons and the few low-energy "evaporation" particles. The secondary protons which have energies of some hundreds of Mev or more are again relatively unaffected by ionization loss, and will induce further nuclear disintegrations after traveling, on

[1] G. W. Anderson, P. S. Frier, and J. E. Naugle, *Phys. Rev.*, vol. 94, p. 1317, 1954.

the average, about 120 grams per cm², forming a "nucleon cascade" through the atmosphere. In each encounter the energy of the incident particle is shared among the several products, and, eventually, when the available energy becomes less than 100 Mev per particle, the protons will have little opportunity to produce further disintegrations before being stopped by ionization loss (ionization losses will bring a 100-Mev proton to rest in about 10 grams per cm²). Secondary neutrons, on the other hand, continue to be effective in inducing disintegrations and so may propagate the cascade until they reach thermal energy, where they finally disappear in the $N^{14}(n,p)C^{14}$ reaction, producing radioactive C^{14}.

The nucleon cascades account for the penetrating showers and for the bulk of the low-energy stars and protons and neutrons observed in the lower atmosphere. For each primary incident upon the top of the atmosphere, about seven nuclear disintegrations occur farther down, each producing several neutrons and protons.[1] Because of their ionization loss, very few protons reach sea level, and practically all the low-energy stars observed are due to neutrons (cf. Sec. 219a). The total number of slow neutrons absorbed in the atmosphere (at latitude 51°) is about 7.1 per second in a vertical column of 1 cm² cross section.[2]

c. Penetrating Component. In the same high-energy primary interactions in which the larger nucleonic cascades have their origin, considerable numbers of π mesons, both charged and neutral, are produced. The number ranges from one or two for a 2-Bev star to fifty or more for the high-energy (10^{13}-ev) stars of the type described in Sec. 219d. As we have seen earlier (Sec. 217), π mesons also have strong nuclear interactions and will presumably induce further disintegrations after traveling, on the average, about 120 grams per cm² or, if they are produced at an altitude near 15 kilometers, a few kilometers downward. Charged π mesons decay, however, with a half-life of $2.6 \times 10^{-8}W/W_0$ sec (W and W_0 are the total and rest energies: cf. Sec. 217). With a velocity near c, such a particle will travel a mean distance of

$$2.6 \times 10^{-8} \times 3 \times 10^{8}W/W_0 \cong 10 \times W/W_0$$

meters before decaying. Thus only those exceptional ones with energies greater than $100W_0$, or about 10 Bev, will produce nuclear disintegrations. Most of the charged π mesons will decay in flight near their source into μ mesons (and neutrinos). The μ mesons, having little radiation loss and almost no nuclear interaction, travel great distances through the atmosphere and even to depths of many hundreds of meters below the earth's surface. These, then, comprise the bulk of the penetrating component at all except the highest altitudes and are responsible for all the observed

[1] Wilson, op. cit., p. 379.
[2] L. C. L. Yuan, Phys. Rev., vol. 81, p. 175, 1951.

effects at great depths underground. As shown by curve μ in Fig. 246, the μ meson intensity builds up to a maximum in the first 150 grams per cm^2 or so and thereafter falls very much more slowly than does the high-energy-proton component.

On their way down through the atmosphere, many of the μ mesons decay, producing electrons or positrons, and many others eject high-energy electrons ("knock-ons" or "δ-rays") from the atoms through which they pass. The electrons then are multiplied through cascade processes (Sec. 213) and contribute to the "soft" component. Most of the electrons, positrons, and γ-rays observed at sea level and all those observed underground are secondaries of the μ-meson component.

d. *Soft Component.* The neutral π mesons produced in large stars near the top of the atmosphere are so short-lived ($\tau_0 < 10^{-14}$ sec) that none of them travels more than a few microns before decaying. The decay of a π^0 meson results in two high-energy γ-quanta, and these, through the process of pair formation, initiate cascade showers which may, given sufficient energy, extend clear down through the atmosphere. Most of the soft component observed at high altitude results from the decay of π^0 mesons. Curve e of Fig. 246 shows the rise and fall of the soft component.

222. Origin of Cosmic Rays.[1] The principal known facts which must be accounted for by a theory of the origin of cosmic rays are the following:

1. The energy spectrum has the form $N(E)\ dE \propto (1 + E)^{-n}\ dE$, where $N(E)\ dE$ is the number of particles having energy E in the range dE. The exponent n is about 2.1 for protons of energy 2 to 15 Bev and about 2.5 for higher energies, up to at least 10^{15} ev. For heavier particles, the spectrum is roughly the same when expressed in terms of energy per nucleon.

2. Individual particles may have energies as high as 10^{18} ev.

3. The relative abundance of heavy elements in the cosmic-ray primaries seems to be about the same as that in the universe as a whole, or perhaps somewhat greater.

4. Aside from variations due to changes in conditions in the earth's atmosphere or magnetic field, periodic variations with sidereal or solar time amount to only a fraction of 1 per cent or less for the bulk of the cosmic radiation.[2]

5. The density of cosmic-ray energy in space, about 10^{-12} erg per cm^3, is approximately equal to that of the total thermal radiation (including visible light).

6. Few if any high-energy electrons occur.

[1] L. Biermann, *Ann. Revs. Nuclear Sci.*, vol. 2, 1953; Heisenberg, *op. cit.*

[2] Cf. Wilson, *op. cit.*, article by H. Elliott; J. W. Fonger, W. H. Fonger, and J. A. Simpson, *Phys. Rev.*, vol. 94, p. 1031, 1954.

7. Pronounced increases in the intensity of particles of more than 10 Bev are occasionally observed in connection with solar eruptions.[1]

In broad outline, the problem presented by the primary cosmic radiation may be divided into three parts. Where are the sources of cosmic-ray particles located? What are the mechanisms by which the particles are liberated from their sources? How are the particles propagated through space? In the following we shall deal briefly with these three questions, more with the objective of illustrating current thinking on the subject than with any conviction that the conclusions suggested have any but the most tentative character.

a. Source of Cosmic Rays. Three possible regions may be considered as sources of the cosmic radiation: the solar system, the galaxy in which we live, or other galaxies. Although it appears from item 7 above that some high-energy particles probably have their source in the sun, the fact that the diurnal variation is small (4) suggests that the sun is not the main source.[2] Extragalactic sources seem improbable since only about 1 per cent of the thermal energy comes from outside our galaxy, and item 5 above would then require that extragalactic sources supply a much higher ratio of cosmic-ray energy to thermal energy—by a factor of 100—than does our own galaxy. It appears then most likely that the cosmic rays are produced within our own galaxy, and that relatively little energy of this sort exists in intergalactic space.

b. Initial Production. The fact that exceptional activity on the surface of the sun is accompanied by an increase in the cosmic radiation shows that some mechanism for accelerating charged particles must exist in such disturbances on the sun and, presumably, other stars. Such a mechanism may conceivably be found in rapidly changing magnetic fields —as observed for example in the sun spots. In such fields, slowly moving ions could be accelerated by something akin to the betatron principle (Sec. 191). There are a number of difficulties with this view, however, and it is not at all clear that the main source of cosmic rays is of this character. In particular, the energies which can be obtained seem to be rather low, perhaps less than 1 Bev, and further acceleration of the particles after they escape from the source is probably required. Also, the amount of energy which can be radiated by any ordinary star in the form of high-energy charged particles must be a very small fraction indeed of the total radiation. It follows that there must exist some means by which

---

[1] H. Elliott, *op. cit.*

[2] A theory advanced by R. D. Richtmyer and E. Teller, *Phys. Rev.*, vol. 75, p. 1729, 1949, overcomes this difficulty by allowing the particles to circulate in the solar system under the influence of a magnetic field until they become essentially isotropic. The theory meets with other difficulties, however, and has been generally abandoned in favor of the hypothesis of galactic origin. Cf. Biermann, *op. cit.*, p. 353.

the cosmic-ray particles are trapped within the galaxy until the energy density is built up by many orders of magnitude.

c. Trapping and Acceleration.[1]   There are a number of reasons for believing that there exist weak magnetic fields in interstellar space.   The most direct evidence for the existence of such fields comes from the observed polarization of starlight, which is believed to be due to an ordered orientation of nonspherical dust grains containing paramagnetic materials.[2]   These fields, which may have been established in the course of the evolution of the galaxy, are strongly affected by the motion of clouds of ions moving in interstellar space under the action of pressure gradients, light pressure, and other forces.   Because of the high electrical conductivity of the ion clouds, the magnetic lines of force will be effectively "frozen" in the clouds and will follow the mass motion.[3]   Observations on the polarization suggest that the field in that part of the galaxy in which the sun is located has a magnitude of the order of 10^{-6} to 10^{-4} gauss, is roughly homogeneous, and is directed along a spiral arm of the galaxy.

In a theory proposed by Fermi, charged cosmic-ray particles are assumed to be partially trapped within the galaxy and accelerated through the operation of local variations in the general field.   Consider a particle of momentum 10 Bev/c, moving in a field of 10^{-5} gauss. The radius of curvature of its trajectory will be about 3×10^{12} cm, somewhat less than the distance from the earth to the sun.   From the point of view of galactic dimensions,[4] the particle will appear simply to execute a close helix about a line of force, and the general motion in a uniform field will be given essentially by the direction of the magnetic field.   If now such a particle traveling along the field lines in a region of low field should come to a region where the magnetic field is appreciably larger, the particle may be reflected, reversing the sense of the helix and traveling back in approximately the direction from which it came.   In this direction, too, it is likely to encounter a region of high field, and it may spend some time traveling back and forth in this trap.   If the two "jaws" of the trap are at relative rest, the particle neither gains nor loses kinetic energy.   If, on the other hand, the regions of high field are in motion or are changing with time,[5] the action of the induced electric fields may cause either an increase or a decrease in the energy of the particle.   Statistical

[1] E. Fermi, *Phys. Rev.*, vol. 75, p. 1169, 1949; *Astrophys. J.*, vol. 119, p. 1, 1954; P. Morrison, S. Olbert, and B. Rossi, *Phys. Rev.*, vol. 94, p. 440, 1954.

[2] L. Davis and J. S. Greenstein, *Astrophys. J.*, vol. 114, p. 206, 1951.

[3] Conversely, if the magnetic fields are sufficiently intense, they will affect the motion of the cloud.

[4] Our galaxy is roughly a spiral, of mean diameter 10^5 light-years and thickness about 10^3 light-years; the developed length of an arm may be as much as 10^6 light-years.   One light-year $= 3 \times 10^{18}$ cm.

[5] L. Davis, *Phys. Rev.*, vol. 93, p. 947, 1954.

considerations indicate that on the average there should be a net gain in this process: in fact the tendency will be toward a situation of equipartition, in which each particle and moving cloud has the same kinetic energy.

Actually the equilibrium condition is never even remotely approached, according to the theory, because particles gradually disappear in some way, possibly by leaking out of the ends of the galactic arms. An upper limit to the mean life of a cosmic-ray particle in the galaxy may be set from the observation that an appreciable fraction of heavy nuclei is observed. As these particles traverse matter they are quickly broken up, with a mean free path of only a few tens of grams per square centimeter, into lighter particles. The heavy primaries observed above the earth must then have traveled through a total amount of matter something less than this figure. Interstellar matter consists largely of hydrogen, with an average density of about 0.5 atoms per cubic centimeter, or about 10^{-24} grams per cm^3. To have traversed less than 10 grams per cm^2, a particle must have had a total path less than 10^{25} cm or 10^7 light-years. This is a long distance compared to the 10^3 or so light-years traveled by a light photon in the galaxy, but not unreasonable if the particles are required to diffuse out along a spiral arm.

The intragalactic magnetic fields thus serve two important functions: they greatly delay the escape of charged particles, permitting a large energy density to be built up even though the sources may be weak, and they provide a means by which the energies of individual particles may be enormously multiplied. It is obvious, however, that the present theory leaves many important questions unanswered, and it is not impossible that quite different processes will be discovered as our information about cosmic rays and the properties of interstellar space is improved by further experimental and theoretical investigations.

APPENDIX I

ELECTROMAGNETIC ENERGY, MOMENTUM, AND RADIATION

There are a few features of the electromagnetic field which it is useful to bear in mind in considering the new conceptions introduced by the quantum theory but which are not adequately treated in most textbooks. For reference, these results will be described in this appendix, but with omission of all proofs.

223. Electromagnetic Units. The principal relations will be stated both in Gaussian-cgs units and in absolute practical or "rationalized" mks units, hereafter called simply mks units. In dealing with charged particles moving about in space, the Gaussian units have the advantage that the permittivity ϵ_0 and permeability μ_0 of empty space are both unity; and in such cases no inconvenience results from the small sizes of the centimeter and the gram. In the absolute practical, or mks, units

$$\epsilon_0 = (36\pi \times 10^9)^{-1} \text{ farad per meter} \qquad \mu_0 = 4\pi \times 10^{-7} \text{ henry per meter}$$

(The value of μ_0 is exact by definition, but $\epsilon_0 = 1/\mu_0 c^2$ in terms of the speed of light c in meters per second.) In these latter units, charges are expressed in coulombs, the electric field strength in volts per meter, the magnetic induction B in webers per square meter, and the magnetic field strength H in ampere-turns per meter; masses, lengths, times, forces, and work, respectively, are in kilograms, meters, seconds, newtons, and joules. A few useful conversion ratios are listed just ahead of the index.

224. Electromagnetic Energy. Consider a homogeneous medium of permittivity ϵ and permeability μ, in which there may be moving electric charges or streams of charges constituting currents. From the Maxwell-Lorentz equations for the electromagnetic field, of which all but the force equation were written down in Sec. 67, the following mathematical theorem can be deduced,[1] stated in Gaussian units:

$$-\frac{d}{dt} \int_\tau \frac{1}{8\pi} (\epsilon E^2 + \mu H^2)\, d\tau = \frac{dW}{dt} + \int_S \frac{c}{4\pi} (\mathbf{E} \times \mathbf{H})_n\, dS \qquad (301)$$

Here E is the electric field intensity and H the magnetic field strength (in oersteds); and in free space $\epsilon = \mu = 1$. The first integral is taken throughout the volume τ enclosed by any surface S; and dW/dt represents the rate at which work is being done by forces due to the field acting upon the moving charges (if any) inside this surface. The second integral is taken over the surface S itself. The symbol $\mathbf{E} \times \mathbf{H}$ stands for the vector product[2] of the electric vector $\mathbf{E}$ and the magnetic vector $\mathbf{H}$ and $(\mathbf{E} \times \mathbf{H})_n$ for the component of this vector in the direction of the outward-drawn normal to S, and c denotes the speed of light in a vacuum in centimeters per second.

---

[1] See J. C. Slater and N. H. Frank, "Electromagnetism," 1947, or W. R. Smythe, "Static and Dynamic Electricity," 1939.

[2] The vector product is defined in Sec. 40.

In mks units the same equation holds except that the coefficient $1/8\pi$ in the first integral is replaced by $\frac{1}{2}$ and the factor $c/4\pi$ in the last term disappears; in these units, in free space, $\epsilon = \epsilon_0$ and $\mu = \mu_0$.

The theorem expressed by Eq. (301), representing a mathematical consequence of the Maxwell-Lorentz equations, at once poses a question as to the conservation of energy. The accepted procedure is to preserve this principle by inventing a new form of energy. "Electromagnetic" energy is commonly assumed to be distributed throughout the field with a density

$$u = \frac{1}{8\pi}(\epsilon E^2 + \mu H^2) \qquad \text{ergs per cm}^3 \tag{302a}$$

if ϵ, μ, E, and H are in Gaussian units, or

$$u = \frac{1}{2}(\epsilon E^2 + \mu H^2) \qquad \text{joules per m}^3 \tag{302b}$$

if mks units are used. The integral on the left in the equation then represents the rate of loss of electromagnetic energy from the volume enclosed by S.

Part of this lost energy appears as the work dW/dt. To interpret the last term in the equation, it is usually assumed that the electromagnetic energy is streaming in the field in the direction of "Poynting's vector" $\mathbf{\Pi}$ defined as

$$\mathbf{\Pi} = \frac{c}{4\pi}\, \mathbf{E} \times \mathbf{H} \qquad \text{ergs per cm}^2 \text{ per sec} \tag{303a}$$

in Gaussian units or

$$\mathbf{\Pi} = \mathbf{E} \times \mathbf{H} \qquad \text{joules per m}^2 \text{ per sec} \tag{303b}$$

in the mks system. If a small plane surface is drawn in the field perpendicular to the vector $\mathbf{\Pi}$ (Fig. 247), the magnitude Π expresses the amount of energy that crosses unit area of this surface per second. The second integral in the equation then represents the rate at which electromagnetic energy is passing outward across S, and the conservation of energy is obviously preserved.

225. Electromagnetic Momentum. In mechanics, the principles of the conservation of momentum and of moment of momentum are second in importance only to the energy principle. It is easily seen that the resultant of all the electrostatic forces exerted on each other by a set of stationary charges always vanishes, and that the total moment of these forces about any axis also vanishes. The same is true of the mutual forces exerted on a set of *steady currents* by their magnetic fields. In the case of *nonsteady* electromagnetic fields, however, the resultant force may not vanish. A good example is the force on an electron in space due to an isolated patch of electromagnetic waves; in this case there may be no simultaneously acting reaction on any material particle or body anywhere.

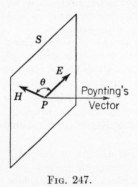

Fig. 247.

It would not be illogical to say that in such cases the principles of momentum simply do not hold. On the other hand, it has been found possible to preserve both momentum principles by assuming that there is a distribution of *electromagnetic momentum* in the field itself and that what is conserved is the sum of the momenta of all material particles and of the integrated field momentum.

The situation is simplest in free space, and only this case is of interest in this book. It can be shown[1] that both principles of momentum are satisfied if the volume density of vector momentum in the field is assumed to be equal at every point to Poynting's vector divided by c^2. Thus in free space, in Gaussian-cgs units,

$$g = \frac{1}{4\pi c} \mathbf{E} \times \mathbf{H} \qquad \text{grams per sec per cm}^2 \qquad (304a)$$

c being expressed in centimeters per second; or, in mks units, with c in meters per second,

$$g = \frac{1}{c^2} \mathbf{E} \times \mathbf{H} \qquad \text{kilograms per sec per m}^2 \qquad (304b)$$

It may be of interest to note in passing that in free space the electromagnetic momentum can be accounted for physically by making the following arbitrary assumptions:

1. The electromagnetic energy u has a mass u/c^2 (in either set of units), in accord with the general relation suggested by relativity between mass and energy (Sec. 39);

2. this energy is in motion with such a vector velocity $\mathbf{v}$ as will give the correct value to Poynting's vector, i.e., so that $u\mathbf{v} = \mathbf{\Pi}$; and, finally,

3. momentum equals mass times velocity, according to the standard definition.

226. Electromagnetic Waves. It is shown in many books that certain solutions of Maxwell's equations for a homogeneous isotropic insulator represent plane waves of uniform amplitude. The waves are propagated in a direction perpendicular to the wave front at a speed V, whose value can be written, in either set of units,

$$V = \frac{c}{\sqrt{\epsilon_m \mu_m}} \qquad (305)$$

where c is the speed of light in a vacuum in the proper units and ϵ_m and μ_m stand for the ordinary dielectric constant and permeability of the medium relative to vacuum. Thus $\epsilon_m = \epsilon/\epsilon_0$, $\mu_m = \mu/\mu_0$, and in free space $\epsilon_m = \mu_m = 1$. In Gaussian units we can also write $V = c/\sqrt{\epsilon\mu}$; whereas in mks units

$$V = \frac{1}{\sqrt{\epsilon\mu}} \qquad c = \frac{1}{\sqrt{\epsilon_0\mu_0}} \qquad \text{meters per sec} \qquad (305a,b)$$

In any wave front, the electric vector E and the magnetic vector H both lie in the plane of the wave front and hence are perpendicular to the direction of propagation of the waves. These vectors are also perpendicular to each other and are so oriented that Poynting's vector $\mathbf{\Pi}$ as defined by Eq. (303a,b) points in the direction of propagation (see Fig. 247). In either set of units, the magnitudes of E and H (but not of B, in general) are in the ratio

$$\frac{H}{E} = \sqrt{\frac{\epsilon}{\mu}} \qquad (306)$$

Thus, in free space, in Gaussian units $B = H = E$; whereas in the mks units $B = E/c$, where $c = 3 \times 10^8$ meters per sec.

If, in Eq. (302a) or (302b), we insert $H = E\sqrt{\epsilon/\mu}$, we see that in plane waves the magnetic and electric parts of the energy are equal to each other and the total energy density is

$$u = \frac{\epsilon E^2}{4\pi} \qquad \text{ergs per cm}^3 \qquad \text{or} \qquad u = \epsilon E^2 \qquad \text{joules per meter}^3$$

[1] See L. Page and N. I. Adams, "Principles of Electricity," 2d ed., 1949.

the corresponding unit for ϵ and for E being understood in each case. Since this energy obviously travels with the waves, the average amount of energy that passes per second across a unit area drawn perpendicular to the direction of propagation will be the energy contained in a column standing on the area and of length equal to the distance traveled by the waves in a second, or to their velocity V. This quantity is called the *intensity* of the waves, symbol I. Thus, if a bar over a symbol denotes the average value along the wave train, $I = V\bar{u}$; and, substituting the values of V and u,

$$I = \frac{c}{4\pi} \sqrt{\frac{\epsilon}{\mu}} \, \overline{E^2} \qquad \text{ergs per cm}^2 \text{ per sec} \qquad (307a)$$

in Gaussian-cgs units, in which in free space $\epsilon/\mu = 1$; whereas in mks units

$$I = \sqrt{\frac{\epsilon}{\mu}} \, \overline{E^2} \qquad \text{joules per m}^2 \text{ per sec} \qquad (307b)$$

It is easily seen that I is equal also to the time average of the magnitude of Poynting's vector.

Besides energy, the waves also carry electromagnetic *momentum*. According to Eqs. (304a,b), in free space the vector momentum has the direction in which the waves are being propagated; also, since the vectors **E** and **H** are perpendicular to each other, the magnitude of $\mathbf{E} \times \mathbf{H}$ is just EH or E^2 in Gaussian units, since $H = E$. Hence in plane waves in free space, $g = E^2/4\pi c$ in Gaussian units; the corresponding formula in mks units is $g = (1/c^2)E^2 \sqrt{\epsilon_0/\mu_0}$. In either case, $g = u/c$; this follows in mks units because $c = 1/\sqrt{\epsilon_0\mu_0}$. Thus in free space electromagnetic waves carry momentum equal to the energy that they carry divided by the speed of light. It is as if energy W had a mass W/c^2 and were moving at speed c. Pressure due to radiation falling on a material body is readily explained as resulting from the electromagnetic momentum delivered to the body by the incident waves.

Many other types of electromagnetic waves can occur. Besides plane waves of nonuniform amplitude, there are, for example, waves diverging from a center (or converging toward it), of dipole or quadrupole or more complex form. An example of dipole waves will be described presently.

227. Field of a Moving Point Charge. It is obvious from Maxwell's equations that an isolated moving charge must always be accompanied by a magnetic field of some sort; for its electric field cannot be steady in time and the equations require therefore the presence of the derivatives of a magnetic field. For the case of *steady* motion the field is completely described in Sec. 40. In this case it is easily seen from the magnitude of Poynting's vector that no energy is streaming off to infinity.

If the charge is *accelerated*, on the other hand, its field becomes modified in such a way that at sufficiently great distances the field falls off with increasing distance r from the charge only as $1/r$. This distant part of the field is called a radiation field.[1] A useful idea, which can be derived from the Maxwell-Lorentz equations, is that the entire field is continually being emitted by the charge and spreading outward with the speed of light. Thus the radiation field at any point Q at time t is determined by the acceleration that the charge possessed at an earlier time $t - r/c$, at which time the charge was at a point P; r denotes the distance from P to Q [see Fig. 248(a)]. The vectors **E** and **H** at Q are perpendicular to each other and to the line PQ, and are so oriented that the vector product $\mathbf{E} \times \mathbf{H}$ is directed from P to Q. Thus the radiation field consists of outgoing waves, and it can be shown that these waves necessarily carry energy off to infinity.

[1] J. A. Stratton, "Electromagnetic Theory," Sec. 8.17, 1941.

If the charge was momentarily at rest at time $t - r/c$ but had at that time the instantaneous acceleration $a_{t-r/c}$, then the magnitude of E in terms of Gaussian and cgs units (and also the magnitude of H or B) is, at Q at time t,[1]

$$E = \frac{q}{c^2 r} a_{t-r/c} \sin \theta \tag{308}$$

Here θ is the angle between the line PQ and the direction of the vector acceleration **a**. The electric vector **E** lies in the plane containing PQ and the direction of **a**, and, for a positive charge, is so oriented as to have a component opposite to the direction of **a**. See Fig. 248(b). For an electron, $q = -e$.

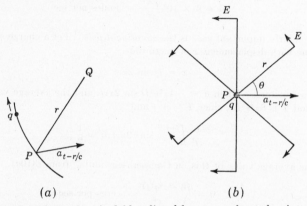

(a) (b)

Fig. 248. Illustration of the electric field radiated by an accelerated point charge q: (a) in general, (b) when moving at negligible velocity, q being positive.

The last formula holds also to a good approximation if the charge was already moving at time $t - r/c$ but at a speed small relatively to c. The general effect of a velocity of the charge is to change the magnitudes of **E** and **H** in such a way that they are strengthened on the side toward which the charge is moving and weakened on the opposite side; if the velocity is not coplanar with PQ and **a**, **E** is likewise not in this plane. In the simple case of a charge moving at variable speed v along a straight line, the electric vector **E** lies in a plane containing this line and has the magnitude

$$E = -\frac{1}{(1 - \beta \cos \theta)^3} \frac{q}{c^2 r} a_{t-r/c} \sin \theta \qquad \beta = \frac{v}{c} \tag{309a,b}$$

Here a and v are to be taken positive in the direction $\theta = 0$.

228. Energy Radiated by Accelerated Point Charges. Insertion of the value of E given by Eq. (308) in Eq. (307a), with $\epsilon = \mu = 1$ for free space, gives as the rate at which energy is streaming outward across unit area in the radiation field

$$I = \frac{q^2 a^2}{4\pi c^3 r^2} \sin^2 \theta$$

For simplicity, the subscript $t - r/c$ has been omitted here.

To find the *total* emission, let a sphere of radius r be drawn about the point of emission P as center. Then the integral of I over this sphere will represent the total rate

[1] See Smythe. *loc cit.*

at which energy is streaming outward across the surface of the sphere, and this **can** be taken to represent the rate Ω at which the accelerated charge was radiating energy when it was at P. Taking a ring-shaped element of area $2\pi r^2 \sin \theta \, d\theta$ on the sphere, in a plane perpendicular to the axis from which θ is measured, we have

$$\Omega = \int_0^\pi \frac{q^2 a^2}{4\pi c^3 r^2} \, 2\pi r^2 \sin^3 \theta \, d\theta = \frac{2}{3} \frac{q^2 a^2}{c^3} \qquad \text{ergs per sec} \qquad (310a)$$

Here Gaussian and cgs units are assumed, and the velocity of the charge is assumed small relative to c. In mks units (in which $c = 3 \times 10^8$ meters per sec), the formula becomes

$$\Omega = 6 \times 10^9 \frac{q^2 a^2}{c^3} \qquad \text{joules per sec} \qquad (310b)$$

A particularly important case is the *vibrating dipole*. Let a charge q vibrate along a fixed line with displacement x of magnitude

$$x = D \sin 2\pi \nu t$$

D being a constant. Then $a = -4\pi^2 \nu^2 D \sin 2\pi \nu t$; and the average value of a^2 over each period T is $8\pi^4 \nu^4 D^2$, since $T = 1/\nu$ and

$$\frac{1}{T} \int_{t_1}^{t_1 + T} \sin^2 2\pi \nu t \, dt = \frac{1}{2}$$

Hence the average value of Ω is, in Gaussian-cgs units,[1] from (310a),

$$\bar{\Omega} = \frac{16}{3} \frac{\pi^4 \nu^4 q^2 D^2}{c^3} \qquad \text{ergs per sec} \qquad (311)$$

In mks units the coefficient $16/3$ is replaced by 4.8×10^{10}. An additional stationary charge of magnitude $-q$ may be supposed to be located at $x = 0$ without affecting the radiation field; the resulting combination of two charges is equivalent to a dipole of variable moment qx or of moment amplitude qD.

[1] See Smythe, *loc cit.*

APPENDIX II

COMPOSITION OF THE ELEMENTS
AND MASSES OF ISOTOPES

The data below are taken from a compilation by K. T. Bainbridge which appears in E. Segrè, "Experimental Nuclear Physics," Vol. I (Wiley, 1953). The masses cited represent the best averages (as of 1952) of values obtained by direct mass-spectrograph measurements and nuclear-reaction Q values, except that for Z less than 10 only values from nuclear reactions are used. Most of the known radioactive nuclides are listed up to and including $Z = 10$; beyond this point, only nuclides which occur in nature have been listed. The isotopic abundances depend upon the source in some cases, particularly among the light elements and for some species derived from radioactive materials.

Element Z		Mass number A of isotopes	Atomic mass, amu ($O^{16} = 16$)	Relative abundance per cent
n	0	1	1.008 982	unstable
H	1	1	1.008 142	99.9851
		2	2.014 735	0.0149
		3	3.016 997	unstable
He	2	3	3.016 977	1.3×10^{-4}
		4	4.003 873	99.9999
		6	6.020 474	unstable
Li	3	6	6.017 021	7.52
		7	7.018 223	92.47
		8	8.025 018	unstable
Be	4	7	7.019 150	unstable
		8	8.007 850	unstable
		9	9.015 043	100
		10	10.016 711	unstable
B	5	9	9.016 190	unstable
		10	10.016 114	18.5

Element Z		Mass number A of isotopes	Atomic mass, amu ($O^{16} = 16$)	Relative abundance per cent
		11	11.012 789	81.5
		12	12.018 162	unstable
C	6	10	10.020 61	unstable
		11	11.014 916	unstable
		12	12.003 804	98.892
		13	13.007 473	1.108
		14	14.007 682	unstable
N	7	13	13.009 858	unstable
		14	14.007 515	99.635
		15	15.004 863	0.365
		16	16.010 74	unstable
		17	17.014 04	unstable
O	8	15	15.007 768	unstable
		16	16.000 000	99.758
		17	17.004 533	0.0373
		18	18.004 874	0.2039
		19	19.009 48	unstable
F	9	17	17.007 486	unstable
		18	18.006 670	unstable
		19	19.004 456	100
		20	20.006 352	unstable
Ne	10	19	19.007 915	unstable
		20	19.998 860	90.92
		21	21.000 589	0.257
		22	21.998 270	8.82
		23	23.001 680	unstable
Na	11	23	22.997 139	100
Mg	12	24	23.992 696	78.60
		25	24.993 815	10.11
		26	25.990 871	11.29
Al	13	27	26.990 140	100
Si	14	28	27.985 837	92.27
		29	28.985 719	4.68
		30	29.983 313	3.05
P	15	31	30.983 622	100

Element Z	Mass number A of isotopes	Atomic mass, amu ($O^{16} = 16$)	Relative abundance per cent
S 16	32	31.982 265	95.1
	33	32.981 961	0.74
	34	33.978 773	4.2
	36		0.016
Cl 17	35	34.980 175	75.4
	37	36.977 624	24.6
A 18	36	35.978 93	0.337
	38	37.974 88	0.063
	40	39.975 10	99.600
K 19	39	38.975 93	93.08
	40	39.976 58	0.0119
	41	40.974 84	6.91
Ca 20	40	39.975 42	96.97
	42	41.972 04	0.64
	43	42.972 37	0.145
	44	43.969 20	2.06
	46		0.0033
	48	47.967 63	0.185
Sc 21	45	44.970 000	100
Ti 22	46		7.95
	47	46.967 0	7.75
	48	47.964 05	73.45
	49		5.51
	50		5.34
V 23	50	49.962 15	0.24
	51	50.959 53	99.76
Cr 24	50	49.959 99	4.31
	52	51.956 93	83.76
	53		9.55
	54		2.38
Mn 25	55	54.955 64	100
Fe 26	54	53.956 54	5.84
	56	55.952 86	91.68
	57	56.953 65	2.17
	58		0.31

Element Z		Mass number A of isotopes	Atomic mass, amu (O^{16} = 16)	Relative abundance per cent
Co	27	59	58.951 82	100
Ni	28	58	57.953 60	67.76
		60	59.949 48	26.16
		61		1.25
		62		3.66
		64	63.947 33	1.16
Cu	29	63	62.948 62	69.1
		65	64.947 49	30.9
Zn	30	64		48.89
		66		27.81
		67		4.11
		68		18.56
		70		0.62
Ga	31	69		60.2
		71		39.8
Ge	32	70		20.55
		72		27.37
		73		7.61
		74		36.74
		76		7.67
As	33	75		100
Se	34	74		0.87
		76		9.02
		77		7.58
		78		23.52
		80		49.82
		82		9.19
Br	35	79		50.52
		81		49.48
Kr	36	78		0.354
		80		2.27
		82	81.938 42	11.56
		83		11.55
		84	83.938 49	56.90
		86	85.936 58	17.37
Rb	37	85	84.931 0	72.15
		87	86.929 5	27.85

Element Z		Mass number A of isotopes	Atomic mass, amu $(O^{16} = 16)$	Relative abundance per cent
Sr	38	84		0.56
		86	85.935 4	9.86
		87	86.935 2	7.02
		88	87.933 60	82.56
Y	39	89	88.937 12	100
Zr	40	90		51.46
		91		11.23
		92		17.11
		94		17.40
		96		2.80
Nb	41	93		100
Mo	42	92		15.86
		94	93.935 2	9.12
		95		15.70
		96	95.935 58	16.50
		97	96.936 93	9.45
		98		23.75
		100	99.938 29	9.62
Ru	44	96		5.7
		98		2.2
		99		12.8
		100		12.7
		101		17.0
		102		31.3
		104		18.3
Rh	45	103		100
Pd	46	102		0.8
		104	103.936 9	9.3
		105		22.6
		106		27.2
		108	107.936 90	26.8
		110	109.940 98	13.5
Ag	47	107		51.35
		109		48.65
Cd	48	106		1.215
		108		0.875
		110	109.939 11	12.39

Element Z	Mass number A of isotopes	Atomic mass, amu ($O^{16} = 16$)	Relative abundance per cent
	111		12.75
	112	111.939 99	24.07
	113	112.942 06	12.26
.	114	113.940 13	28.86
	116	115.942 12	7.58
In 49	113		4.23
	115	114.942 07	95.77
Sn 50	112		0.95
	114	113.941 09	0.65
	115	114.941 54	0.34
	116	115.938 06	14.24
	117	116.941 71	7.57
	118		24.01
	119		8.58
	120	119.939 04	32.97
	122	121.942 6	4.71
	124		5.98
Sb 51	121		57.25
	123		42.75
Te 52	120		0.089
	122		2.46
	123		0.87
	124		4.61
	125		6.99
	126	125.942 7	18.71
	128	127.947 1	31.79
	130	129.946 7	34.49
I 53	127	126.946	100
Xe 54	124		0.096
	126		0.090
	128		1.919
	129	128.945 33	26.44
	130		4.08
	131		21.18
	132	131.947 3	26.89
	134		10.44
	136		8.87
Cs 55	133		100

Element Z	Mass number A of isotopes	Atomic mass, amu $(O^{16} = 16)$	Relative abundance per cent
Ba 56	130		0.101
	132		0.097
	134		2.42
	135		6.59
	136		7.81
	137		11.32
	138		71.66
La 57	138		0.089
	139		99.911
Ce 58	136		0.193
	138		0.250
	140		88.48
	142		11.07
Pr 59	141		100
Nd 60	142		27.13
	143		12.20
	144	143.956 07	23.87
	145		8.30
	146		17.18
	148		5.72
	150	149.968 78	5.60
Sm 62	144		3.16
	147		15.07
	148		11.27
	149		13.84
	150		7.47
	152		26.63
	154		22.53
Eu 63	151		47.77
	153		52.23
Gd 64	152		0.20
	154		2.15
	155		14.73
	156		20.47
	157		15.68
	158		24.87
	160		21.90
Tb 65	159		100

Element Z	Mass number A of isotopes	Atomic mass, amu ($O^{16} = 16$)	Relative abundance per cent
Dy 66	156		0.0524
	158		0.0902
	160		2.294
	161		18.88
	162		25.53
	163		24.97
	164		28.18
Ho 67	165		100
Er 68	162		0.136
	164		1.56
	166		33.41
	167		22.94
	168		27.07
	170		14.88
Tm 69	169		100
Yb 70	168		0.140
	170		3.03
	171		14.31
	172		21.82
	173		16.13
	174		31.84
	176		12.73
Lu 71	175		97.40
	176		2.60
Hf 72	174		0.18
	176	175.992 3	5.15
	177		18.39
	178	177.993 8	27.08
	179		13.78
	180	180.004 4	35.44
Ta 73	181		100
W 74	180		0.135
	182	182.003 8	26.4
	183	183.003 21	14.4
	184	184.006 0	30.6
	186		28.4

Element Z	Mass number A of isotopes	Atomic mass, amu ($O^{16} = 16$)	Relative abundance per cent
Re 75	185		37.07
	187		62.93
Os 76	184		0.018
	186		1.59
	187		1.64
	188		13.3
	189		16.1
	190		26.4
	192		41.0
Ir 77	191		38.5
	193		61.5
Pt 78	190		0.012
	192		0.78
	194	194.024 0	32.8
	195	195.026 42	33.7
	196		25.4
	198		7.23
Au 79	197		100
Hg 80	196		0.146
	198		10.02
	199		16.84
	200		23.13
	201		13.22
	202		29.80
	204		6.85
Tl 81	203	203.035 0	29.50
	205	205.037 9	70.50
Pb 82	204	204.036 1	1.48
	206	206.038 6	23.6
	207	207.040 3	22.6
	208	208.041 4	52.3
Bi 83	209	209.045 5	100
Th 90	232	232.110 3	100
U 92	234	234.113 8	0.0058
	235	235.117 0	0.715
	238	238.124 9	99.28

FIRST IONIZATION POTENTIAL V, LOWEST SPECTRAL TERM T, AND ELECTRON CONFIGURATION OF THE ELEMENTS

X-ray symbol n, l Spectroscopic symbol			K 1, 0 $1s$	L_I 2, 0 $2s$	II.III 2, 1 $2p$	M_I 3, 0 $3s$	II.III 3, 1 $3p$	IV.V 3, 2 $3d$	N_I 4, 0 $4s$
Element	V	T							
H	1	13.598	$^2S_{1/2}$	1					
He	2	24.584	$^1S_0$	2					
Li	3	5.39	$^2S_{1/2}$	2	1				
Be	4	9.322	$^1S_0$	2	2				
B	5	8.28	$^2P_{1/2}$	2	2	1			
C	6	11.267	$^3P_0$	2	2	2			
N	7	14.55	$^4S_{3/2}$	2	2	3			
O	8	13.617	$^3P_2$	2	2	4			
F	9	17.3	$^2P_{3/2}$	2	2	5			
Ne	10	21.56	$^1S_0$	2	2	6			
Na	11	5.14	$^2S_{1/2}$	2	2	6	1			
Mg	12	7.65	$^1S_0$				2			
Al	13	5.99	$^2P_{1/2}$		K, L		2	1		
Si	14	8.15	$^3P_0$		10		2	2		
P	15	10.9	$^4S_{3/2}$		electrons		2	3		
S	16	10.4	$^3P_2$				2	4		
Cl	17	13.02	$^2P_{3/2}$				2	5		
A	18	15.76	$^1S_0$				2	6		
K	19	4.34	$^2S_{1/2}$				2	6		1
Ca	20	6.11	$^1S_0$				2	6		2
Sc	21	6.7	$^2D_{3/2}$				2	6	1	2
Ti	22	6.84	$^3F_2$				2	6	2	2
V	23	6.8	$^4F_{3/2}$				2	6	3	2
Cr	24	6.76	$^7S_3$				2	6	5	1
Mn	25	7.43	$^6S_{5/2}$				2	6	5	2
Fe	26	7.86	$^5D_4$				2	6	6	2
Co	27	7.81	$^4F_{9/2}$				2	6	7	2
Ni	28	7.634	$^3F_4$				2	6	8	2
Cu	29	7.72	$^2S_{1/2}$				2	6	10	1

X-ray symbol n, l Spectroscopic symbol			K, L, M	N_I 4, 0 $4s$	II,III 4, 1 $4p$	IV,V 4, 2 $4d$	VI,VII 4, 3 $4f$	O_I 5, 0 $5s$	II,III 5, 1 $5p$	IV,V 5, 2 $5d$	P_I 6, 0 $6s$
Zn	30	9.39	$^1S_0$	K, L, M	2							
Ga	31	6.00	$^2P_{1/2}$	28	2	1						
Ge	32	8.13	$^3P_0$	elec-	2	2						
As	33	10.5	$^4S_{3/2}$	trons	2	3						
Se	34	9.7	$^3P_2$		2	4						
Br	35	11.85	$^2P_{3/2}$		2	5						
Kr	36	13.999	$^1S_0$		2	6						
Rb	37	4.177	$^2S_{1/2}$		2	6			1			
Sr	38	5.693	$^1S_0$		2	6			2			
Y	39	6.6	$^2D_{3/2}$		2	6	1		2			
Zr	40	6.95	$^3F_2$		2	6	2		2			
Cb	41		$^6D_{1/2}$		2	6	4		1			
Mo	42	7.38	$^7S_3$		2	6	5		1			
Tc	43				2	6	6		1			
Ru	44	7.7	$^5F_5$		2	6	7		1			
Rh	45	7.7	$^4F_{9/2}$		2	6	8		1			
Pd	46	8.3	$^1S_0$		2	6	10					
Ag	47	7.58	$^2S_{1/2}$		2	6	10		1			
Cd	48	8.99	$^1S_0$		2	6	10		2			
In	49	5.79	$^2P_{1/2}$		2	6	10		2	1		
Sn	50	7.34	$^3P_0$		2	6	10		2	2		
Sb	51	8.5	$^4S_{3/2}$		2	6	10		2	3		
Te	52	8.9	$^3P_2$		2	6	10		2	4		
I	53	10.	$^2P_{3/2}$		2	6	10		2	5		
Xe	54	12.130	$^1S_0$		2	6	10		2	6		
Cs	55	3.89	$^2S_{1/2}$		2	6	10		2	6		1
Ba	56	5.21	$^1S_0$		2	6	10		2	6		2
La	57	5.6	$^2D_{3/2}$		2	6	10		2	6	1	2
Ce	58	6.54	$^2F_{5/2}$		2	6	10	2	2	6		2
Pr	59	5.8	$^4K_{11/2}$		2	6	10	3	2	6		2
Nd	60	6.3	$^5L_6$		2	6	10	4	2	6		2
Pm	61		$^6L_{11/2}$		2	6	10	5	2	6		2
Sm	62	6.6	$^7K_4$		2	6	10	6	2	6		2
Eu	63	5.64	$^8H_{3/2}$		2	6	10	7	2	6		2
Gd	64	6.7	$^9D_2$		2	6	10	7	2	6	1	2
Tb	65	6.7	$^8H_{17/2}$		2	6	10	9	2	6		2
Dy	66	6.8	$^7K_{10}$		2	6	10	10	2	6		2
Ho	67		$^6L_{5/2}$		2	6	10	11	2	6		2
Er	68		$^5L_{10}$		2	6	10	12	2	6		2
Tm	69		$^4K_{17/2}$		2	6	10	13	2	6		2
Yb	70	7.1	$^3H_6$		2	6	10	14	2	6		2

X-ray symbol n, l Spectroscopic s			$K, L,$ M, N	O_I 5, 0 $5s$	II,III 5, 1 $5p$	IV,V 5, 2 $5d$	VI,VII 5, 3 $5f$	P_I 6, 0 $6s$	II,III 6, 1 $6p$	IV,V 6, 2 $6d$	Q_I 7, 0 $7s$
Lu	71		$^2D_{3/2}$	$K, L,$	2	6	1		2			
Hf	72		$^3F_2$	M, N	2	6	2		2			
Ta	73		$^4F_{3/2}$	60	2	6	3		2			
W	74	8.1	$^5D_0$	elec-	2	6	4		2			
Re	75		$^6S_{5/2}$	trons	2	6	5		2			
Os	76				2	6	6		2			
Ir	77		$^2D_{5/2}$		2	6	7		2			
Pt	78	8.9	$^3D_3$		2	6	9		1			
Au	79	9.2	$^2S_{1/2}$		2	6	10		1			
Hg	80	10.44	$^1S_0$		2	6	10		2			
Tl	81	6.11	$^2P_{1/2}$		2	6	10		2	1		
Pb	82	7.42	$^3P_0$		2	6	10		2	2		
Bi	83	8.0	$^4S_{3/2}$		2	6	10		2	3		
Po	84		$^3P_2$		2	6	10		2	4		
At	85		$^2P_{3/2}$		2	6	10		2	5		
Rn	86	10.75	$^1S_0$		2	6	10		2	6		
Fr	87		$^2S_{1/2}$		2	6	10		2	6		1
Ra	88	5.25	$^1S_0$		2	6	10		2	6		2
Ac	89		$^2D_{3/2}$		2	6	10		2	6	1	2
Th	90		$^3F_2$		2	6	10		2	6	2	2
Pa	91		$^4F_{3/2}$		2	6	10	2	2	6	1	2
U	92		$^5D_0$		2	6	10	3	2	6	1	2
Np	93				2	6	10	4	2	6	1	2
Pu	94				2	6	10	5	2	6	1	2
Am	95				2	6	10	6	2	6	1	2
Cm	96				2	6	10	7	2	6	1	2

Note 1. The ionization potentials were mostly calculated as explained in Sec. 87d.
Note 2. A few names are: Tc 43, technetium; Pm 61, promethium; At 85, astatine; Fr 87, francium; Pa 91, protactinium; Np 93, neptunium; Pu 94, plutonium; Am 95, americium; Cm 96, curium.

SOME USEFUL CONSTANTS AND RELATIONS

(The last digit shown is probably correct within 1)

c velocity of light in vacuum............ 2.99793×10^{10} cm per sec

h Planck's constant (Sec. 71)............ 6.625×10^{-27} erg sec

k Boltzmann's constant (Sec. 66)........ 1.3804×10^{-16} erg per deg
                           $= 8.616 \times 10^{-5}$ ev per deg

N_0 Avogadro's number (Sec. 48).......... (chemical scale) 6.023×10^{23} mole^{-1}
                           (physical scale) 6.025×10^{23} mole^{-1}

e electronic charge.................... 4.803×10^{-10} esu
                           $= 1.6021 \times 10^{-20}$ emu

m electronic rest mass.................. 0.9108×10^{-27} gram

e/m for electrons........................ 1.7589×10^{7} emu per gram

M_p mass of the proton................... 1.00759 amu

M_n mass of the neutron.................. 1.00898 amu

M_p/m... $1{,}836.1$

$a_0 = h^2/4\pi^2 me^2$ (smallest Bohr radius, Sec. 81). 5.2917×10^{-9} cm

$\alpha = 2\pi e^2/ch$ fine-structure constant (Sec. 120). $1/137.04$

mc^2 rest energy of electron............... 0.5110 Mev

M_1c^2 rest energy of 1 atomic unit of mass.... 931.2 Mev

M_pc^2 rest energy of proton................. 938.2 Mev

M_nc^2 rest energy of neutron............... 939.5 Mev

kT at 15°C ($T = 288.1°$).................... 0.0248 ev

R_∞ Rydberg's wave number (Sec. 75)...... $109{,}737.31$ cm^{-1}

1 X.U. (X unit, Sec. 151) $= 1.002020 \times 10^{-11}$ cm

If $h\nu = eV_v/299.79$ (V_v = potential difference in volts or energy in ev), $\lambda = c/\nu$, $\lambda_A = \lambda \times 10^8$ = wavelength in vacuum in angstroms, $\tilde{\nu} = 1/\lambda$ or waves per centimeter in vacuum (Secs. 73, 83)

$$\lambda_A = \frac{12{,}398}{V_v} \qquad \tilde{\nu} = 8{,}066 V_v$$

1 ev (electron-volt, Sec. 83) $= 1.6021 \times 10^{-12}$ erg
    (1 Mev $= 10^6$ ev, 1 Bev $= 10^9$ ev)

1 atomic mass unit (amu, Sec. 181) $= 1.6598 \times 10^{-24}$ gram

1 coulomb $= 0.1$ emu $= 2.99793 \times 10^9$ esu, 1 volt $= 1/299.793$ esu
    1 weber per square meter $= 10^4$ gauss

If ϵ denotes permittivity and μ permeability, and if a subscript indicates the units, then

$$\epsilon_{mks} = \frac{\epsilon_{esu}}{35.950\pi \times 10^9}$$

$$\mu_{mks} = \mu_{emu} \times 4\pi \times 10^{-7}$$

651

INDEX

A, nuclear mass number, 441
a_o, 209, 651
Aamodt, R. L., 608
Aberration, stellar, 28
Absorption of light, 164, 222
  by molecules, 318, 321
Accelerators (nuclear), 498–504
  electrostatic, 499
  high-tension, 498
  induction, 503
  linear, 504
  magnetic-resonance, 500
Adiabatic principle, 416
Age of earth, 444
Air showers (*see* Cosmic rays)
Airy, Sir George B., 52
Albedo, 623
Alhazen, 10
Alkali metals, term energies and spectra
  of, 241–250, 254–258
Alpha-decay
  stability against, 476
  theory of, 487
Alpha-particles, 142, 434
  energy loss by, 444
    (*See also* Charged particles)
  nature of, 434–436
  range of, 433, 448, 449
  scattering of, 142, 144–146, 463, 471
  spectra of, 448
  transmutations by, 463–466
  velocity of, 434
Amaldi, E., 529
Ammonia, inversion spectrum, 339–344
amu = atomic mass unit, 461, 651
Anaxagoras, 5
Anderson, C. D., 491, 577, 591, 592
Andrade, E. N., 451
Andrychuk, D., 335
Ångström, A. J., 138
angstrom (A), 134
Angular momentum
  of atom, 205, 240–242, 269
    with one electron, 204–207
  in Bohr's theory, 149, 151

Angular momentum, of electron in central field, 226
  of electron spin, 212, 269
  indeterminacy of, 206, 253
  in magnetic field, 285
  of molecules, 316, 325
  of neutron, 302, 303
  of nucleus (*see* Nucleus)
  orbital, 269
  of proton, 302, 303
  in wave mechanics, 197, 206
Annihilation radiation, 493
Antiproton, 614
Arago, 34, 35, 39
Araki, G., 598
Archimedes, 9
Aristarchus, 9
Aristotle, 6
Aston, F. W., 458
Atmosphere, pressure vs. altitude, **561**
Atom
  Bohr theory of, 148–156, 169
  many-electron, 266–282
  one-electron, 149–154, 203–211, **258**–
    266
  structure of, **141, 144, 147, 227, 239**
    table, 648
  theories of, 141–142, 144
Atomic bomb, 549–552, 554
Atomic energy (*see* Nuclear fission)
Atomic mass unit, 461, 651
  energy equivalent of, 476, 651
Atomic masses, 455–463, 475, 510
  table, 639–647
Atomic number (Z), 144, 147, **441**
  table, 648
Auger, P., 399, 581
Auger effect, 398
Auger showers (*see* Cosmic **rays**)
Avogadro's number (N_o), **80, 88**

Back, E., 290, 296
Bäcklin, E., 87
Bacon, Roger, 10

Bainbridge, K. T., 458
Balard, A. J., 35
Balmer, J. J., 136–138
Balmer formula, 135, 154
Balmer series (photograph), 137
Bands (spectral), 314, 320, 328–331
  alternating intensities in, 337
Barkla, C. G., 351–354, 470
Barn, definition of, 524
Barrett, P. H., 560
Barrier penetration (nuclear), 487, 496
Bartholinus, 34
Bartlett, R. S., 535
Bearden, J. A., 393
Becker, H., 466, 491
Becquerel, H., 431–434
Bernoulli, D., 27
Bertin-Sans, 347
Beta-decay
  nature of, 474
  spectra, 453
  stability rules, 478
Beta-particles
  nature of, 433
  spectra of, 453
  velocity of, 434
  (See also Electrons)
Betatron, 503
Bethe, H. A., 264, 265, 586
Bethe-Heitler theory, 586, 591
Bev = billion electron volt, 651
Bev/c, unit of momentum, 567
Bevatron (Berkeley), 503
Binding energy, nuclear, 474–479
Biot and Savart, 36
Bjorklund, R., 606
Black, J., 27
Blackett, P. M. S., 465, 492, 494, 576
Bless, A. A., 389
Bloch, F., 426
Bohr, N., 148, 153, 169, 394, 454, 520,
  542, 543
Boltwood, 440
Boltzmann, L., 110
Boltzmann constant, k, 120, 651
Boltzmann distribution law, 168
Bose-Einstein molecules, 335, 415
Bose-Einstein statistics, 415, 472
Bothe, W., 389, 466, 491, 574
Bowen, I. S., 564, 565
Boyle, 27
Bradley, 28
Bradt, H. L., 620
Bragg, W. H., 359, 360, 362
Bragg, W. L., 357, 359, 360
Bragg planes and spacings, 357
Bragg's law, 359, 392, 393

Brahe, Tycho, 16
Breadth of lines, 311
  x-rays, 400
Breit, G., 306
Breit-Wigner resonance formula, 516
Bremsstrahlung, 584, 586
Brode, R. B., 594
Brown, W. W., 617, 619
Buguet, 353
Buisson, 312
Bunsen, 35
Burmeister, 322
Bursts of ionization (see Cosmic rays)
Byfield, H., 609

Cabeo, 19
Calutron, 550
Cameron, G. H., 556–559, 562, 575
Canal rays, 455
Cario, G., 166
Carlisle, 36
Carnot, 32
Cascade showers (see Cosmic rays)
Cavalieri, 19
Cavendish, 30
Central field, 224
  for argon, 226
Chain reactions (see Nuclear fission)
Chao, C. Y., 491
Characteristic functions and values, 196
Charge cloud, 209
  H, 211, 236
  Na, 248
Charged particles
  detection of, 444–448
  determination of mass, 600–602
  energy loss by, 445, 584–587, 601
  ionization by, 445, 585, 601
  radiation by, 586
  range of, 449, 601
  scattering of, 142–146, 584, 601
Chedester, C., 609
Chemical binding, 235
Chinowsky, W., 608
Clark, G. L., 356
Clausius, 32
Clay, J., 562, 563
Cleeton, C. E., 342
Cloud chamber, 447, 576
cm^{-1}, 134, 156
  and ev, 157
Coblentz, 131
Cockroft, J. D., 497, 498
Cohen, E. R., 88
Cohesion, 236
Coincidence technique, 574–575

Coles, D. K., 343
Collective-motion model of nucleus, 540
Collisions of the second kind, 166
Compound nucleus, 520
Compton, A. H., 352, 386, 393, 558, 562–564
Compton, K. T., 91, 92
Compton effect, 386–392, 394
  cross section for, 583 (fig.)
Condon, E. U., 488
Conductivity, electronic, 423, 427
Configurations, electronic, 268, 648
Contact potentials, 104
Contractions in space and time, 61
Conversi, M., 599, 600
Copernicus, 11
Cosmic rays
  absorption of, in air, 556, 575, 625
    in dense materials, 574–575
    underground, 559
    in water, 556, 559
  discovery of, 555
  east-west effect, 572
  energy flux, 558, 561, 569–573
  geomagnetic effects, 566–569
  ionization by, in atmosphere, 555–566
    bursts of, 579
    at sea level, 559
  latitude effect (see variation of intensity, below)
  mesons in (see Mesons)
  N component of, 619, 626
  neutrons in, 627
  nuclear interactions of, 616–622, 625–628
  origin of, 628–631
  particles in, absorption of, 574–576
    energy of, 573–576
    energy loss of, 590–594
    flux of, 571–573, 624
  penetrating component, 576, 581, 627
    (See also Mesons, mu)
  primaries, composition of, 622–625, 628
    energy spectrum, 569–573, 628
    flux of, 571–573, 624
    interaction with atmosphere, 625
    momentum spectrum, 569–573
  protons in, 623, 625, 626
  showers, cascade, 577–590, 628
    extensive air (Auger), 590, 620, 628
    local penetrating, 619, 627
  soft component, 576, 581, 628
  stars due to, 616, 620
  variation of intensity, with altitude, 556, 560, 564–565
    with depth underground, 559

Cosmic rays, variation of intensity, with latitude, 562–572
  with longitude, 563
  with temperature, 563
  with time, 628
Cosmotron (Brookhaven), 503
Coster, D., 398
Coulomb, C. A. de, 30
Coulomb barrier (see Nuclear barrier)
Coulomb excitation of nucleus, 506
Coulomb field, 226
Counters
  Geiger, 446
  neutron, 526
  proportional, 445
  scintillation, 446, 452
  telescope, 575
Coupling, 269, 281
  jj, 279–281
  ΛS (in molecules), 325
  LS or Russell Saunders, 269–278
  with nucleus, 303
  Ω (in molecules), 327
Crandall, W. E., 606
Crane, H. R., 496, 498
Critchfield, C. L., 623
Cross section, 523
  classical scattering, 351
  differential, 525
  gamma-ray absorption, 583 (fig.)
  neutron-proton scattering, 525 (fig.)
Crystal diffraction grating, 355
Crystals
  electronic conductivity of, 423, 427
  electronic levels in, 426, 427
  energy bands of, 422, 424, 427
  wave mechanics of, 420–430
    atomic approach, 421–425
    collective electron approach, 426–430
Curie, M., 432, 433
curie unit, definition of, 443
Cyclotron, 500
Czerny, 318

da Vinci, Leonardo, 10
Davisson, C., 180
Davy, Sir Humphry, 32
de Broglie, L., 173, 174, 175, 177
de Broglie wavelength, 178
  of neutrons, 528, 530
Debye, P., 412
Dee, P. I., 498
Degeneracy of states or wave functions, 204, 207, 227
  classical analogy of, 208, 214

Degeneracy of states or wave functions, exchange, 214
  nuclear, 302
Degrees of freedom, 119, 121
  of elastic waves, 412
  of waves in an enclosure, 121–123
Delta-rays, 586, 624, 628
Democritus, 6
Dempster, A. J., 458
Dennison, D. M., 342
Descartes, 22
Deuteron
  binding energy of, 476
  photodisintegration of, 506
  singlet state of, 483
  theory of, 480
Dewar, Sir James, 135
Dieke, G. H., 334
Dirac, P. A. M., 212
Dirac electron theory, 212, 492
Disintegration of nucleus (see Nuclear reactions)
Disintegration constant, 438
Displacement currents, 47
Displacement law (Wien), 117
Dissociation of molecule, 323
Doan, R. L., 393
Dolland, 23
Doppler, 35
Dorn, E., 433
Drude, P., 100
Druyvesteyn, M. J., 398
Du Fay, 29
Dulong and Petit, 409
DuMond, J. W. M., 88, 451
Durbin, R. P., 605
Dwight, K., 624

e, 88, 651
Earth
  age of, 444
  heat of, 436
  magnetism of, 566
  radioactivity of, 436
Edison, Thomas A., 95
Ehrenfest, P., 416
Eigenfunctions, eigenvalues, 196
Einstein, A., 56, 57, 73, 74, 75, 94, 410
Einstein frequency condition, 149
Einstein's photoelectric equation, 94
Electric quadrupole moment, 343, 473
Electricity
  discoveries in, 35, 39–44, 46
  in matter, 79
Electromagnetic field, 47, 633–638
  energy and momentum in, 633–635

Electromagnetic field, Maxwell's equations for, 121
  of point charges, 71–73, 636–638
  transformation of, 71
  waves in, 635
Electron-volt (ev), 96, 651
Electrons
  capture of, by nucleus, 474, 478
  charge of, 86–88
  classical radius of, 265
  in complex atoms, 224, 648
  creation of, 492
  discovery of, 80, 83–86
  e/m of, 85, 89
  energy loss by, 444, 584, 587, 591–592
  "free," 100–102, 429
  internal conversion, 452
  magnetic moment of, 212, 251, 287
  mass of, 88
  motion in magnetic field, 382
  radiation by, 586–587
  recoil, 389
  rest energy of, 651
  wavelength of, 179
  (See also Beta-particles)
Electroscope, 558
Elements
  isotopic composition of, 459
    tables, 639–647
  transuranic, 540, 551
Ellis, C. D., 453, 454
Elsasser, W. M., 535
Elster, J., 78, 91, 95, 555
Emission of light (see Radiation; Spectra)
Emissive power, 113
Empedocles, 5
Endoergic and exoergic reaction, 508
Energy
  binding, 474–479
  conservation of, 31–33, 42, 634
  electromagnetic, 633
  equipartition of, 119
  of gas molecules, 120
  loss by charged particles, 584–587
  per degree of freedom, 119
  relativistic, 67–70
  released, in fission, 542, 544
    in nuclear reactions, 507
  rest, 68
  separation, 477
  (See also Radiation)
Energy levels, 127, 196
  in central field, 227
  in magnetic field, 287, 288, 290, 292, 296
  molecular, 316, 320, 325, 328

Energy levels, nuclear (*see* Nucleus, quantum states of)
  resonance, 400, 422
  (*See also* Wave mechanics; special topics)
Enhanced spectrum, 135
Epstein, P. S., 566
Equipartition of energy, 119
Equivalent electrons, 278
Estermann, I., 184
Euler, 27
ev (electron-volt), 96, 651
Exchange effects, 214, 216–217, 236
Exchange forces, 484
Excitation of atoms, 162
  removal of, by collisions, 166
Excitation function (nuclear), 515
Excitation potential, 162
Exciton, 423
Exclusion principle, 218, 220, 279
Expansion chamber (cloud chamber), 447, 576

Fabry, 312
Fahrenheit, 27
Faraday, M., 36–43, 79, 80
faraday (unit), 80, 88
Feather, N., 469
Fermi, E., 454, 525, 527, 529, 541, 550, 600, 630
Fermi-Dirac molecules or statistics, 335, 415, 472
Fine structure
  in alkali-type spectra, 254–258
  in molecular spectra, 327
  in NH_3 inversion line, 342
  for one-electron atoms, 258–266
  (*See also* Hyperfine structure; Isotope structure)
Fine-structure constant, α, 259
Fission (*see* Nuclear fission)
FitzGerald, George F., 55
Fizeau, A. H. L., 52
Fluorescence, 164, 353, 355, 370
Foote, P. D., 162
Foucault, 34
Frame of reference, 50, 73
Franck, J., 162
Franklin, B., 29
Fränz, H., 466
Fraunhofer, 35
Freier, P., 624
Frenkel, J., 423
Fresnel, 34, 51
Fretter, W. B., 594
Friedrich, W., 355, 356

Frisch, O. R., 541, 542
Frisch, R., 184
Frost, R. H., 594
Functions, complete set of, 198
Fusion of light nuclei, 550

Galileo, 12
Galvani, 35
Gamma-rays
  absorption of, 491, 582–584
    anomalous, 491
  detection of, 445
  discovery of, 433
  energy measurement, 451
  internal conversion of, 452
  nature of, 436
  from nuclear reactions, 466, 515, 516
  origin of, 450, 515
  pair production by, 492, 582–584
  scattering of, 383–392, 583 (fig.)
  spectra of, 451
Gamow, G., 488
Gases
  Bose-Einstein, 415–416, 418, 420
  Fermi-Dirac, 415–420
  specific heats of, 405
  wave mechanics of, 414–420
Geiger, H., 143, 146, 147, 435, 446, 470
Geiger counter, 446
Geitel, H., 78, 91, 95, 555
Gellibrand, 19
George, E. P., 559–560
Gerlach, W., 299
Germer, L. H., 180
Giesel, 433
Gilbert, 19
Gill, P. S., 579
Gockel, A., 551
Goldstein, E., 455
Good, W. E., 342, 343
Goudsmit, S., 212
Gram-mole, molecules in, 88
Gravitation, 25, 73–75
Gray, L. H., 491
Gray, S., 29
Green, G., 35
Ground state, 151
Group velocity, 177
Guericke, 19
Guggenheimer, K., 535
Gurney, R. W., 466, 488
Gyromagnetic ratio, 284

h (Planck's constant), 132
Hadley, J., 608

Haga, 347
Hagenow, C. F., 352
Hahn, O., 541, 551
Half-life, 438
Hallwachs, W., 78
Hamilton, 31
Hardy, J. D., 342
Hartley, W. N., 136
Hartley's law, 136
Havens, W. W., 605
Hawksbee, 29
Haxel, O., 538
Haynes, S. K., 560
Hazen, W. E., 594
HCl, molecular spectrum of, 321–323, 334
Heat
    discoveries in, 27, 31
    of dissociation, 323
    theories of, 28, 32
Heisenberg, W., 330
Heitler, W., 586
Helium
    ionized, 158
    in radioactive minerals, 435, 443
    spectrum, of neutral, 278
        of ionized, 158, 265
Helmholtz, 32
Henry, J., 43
Herb, R. G., 500
Hertz, G., 162
Hertz, H., 48, 77
Hess, V. F., 556
High potentials, production of, 498
Hilberry, N., 595
Historical sketch, 5–48
Hjalmar, E., 392
Hoag, J. B., 595
Hoffman, G., 579
Homonuclear molecules, 324, 335–339
Hooke, 27
Huggins, 137
Hund, F., 335, 339
Hupfield, H. H., 491
Huygens, 27
Hydrogen
    Bohr's theory of, 148
    energy levels of, 153, 258, 265
        plot, 160
        tables, 156–157
    heavy, 301
    mass relative to electron, 89
    ortho- and para-, 339
    specific heat of, 339, 408
    spectrum of, 154–158
        diagram, 160
        fine structure of, 261–265
        table, 157

Hyperfine structure (in spectra), 300,
    302–305, 343
Hyperon, 609, 611–616, 618

Imbert, 347
Imes, E. S., 321
Impenetrability, 236
Indeterminacy principle, 191, 193, 313,
    394, 395
Induction accelerator (betatron), 503
Intercombination line, 277
Inversion spectrum of NH_3, 339
Ionization
    of atoms, 161, 163
        by charged particles, 445, 584, 601
        inner, 366, 396
        multiple, 167, 397
    bursts of, 579
Ionization chamber, 445, 558
Ionization energy or potential, 164
    plot, 250
    tables, 167, 648–650
Ions, structure and spectra of, 235
Isobars, 441
    energy levels of, 532–534
    stability of, 479
Isoelectronic atoms, 278
Isothermal enclosure, 106
Isotone, 537
Isotope effects, 301, 330
Isotope structure, 300–301
Isotopes
    abundance of, 459
        tables, 639–647
    definition of, 440, 441
    discovery of, 440
    identification of, 459
    masses of, 461, 510
    radioactive, 440
    separation of, 460, 550
Isotopic spin, 534

Jeans, J. H., 119, 121
Jensen, J. H. D., 538
Jesse, W. P., 622
Joliot-Curie, F., 467, 468, 491, 495, 542
Joliot-Curie, I., 467, 468, 491, 495, 541
Joule, 32

k (Boltzmann constant), 120, 651
K-particle, 609, 611
    table, 616
Kalckar, F., 542
Kaplon, M. F., 620

Kaufmann, W., 434
Keetman, 440
Kellogg, J. M. B., 308
Kelvin, Lord, 32, 33
Kent, N. A., 298
Kepler, Johannes, 16
Kepler's laws, 18
Kerst, D. W., 500, 503
Kessler, J., 609
kev = thousand electron volts, 497
Kikuchi, S., 183
Kinetic energy, relativistic, 67, 68
Kinsey, B. B., 498
Kircher, 19, 27
Kirchhoff, 35
Knipping, P., 355, 356
Knock-on electrons (delta-rays), 586, 624, 628
Knox, 35
Kolhörster, W., 556, 557, 574
Kramers, H. A., 330
Krishnan, 332
Kronig, R. de L., 398
Kulenkampff, H., 595

Lagrange, 27
Lamb, W. E., 262
Landé g factor, 287
Landé's interval rule, 274
Laplace, P. S. de, 35
Larmor precession, 286
Larsson, A., 393
Lattes, C. M. G., 602
Laue, M., 355
Lauritsen, C. C., 496, 498
Lawrence, E. O., 498, 500, 550
Lederman, L. M., 605, 609
Leibnitz, 27
Lemaitre, G., 566
Lenard, P., 79, 89
Leu, A., 300
Light
  absorption of, 164, 222
  corpuscular theory of, 23, 24, 98
  discoveries in, 33, 42, 43
  (See also Radiation)
Linear accelerator, 504
Liouville's theorem, 568
Lipperhey, 14
Liquid-drop model of nucleus, 519
Liveing, G. D., 135
Livingston, M. S., 498, 500
Loar, H. H., 605
Locher, G. L., 576
Lorentz, H. A., 48, 52, 55, 61, 80, 100

Lorentz transformation, 59
Lorentz unit, 290
Lorenz, L., 80
Lummer, 118

McMillan, E. M., 502, 551
Magic number, nuclear, 535–538
Magnetic-beam method, 305–311
Magnetic field
  of earth, 566
  effect of, on angular momentum, 285
    on atomic energy, 287, 288
    on atoms, 282
  of galaxy, 630
  motion of electron in, 382
  of sun, 571
Magnetic moment
  of atoms, 283–284, 287–288
    measurement of, 299
  due to orbital motion, 283
  of electron spin, 212, 284, 287
  of nuclei, 301–302, 472, 539
    table, 303
Magnetic-resonance accelerator, 500
Magnetic-resonance method, 309
Magnetic rigidity, 434
Magnetism, 286
Magneton
  Bohr, 287
  nuclear, 303
Majorana force (nuclear), 485
Marckwald, 440
Marsden, E., 143, 146, 147, 463, 470
Martinelli, E. A., 605
Marshak, R. E., 600
Mass
  atomic unit of, 461, 651
  of energy, 68
  reduced, 153
  variation of, 64
Mass correction, 152, 211, 227
Mass number (nuclear), 441
Mass spectrometer, 458, 461
Matrix, diagonalized, 214
Matrix components, 202
Mattauch, J., 458
Maxwell, J. C., 44–47
Maxwell's equations, 121
Mayer, M. G., 537, 538
Mayer, R. J., 32
Mean life, 222, 438
Mechanics
  discoveries in, 27
  geometrical optics, 175
  relativistic, 64

Meggers, W. F., 162
Meitner, L., 491, 541
Mercury, arc spectrum of, 275
Mersenne, 19
Mesonic atom, 598
Mesons
  heavy, 609–611
    table, 616
  hyperon, 609, 611–616, 618
  K-particle, 609, 611
    table, 616
  mu (muon), 593
    discovery of, 590
    energy loss of, 585 (fig.)
    production of, 605
    properties of, 594–600, 616
  pi (pion), 603
    discovery of, 602
    production of, 603, 606
    properties of, 604–609, 616
  sigma, 603
  tau, 609, 616
  theory of nuclear forces, 593
Metals
  electronic states in, 402, 403
  theory of, 100
Metastable levels, 277
Mev = million electron volts, 445, 651
Michelson, A. A., 52, 261, 313
Michelson-Morley experiment, 52, 62
Micron, 134
Microwaves, uses of, 262, 342
Millikan, R. A., 86, 87, 93, 94, 470, 556–560, 562–565, 575, 591
Millman, S., 310
Minerals, age of, 444
Mirror nuclides
  energy levels of, 532–534
  masses of, 510
mks units, 633
Moderator, neutron, 527–529, 547
Mohler, F. L., 162
Momentum
  electromagnetic, 634
  relativistic, 67
  in wave mechanics, 191, 197
Morley, E. W., 52, 261
Moseley, H. G. J., 364, 365, 470
Moseley's law, 364
Mott-Smith, H., 576
Moyer, B. J., 606
μ_I, table, 303
Muirhead, H., 602
Multiplets, 274
Multiplicity of a term, 273
Muon (see Mesons)

N_0 (Avogadro's number), 80, 88
Neddermeyer, S. H., 577, 591, 592
Neher, H. V., 560, 563–565
Neon (spectrum), 164
Neptunium, 551
Nereson, N. G., 597
Neumann, F., 41
Neutrino, 454, 478
Neutrons
  capture of, 527, 529–531
  crystal spectrometer for, 530
  decay of, 622
  detection of, 524, 526
  discovery of, 466
  energy loss in hydrogen, 527
  magnetic moment of, 303
  mass of, 469, 470, 509, 651
  mean free path of, 528, 547
  production of, 469, 522
  proton scattering by, 482, 524, 527
  reactions induced by, 522–531
    (See also Nuclear reactions)
  released in fission, 542, 544–546
  resonance absorption of, 529–531
  scattering of, 482
  slow and thermal, 527
  spin of, 303
  total cross section, 523
  velocity selector for, 530
  wavelength of, 528
Newton, 20–27, 49
Ney, E. P., 623
Nicholson, 36
Nier, A. O., 458
Nitrogen nucleus, 338
Normal quantum state, 151
Normalization, 191
$\bar{\nu}$, 134
Nuclear barrier, 487, 496
Nuclear bomb, 549–552, 554
Nuclear emulsion, 447, 600
Nuclear energy in stars, 552
  (See also Nuclear fission)
Nuclear fission, 540–554
  bomb, 549–552
  chain reactions, 545–552
  cross sections, 456, 552
  delayed neutrons, 544, 549
  discovery of, 540
  energy release in, 542, 544, 549
  fast, 549
  neutrons emitted in, 542, 544–546
  power production, 549
  reactors (see Nuclear reactor)
  spontaneous, 544
  theory of, 543
  of thorium, 542, 550

Nuclear fission, threshold for, 544
Nuclear force, 479–490
  charge independence, 483, 511, 532–534
  exchange character, 484
  potential, 480, 486
  range of, 471
  saturation, 484
  spin dependence, 482
  Yukawa theory of, 593
Nuclear models
  collective-motion, 540
  independent-particle, 534–540
  liquid-drop, 519
  shell, 534–540
Nuclear reactions, 504–510
  alpha-particle induced, 463–466
  artificially induced, 496
  conservation laws in, 506
  in cosmic rays (see Cosmic rays)
  determination of mass by, 508–510
  endo- and exoergic, 508
  energy balance, Q, 507
  excitation function, 515
  fission (see Nuclear fission)
  fusion, 550
  kinetics of, 507
  of neutrons, 522–531
  notation for, 506
  particle groups in, 512
  resonances, 466, 515, 529
  types of, 505
  yield, 515
Nuclear reactor (pile), 545–552
  control of, 549
  critical size, 548
  moderator, 547
  multiplication factor, 547
  neutron production by, 523
Nucleon, 474
Nucleus
  angular momentum (spin), 301–303, 539
    measurement of, 305
    table, 472
  binding energy of, 474–479
  charge of, 470
  compound, 520
  constituents of, 470, 473
  electric quadrupole moment, 343, 473
  electrostatic energy of, 486, 543
  energy levels of (see Quantum states)
  fission of (see Nuclear fission)
  isotopic spin of, 534
  liquid-drop model of, 519, 543
  magnetic moment of, 301–303, 539
    measurement of, 305

Nucleus, magnetic moment of, table, 303
  mass of, 510
    (See also Atomic masses)
  motion of, in atoms, 152, 159, 227
  nitrogen, 338
  parity of, 473
  quantum states of, 450, 488, 512, 515, 516, 531–540
  radius of, 471, 524
  shell model of, 534–540
  spin of, 301–303, 539
    table, 303
  stability of, 474–479, 543
  statistics of, 472
  structure of, 479–490, 519, 534–540
  surface tension of, 542, 543
  transformation of (see Nuclear reactions)
Nuclide, 441
  mirror, 510, 532

Occhialini, G. P. S., 492, 494, 576, 602
Oersted, 36
Oleksa, S., 623
Oliphant, M. L. E., 498
Operators, 197
Oppenheimer, J. R., 606
Orbits in one-electron atoms, 149, 152 (fig.), 153–155
  elliptical, 170
Ornstein, L. S., 338
Ortho states, 335
Orthogonality of functions, 200, 215
Oscillators
  Planck's theory of, 127–130
  radiation by, 638
  in thermal equilibrium, 125–127, 129
  wave mechanics of, 200

p, s lines, 289
Packing fraction, 462
Pair production (electron-positron), 492, 582
Pancini, E., 599
Panofsky, W. K. H., 605, 607, 608
Para states, 335
Parity
  in nuclear reactions, 507
  of nucleus, 473
Parkinson, D. B., 500
Parratt, L. G., 404
Particles in a box, 199, 341, 414
  two, 213
    electrons, 218
Pascal, 19

Paschen, F., 290, 296
Paschen-Back effect, 295
Pasternak, S., 262
Pauli, W., 220, 301, 454
Peregrinus, Petrus, 10
Periodic table, 228–235, 238–240
  Bohr's, 229
Perrin, F., 84
Perturbation theory, 201, 216
Peters, B., 620
Peterson, V. Z., 565
Phase waves, 174
Photoelectric effect and Compton effect, 391
  cross section for, 583 (fig.)
  discovery of, 77
  due to x-rays, 380
  nature and properties of, 89–95, 97–99, 102–103
Photographic emulsion detector (*see* Nuclear emulsion)
Physical scale, 88, 463
Physical significance of Ψ, 189
π, σ lines, 289
Piccioni, O., 599
Pile (*see* Nuclear reactor)
Pion (pi meson) (*see* Mesons)
Planck, M., 124, 127
Planck radiation law, 130–132
Planck's constant, 132
Plutonium, 550
Poisson, 35
Polonium, 433
Pose, 466
Positive rays, 455–458
Positron, 490–495
  annihilation of, 493
  discovery of, 491
  mass of, 495
  production of, 492, **582**
  theory of, 492
Positron decay, 474
  stability against, 478
Powell, C. F., 600, 602
Powell, W. M., 616, **617**
Poynting's vector, 634
Preston's rule, 294
Pringsheim, 118
Probability amplitude, density, **191–192**, 208
  for hydrogen atom, 211
Proportional counter, 445
Protons
  angular momentum of, 303
  energy loss by, 585 (fig.)
  (*See also* Charged particles)
  magnetic moment of, 303

Protons, mass of, 651
  ratio to electron, 89
  range of, 449 (fig.)
  rest energy of, 651
Prout, 141, 440
Ptolemy, 9
Pythagoras, 5

Q value (nuclear heat of reaction), 507
Quadrupole, electric, in nucleus, 343, 473
Quadrupole lines, 374
Quantum defect, 249
Quantum numbers
  F, M_F, 303
  I, M_I (nucleus), 302
  J, M, 240
  LS, 243, 269, 271
  $LSJM$, 272
  $LS\Lambda\Sigma$, 269, 271
  magnetic, 287
  for molecules, J, 316
    K, S, 326, 328
    Λ, 325
    Ω, 327
    v, 319
  $nljm$, 252, 372
  $nl\lambda\mu$, 204, 226
  principal, 207
    effective, 248
  $s\mu$, 213
  $S\Sigma$, 219–220
Quantum states, 127, 148, **195**
  continuous, 154
  molecular, 316, 319, 324, **328**
  multiple, 168
  nuclear (*see* Nucleus)
  x-ray, 366
  (*See also* Wave mechanics; special topics)
Quantum theory, 124, 127, 148–155, 169
  (*See also* Wave mechanics; special topics)

Rabi, I., 306, 308
Radiation
  absorption and emission of, 110, 113, 164, 221–222
    by charged particles, 586–587
    by dipole or harmonic oscillator, 223, 638
    by point charges, 637
    quadrupole, 223
  annihilation, 493
  black-body, 106, 110–113, 115–119, 123–132

Radiation, electromagnetic, 635, 637
  intensity of, 108
  nature of, 393
  pressure due to, 109
  resonance, 164
  thermal, 106
Radiation length, 586
  table, 587
Radioactive series, 442
Radioactive transformations, 437
Radioactivity, 431–454
  discovery of, 432
  of earth, 436
  energy release in, 436
  induced, 495, 525
  secular equilibrium, 439
  successive transformations in, 438
Radioisotopes, 496, 525
Radium
  discovery of, 433
  half-life of, 443
Radon, disintegration constant of, 438
Raman, C. V., 332
Raman effect, 330
Randall, H. M., 342
Rasetti, F., 338, 597
Rayleigh, Lord, 118
Rayleigh, Lord (fourth), 165
Rayleigh-Jeans formula, 123, 131
Reactor (see Nuclear reactor)
Reflection from moving mirror, 113
Regener, E., 559
Relativity, 49–76
  in electromagnetism, 70–73
  in light propagation, 50, 55, 56
  in mechanics, 64–70
  Newtonian, 49
  theory of, general, 73–76
    special, 56–73
  in wave mechanics, 212, 251, 259, 260
Residual electrostatic interaction, 268
Resonances (nuclear) (see Nuclear reactions)
Retherford, R. C., 262
Richardson, J. R., 605
Richardson, O. W., 91, 92, 96
Richtmyer, F. K., 379
Ritz combination principle, 140
Robinson, H. R., 381, 383
Roentgen, W. K., 345–347, 350
Römer, 28
Rossi, B., 575, 580, 595, 597
Rossi transition curve, 580
Rowland, 48
Royds, T., 436
Rumford, 32

Rutherford, E., 143, 144, 433–437, 439, 446, 451, 463–466, 469, 498, 557
rutherford unit, definition, 443
Rydberg, J. R., 138, 140
Rydberg constant, 139, 155
  mass correction of, 159
Rydberg formula, 138, 140, 249, 274
Rydberg-Schuster law, 140

S, P, D, F terms, 243, 245
s, p, d, f, 210
S_α, S_β, S_μ, 217
$S_{\alpha\alpha}$, etc., 218
Sabin, R., 624
Satellite lines, 257
Savitch, 541
Scattering
  of charged particles, 142–146, 601
  neutron-proton, 482, 524, 527
Schein, M., 579, 622
Scheiner, 19
Schmidt, G. C., 433
Schmidt, T., 539
Schrödinger, E., 173, 174, 185, 195
Schuster, A., 140
Scintillation counter, 446, 452
Seaborg, G. T., 551
Secular equilibrium, 439
Selection rules, 241
  nuclear, 507, 519
  (See also Quantum numbers; special topics)
Self-consistent field, 267
Separation energy, nuclear, 477
Series (spectral), 135–141, 277
  diffuse, fundamental, principal, sharp, 138, 244–245
  relation to terms, 140
  x-ray, 366–367
  (See also Spectra)
Shell model of nucleus, 534–540
Shells and subshells in atoms, 227, 242
  tables of, 228, 239, 648
Siegbahn, M., 361
Simultaneity, 57
Singer, S. F., 625
Skobeltzyn, D., 573, 577
Smekal, 332
Smyth, H. D., 545
Snell, 19
Soddy, F., 436, 437, 439, 440, 458
Sodium
  charge cloud for, 248
  energy levels (diagram), 160, 246
    table, 256
  spectrum, 161, 164

Sodium, spectrum, excitation of, 163, 169
    table, 256
    Zeeman effect for, 294
Sodium chloride crystal, 424
Soltan, A., 498
Sommerfeld, A., 100, 169, 170, 259, 376
Space quantization, 206, 299
Space-time, 50, 60–63
Specific heats
    of gases, 405–409
    of hydrogen, 339, 408
    of solids, 409–414
Spectra, 135, 240–344
    absorption, 164, 318, 321
    alkali type of, 242–250
        fine structure in, 254–258
    arc and spark, 135, 158
    continuous, 155
    hydrogen, 156, 261
    from ionized atoms, 243, 278
    molecular, 314–330
        electronic, 316, 328–330
        homonuclear, 324, 337
        rotation, 315–318, 322, 333
        vibration-rotation, 315, 318–324, 333
    from one-electron atoms, 154–161, 258
    two-electron type of, 275–278
    (See also Series; x-rays)
Spectral notation (see Quantum numbers; S, P, D, F; s, p, d, f)
Spectrograph
    magnetic, 448, 509
    mass, 458, 461
Spin
    electron, 212, 217, 251
    neutron and proton, 303
    nuclear, 302, 472, 539
        measurement of, 305
        table, 303
Spin-orbit effect
    in central field, 250–254
    on LS terms, 272
    on magnetic levels, 290
    in molecules, 326, 327
    in nucleus, 538
    in one-electron atoms, 258, 266
Stark effect, 282
Stationary states, 149, 195
Statistical weight, 169
Statistics
    Bose-Einstein and Fermi-Dirac, 415, 472
    of nuclei, 472
Stefan-Boltzmann law, 110–113
Steinberger, J., 607, 608
Stellar energy sources, 552

Steller, J., 607
Stenström, W., 392
Stern, E. A., 565
Stern, O., 184, 299, 306
Stern-Gerlach experiment, 298
Stevenson, E. C., 594
Stix, T., 624
Stoletow, 78
Stoney, G. J., 80
Störmer, C., 566
Strassman, F., 541, 551
Straubel, 353
Street, J. C., 594
Suess, H. E., 538
Synchrocyclotron, 502
Synchrotron, 503

Tarrant, G. T. P., 491
Taylor, J. B., 300
Technetium, 444
Teller, E., 600
Terms (spectral), 140, 157
    lowest, table, 648
    (See also Energy levels; special topics)
Thales, 5
Thermalizer, neutron, 529
    (See also Moderator)
Thermionic emission, 95–97, 104
Thermonuclear processes in stars, 552
Thermonuclear weapons, 554
Thomas, L. H., 251
Thomson, J. J., 84, 85, 95, 142, 350, 455–458
Time, 49, 57, 62
Tomonaga, S., 598
Torricelli, 19
Townsend, J. S., 86
Transition probabilities, 221–222
Transmutations (see Nuclear reactions)
Transuranic elements, 540, 551
Triton, 505
Tunnel effect, 203, 341
Turner, R. N., 563
Tycho Brahe, 16

Uhlenbeck, G. E., 212
Uncertainty principle, 193
Uranium
    fission of (see Nuclear fission)
    half-life of, 443
    radioactive series, 442
Urey, H. C., 301

V-particle (see Mesons)
Valence bonds, 235

Vallarta, M. S., 566
Van Allen, J. A., 571, 625
Van de Graaff, R. J., 500
Van de Graaff generator, 499
van der Waals attraction, 236
Van Wyk, W. R., 338
Vector diagrams, 206, 219
  for J, M, 241
  for L, S, J, 273
  for Zeeman effect, 291
Vector product defined, $71n$.
Veksler, V., 502
Velocities, transformation of, 63
Villard, 433
Volta, 35
von Welsbach, A., 440

Walton, E. T. S., 497, 498
Wave equation, Schrödinger, 185–188, 196
  (See also special topics)
Wave functions, 196, 220
  of electron with spin, 212–213, 252
  symmetry of, 218, 335
  (See also Wave mechanics; special topics)
Wave mechanics, 172–223
  of complex atoms, 224–227, 266
  of crystalline solids (see Crystals)
  of electron, in central field, 226, 247
    with spin, 212, 266
  of molecules, 324–327
  of a particle, 188–212
  relativistic, 212
  significance of Ψ in, 189
  (See also Quantum states; Wave functions; special cases)
Wave number ($\bar{\nu}$), 134, 156
  and ev, 157, 651
Wave packet, 190, 196
Wavelength and ev, 157, 651
Waves
  electromagnetic, 635
  matter, 172–185
    experiments on, 180
    molecular, 184
    physical significance of, 189
    refraction of, 176
    scattering of, 190
    wavelength of, 178, 179
Weber, 409
Weisskopf, V. F., 600
Wentzel, G., 398
Wheeler, J. A., 543
White, M. G., 498
Wien, W., 118. 455

Wien's formula, 118, 131
Wigner, E. P., 483
Williams, E. J., 591
Williams, N. H., 342
Williams, R. C., 261
Wilson, C. T. R., 389, 447, 555
Winckler, J. R., 571, 624
Wind, C. H., 347
Winkelmann, A., 353
Wollan, E. O., 622
Wood, R. W., 165, 334
Wooster, W. A., 453
Wright, N., 342

X-rays, 345–404
  absorption of, 353, 368–370, 372, 377–383, 391, 400, 403
  Auger effect on, 398
  Bragg's law for, 369
  characteristic, 354, 362
  discovery and properties of, 345–347
  energy levels for, 370–374, 397
    resonance, 400
  excitation of, 369, 397
  first-order or diagram lines, 368, 396
  fluorescent, 353, 355, 370
  intensity of, 373, 375, 399
  measurement of, 348
  photoelectric effect of, 380–383, 391
  polarization of, 351
  pulse theory of, 349, 385
  quadrupole lines, 374
  quantum theory of, 372
  reflection of, from crystals, 355
    from ruled gratings, 393
  refraction of, 392
  scattering of, 350, 383–392
    classical cross section, 351
    Compton, 386
  second-order (satellite) lines, 367, 396–399
  spectra, 355–377
    continuous, 374–377
    discrete, 355
      plot, 367
      table, 368
    involving outer electrons, 400
    K, L, M, N, lines, 355, 366
    satellite lines, 367, 396–399
    series in, 366, 367
    of solids, 402
    theory of, 365–375
  spectrometer for, 359
  wavelengths, measurement of, 359, 393
    table, 368
X-unit (X.U.), 134, 361, 362

Y-particle (hyperon), 609, 611–616, 618
York, H. F., 606
Young, Thomas, 33, 35
Yukawa, H., 593, 594, 595

Z (atomic number), 144, 147, 228, 441
    table, 648
Zacharias, J. R., 308
Zeeman, P., 80, 83, 294

Zeeman effect, 80, 282–298
    anomalous, 282
    classical theory of, 80–83
    in huge field, 287
    normal triplet, 282, 289
    photographs, 283
    in strong field, 298
    in weak field, 291
Zero-point energy, 419